interactive SCIENCE

Go to **MyScienceOnline.com** to experience science in a whole new way.

Interactive tools such as My Planet Diary connect you to the latest science happenings.

MY PLANET DiaRY

- Search **Earth's Journal** for important science news from around the world.

- Use **Earth's Calendar** to find out when cool scientific events occur.

- Explore science **Links** to find even more exciting information about our planet.

- Visit **Jack's Blog** to be the first to know about what is going on in science!

PEARSON

Glenview, Illinois • Boston, Massachusetts • Chandler, Arizona • Upper Saddle River, New Jersey

Ohio • Science • Ohio • Science • Ohio • Science • Ohio • Science • Ohio • Science • Ohio • Science • Ohio • Science

Ohio

You're an author!

As you write in this science book, your answers and personal discoveries will be recorded for you to keep, making this book unique to you. That is why you are one of the primary authors of this book.

✎ **In the space below, print your name, school, town, and state. Then write a short autobiography that includes your interests and accomplishments.**

YOUR NAME _____

SCHOOL _____

TOWN, STATE _____

AUTOBIOGRAPHY _____

_____

_____

_____

_____

Your Photo

Taken from:

Interactive Science: Earth's Structure, Forces and Energy, Cells and Heredity, Earth's Surface, and Ecology and the Environment
by Don Buckley, M.Sc., Zipporah Miller, M.A.Ed., Michael J. Padilla, Ph.D., Kathryn Thornton, Ph.D., and Michael E. Wysession, Ph.D.
Copyright © 2011 by Pearson Education, Inc.
Published by Prentice Hall
Upper Saddle River, New Jersey 07458

Louisiana Interactive Science, Grade 7
by Don Buckley, M.Sc., Zipporah Miller, M.A.Ed., Michael J. Padilla, Ph.D., Kathryn Thornton, Ph.D., and
Michael E. Wysession, Ph.D.
Copyright © 2012 by Pearson Education, Inc.
Published by Prentice Hall
Upper Saddle River, New Jersey 07458

Indiana Interactive Science, Grade 8
by Don Buckley, M.Sc., Zipporah Miller, M.A.Ed., Michael J. Padilla, Ph.D., Kathryn Thornton, Ph.D., and Michael E. Wysession, Ph.D.
Copyright © 2012 by Pearson Education, Inc.
Published by Prentice Hall
Upper Saddle River, New Jersey 07458

Certain materials herein are adapted from *Understanding by Design, 2nd Edition*, by Grant Wiggins & Jay McTighe © 2005 ASCD. Used with permission.

UNDERSTANDING BY DESIGN® and UbD® are trademarks of ASCD, and are used under license.

Pearson Learning Solutions, 501 Boylston Street, Suite 900, Boston, MA 02116
A Pearson Education Company
www.pearsoned.com

Printed in the United States of America

19 16

000200010270768896

CP/CM

PEARSON

ISBN 10: 1-256-27946-3
ISBN 13: 978-1-256-27946-4

Program Authors

DON BUCKLEY, M.Sc.
*Information and Communications Technology Director,
The School at Columbia University, New York, New York*
A founder of New York City Independent School Technologists (NYCIST) and long-time chair of New York Association of Independent Schools' annual IT conference, Mr. Buckley has taught students on two continents and created multimedia and Internet-based instructional systems for schools worldwide.

ZIPPORAH MILLER, M.A.Ed.
Associate Executive Director for Professional Programs and Conferences, National Science Teachers Association, Arlington, Virginia
Ms. Zipporah Miller is a former K–12 science supervisor and STEM coordinator for the Prince George's County Public School District in Maryland. She is a science education consultant who has overseen curriculum development and staff training for more than 150 district science coordinators.

MICHAEL J. PADILLA, Ph.D.
Associate Dean and Director, Eugene P. Moore School of Education, Clemson University, Clemson, South Carolina
A former middle school teacher and a leader in middle school science education, Dr. Michael Padilla has served as president of the National Science Teachers Association and as a writer of the National Science Education Standards. He is professor of science education at Clemson University.

KATHRYN THORNTON, Ph.D.
Professor and Associate Dean, School of Engineering and Applied Science, University of Virginia, Charlottesville, Virginia
Selected by NASA in May 1984, Dr. Kathryn Thornton is a veteran of four space flights. She has logged more than 975 hours in space, including more than 21 hours of extravehicular activity. As an author on the *Scott Foresman Science* series, Dr. Thornton's enthusiasm for science has inspired teachers around the globe.

MICHAEL E. WYSESSION, Ph.D.
Associate Professor of Earth and Planetary Science, Washington University, St. Louis, Missouri
An author on more than 50 scientific publications, Dr. Wysession was awarded the prestigious Packard Foundation Fellowship and Presidential Faculty Fellowship for his research in geophysics. Dr. Wysession is an expert on Earth's inner structure and has mapped various regions of Earth using seismic tomography. He is known internationally for his work in geoscience education and outreach.

Instructional Design Author

GRANT WIGGINS, Ed.D.
President, Authentic Education, Hopewell, New Jersey
Dr. Wiggins is a co-author with Jay McTighe of *Understanding by Design, 2nd Edition* (ASCD 2005). His approach to instructional design provides teachers with a disciplined way of thinking about curriculum design, assessment, and instruction that moves teaching from covering content to ensuring understanding.
UNDERSTANDING BY DESIGN® and UbD® are trademarks of ASCD, and are used under license.

Planet Diary Author

JACK HANKIN
*Science/Mathematics Teacher, The Hilldale School, Daly City, California
Founder, Planet Diary Web site*
Mr. Hankin is the creator and writer of Planet Diary, a science current events Web site. Mr. Hankin is passionate about bringing science news and environmental awareness into classrooms.

ELL Consultant

JIM CUMMINS, Ph.D.
Professor and Canada Research Chair, Curriculum, Teaching and Learning department at the University of Toronto
Dr. Cummins's research focuses on literacy development in multilingual schools and the role technology plays in learning across the curriculum. Interactive Science incorporates research-based principles for integrating language with the teaching of academic content based on Dr. Cummins's work.

Reading Consultant

HARVEY DANIELS, Ph.D.
Professor of Secondary Education, University of New Mexico, Albuquerque, New Mexico
Dr. Daniels serves as an international consultant to schools, districts, and educational agencies. Dr. Daniels has authored or coauthored 13 books on language, literacy, and education. His most recent works include *Comprehension and Collaboration: Inquiry Circles in Action* and *Subjects Matter: Every Teacher's Guide to Content-Area Reading*.

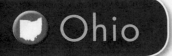

Ohio

Contributing Writers

Edward Aguado, Ph.D.
Professor, Department of
Geography
San Diego State University
San Diego, California

Elizabeth Coolidge-Stolz, M.D.
Medical Writer
North Reading, Massachusetts

Donald L. Cronkite, Ph.D.
Professor of Biology
Hope College
Holland, Michigan

Jan Jenner, Ph.D.
Science Writer
Talladega, Alabama

Linda Cronin Jones, Ph.D.
Associate Professor of Science and
Environmental Education
University of Florida
Gainesville, Florida

T. Griffith Jones, Ph.D.
Clinical Associate Professor
of Science Education
College of Education
University of Florida
Gainesville, Florida

Andrew C. Kemp, Ph.D.
Teacher
Jefferson County Public Schools
Louisville, Kentucky

Matthew Stoneking, Ph.D.
Associate Professor of Physics
Lawrence University
Appleton, Wisconsin

R. Bruce Ward, Ed.D.
Senior Research Associate
Science Education Department
Harvard-Smithsonian Center for
Astrophysics
Cambridge, Massachusetts

Ohio

K-8 Teacher Reviewers

Misty Anness
Wilson Elementary School
Cincinnati, Ohio

Sunshine Craven
Liberty Local School District
Liberty, Ohio

Dr. Richard Fairman
Antioch University Midwest
Yellow Springs, OH

John Farmer
Ayer Elementary School
Cincinnati, Ohio

Brice Harris
Trumbull County
Educational Service Center
Niles, Ohio

Lorraine Turner
Cleveland Heights-University
Heights City Schools
University Heights, Ohio

Content Reviewers

Paul D. Beale, Ph.D.
Department of Physics
University of Colorado at Boulder
Boulder, Colorado

Jeff R. Bodart, Ph.D.
Professor of Physical Sciences
Chipola College
Marianna, Florida

Joy Branlund, Ph.D.
Department of Earth Science
Southwestern Illinois College
Granite City, Illinois

Marguerite Brickman, Ph.D.
Division of Biological Sciences
University of Georgia
Athens, Georgia

Bonnie J. Brunkhorst, Ph.D.
Science Education and Geological
Sciences
California State University
San Bernardino, California

Michael Castellani, Ph.D.
Department of Chemistry
Marshall University
Huntington, West Virginia

Charles C. Curtis, Ph.D.
Research Associate Professor
of Physics
University of Arizona
Tucson, Arizona

Diane I. Doser, Ph.D.
Department of Geological
Sciences
University of Texas
El Paso, Texas

Rick Duhrkopf, Ph.D.
Department of Biology
Baylor University
Waco, Texas

Alice K. Hankla, Ph.D.
The Galloway School
Atlanta, Georgia

Mark Henriksen, Ph.D.
Physics Department
University of Maryland
Baltimore, Maryland

Chad Hershock, Ph.D.
Center for Research on Learning
and Teaching
University of Michigan
Ann Arbor, Michigan

Jeremiah N. Jarrett, Ph.D.
Department of Biology
Central Connecticut State
University
New Britain, Connecticut

Scott L. Kight, Ph.D.
Department of Biology
Montclair State University
Montclair, New Jersey

Jennifer O. Liang, Ph.D.
Department of Biology
University of Minnesota–Duluth
Duluth, Minnesota

Candace Lutzow-Felling, Ph.D.
Director of Education
The State Arboretum of Virginia
University of Virginia
Boyce, Virginia

Cortney V. Martin, Ph.D.
Virginia Polytechnic Institute
Blacksburg, Virginia

Joseph F. McCullough, Ph.D.
Physics Program Chair
Cabrillo College
Aptos, California

Heather Mernitz, Ph.D.
Department of Physical Science
Alverno College
Milwaukee, Wisconsin

Sadredin C. Moosavi, Ph.D.
Department of Earth and
Environmental Sciences
Tulane University
New Orleans, Louisiana

David L. Reid, Ph.D.
Department of Biology
Blackburn College
Carlinville, Illinois

Scott M. Rochette, Ph.D.
Department of the Earth Sciences
SUNY College at Brockport
Brockport, New York

Karyn L. Rogers, Ph.D.
Department of Geological
Sciences
University of Missouri
Columbia, Missouri

Laurence Rosenhein, Ph.D.
Department of Chemistry
Indiana State University
Terre Haute, Indiana

Sara Seager, Ph.D.
Department of Planetary Sciences
and Physics
Massachusetts Institute of
Technology
Cambridge, Massachusetts

Tom Shoberg, Ph.D.
Missouri University of Science
and Technology
Rolla, Missouri

Teacher Reviewers

Master Teacher Board

Museum of Science.

Special thanks to the Museum of
Science, Boston, Massachusetts,
and Ioannis Miaoulis, the
Museum's president and director,
for serving as content advisors for
the technology and design strand
in this program.

CONTENTS

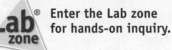 Enter the Lab zone for hands-on inquiry.

Chapter Lab Investigation:
• Directed Inquiry: Become a Learning Detective
• Open Inquiry: Become a Learning Detective

Inquiry Warm-Ups: • How Does a Scientist Think? • Developing a Theory • What's the Question? • Posing Questions

Quick Labs: • Scientific Skills • Activities of Science • Scientific Thinking • Science and Its Methods • It Starts With a Question • How Can You Explain It? • Scientific Literacy Survey • Analyzing Claims • Sources of Information

my science online .com

Go to MyScienceOnline.com to interact with this chapter's content.
Keyword: **Using Scientific Inquiry**

> PLANET DIARY
• Using Scientific Inquiry

> INTERACTIVE ART
• Inquiry Diagram

> REAL-WORLD INQUIRY
• Where's the Evidence? • When Science Sparks Controversy

> VIRTUAL LAB
• What Is Scientific Inquiry?

CHAPTER 2
Mathematics and Models in Science

 Enter the Lab zone for hands-on inquiry.

Chapter Lab Investigation:
  • Directed Inquiry: Selecting Models
  • Open Inquiry: Selecting Models

Inquiry Warm-Ups: • What Is Scientific Measurement? • How Do Math and Science Work Together? • What's in a Graph? • Models in Science • Can You Name the Safety Equipment?

Quick Labs: • Measuring With SI • A Unit of SI • Is It Accurate? • Math Tools in Science • Recognizing Trends • Working With Models • Characteristics of Systems • Be Prepared to Be Safe in the Field • How Would You Respond to These Emergencies?

my science online.com

Go to MyScienceOnline.com to interact with this chapter's content. Keyword: Mathematics and Models in Science

> UNTAMED SCIENCE
• Grams and Meters and Liters—Oh My!

> PLANET DIARY
• Mathematics and Models in Science

> INTERACTIVE ART
• The Need for Numbers • Plotting a Line Graph • Modeling a System

> VIRTUAL LAB
• How Are Units Useful?

CONTENTS

Lab zone® Enter the Lab zone for hands-on inquiry.

△ **Chapter Lab Investigation:**
• Directed Inquiry: Modeling Mantle Convection Currents
• Open Inquiry: Modeling Mantle Convection Currents

△ **Inquiry Warm-Ups:** • What Is a System?
• Earth's Interior • Tracing Heat Flow

△ **Quick Labs:** • Parts of Earth's System • What Forces Shape Earth? • How Do Scientists Find Out What's Inside Earth? • Build a Model of Earth • How Can Heat Cause Motion in a Liquid?

my science online.com

Go to MyScienceOnline.com to interact with this chapter's content.
Keyword: **Introducing Earth**

> **UNTAMED SCIENCE**
• Beyond the Dirt

> **PLANET DIARY**
• Introducing Earth

> **INTERACTIVE ART**
• Earth's System • Heat Transfer

> **ART IN MOTION**
• Convection in Earth's Mantle

> **REAL-WORLD INQUIRY**
• Exploring Earth's Layers

 Enter the Lab zone for hands-on inquiry.

Chapter Lab Investigation:
• Directed Inquiry: Modeling Sea-Floor Spreading
• Open Inquiry: Modeling Sea-Floor Spreading

Inquiry Warm-Ups: • How Are Earth's Continents Linked Together? • What Is the Effect of a Change in Density? • Plate Interactions

Quick Labs: • Moving the Continents • Mid-Ocean Ridges • Reversing Poles • Mantle Convection Currents

MY SCIENCE online.com

Go to MyScienceOnline.com to interact with this chapter's content.
Keyword: Plate Tectonics

> **UNTAMED SCIENCE**
• Diving Toward Divergence

> **PLANET DIARY**
• Plate Tectonics

> **INTERACTIVE ART**
• Continental Drift • Sea-Floor Spreading

> **ART IN MOTION**
• Changing Earth's Crust

> **REAL-WORLD INQUIRY**
• Predicting Plate Motions

CONTENTS

Lab® zone Enter the Lab zone for hands-on inquiry.

Chapter Lab Investigation:
• Directed Inquiry: Finding the Epicenter
• Open Inquiry: Finding the Epicenter

Inquiry Warm-Ups: • How Does Stress Affect Earth's Crust? • How Do Seismic Waves Travel Through Earth? • How Can Seismic Waves Be Detected?

Quick Labs: • Effects of Stress • Modeling Faults • Modeling Stress • Properties of Seismic Waves • Measuring Earthquakes • Design a Seismograph • Earthquake Patterns

MY SCIENCE online.com

Go to MyScienceOnline.com to interact with this chapter's content.
Keyword: **Earthquakes**

> UNTAMED SCIENCE
• Why Quakes Shake

> PLANET DIARY
• Earthquakes

> INTERACTIVE ART
• Seismic Waves • Earthquake Engineering

> ART IN MOTION
• Stresses and Faults

> REAL-WORLD INQUIRY
• Placing a Bay Area Stadium

Enter the Lab zone for hands-on inquiry.

Chapter Lab Investigation:
• Directed Inquiry: Gelatin Volcanoes
• Open Inquiry: Gelatin Volcanoes

Inquiry Warm-Ups: • Moving Volcanoes
• How Fast Do Liquids Flow? • How Do
Volcanoes Change Land?

Quick Labs: • Where Are Volcanoes
Found on Earth's Surface? • Volcanic Stages
• Identifying Volcanic Landforms • How Can
Volcanic Activity Change Earth's Surface?

my science online.com

Go to MyScienceOnline.com to
interact with this chapter's content.
Keyword: Volcanoes

> **UNTAMED SCIENCE**
• Why Some Volcanoes Explode

> **PLANET DIARY**
• Volcanoes

> **INTERACTIVE ART**
• Composite Volcano • Volcanoes and
Volcanic Landforms

> **ART IN MOTION**
• Volcanic Boundaries and Hot Spots

> **REAL-WORLD INQUIRY**
• Monitoring a Volcano

CONTENTS

CHAPTER 7

A Trip Through Geologic Time

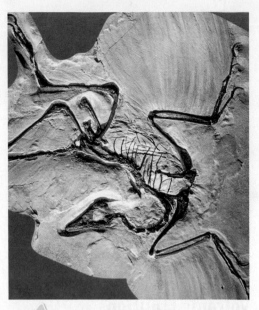

Lab zone Enter the Lab zone for hands-on inquiry.

Chapter Lab Investigation:
• Directed Inquiry: Exploring Geologic Time Through Core Samples
• Open Inquiry: Exploring Geologic Time Through Core Samples

Inquiry Warm-Ups: • What's in a Rock?
• Which Layer Is the Oldest? • How Long Till It's Gone? • This Is Your Life! • How Could Planet Earth Form in Space? • Dividing History

Quick Labs: • Sweet Fossils • Modeling Trace Fossils • Modeling the Fossil Record • How Did It Form? • The Dating Game • How Old Is It? • Going Back in Time • Learning From Fossils • Graphing the Fossil Record • Modeling an Asteroid Impact • Cenozoic Timeline

my science online.com

Go to MyScienceOnline.com to interact with this chapter's content. Keyword: **A Trip Through Geologic Time**

> **PLANET DIARY**
• A Trip Through Geologic Time

> **ART IN MOTION**
• Change Over Geologic Time

> **INTERACTIVE ART**
• Fossil Formation • Piecing Together the Past
• Index Fossils

> **REAL-WORLD INQUIRY**
• How Do You Find the Age of a Rock?

CHAPTER 8
Plant and Animal Life Cycles

 Enter the Lab zone for hands-on inquiry.

Chapter Lab Investigation:
• Directed Inquiry: Investigating Stomata
• Open Inquiry: Investigating Stomata

Inquiry Warm-Ups: • Which Plant Part Is It? • Make the Pollen Stick • Making More • "Eggs-amination"

Quick Labs: • The In-Seed Story • Modeling Flowers • Plant Life Cycles • Where Are the Seeds? • Types of Reproduction • Types of Fertilization • "Eggs-tra" Protection • Cycles of Life • To Care or Not to Care

my science online.com

Go to MyScienceOnline.com to interact with this chapter's content.
Keyword: **Plant and Animal Life Cycles**

> **UNTAMED SCIENCE**
• Amazing Plant Defenses

> **PLANET DIARY**
• Plant and Animal Life Cycles

> **INTERACTIVE ART**
• Seed Dispersal • The Structure of a Flower
• Build a Life Cycle

> **REAL-WORLD INQUIRY**
• Break in the Life Cycle

CONTENTS

Lab® zone Enter the Lab zone for hands-on inquiry.

Chapter Lab Investigation:
• Directed Inquiry: Make the Right Call!
• Open Inquiry: Make the Right Call!

Inquiry Warm-Ups: • What Does the Father Look Like? • What's the Chance? • Observing Traits • Which Chromosome Is Which? • Oops!

Quick Labs: • Observing Pistils and Stamens • Inferring the Parent Generation • Coin Crosses • Patterns of Inheritance • Is It All in the Genes? • Chromosomes and Inheritance • Modeling Meiosis • Comparing Mitosis and Meiosis • Effects of Mutations • What Happens When There Are Too Many Cells?

my science online.com

Go to MyScienceOnline.com to interact with this chapter's content.
Keyword: **Genetics: The Science of Heredity**

> **UNTAMED SCIENCE**
• Where'd You Get Those Genes?

> **PLANET DIARY**
• Genetics: The Science of Heredity

> **INTERACTIVE ART**
• Punnett Squares • Effects of Environment on Genetic Traits

> **VIRTUAL LAB**
• Mendel's Experiments 101 • Track Down the Genetic Mutation

Enter the Lab zone for hands-on inquiry.

Chapter Lab Investigation:
• Directed Inquiry: How Are Genes on the Sex Chromosomes Inherited?
• Open Inquiry: How Are Genes on the Sex Chromosomes Inherited?

Inquiry Warm-Ups: • How Tall Is Tall?
• How Many Chromosomes? • What Do Fingerprints Reveal? • Using Genetic Information

Quick Labs: • The Eyes Have It • What Went Wrong? • Family Puzzle • Selective Breeding • Extraction in Action

my science online.com

Go to MyScienceOnline.com to interact with this chapter's content.
Keyword: **Human Genetics and Genetic Technology**

> **UNTAMED SCIENCE**
• The Case of the X-Linked Gene

> **PLANET DIARY**
• Human Genetics and Genetic Technology

> **INTERACTIVE ART**
• Pedigree • DNA Fingerprinting

> **ART IN MOTION**
• Understanding Genetic Engineering

> **VIRTUAL LAB**
• Why Does My Brother Have It and I Don't?

CONTENTS

Lab zone® Enter the Lab zone for hands-on inquiry.

△ **Chapter Lab Investigation:**
• Directed Inquiry: Nature at Work
• Open Inquiry: Nature at Work

△ **Inquiry Warm-Ups:** • How Do Living Things Vary? • How Can You Classify a Species? • Making a Timeline • How Much Variety Is There?

△ **Quick Labs:** • Bird Beak Adaptations • Finding Proof • Large-Scale Isolation • Slow or Fast? • Modeling Keystone Species • Grocery Gene Pool • Humans and Biodiversity

my science online.com

Go to MyScienceOnline.com to interact with this chapter's content.
Keyword: **Change Over Time**

> **UNTAMED SCIENCE**
• Why Would a Fish Have Red Lips?

> **PLANET DIARY**
• Change Over Time

> **INTERACTIVE ART**
• What Is It Adapted To?
• Homologous Structures

> **ART IN MOTION**
• Rate of Evolution

> **REAL-WORLD INQUIRY**
• What Affects Natural Selection?

Forces and Motion

CHAPTER 12

Lab® zone Enter the Lab zone for hands-on inquiry.

△ **Chapter Lab Investigation:**
- Directed Inquiry: Sticky Sneakers
- Open Inquiry: Sticky Sneakers

△ **Inquiry Warm-Ups:** • Will You Hurry Up?
- Is the Force With You? • Observing Friction
- What Changes Motion? • How Pushy Is a Straw?
- What Makes an Object Move in a Circle?

△ **Quick Labs:** • Describing Acceleration
- Graphing Acceleration• What Is Force?
- Modeling Unbalanced Forces • Calculating
- Around and Around • Newton's Second Law
- Interpreting Illustrations • Colliding Cars
- Which Lands First? • Orbiting Earth

my science online.com

Go to MyScienceOnline.com to interact with this chapter's content.
Keyword: **Forces and Motion**

> **UNTAMED SCIENCE**
- Sir Isaac Visits the Circus

> **PLANET DIARY**
- Forces and Motion

> **INTERACTIVE ART**
- Balanced and Unbalanced Forces
- Conservation of Momentum

> **ART IN MOTION**
- Friction

> **VIRTUAL LAB**
- Investigating Newton's Laws of Motion

CONTENTS

Lab zone® Enter the Lab zone
for hands-on inquiry.

Chapter Lab Investigation:
• Directed Inquiry: Detecting Fake Coins
• Open Inquiry: Detecting Fake Coins

Inquiry Warm-Ups: • Natural Magnets
• Predict the Field • Can You Move a Can
Without Touching It? • How Can Current Be
Measured? • Electromagnetism • How Are
Electricity, Magnets, and Motion Related?
• Electric Current Without a Battery

Quick Labs: • Magnetic Poles • Spinning
in Circles • Earth's Magnetic Field • Drawing
Conclusions • Sparks Are Flying • Producing
Electric Current • Conductors and Insulators
• Modeling Potential Difference • Electric
Current and Magnetism • Magnetic Fields
From Electric Current • Electromagnet • Can a
Magnet Move a Wire? • How Galvanometers
Work • Parts of an Electric Motor • Inducing
an Electric Current • How Generators Work
• How Transformers Work

my science online.com

Go to MyScienceOnline.com to interact with this chapter's content.
Keyword: Electromagnetism

> PLANET DIARY
• Electromagnetism

> INTERACTIVE ART
• Magnetic Fields • Motors and Generators

> ART IN MOTION
• Maglev Train

> REAL-WORLD INQUIRY
• Exploring Electromagnetism

interactive SCIENCE

This is your book.
You can write in it!

Get Engaged!

At the start of each chapter, you will see two questions: an Engaging Question and the Big Question. Each chapter's Big Question will help you start thinking about the Big Ideas of Science. Look for the Big Q symbol throughout the chapter!

HOW CAN WIND KEEP YOUR LIGHTS ON?

THE BIG Q What are some of Earth's energy sources?

This man is repairing a wind turbine at a wind farm in Texas. Most wind turbines are at least 30 meters off the ground where the winds are fast. Wind speed and blade length help determine the best way to capture the wind and turn it into power. **Develop Hypotheses** Why do you think people are working to increase the amount of power we get from wind?

Wind energy collected by the turbine does not cause air pollution.

> UNTAMED SCIENCE Watch the Untamed Science video to learn more about energy resources.

174 Energy Resources

Untamed Science

Follow the Untamed Science video crew as they travel the globe exploring the Big Ideas of Science.

Interact with your textbook.   Interact with inquiry.   Interact online.

Build Reading, Inquiry, and Vocabulary Skills

In every lesson you will learn new 🔁 **Reading** and ◢ **Inquiry** skills. These skills will help you read and think like a scientist. Vocabulary skills will help you communicate effectively and uncover the meaning of words.

Energy Resources

CHAPTER 5

175

My Science online.com

Go Online!

Look for the MyScienceOnline.com technology options. At MyScienceOnline.com you can immerse yourself in amazing virtual environments, get extra practice, and even blog about current events in science.

Explore the Key Concepts.

Each lesson begins with a series of Key Concept questions. The interactivities in each lesson will help you understand these concepts and Unlock the Big Question.

my planeT DiaRY

At the start of each lesson, My Planet Diary will introduce you to amazing events, significant people, and important discoveries in science or help you to overcome common misconceptions about science concepts.

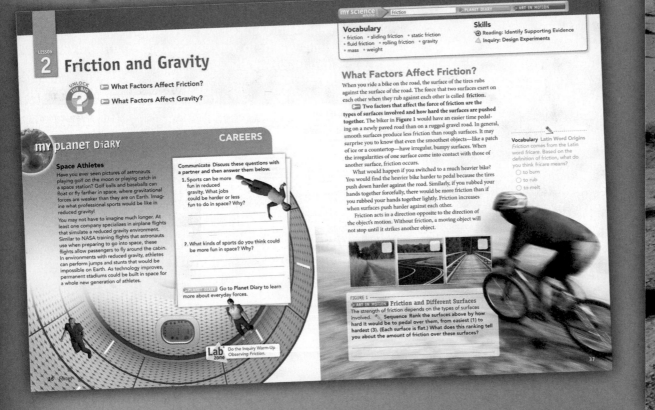

Desertification If the soil in a
of moisture and nutrients, the a
advance of desertlike conditions
fertile is called **desertification** (

One cause of desertification i
is a period when less rain than r
droughts, crops fail. Without pla
blows away. Overgrazing of gras
cutting down trees for firewood

Desertification is a serious pr
and graze livestock where desert
people may face famine and star
central Africa. Millions of rural
cities because they can no longe

apply it!

Desertification affects many
areas around the world.

❶ Name Which continent
has the most existing desert?

❷ Interpret Maps Where in
the United States is the greatest
risk of desertification?

❸ Infer Is desertification a thr
is existing desert? Explain. Circle
your answer.

❹ CHALLENGE If an area is facin
things people could do to possib

132   Land, Air, and Water Reso

Explain what you know.

Look for the pencil. When you see it, it's time to interact with your book and demonstrate what you have learned.

apply it

Elaborate further with the Apply It activities. This is your opportunity to take what you've learned and apply those skills to new situations.

Lab Zone

Look for the Lab zone triangle. This means it's time to do a hands-on inquiry lab. In every lesson, you'll have the opportunity to do a hands-on inquiry activity that will help reinforce your understanding of the lesson topic.

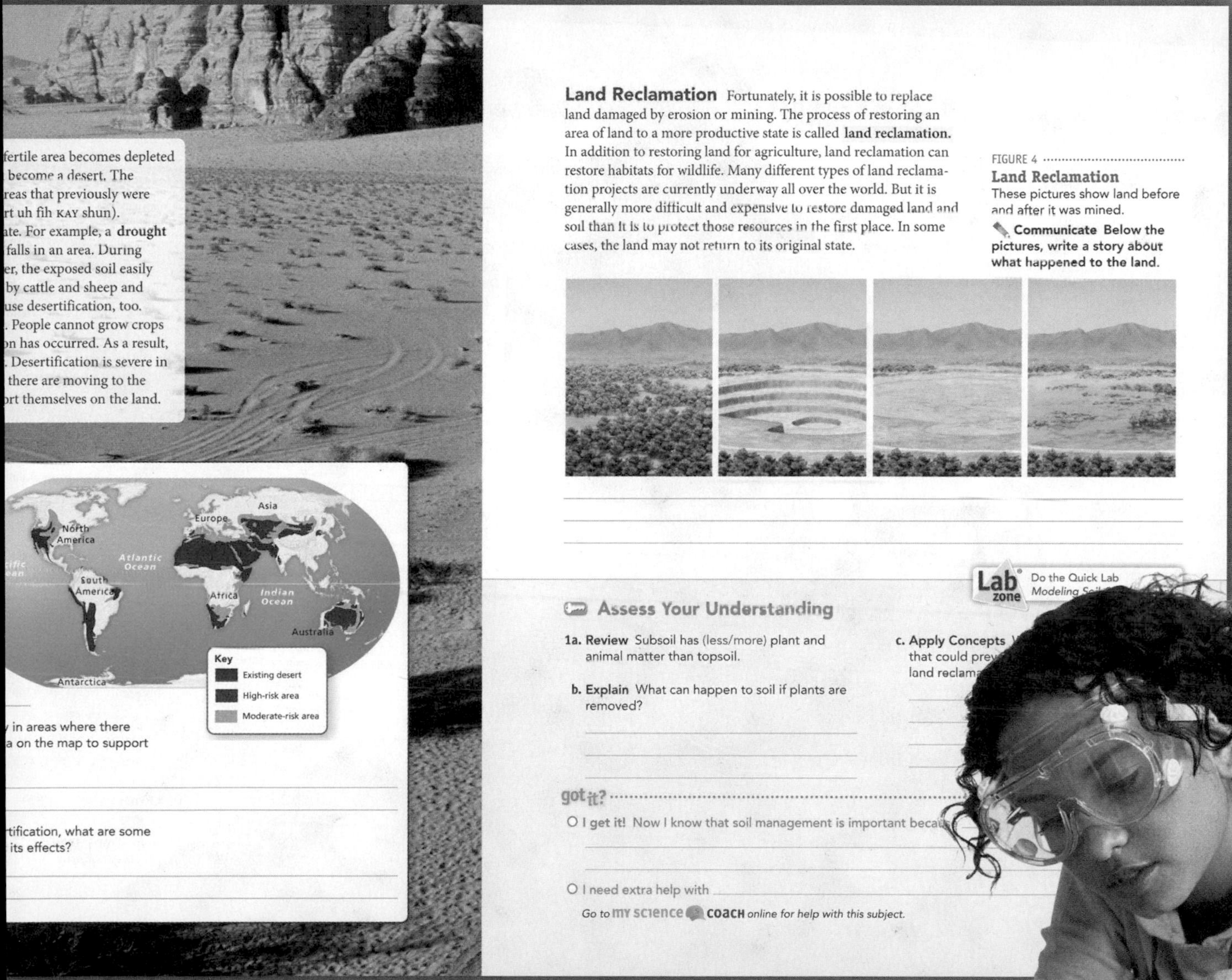

fertile area becomes depleted
become a desert. The
reas that previously were
rt uh fih KAY shun).
te. For example, a **drought**
falls in an area. During
er, the exposed soil easily
by cattle and sheep and
use desertification, too.
. People cannot grow crops
n has occurred. As a result,
. Desertification is severe in
there are moving to the
rt themselves on the land.

Key
- Existing desert
- High-risk area
- Moderate-risk area

y in areas where there
a on the map to support

tification, what are some
its effects?

Land Reclamation Fortunately, it is possible to replace land damaged by erosion or mining. The process of restoring an area of land to a more productive state is called **land reclamation**. In addition to restoring land for agriculture, land reclamation can restore habitats for wildlife. Many different types of land reclamation projects are currently underway all over the world. But it is generally more difficult and expensive to restore damaged land and soil than it is to protect those resources in the first place. In some cases, the land may not return to its original state.

FIGURE 4

Land Reclamation
These pictures show land before and after it was mined.

✎ **Communicate** Below the pictures, write a story about what happened to the land.

📖 Assess Your Understanding

1a. Review Subsoil has (less/more) plant and animal matter than topsoil.

b. Explain What can happen to soil if plants are removed?

c. Apply Concepts
that could prev
land reclam

Lab zone — Do the Quick Lab
Modeling S

got it?

○ **I get it!** Now I know that soil management is important becaus

○ **I need extra help with**

Go to MY SCIENCE COACH online for help with this subject.

got it?

Evaluate Your Progress.

After answering the Got It question, think about how you're doing. Did you get it or do you need a little help? Remember, MY SCIENCE COACH is there for you if you need extra help.

Explore the Big Question.

At one point in the chapter, you'll have the opportunity to take all that you've learned to further explore the Big Question.

Pollution and Solutions

What can people do to use resources wisely?

FIGURE 4 ....

▶ REAL-WORLD INQUIRY All living things depend on land, air, and water. Conserving these resources for the future is important. Part of resource conservation is identifying and limiting sources of pollution.

▶ Interpret Photos On the photograph, write the letter from the key into the circle that best identifies the source of pollution.

Land
Describe at least one thing your community could do to reduce pollution on land.

Air
Describe at least one thing your community could do to reduce air pollution.

Water
Describe at least one thing your community could do to reduce water pollution.

Pollution Sources
A. Sediments
B. Municipal solid waste
C. Runoff from development

Lab zone   Do
            Get

▭ Assess Your Under

1a. Define What are sediments?

b. Explain How can bacteria he spill in the ocean?

c. ANSWER What can people do resources wisely?

d. CHALLENGE Why might a c to recycle the waste they p would reduce water polluti

got it? ....

◯ I get it! Now I know that can be reduced by

◯ I need extra help with

Go to MY SCIENCE coa with this subject.

Answer the Big Question.

Now it's time to show what you know and answer the Big Question.

Review What You've Learned.

Use the Chapter Study Guide to review the Big Question and prepare for the test.

Practice Taking Tests.

Apply the Big Question and take a practice test in standardized test format.

159

INTERACT... WITH YOUR TEXTBOOK...

Go to MyScienceOnline.com and immerse yourself in amazing virtual environments.

THE BIG QUESTION

Each online chapter starts with a Big Question. Your mission is to unlock the meaning of this Big Question as each science lesson unfolds.

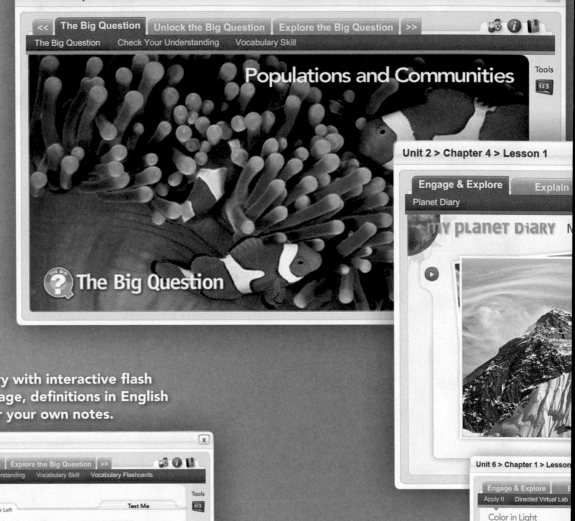

VOCAB FLASH CARDS

Practice chapter vocabulary with interactive flash cards. Each card has an image, definitions in English and Spanish, and space for your own notes.

Unit 4 > Chapter 1 > Lesson 1

The Big Question | Untamed Science | Check Your Understanding | Vocabulary Skill | Vocabulary Flashcards

Vocabulary Flashcards

Card List — Create-a-Card — 10 Cards Left — Test Me

Lesson Cards | My Cards

Birth Rate
Carrying Capacity
Commensalism
Community
Competition
Death Rate
Ecology
Ecosystem
Emigration
Habitat
Host
Immigration
Limiting Factor

Science Vocabulary

Term: **Community**

Definition: **All the different populations that live together in a particular area.**

Add Notes — View Spanish

Card 5 of

Unit 6 > Chapter 1 > Lesson 1

Engage & Explore | Explain | Elaborate | Evaluate
Apply It | Do the Math | Art in Motion | Interactive Art | Real World Inquiry

The Nebraska Plains

▶ Bald Eagle

Information | Media

Haliaeetus leucocephalus
Bald Eagles are 80-95 cm tall with a wingspan of 180-230 cm. These birds are born with all brown feathers but grow white feathers on their head, neck, and tail.

Layers List — ▲ Show

INTERACTIVE ART

At MyScienceOnline.com, many of the beautiful visuals in your book become interactive so you can extend your learning.

WITH INQUIRY...

interactive SCIENCE
GO ONLINE

my science online.com > Populations and Communities > PLANET DIARY > LAB ZONE > VIRTUAL LAB

🔄 ➕ 🌐 http://www.myscienceonline.com/

▷ PLANET DIARY

My Planet Diary online is the place to find more information and activities related to the topic in the lesson.

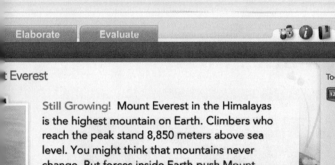

Elaborate | Evaluate

t Everest

Tools
123

Still Growing! Mount Everest in the Himalayas is the highest mountain on Earth. Climbers who reach the peak stand 8,850 meters above sea level. You might think that mountains never change. But forces inside Earth push Mount Everest at least several millimeters higher each year. Over time, Earth's forces slowly but constantly lift, stretch, bend, and break Earth's crust in dramatic ways!

Planet Diary Go to Planet Diary to learn more about forces in the Earth's crust.

▶ Next

22 of 22

Back ◀

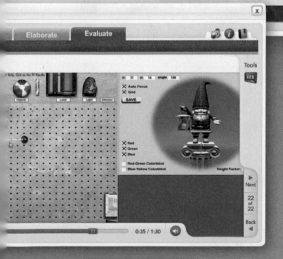

0:35 / 1:30

▷ VIRTUAL LAB

Get more practice with realistic virtual labs. Manipulate the variables on-screen and test your hypothesis.

Find Your Chapter

1 Go to www.myscienceonline.com.

2 Log in with username and password.

3 Click on your program and select your chapter.

Keyword Search

1 Go to www.myscienceonline.com.

2 Log in with username and password.

3 Click on your program and select Search.

4 Enter the keyword (from your book) in the search box.

Other Content Available Online

▷ **UNTAMED SCIENCE** Follow these young scientists through their amazing online video blogs as they travel the globe in search of answers to the Big Questions of Science.

▷ **MY SCIENCE COACH** Need extra help? My Science Coach is your personal online study partner. My Science Coach is a chance for you to get more practice on key science concepts. There you can choose from a variety of tools that will help guide you through each science lesson.

▷ **MY READING WEB** Need extra reading help on a particular science topic? At My Reading Web you will find a choice of reading selections targeted to your specific reading level.

? BIG IDEAS OF SCIENCE

Have you ever worked on a jigsaw puzzle? Usually a puzzle has a theme that leads you to group the pieces by what they have in common. But until you put all the pieces together you can't solve the puzzle. Studying science is similar to solving a puzzle. The big ideas of science are like puzzle themes. To understand big ideas, scientists ask questions. The answers to those questions are like pieces of a puzzle. Each chapter in this book asks a big question to help you think about a big idea of science. By answering the big questions, you will get closer to understanding the big idea.

✎ **Before you read each chapter, write about what you know and what more you'd like to know.**

BIGIDEA

Scientists use scientific inquiry to explain the natural world.

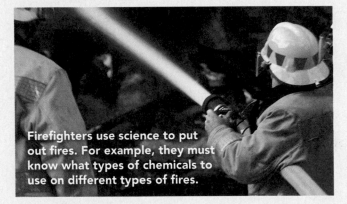

Firefighters use science to put out fires. For example, they must know what types of chemicals to use on different types of fires.

What do you already know about how science affects your everyday life? ✎ **What more would you like to know?**

_____

_____

_____

Big Question:

? How do science and society affect each other? Chapter 1

✎ **After reading the chapter, write what you have learned about the Big Idea.**

_____

_____

_____

BIGIDEA

Scientists use mathematics in many ways.

Scientists rely on estimates when they cannot obtain exact data. Estimating is a quick way of determining how many birds are in this photo.

Which math skills have you used to study science? ✎ **Which math skills do you need to practice?**

_____

_____

_____

Big Question:

? How do scientists use measurement and mathematics? Chapter 2

✎ **After reading the chapter, write what you have learned about the Big Idea.**

_____

_____

_____

BIGIDEA
Earth's land, water, air, and life form a system.

Many forms of marine life, such as this orca breaching near the coastline, interact every day with Earth's land, air, and water.

What do you already know about how land, water, air, and life interact on Earth?

✏️ **What would you like to know?**

_____

_____

_____

Big Question

❓ What is the structure of Earth? Chapter 3

✏️ **After reading the chapter, write what you have learned about the Big Idea.**

_____

_____

_____

_____

_____

_____

_____

_____

BIGIDEA
Earth is a continually changing planet.

In 2009, this eruption of an underwater volcano off the coast of Tonga formed a small new island in the Pacific Ocean.

What do you already know about how Earth changes every day?

✏️ **What would you like to know?**

_____

_____

_____

_____

Big Questions

❓ How do moving plates change Earth's crust? Chapter 4

❓ Why do earthquakes occur more often in some places than in others? Chapter 5

❓ How does a volcano erupt? Chapter 6

✏️ **After reading the chapters, write what you have learned about the Big Idea.**

_____

_____

_____

_____

Earth is 4.6 billion years old and the rock record contains its history.

This fossil of a turtle is millions of years old.

What do you already know about Earth's history? ✏️ **What more would you like to know?**

_____
_____
_____

Big Question:

❓ How do scientists study Earth's past? Chapter 7

✏️ **After reading the chapter, write what you have learned about the Big Idea.**

_____
_____
_____
_____
_____
_____
_____
_____
_____

Living things grow, change, and reproduce during their lifetimes.

Tadpoles hatch from frog eggs and grow into adults.

What do you already know about how animals survive and produce offspring? ✏️ **What more would you like to know?**

_____
_____
_____

Big Question:

❓ How do plants and animals reproduce and grow? Chapter 8

✏️ **After reading the chapter, write what you have learned about the Big Idea.**

_____
_____
_____
_____

BIGIDEA

Genetic information passes from parents to offspring.

Once in a while, a koala joey is born with white fur instead of the usual gray fur. Even with such a striking difference, you can tell the joey is related to its mother.

What do you already know about how offspring resemble their parents? ✏️ **What more would you like to know?**

_____

_____

_____

Big Questions:

❓ Why don't offspring always look like their parents? Chapter 9

❓ How can genetic information be used? Chapter 10

✏️ **After reading the chapters, write what you have learned about the Big Idea.**

_____

_____

_____

BIGIDEA

Living things change over time.

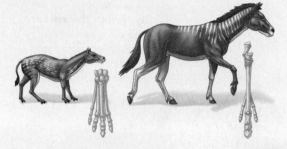

Modern horses are descended from much smaller animals with toes instead of hooves.

What do you already know about how life forms change? What more would you like to know?

_____

_____

_____

Big Question:

❓ How do life forms change over time? Chapter 11

✏️ **After reading the chapter, write what you have learned about the Big Idea.**

_____

_____

_____

By hitting the soccer ball with her head, this athlete changes the direction of the soccer ball.

A net force causes an object's motion to change.

What do you already know about how the force of one object can affect the movement of another object? ✎ **What more would you like to know?**

_____

_____

_____

_____

Big Questions

❓ How do objects react to forces? Chapter 12

✎ **After reading the chapters, write what you have learned about the Big Idea.**

_____

_____

_____

_____

As these skydivers fall, they don't lose any energy—the energy just takes different forms.

HOW COULD POLLUTION FROM ASIA AFFECT PEOPLE IN THE ARCTIC?

THE BIG ?

How do science and society affect each other?

These children are sledding in Igloolik, Nunavut, in northern Canada. The sky is so blue and clear that you would think that the cold arctic air would be fresh and clean. However, pollution generated thousands of kilometers away affects the air, snow, water, wildlife, and people of the Arctic. Pollutants from burning fossil fuels migrate north. High concentrations of chemicals that evaporate from televisions, paints, and pesticides in countries worldwide, have been found in the people that live in small Arctic towns like Igloolik.

Develop Hypotheses How do you think pollution produced thousands of kilometers away ends up in the Arctic?

_____

_____

_____

_____

> **UNTAMED SCIENCE** Watch the **Untamed Science** video to learn more about scientific inquiry.

Using Scientific Inquiry

1 Getting Started

Check Your Understanding

1. **Background** Read the paragraph below and then answer the question.

Emi studied hard to prepare for her science lab investigation. She was concerned because her **research** was complex. However, it was also well **organized**. Emi wanted to use her lab report as a **sample** of her science work.

> **Research** is information collected from careful study of a subject.
>
> To be **organized** is to be arranged in an orderly way.
>
> A **sample** is a portion of something that is used to represent the whole thing.

- Why would being organized help Emi prepare for her lab investigation?

_____

_____

_____

> **MY READING WEB** If you have trouble completing the question above, visit **My Reading Web** and type in *Using Scientific Inquiry.*

Vocabulary Skill

Identify Multiple Meanings Words you use every day may have different meanings in science. Look at the different meanings of the words below.

Word	Everyday Meaning	Scientific Meaning
model	n. A person who poses for an artist. Example: Julio worked as a *model* for a sculptor in Daytona Beach.	n. A representation of an object or process. Example: A globe is a *model* of Earth.
cost	n. The price paid by someone for a certain object or service. Example: The *cost* of the train ticket was $35.	n. An undesirable outcome of a decision. Example: Dirty air might be one *cost* of not using "clean" energy.

2. **Quick Check** Circle the sentence below that uses the scientific meaning of the word *cost.*
- The cost of repairing the highway was $12 million.
- One cost of building a new highway might be more cars on the road.

science

subjective reasoning

controlled experiment

A B C

opinion

Chapter Preview

LESSON 1
- science • observing
- quantitative observation
- qualitative observation
- classifying • inferring
- predicting • analyzing
- ⊙ Identify Supporting Evidence
- △ Observe

LESSON 2
- skepticism • data
- empirical evidence
- objective reasoning
- subjective reasoning
- pseudoscience
- ⊙ Outline
- △ Interpret Data

LESSON 3
- scientific inquiry • hypothesis
- independent variable
- dependent variable
- controlled experiment • bias
- repeated trial • replication
- scientific explanation
- ⊙ Summarize
- △ Develop Hypotheses

LESSON 4
- scientific literacy
- evidence • opinion
- ⊙ Summarize
- △ Interpret Data

> VOCAB FLASH CARDS For extra help with vocabulary, visit **Vocab Flash Cards** and type in *Using Scientific Inquiry.*

3

How Scientists Work

 **How Do Scientists Explore the Natural World?**

MY PLANET DIARY

BIOGRAPHY

Model of the
paclitaxel molecule

The Road to Discovery

Today, paclitaxel is one of the most effective drugs against cancer. But it was not well known until Dr. Susan Horwitz's work drew attention to it. Horwitz went to college to study history, but after taking a biology class, she became fascinated with how scientists form and test their ideas. After graduating with a biology degree, she went on to a graduate program in biochemistry. At the time, there were very few women in graduate schools, but that didn't stop Dr. Horwitz. Armed with a doctorate degree, Horwitz eventually moved to her current position at Albert Einstein School of Medicine. It was there that she discovered how paclitaxel stopped the growth of cancer cells. Her work convinced pharmaceutical companies to turn paclitaxel into a medicine that now saves many lives.

Write your answers to each question below.

1. Why did Susan Horwitz decide to become a scientist?

_____

_____

_____

_____

2. What do you think is the difference between the way historians and scientists think?

_____

_____

_____

_____

> **PLANET DIARY** Go to **Planet Diary** to learn more about how scientists work.

Lab zone® Do the Inquiry Warm-Up
How Does a Scientist Think?

Vocabulary

- science • observing • quantitative observation
- qualitative observation • classifying • inferring
- predicting • analyzing

Skills

↻ **Reading:** Identify Supporting Evidence
△ **Inquiry:** Observe

How Do Scientists Explore the Natural World?

Paclitaxel is one of the many great success stories of science. **Science** is a way of learning about the natural world. Science is also the knowledge gained through this exploration. 🗝 **Scientists explore the natural world by using skills such as observing, classifying, making models, inferring, and predicting. They form and test their ideas through scientific investigation.**

Observing Paclitaxel is a drug made from the bark of the Pacific yew tree, shown in **Figure 1.** The seeds and leaves of all yew trees are poisonous, but Native Americans found that they could make teas from the bark and needles. They observed that drinking the tea sometimes made people who were sick feel better. **Observing** means using one or more of your senses to gather information. Native Americans observed the effects of the tea on sick people and decided that the tea could help treat headaches and other health problems. Observing also means using tools, such as a microscope, to help your senses.

Observations can be quantitative or qualitative. A **quantitative observation** deals with numbers, or amounts. For example, seeing that a person has a fever of 101 degrees Fahrenheit is a quantitative observation. A **qualitative observation** deals with descriptions that cannot be expressed in numbers. Feeling that a person's head is warm is a qualitative observation.

FIGURE 1 ···

What Do You Observe?

The photo shows the berries and bark of the slow-growing and ancient Pacific yew tree.

✎ △**Observe** Write one quantitative observation and one qualitative observation about the tree.

_____

_____

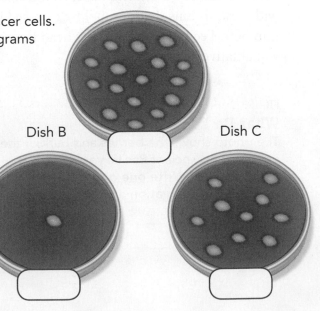

did you know?

The bark of the Florida yew tree also contains a compound that can treat cancer. Threats of harvesting this endangered tree worried many conservationists. Fortunately, in 1993, researchers found a way to make the compound synthetically in a laboratory.

Organizing Data

In 1962, plant biologists collected samples of different types of trees. They were searching for a cure to cancer. They sent the samples back to a laboratory that ran tests to see what effect these samples had on cancer cells. Then the samples were classified according to their results. **Classifying** is grouping together items that are alike in some way. Paclitaxel, from the yew tree sample, was classified as having anticancer effects. **Figure 2** shows a test that can be used to classify samples.

Making Models

Once people realized that paclitaxel had an effect on cancer cells, they needed to figure out what it was made of. They built a model that showed the arrangement of atoms in a molecule of paclitaxel. Making models involves creating representations of complex objects or processes. Some models can be made of actual objects, such as balls and sticks. Others are in the form of drawings or mathematical equations. Models help people study things that can't be observed directly. By using models, scientists were able to better understand the properties of paclitaxel.

Inferring

Susan Horwitz examined how paclitaxel affected cancer cells. The invention of the electron microscope allowed scientists to observe how cells divide. From her observations, Horwitz inferred that paclitaxel stopped cancer cells from dividing.

When you explain or interpret things that you observe, you are **inferring.** Making an inference is not guessing. Inferences are based on reasoning from your prior knowledge and from what you observe. By making inferences about how paclitaxel worked, Horwitz was able to show that paclitaxel could be an effective anticancer drug.

FIGURE 2 ·······

Classifying Cancer Colonies

Scientists observed the effects of different tree samples on cancer cells. Each petri dish began with 10 colonies of cancer cells. The diagrams show the results after being treated with the tree samples.

✎ **Complete these tasks.**

1. **Observe** Count and record the number of cancer cell colonies below each petri dish.

2. **Infer** What can you infer about each of the samples from the petri dishes that were treated?

_____

_____

3. **Classify** Which sample(s) should be classified as possible cancer treatment(s)? Explain.

_____

Dish A

Dish B

Dish C

Predicting

Predicting Paclitaxel only kills some kinds of cancer cells. After running tests on mice, scientists made predictions about what types of human cancer paclitaxel might treat. **Predicting** means making a statement or a claim about what will happen in the future based on past experience or evidence.

Scientists planted human tumors onto mice. Then they gave the mice paclitaxel. The mice with breast tumors showed signs of recovery. From this observation, scientists predicted that paclitaxel could help treat breast cancer.

Predictions and inferences are related. While inferences are attempts to explain what has already happened, predictions are forecasts about what will happen. If you see a puddle of water on the floor, you might infer that a glass spilled. If, however, you see someone bump into a glass, you can predict that it's about to make a mess.

Identify Supporting Evidence Determine if the statement below is a prediction or an inference. Then underline the sentence in the text that supports your answer. "The alarm clock is blinking 12:00 because the electricity went out temporarily."

do the math!

Only a small amount of paclitaxel can be produced from the bark of a single Pacific yew. It requires 120 kilograms of paclitaxel to treat 60,000 patients with 2 grams each of the drug per year.

1 Calculate If 1 kilogram of bark can produce about 0.015 kilogram of paclitaxel, how much bark is needed to make 120 kilograms of paclitaxel?

2 CHALLENGE You need to cut down 3 trees to get about 5 kilograms of bark. About how many trees do you have to cut down each year to make enough paclitaxel for 60,000 patients?

3 Evaluate the Impact on Society Some people think that the destruction of so many trees and the habitat of forest animals was too high a price to pay for paclitaxel. Explain why you agree or disagree with this opinion.

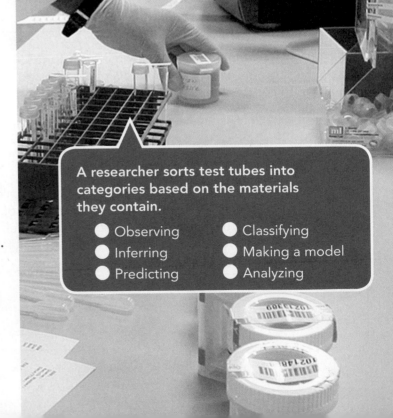

This scientist places a sample under a microscope in order to see objects she can't see with her eyes alone.

- ○ Observing
- ○ Inferring
- ○ Predicting
- ○ Classifying
- ○ Making a model
- ○ Analyzing

Analyzing Before paclitaxel could be sold as a medicine, scientists had to run experiments on people. They measured the size of individuals cancerous tumors throughout the experiment. They also recorded any side effects they observed. Then they analyzed this data. **Analyzing** involves evaluating observations and data to reach a conclusion about them. Scientists compared the data and concluded that paclitaxel was a very effective treatment for women with cancer in their ovaries.

Scientific Investigations The story of paclitaxel involves many scientific investigations. A scientific investigation is the forming and testing of ideas about the natural world. When people carry out scientific investigations, they use all the skills discussed above. These include observing, making models, classifying, inferring, predicting, and analyzing. Scientists use these skills when they investigate questions in science. **Figure 3** shows people using these skills.

FIGURE 3 ·······································

 INTERACTIVE ART **Scientific Investigations**
Scientific investigations involve observing, making models, classifying, inferring, predicting, and analyzing.

✎ **Interpret Photos** Determine which skill is being described in each box in the lab photo.

A researcher sorts test tubes into categories based on the materials they contain.

- ○ Observing
- ○ Inferring
- ○ Predicting
- ● Classifying
- ○ Making a model
- ○ Analyzing

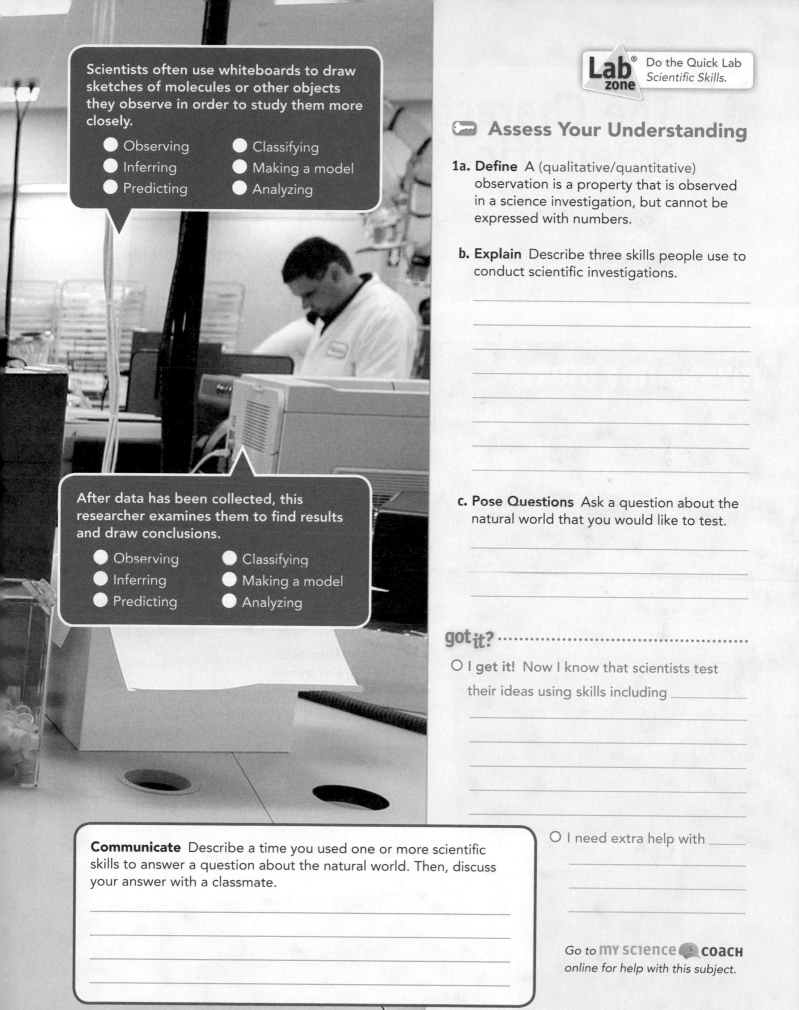

Scientists often use whiteboards to draw sketches of molecules or other objects they observe in order to study them more closely.

- ○ Observing
- ○ Inferring
- ○ Predicting
- ○ Classifying
- ○ Making a model
- ○ Analyzing

After data has been collected, this researcher examines them to find results and draw conclusions.

- ● Observing
- ● Inferring
- ● Predicting
- ● Classifying
- ● Making a model
- ● Analyzing

Communicate Describe a time you used one or more scientific skills to answer a question about the natural world. Then, discuss your answer with a classmate.

_____

_____

_____

Lab ® Do the Quick Lab
zone *Scientific Skills.*

🔑 Assess Your Understanding

1a. Define A (qualitative/quantitative) observation is a property that is observed in a science investigation, but cannot be expressed with numbers.

b. Explain Describe three skills people use to conduct scientific investigations.

_____

_____

_____

_____

_____

_____

_____

_____

_____

c. Pose Questions Ask a question about the natural world that you would like to test.

_____

_____

_____

got it? ....

○ **I get it!** Now I know that scientists test their ideas using skills including _____

_____

_____

_____

○ **I need extra help with** _____

_____

_____

Go to **MY SCIENCE** 🄢 **COACH**
online for help with this subject.

9

The Characteristics of Scientific Knowledge

UNLOCK THE BIG ?

🔑 **What Do Scientific Investigations Involve?**

🔑 **What Are Scientific and Pseudoscientific Thinking?**

🔑 **What Characterizes Science and Its Methods?**

my PLANET DiARY

BIOGRAPHY

A Scientific Success

Dr. Percy Lavon Julian (1899–1975) was a renowned research chemist who grew up and studied in Indiana. His first experiments isolated simple compounds found in plants. He used this knowledge to later develop drugs to treat glaucoma, slow down the effects of Alzheimer's disease, and prevent miscarriages. Julian also created aerofoam, a flame retardant that saved the lives of countless sailors during World War II.

Dr. Percy Julian became the first African-American chemist inducted into the National Academy of Sciences in 1973.

Communicate Discuss the question with a partner. Write your answer below.

Why do you think it's important for scientists like Dr. Julian to be curious?

_____

_____

_____

_____

 Lab zone® Do the Inquiry Warm-Up *Developing a Theory.*

▶ **PLANET DIARY** Go to **Planet Diary** to learn more about scientific investigations.

Vocabulary
- skepticism
- data
- empirical evidence
- objective reasoning
- subjective reasoning
- pseudoscience

Skills
- ➲ Reading: Outline
- △ Inquiry: Interpret Data

What Do Scientific Investigations Involve?

As you just read, scientists use certain skills, such as observing and inferring, in scientific investigations. They also bring important attitudes to investigations. These attitudes include curiosity, honesty, creativity, and open-mindedness, or the willingness to accept new ideas. But scientists are also skeptical. Their **skepticism,** which is an attitude of having doubt, keeps scientists from accepting faulty ideas and may lead to new understandings.

🔑 **In addition to the skills and attitudes of scientists, scientific investigations involve collecting evidence in a scientific way and using that evidence to make inferences and to reach conclusions. Figure 1** shows an investigation that researchers performed with crows to find out if crows could recognize an individual human face. To test their idea, researchers wore caveman masks while they trapped, banded, and released several of the crows living in a group in a specific area. During this process, the captured crows cawed loudly. Later, researchers walked among the group of crows to observe how the banded crows reacted. On different walks, the researchers wore the caveman masks, different masks, or no masks.

FIGURE 1 ···
Cause and Effect
Researchers wanted to see if crows could recognize a specific human face.

✎ **Complete these tasks.**

1. **Classify** Read the two statements below. Write *O* next the statement that is an observation. Write *I* next to the statement that is an inference.

    _____ The crow caws because it does not like to be handled.

    _____ The crow caws when it is banded.

2. **Observe** Use the evidence from the During Capture picture to circle the banded crows in the After Capture picture.

3. **Identify** Look at the After Capture picture. What are some other ways besides cawing that the crows reacted?

    _____

    _____

    _____

During Capture

After Capture

Collecting Empirical Evidence

In the crow investigation, the researchers walking among the crows recorded their observations in notebooks. The information they recorded is called data. **Data** (singular: *datum*) are facts, figures, and other evidence collected during a scientific investigation.

When data are collected in a precise, logical, and consistent manner, the data are called empirical evidence. **Empirical evidence** is data that are collected using scientific processes that describe particular observations. All scientific investigations involve the collection of relevant empirical evidence. **Figure 2** shows some of the data that the crow researchers collected on some of their walks.

FIGURE 2 ···

> REAL-WORLD INQUIRY **Conclusions and Empirical Evidence**

The table below uses tally marks to show the number of times that a banded crow had a specific type of reaction to two different researchers at a certain site.

✎ **Answer the questions on each notebook page.**

1. Make Generalizations Why might a scientist choose to use a table to record this kind of data?

_____

_____

A Banded Crow's Reactions	Researcher Wearing Caveman Mask	Researcher Wearing Different Mask
No reaction	–	|||| ||||	
Looking at researcher	||	–
Looking at and cawing at researcher	|||	–
Cawing and following researcher	||||		–

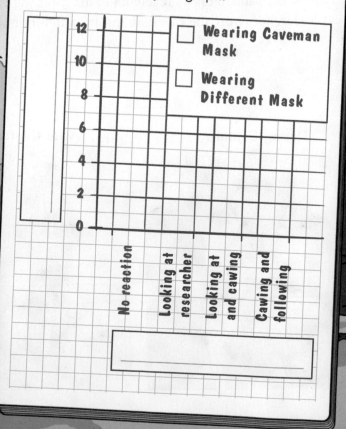

2. Interpret Data Using the data from the table, make a bar graph in the space below, or on a computer or calculator. Label the *x*- and *y*-axes of your graph.

☐ Wearing Caveman Mask

☐ Wearing Different Mask

Analyzing Empirical Evidence

After scientists collect empirical evidence, they carefully look for patterns in it that allow them to make inferences and predict trends. Once they have collected a lot of data that show the same patterns, they use logic and reasoning to state a conclusion. In the crow investigation, the researchers studied all the data they collected. Each set of data showed a similar pattern. Crows banded by the researchers cawed at and followed researchers wearing caveman masks more often than other researchers without masks or with different masks. Therefore, the researchers concluded that crows can recognize an individual human face.

3. Infer Based on the information in the graph, make an inference about whether or not crows can recognize an individual human face. Explain the reasoning that led to your inference.

Crow Study

Inference: _____

Reasoning: _____
_____
_____
_____
_____
_____
_____
_____
_____

Lab ® Do the Quick Lab
zone Activities of Science.

Assess Your Understanding

1a. Review (Empirical evidence/Logical reasoning) is data collected using scientific processes that describe particular observations.

b. Relate Evidence and Explanation What evidence allowed the crow researchers to conclude that crows can recognize an individual human face?
_____
_____
_____
_____
_____
_____

c. Apply Concepts Some people might tell stories about an animal recognizing them. How might skepticism about such stories lead to new explanations?
_____
_____
_____
_____
_____
_____

got it? ....

O **I get it!** Now I know scientific investigations involve _____
_____
_____

O **I need extra help with** _____
_____

Go to **MY SCIENCE COACH** online for help with this subject.

What Are Scientific and Pseudoscientific Thinking?

Recall that the crow researchers used reasoning to review their data. Then the researchers drew a logical conclusion from their data. Scientific thinking requires a logical way of reasoning based on gathering and evaluating evidence. Look at **Figure 3**. Scientific thinking can be divided into two general types of reasoning: objective reasoning and subjective reasoning.

Objective and Subjective Reasoning

Objective reasoning is reasoning that is based on evidence. Because scientific reasoning relies on gathering and evaluating evidence, it is objective reasoning.

In contrast, **subjective reasoning** is reasoning that is based on personal feelings or personal values. For instance, you might think crows are stupid. As a result, you might conclude crows could not possibly recognize humans. If you based your conclusion on your personal feelings, you could reach the wrong conclusion.

Look at the photograph in **Figure 3**. By being able to distinguish between objective and subjective reasoning, you can distinguish between strong scientific claims and less reliable assertions.

✏️ **Outline** Read the text and complete the outline.

1. _____

   a. Based on evidence

   b. Example: _____

   _____

2. Subjective Reasoning

   a. _____

   _____

   b. Example: Crows are stupid.

FIGURE 3 ··

Subjective Reasoning

Personal feelings can be misleading. In science, conclusions are based on objective reasoning.

✏️ **Look at the photograph of a horseshoe crab and answer the questions.**

1. **Describe** What words would you use to describe horseshoe crabs? Are your words based on opinion or on objective reasoning?

_____

_____

_____

_____

2. **Apply Concepts** The blood of horseshoe crabs is often used to ensure that some vaccines do not contain potentially deadly contamination from bacteria. Knowing this, what new words would you use to describe this animal?

_____

_____

_____

Science Versus Pseudoscience

Science Versus Pseudoscience For thousands of years, people imagined that patterns in the stars looked like humans, animals, or objects. What does the star pattern in **Figure 4** look like to you? Perhaps you know that astronomy is the scientific study of stars. But do you know what astrology is? It is the use of stars to predict the course of human events. Unlike astronomy, astrology is not a science.

Astrologers claim that the course of human life in part depends on the stars. They make use of data regarding the positions of the stars. But they base their predictions on subjective reasoning rather than empirical evidence. So astrology can be classified as a pseudoscience. A **pseudoscience** is a set of beliefs that may make use of science. But the conclusions and predictions of a pseudoscience are not based on observation, objective reasoning, or scientific evidence.

🔑 **Science is based on empirical evidence and well-reasoned interpretation of data. Pseudoscience may make use of scientific data. But the conclusions of pseudoscience are based on subjective reasoning, faulty reasoning, or faulty beliefs, not on careful examination of evidence.**

Taurus

Aldebaran

FIGURE 4 ··

Starry-Eyed

Scientists make use of empirical evidence and relevant data to draw conclusions. People who practice pseudoscience do not.

✎ **Identify Faulty Reasoning** Look at the outline above of the star pattern called Taurus (also known as "the bull"). Identify whether each statement below is based on science (S) or on pseudoscience (P).

_____ People whose zodiac sign is Taurus tend to be loyal.

_____ Aldebaran is the brightest star in the constellation Taurus.

_____ Each year, Taurus reaches its highest point in the sky in January.

_____ Taurus is a constellation, or pattern of stars.

_____ Scientists know that bulls are colorblind. So many people whose zodiac sign is Taurus cannot tell green and red apart.

15

Nonscientific Ways of Knowing

The study of science provides a logical, well-reasoned understanding of the natural world. But understanding other aspects of the world requires training outside of science. Look at **Figure 5.** Many artists apply their understanding of mathematics when they use points, lines, angles, shapes, and sizes to define spaces. But knowing mathematics would not provide you with a complete understanding of the meaning of an abstract painting. You would need training in the history and principles of art to fully understand the aesthetics, or beauty, of such a painting.

The study of science can also provide only a partial understanding of subjects such as philosophy and history. For example, scientists do not claim to be able to explain the meaning of life. Nor do scientists seek to explain the circumstances that led to major historic events.

"Untitled" (1920) by George Grosz.
© 2009 VAGA

FIGURE 5 ···

Eyes of the Beholder

Many artists create beauty in their art by using the science of defining spaces in a series of lines, angles, and shapes.

✏️ CHALLENGE Find three simple shapes in the painting and outline them. How does your appreciation of this piece of art relate to the science of shapes? How does it relate to your personal sense of beauty?

_____

_____

_____

_____

Lab zone® Do the Quick Lab *Scientific Thinking.*

🗝 Assess Your Understanding

2a. Summarize The conclusions of (science/pseudoscience) are based on subjective reasoning.

b. Identify Faulty Reasoning Is palm-reading a science or a pseudoscience? Explain.

_____

_____

_____

got it?

○ I get it! Now I know that science is based on empirical evidence. Although pseudoscience makes use of scientific data, the conclusions of pseudoscience are based on _____

_____

○ I need extra help with _____

_____

Go to **MY SCIENCE ⓢ COACH** online for help with this subject.

What Characterizes Science and Its Methods?

🔑 **Science is characterized by an ordered approach to learning about the world.** This approach relies on using skills to collect empirical data, analyzing the data to find patterns that lead to inferences and trends, and using objective reasoning to reach conclusions. Because scientific investigations are ordered, other scientists can repeat them.

apply it!

Scientists once thought that coral reefs thrive only in shallow water because sunlight can easily reach them. But in 1999, scientists discovered a reef off Florida's southwest coast that lies at depths between 60 and 80 meters. Scientists think that this reef thrives because the water around it is extremely clear so sunlight can reach it.

1 **Summarize** How did scientists revise their original thinking to explain where coral reefs can thrive?

_____

_____

2 **Discuss** How does the revised idea illustrate the nature of science?

_____

_____

_____

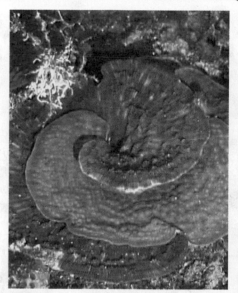

Coral at Florida's Pulley Ridge

Although science is based on empirical evidence and objective reasoning, its results are open to change. Sometimes, scientific investigations produce data that show new patterns. If the new patterns do not contradict existing ones, scientists keep their existing conclusions, or perhaps revise them slightly. However, sometimes, new patterns contradict existing patterns. Scientists must then throw out their old conclusions.

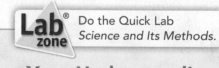

Lab zone®   Do the Quick Lab *Science and Its Methods.*

🔑 Assess Your Understanding

got it?··

O **I get it!** Now I know that science is characterized by _____

_____

_____

O **I need extra help with** _____

Go to MY SCIENCE Ⓢ COACH *online for help with this subject.*

Designing an Experiment

🔑 **What Is Scientific Inquiry?**

🔑 **How Do You Design an Experiment?**

🔑 **What Is a Scientific Explanation?**

MY PLANET DIARY

DISCOVERY

A Galactic Garden

Orbiting Earth is an amazing experience. But eating dehydrated space food can be boring and unappetizing. So, scientists conducted an experiment to see whether they could grow vegetables in space. They picked an old Thanksgiving favorite: sweet potatoes. They grew some cuttings onboard a shuttle and some cuttings on Earth. The cuttings were placed under similar conditions in space and on Earth for five days. They discovered that the number of roots that sprouted were the same in both places. But the roots of those in space actually grew faster! The cuttings that grew in space had more sugar and starch than those on Earth. Astronauts, however, hope that space potatoes taste just as good!

Write your answers to each question below.

1. What was the purpose of the experiment?

_____
_____
_____
_____

2. Why do you think the scientists grew cuttings both in space and on Earth?

_____
_____
_____
_____
_____
_____

> **PLANET DIARY** Go to **Planet Diary** to learn more about designing experiments.

Lab zone Do the Inquiry Warm-Up *What's the Question?*

Vocabulary

- scientific inquiry
- hypothesis
- independent variable
- dependent variable
- controlled experiment
- bias
- repeated trial
- replication
- scientific explanation

Skills

- Reading: Summarize
- Inquiry: Develop Hypotheses

What is Scientific Inquiry?

It's Monday morning. You drag yourself out of bed and go to the kitchen. You pour yourself a bowl of cereal with milk and eat a spoonful. Yuck! Something tastes awful. The milk has gone sour. What happened? Your questioning is the beginning of the **scientific inquiry** process. ⚷ **Scientific inquiry is the process of gathering evidence about the natural world and proposing explanations based on this evidence.**

Posing Questions and Defining a Problem

Scientific inquiry often begins with a question that leads to an observation. Your observation about the sour milk may lead you to ask a question: What made the milk go bad so quickly? Questions come from your experiences, observations, and natural curiosity. Look at **Figure 1** to pose a question about the strawberries.

Once you've posed your question, you should define a problem that can be tested. It is possible that others have already investigated the same problem. You can do research to find what information is known about the topic before you try to answer your question.

Look for the milk icon to follow the steps of the scientific inquiry.

✎ **Identify** In the text, circle the question posed about the sour milk.

FIGURE 1 ···
Posing Questions
Scientific inquiry starts with a question.

✎ **Pose Questions** Observe the photo. Then pose a question you could test about the strawberries.

_____

_____

_____

_____

✎ **Develop Hypotheses**
Underline an explanation about souring milk in the text. Then write your own explanation about why the milk went sour.

_____

_____

_____

Developing a Hypothesis

Developing a Hypothesis How could you answer your question about the milk becoming sour? You start by developing a hypothesis. A **hypothesis** (plural: *hypotheses*) is a possible answer to a scientific question. It is also a possible explanation. For example, you know that you bought the milk five days ago. You also know that you left the milk out overnight. So, you may suspect that the temperature at which the milk is kept contributes to how quickly the milk goes sour. Your hypothesis might be that milk turns sour more quickly if it is left at room temperature for too long. Use **Figure 2** to practice developing a hypothesis.

Hypotheses are not facts. In science, a fact is an observation or description that has been confirmed repeatedly. For example, that milk has calcium is a fact that describes something found in milk. However, a hypothesis is one possible explanation to answer a question.

In science, you must be able to test a hypothesis. Researchers perform investigations and collect data that either support or fail to support a hypothesis.

FIGURE 2 ···
Developing a Hypothesis
Adam wonders why he has been sleeping less than usual.

✎ **Develop Hypotheses** Write an explanation that might answer Adam's question.

_____

_____

_____

Lab ® Do the Quick Lab *It*
zone *Starts With a Question.*

🔑 Assess Your Understanding

1a. Pose Questions Write a testable question about what causes cavities.

_____

_____

b. ✎ **Develop Hypotheses** Write another possible explanation for why milk sours.

_____

_____

got it?

○ **I get it!** Now I know that scientific inquiry is

_____

_____

_____

_____

○ **I need extra help with** _____

Go to **my science** 🔵ˢ **coach** *online for help with this subject.*

How Do You Design an Experiment?

Once you have a hypothesis, you need to test it. 🔑 **You can design an experiment that follows reliable scientific principles to test a hypothesis.** To test a hypothesis that milk will sour quicker if left out at room temperature than at colder temperatures, you could smell the milk periodically when it is left out at room temperature. But how do you know that the milk wouldn't turn sour in the refrigerator? You cannot know unless you smell the milk periodically when it is left in the refrigerator, as well.

Controlling Variables Suppose you want to test the temperature. You could observe how milk smells when it is kept at different temperatures over time. All other variables, or factors that can change in an experiment, must be the same. This includes variables such as the type of milk used and the container it's kept in. By keeping these variables the same, you will know that any differences in the odor of the milk are due to temperature alone.

The one factor that is purposely changed to test a hypothesis is the **independent variable**. In this experiment, the independent variable is air temperature. The factor that may change in response to the independent variable is the **dependent variable**. Here, the dependent variable is the time it takes the milk to sour. Look at **Figure 3**.

✎ **Name** In the text, circle the independent variable and underline the dependent variable for the milk experiment.

FIGURE 3 ···

Controlling Variables

A student wants to test whether shampoo cleans oily hair better than water alone. The student mixes oil with water in one test tube and oil with soapy water in another test tube. She watches to see when the mixture separates.

✎ **Use the data table to complete the activities.**

1. **Classify** What is the independent variable? What is the dependent variable?

   _____

   _____

2. **Identify** Name two other possible variables in this experiment.

   _____

   _____

3. **Draw Conclusions** Write a summary of what was observed in this experiment. What can you conclude?

   _____

   _____

Amount of Soap in Water (mL)	Time of Oil and Water Separation (seconds)
0	15
1.5	105

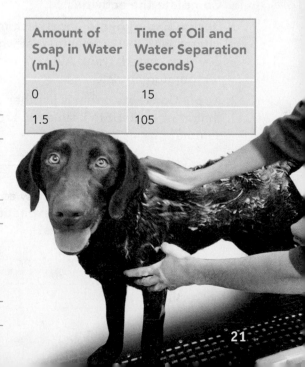

Designing a Controlled Experiment

A scientific experiment in which only one variable is changed at a time is called a **controlled experiment**. You decide to test the milk at three different temperatures, as shown in **Figure 4.** All other variables are kept the same. If your experiment were to have more than one independent variable, there would be no way to tell which variable influenced your results.

For example, in this experiment you are testing the effect of three temperatures on the time it takes milk to sour. You will keep all variables the same, except temperature. However, if you were to use different types of milk for each of your samples or kept each sample in a different kind of container, then you would not know which variable caused the milk to sour quickly. Was it temperature? Was it the type of milk? For this reason, you can only test one variable at a time in a controlled experiment.

Experimental Bias

In any experiment there is a risk of introducing experimental **bias,** an error in the design of the experiment. The error may make a particular result more likely. For example, without meaning to, you might use a carton of milk that is beyond its expiration date.

✎ Summarize Explain how bias can affect an experiment.

_____

_____

_____

_____

_____

FIGURE 4 ·······························

▷ VIRTUAL LAB A Controlled Experiment

In this experiment, the temperatures must be different enough that your results can only be due to temperature.

✎ Complete the activities.

1. **Design Experiments** Label each milk sample with the temperature at which it could be tested. (*Hint:* Average room temperature is 22°C.)

2. **Apply Concepts** What is another variable that must be kept the same for each milk sample?

_____

_____

3. **Analyze Sources of Error** How could testing milk that is past its expiration date introduce experimental bias?

_____

_____

_____

Collecting and Interpreting Data You are almost ready to begin your experiment. You decide to test the milk every 12 hours. Before starting your experiment, determine what observations you will make and what data you will gather. Recall that data are the facts, figures, and other information gathered through qualitative and quantitative observations. A helpful tool to use while collecting data is a data table. A data table is an organized way to collect and record your observations.

After your data have been collected, they need to be interpreted. Tools such as diagrams, graphs, and models can help you interpret data. They can reveal patterns or trends. For example, you might organize the data for the milk experiment in a graph. You could use the graph to compare the time it took for each sample to sour.

do the math!

Information organized in a data table can be made into a graph. This data table shows the percent of students who finished testing over a period of time.

❶ Graph Plot the data on the graph. Identify the independent and dependent data.

Students Finished (%)	Time (min)
0	30
2	45
50	60
98	75

_____

_____

_____

_____

_____

❷ Read Graphs Describe the difference in the percent of students finished testing between 30 and 45 minutes and between 45 and 60 minutes.

_____

_____

_____

_____

_____

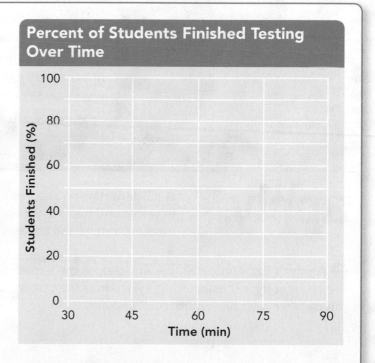

Percent of Students Finished Testing Over Time

❸ [CHALLENGE] After about how many minutes would you predict that all the students will finish their testing?

_____

Drawing Conclusions Once you've collected your data, you can draw a conclusion. A conclusion is a summary of what you have learned from an experiment. When drawing a conclusion, examine the data objectively to see if the results support or fail to support your hypothesis. Also, consider whether the data allow you to draw a conclusion at all based on the results.

You may decide that the data support your hypothesis. The milk at room temperature smelled sour sooner than the milk kept refrigerated. Now, repeat your experiment to see if you get the same results. A conclusion is unreliable if it comes from the results of one experiment. Many trials are needed before a hypothesis can be accepted as true. A **repeated trial** is a repetition of an experiment.

Sometimes your data won't support your hypothesis. When this happens, check your experiment for errors, or bias, and for improvements. Maybe you could have tested the milk every 6 hours. Sometimes you cannot draw a firm conclusion from your data. For example, you might discover that milk left at room temperature, 22°C, soured sooner than milk left at 35°C.

Hypotheses are valuable even when they are not supported by the data. They can lead to further investigation. For example, you may decide to test whether milk's exposure to light has an effect on how quickly it sours. How would you design an experiment to test your new hypothesis?

apply it!

A student dipped squares of nylon, polyester, and cotton in water and hung them up to dry. He then measured the amount of time the squares took to dry.

❶ **Analyze Experimental Results** Before the experiment, the student hypothesized that nylon dries the fastest. Do the data support his hypothesis? Explain.

_____

_____

Fabric	Trial 1	Trial 2	Trial 3	Trial 4
Nylon	28 min	25 min	27 min	33 min
Polyester	17 min	19 min	19 min	25 min
Cotton	44 min	45 min	45 min	51 min

❷ **Identify Experimental Bias** Are the results from one trial different from the others? If so, how might the student have introduced bias that resulted in the different results?

_____

_____

_____

❸ **Apply Concepts** Based on these results, what kind of socks would you want to wear on a fishing trip?

_____

_____

Communicating

Scientists communicate, or share their results with others through writing and speaking. They give talks at meetings, exchange information on the Internet, or publish articles in scientific journals.

When scientists share the results of their research, they describe their procedure and data so that others can repeat their experiments. A **replication** is an attempt by a different group of scientists to conduct the same experiment. Different groups of scientists must run replications and obtain similar results before these results can be used as evidence to support a hypothesis. Even after results are accepted, ongoing skepticism can lead to new understanding of a scientific replication.

Sometimes, scientists from around the world work together on scientific inquiries that are part of a larger project. For example, the International Space Station is one of the largest international scientific projects in history. Sixteen nations participate in it. The goal is to conduct experiments in unusual conditions, such as near-weightlessness. On such a large project, scientists must share their ideas and results regularly.

✏️ **Communicate**
You conclude that milk left at room temperature (22°C) sours quicker than refrigerated milk. Write a catchy newspaper headline that communicates this to other scientists.

VOLUME 22, NO. 03

OHIO SCIENCE WEEKLY

Lab zone® Do the Lab Investigation
Become a Learning Detective.

🔑 Assess Your Understanding

2a. Identify At the beach, a student tests the effectiveness of three sunscreens, each with a different sun protection factor. What is the independent variable in her experiment?

_____

_____

b. Design Experiments Controlling

_____ and eliminating

_____ are important parts

of designing an experiment.

got it? ....

○ **I get it!** Now I know that you design an experiment _____

_____

○ **I need extra help with** _____

Go to **my science** 💬 **coach** *online for help with this subject.*

What Is a Scientific Explanation?

If you are studying chemistry or physics, you can usually design and conduct controlled experiments, as shown in **Figure 5.** If you are studying astronomy or geology, however, it can be difficult or even impossible to carry out controlled experiments.

When you study astronomy or geology, you are often trying to understand how things happened in the past. You must make observations and then use what you already know to draw conclusions. Drawing a conclusion from observations is a way to develop a **scientific explanation.**  **A scientific explanation is a generalization that makes sense of observations by using logical reasoning.** For example, in 2000, workers digging a road in Tennessee discovered a layer of black soil filled with bones. Scientists examined the bones to find out what animals had lived at this site. Scientists knew these animals had lived in North America between 4 and 7 million years ago. Using this data, they reasoned that the site must be the same age! Things in the natural world that cannot be studied through a controlled experiment often rely on scientific explanation.

FIGURE 5 ···

Think Pink

Baby flamingos are born with white feathers, but over time they turn bright pink. Sometimes the feathers of adult flamingos fade back to white. Why does this happen?

✎ **Design Experiments** Plan an investigation to determine if something in their diet causes flamingos' feathers to turn pink.

❶ **Question**
Does a flamingo's diet of shrimp affect the color of its feathers?

❷ **Hypothesis**

_____

_____

🔑 Assess Your Understanding

3a. Review What is one problem that studying the past causes for a geologist?

_____

_____

_____

_____

_____

b. Summarize How does a scientist explain something when a controlled experiment cannot be carried out?

_____

_____

_____

_____

_____

_____

_____

c. Make Generalizations What types of sources might a scientist use to investigate a question about flamingos before designing an experiment?

_____

_____

_____

_____

_____

_____

_____

got it? ···

○ **I get it!** Now I know that a scientific explanation is _____

_____

_____

○ **I need extra help with** _____

Go to **my science** ⓢ **coach** online for help with this subject.

---

❸ Variables

Independent Variable

_____

_____

Dependent Variable

_____

_____

Factors to Control

_____

_____

_____

_____

❹ Procedure

_____

_____

_____

_____

_____

_____

_____

❺ Analyze Information

Scientific Skills Used

_____

_____

_____

Possible Sources of Error

_____

_____

_____

Alternative Explanations

_____

_____

Scientific Literacy

🔑 **Why Is Scientific Literacy Important?**

🔑 **How Do You Analyze Scientific Claims?**

🔑 **How Do You Research Scientific Questions?**

my PLANET DiARY

FUN FACTS

DNA Detective

If you watch TV crime programs, then you know that investigators often use DNA testing to solve a case. How does DNA testing help? Scientists can identify people by examining their DNA. A person's DNA is unique, like a person's fingerprint.

In the future, you may need more information about DNA evidence than what is given in TV programs. For example, if you are selected to sit on a jury in a trial that uses DNA evidence, you will want to know scientific details about DNA to make your decision.

Communicate Discuss the question with a partner. Then write your answer below.

A DNA sample links an accused suspect to a crime. Suppose there is a one in ten million chance that the DNA sample comes from someone else. How would this affect your decision as a juror?

_____

_____

_____

_____

_____

▶ **PLANET DIARY** Go to **Planet Diary** to learn more about scientific literacy.

Lab zone Do the Inquiry Warm-Up *Posing Questions.*

Why Is Scientific Literacy Important?

Suppose someone asks you to sign a petition to protect the Canada geese in your town. "People are trying to keep the geese away from our parks!" he says. A person standing nearby says, "But the geese make an awful mess." You're confused. You know you need to learn more about the issue.

Vocabulary
- scientific literacy
- evidence
- opinion

Skills
- Reading: Summarize
- Inquiry: Interpret Data

Scientific Literacy To understand the many issues you encounter, you need scientific literacy. **Scientific literacy** means understanding scientific terms and principles well enough to ask questions, evaluate information, and make decisions. 🗝 **By having scientific literacy, you will be able to identify good sources of scientific information, evaluate them for accuracy, and apply the knowledge to questions or problems in your life.**

Evidence and Opinion To evaluate scientific information, you must first distinguish between evidence and opinion. In science, **evidence** includes observations and conclusions that have been repeated. Evidence may or may not support a scientific claim. An **opinion** is an idea that may be formed from evidence but has not been confirmed by evidence. In **Figure 1,** try separating evidence from opinion.

Summarize In your own words, summarize the second paragraph.

_____
_____
_____
_____
_____
_____
_____

FIGURE 1 ·····················
Evidence and Opinion
Should your town try to keep Canada geese away from the parks?

✎ **Distinguish Evidence and Opinion** Under each statement in the boxes, label the statement as evidence or opinion.

Geese spend up to 12 hours a day eating grass and roots.
_____

Geese are too messy.
_____

 Do the Quick Lab *Scientific Literacy Survey.*

🗝 Assess Your Understanding

got it? ·····································

○ I get it! Now I know that by having scientific literacy _____
_____

○ I need extra help with _____
Go to MY SCIENCE COACH online for help with this subject.

How Do You Analyze Scientific Claims?

Scientific literacy gives you the tools to analyze scientific claims. Scientific reasoning gives you the process. 🗝 **You can use scientific reasoning to analyze scientific claims by looking for bias and errors in the research, evaluating data, and identifying faulty reasoning.**

FIGURE 2 ···

Analyzing Scientific Claims

✏ **Read about this research and think about the researcher's conclusion. Then answer the question in each box.**

A researcher needs to find out if people in a town have good computer skills. The researcher advertises online for participants to take the test. He offers a free thumb drive as a payment.

Twenty people take the test. Everyone gets a perfect score.

The researcher concludes that the town's residents have excellent computer skills.

Identify Experimental Bias What is an important source of experimental bias in this research?

_____

_____

_____

Analyze Sources of Error What is an important source of error in this research?

_____

_____

_____

_____

apply it!

Read the sample advertisement. Then use scientific reasoning to analyze its claims.

❶ Interpret Data How many subjects were in the study?

_____

❷ Evaluate Scientific Claims Do the research results support the claim that using *KnowHow* helps people get better grades? Explain your answer.

_____

_____

_____

❸ CHALLENGE Was Subject B's score actually 25% higher than Subject A's score? Calculate.

_____

_____

Improve Your Test Scores!

A scientifically *proven* new way to get better grades!

Just look at our research results.

Subject A: Studied for 30 minutes in front of the TV and didn't use our product. Scored 72 points!

Subject B: Studied for 3 hours with a tutor and used KnowHow! Scored 90 points!

That means **25% HIGHER GRADES** with **KnowHow!**

You CAN make the grade! ORDER **KnowHow** TODAY!

 Lab zone Do the Quick Lab *Analyzing Claims.*

🔑 Assess Your Understanding

1a. Identify What is one way to use scientific reasoning to analyze scientific claims?

_____

_____

_____

b. Make Generalizations Would a scientific claim based on one test be a good claim? Why or why not?

_____

_____

_____

got it?

○ **I get it!** Now I know that I can analyze scientific claims by _____

_____

_____

○ **I need extra help with** _____

Go to **my science** 💬 **coach** *online for help with this subject.*

31

How Do You Research Scientific Questions?

Chances are you will need to answer scientific questions to make decisions in your life. For example, suppose you injure your knee and the doctor gives you a choice of treatments. You need to do research before deciding. In science, you also need to do research to design an experiment.

🔑 **To make decisions and design experiments, you need relevant and reliable background information.** Relevant information is knowledge that relates to the question. Reliable, or consistent and truthful, information comes from a person or organization that is not biased. Generally, universities, museums, and government agencies are sources of reliable information. So are many nonfiction books, magazines, and educational Web sites. Look at the sources in **Figure 3**.

Vocabulary Use Context to Determine Meaning Underline the phrase in the text that helps you understand the word *relevant*.

FIGURE 3 ···

Evaluating Sources of Information

✎ **Evaluate Data Reliability** Circle the most relevant and reliable source of information for your research about water use in your community. Explain your choice below.

_____

_____

_____

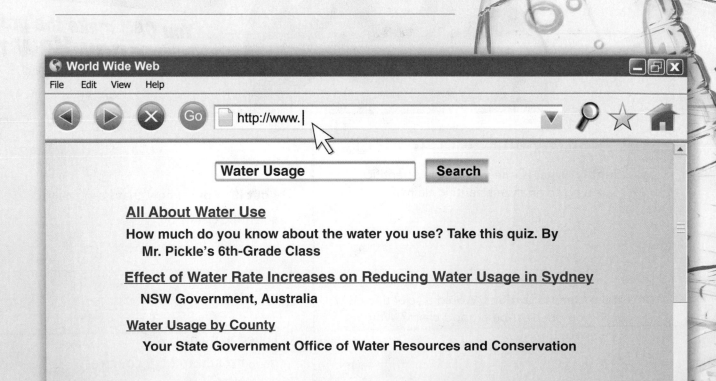

World Wide Web

File   Edit   View   Help

◀ ▶ ✕ Go   📄 http://www. |

Water Usage   **Search**

All About Water Use

How much do you know about the water you use? Take this quiz. By Mr. Pickle's 6th-Grade Class

Effect of Water Rate Increases on Reducing Water Usage in Sydney

NSW Government, Australia

Water Usage by County

Your State Government Office of Water Resources and Conservation

EXPLORE THE BIG Q

All Bottled Up!

How do science and society affect each other?

1 Clear plastics that could be used to make light, cheap bottles were invented.

2 Manufacturers made many plastic bottles for many beverages, which people buy.

3 Empty plastic bottles became litter. Bottle deposit laws encouraged recycling empty bottles.

4 Ways to recycle bottles into new, safe products were invented.

5 People bought products made from recycled bottles.

6 Bottles that use 30% less plastic were designed.

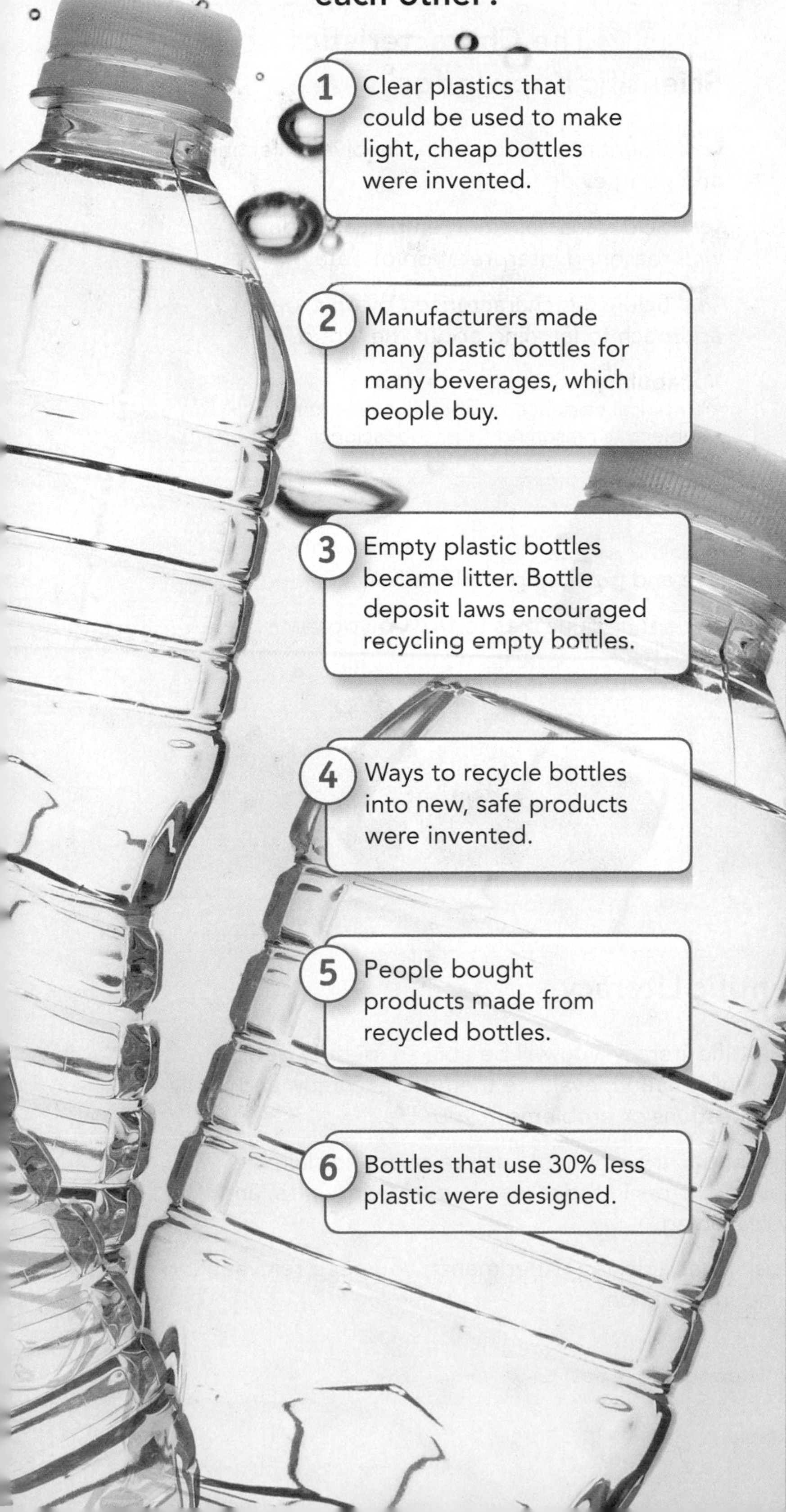

FIGURE 4 ....

▶ **REAL-WORLD INQUIRY** Science and society are interconnected.

✎ **Infer** Circle the boxes that show the work of science. Then explain below how the statements in boxes 3 and 4 show how science and other aspects of society affect each other.

_____

_____

_____

_____

Lab zone Do the Quick Lab *Sources of Information.*

🔑 Assess Your Understanding

2a. Review What is information that relates to a question called?

_____

b. ANSWER THE BIG ❓ How do science and society affect each other?

_____

_____

_____

_____

_____

got it? ....

○ **I get it!** Now I know that to make informed

decisions and design experiments, you

need _____

_____

○ **I need extra help with** _____

Go to **my science** ⑤ **coach** *online for help with this subject.*

33

1 Study Guide

 Science affects society by allowing individuals, communities, and countries to analyze the _____ and _____ of a decision.

LESSON 1 How Scientists Work

🗝 Scientists explore the natural world by using skills such as observing, classifying, making models, inferring, and predicting. They form and test their ideas through scientific investigation.

Vocabulary
- science • observing
- quantitative observation
- qualitative observation
- classifying • inferring
- predicting • analyzing

LESSON 2 The Characteristics of Scientific Knowledge

🗝 Scientific investigations involve collecting and using evidence.

🗝 Science is based on empirical evidence and well-reasoned interpretation of data.

🗝 Science is characterized by an ordered approach to learning about the world.

Vocabulary • skepticism • data
- empirical evidence • objective reasoning
- subjective reasoning • pseudoscience

LESSON 3 Designing an Experiment

🗝 Scientific inquiry is the process of gathering evidence and proposing explanations.

🗝 You can design an experiment that follows reliable scientific principles to test a hypothesis.

🗝 A scientific explanation is a generalization about observations by using logical reasoning.

Vocabulary • scientific inquiry • hypothesis
- independent variable • dependent variable
- controlled experiment • bias
- repeated trial • replication • scientific explanation

LESSON 4 Scientific Literacy

🗝 By having scientific literacy, you will be able to identify good sources of scientific information, evaluate them for accuracy, and apply the knowledge to questions or problems in your life.

🗝 You can use scientific reasoning to analyze scientific claims by looking for bias and errors in the research, evaluating data, and identifying faulty reasoning.

🗝 To make decisions and design experiments, you need relevant and reliable background information.

Vocabulary
- scientific literacy • evidence • opinion

Review and Assessment

LESSON 1 How Scientists Work

1. When scientists group information into categories, they are

   a. analyzing.   **b.** making models.

   c. classifying.   **d.** observing.

2. Finding that the length of a caterpillar is 4.5 centimeters is a(n) _____ observation.

3. Infer What inference might a scientist make if she observed an increase in her energy after eating an afternoon snack?

_____

_____

_____

LESSON 2 The Characteristics of Scientific Knowledge

4. Empirical evidence is data and observations that have been collected through

   a. the Internet.   **b.** inferring.

   c. scientific processes. **d.** the imagination.

5. An attitude of doubt toward ideas is

_____ .

6. **Write About It** Neurology is, in part, the study of the brain's functions to determine how the brain controls the human nervous system. Phrenology is the study of the shape of a person's skull to determine that person's personality. Both neurology and phrenology are based on evidence that specific areas of the brain control specific functions. Which is a science? Which is a pseudoscience? Explain.

LESSON 3 Designing an Experiment

7. What is often the first step in scientific inquiry?

   a. developing a hypothesis

   b. posing a question

   c. designing an experiment

   d. collecting data

8. The variable that is purposely changed in order to be tested is the _____

_____

9. Compare and Contrast How are repetition and replication of an experiment different?

_____

_____

_____

10. Why is it important to have only independent variable?

_____

_____

_____

_____

_____

11. How do tools such as diagrams, graphs, and models help you understand the results of an experiment?

_____

_____

_____

12. A scientific explanation makes sense of observations using _____ reasoning.

1 Review and Assessment

Scientific Literacy

13. Being able to understand basic scientific terms and principles well enough to apply them to your life is called

  a. evidence.   **b.** opinion.

  c. scientific literacy.   **d.** scientific questioning.

14. When you perform scientific research, you should look for information that is _____

15. **Pose Questions** A scientific study proves that frozen fruit is more nutritious than canned fruit. What questions would you want answered before you accept this claim?

_____

_____

_____

_____

_____

16. **Evaluate Data Reliability** You are working on a science fair project and need to gather research on your topic. Where will you look for reliable information? Identify at least three different sources.

_____

_____

_____

_____

_____

_____

How do science and society affect each other?

17. Scientists are studying the effects that melting ice might have on rising sea levels. Describe how the results of these studies might affect society.

_____

_____

_____

_____

_____

_____

_____

_____

_____

_____

_____

_____

_____

_____

_____

_____

_____

Ohio Benchmark Practice

Multiple Choice

Mark only one answer for each question.

1. Lia tested the effect of temperature on plant growth. Before the experiment, she hypothesized that plants grow better in warm temperatures. The results of the experiment are shown below.

   How would you *best* describe the results of Lia's experiment?

   A. The results support the hypothesis.
   B. The results fail to support the hypothesis.
   C. No conclusion can be drawn from the results.
   D. The results are inaccurate.

2. Drew made observations while visiting the pet store. Which of the following is a quantitative observation he may have made?

   A. The store sells hamsters.
   B. The dogs are fed at 4:00 in the afternoon.
   C. The store's employees wear blue aprons.
   D. There are ten more cats than rabbits.

3. A controlled experiment

   A. introduces bias.
   B. tests several variables at once.
   C. tests only one variable and is free of bias.
   D. changes no variables.

4. Determining that the moon is the same age as Earth based on comparison of the age of moon rocks to the age of Earth rocks is an example of

   A. a scientific explanation.
   B. a qualitative observation.
   C. an estimate.
   D. anomalous data.

Short Answer

Write your answer to Question 5 on the lines below.

5. Dowsing is the process of searching for underground water by walking over land while holding a stick. When the person holding the stick senses that the stick is shaking, the person might be standing near water. On what scientific principles, if any, is dowsing based? How might dowsing be based on faulty reasoning?

_____

_____

_____

_____

_____

_____

_____

_____

Extended Reponse

Use the graph below to answer Question 6. Write your answer on a separate sheet of paper.

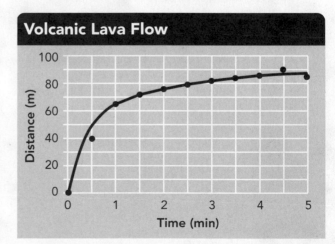

6. A scientist measured the distance that a stream of lava from a volcano flowed over 5 minutes. What logical conclusion you can draw from the graph of the scientist's data?

A RECIPE for Success

Before the 1800s, people thought that living things could appear from nonliving material. But Louis Pasteur did not think that this accepted theory was correct. He suspected that bacteria traveled on particles in the air and reproduced when they landed on biological material—like broth. Pasteur experimented to test his theory. His experiments were successful because they followed a good experimental design. Pasteur tested only one variable, included a control, and repeated his experiments.

Pasteur put broth into two flasks with curved necks. The necks would let in oxygen but keep out bacteria in air. Pasteur boiled the broth in one flask to kill any bacteria in the broth. He did not boil the broth in the other flask.

In a few days, the unboiled broth turned cloudy, showing that new bacteria were growing. The boiled broth remained clear. Pasteur then took the flask with clear broth and broke its curved neck. Bacteria from the air could enter the flask. In a few days, the broth became cloudy. Pasteur's results showed that bacteria were introduced into the broth through the air, and did not grow from the broth itself. He repeated the experiment, and showed that the results were not an accident.

Recipe for a Successful Experiment

1. Make a hypothesis.
2. Write a procedure.
3. Identify the control.
4. Identify the variable.
5. Observe and record data.
6. Repeat.
7. Make a conclusion.

Design It The Dutch scientist Jean-Baptiste van Helmont proposed a recipe for generating mice. He set up an experiment using dirty rags and a few grains of wheat in an open barrel. After about 21 days, mice appeared. The results, he concluded, supported his hypothesis that living things come from nonliving sources. What is wrong with van Helmont's experimental design? Using his hypothesis, design your own experimental procedure. What is your control? What is your variable?

BEWARE of Greenwashing!

Many businesses claim to produce environmentally friendly products. But how can you know the truth? *Greenwashing* is a term that combines the words *green* and *whitewashing*. It refers to the practice of making a product, service, or company appear to be more environmentally friendly than it really is.

Sometimes, identifying greenwashing is difficult because advertisements can be very persuasive. Fortunately, thinking like a scientist can help. As you evaluate a company's environmental claims, consider the following questions.

✓ **Is there proof?** Is there a scientific basis for the claims made by the company?

✓ **Is there a trade-off?** Does creating or delivering the product or service have negative environmental effects that are greater than the benefits of the product or service?

✓ **Are the claims meaningless?** Some labels, such as "100% natural," have no scientific or regulatory meaning.

✓ **Who says so?** Has a reliable source tested the company's claims?

Apply It Find advertisements for products that claim to have environmental benefits. Use the questions above to evaluate the claims. Then, create a brochure to educate the public about greenwashing.

Now Safe for the Environment!

CFC free

With **Eco-sensitive** ingredients

HOW CAN SCIENCE SPEED UP A JET?

How do scientists use measurement and mathematics?

This is a model of an F-16XL jet. The model represents just four percent of the jet's actual size. The model is being tested in a wind tunnel where fans blow air towards the jet. Smoke and lasers are then used to show how the air moves around the jet. The scientists are looking for smooth airflow around the jet to increase the jet's performance and reduce engine noise.

△**Infer** Why do you think scientists would make a model of a jet and wind test it before building it?

_____

_____

_____

_____

> **UNTAMED SCIENCE** Watch the **Untamed Science** video to learn more about how scientists use mathematics.

Mathematics and Models in Science

2 Getting Started

Check Your Understanding

1. **Background** Read the paragraph below and then answer the question.

Jane worked as a scientific **researcher** in the field of genetics. She designed experiments that provided **evidence** certain families can be at higher risk for specific diseases. Joan learned that genetics has had a great impact on how **society** treats diseases.

> A **researcher** is anyone who studies a scientific problem.
>
> **Evidence** is any object or result that indicates a certain theory is true.
>
> **Society** is an organization of individuals, forming a larger unit such as a city or town.

- What is one activity a scientific researcher does?

_____

> **MY READING WEB** If you have trouble completing the question above, visit **My Reading Web** and type in *Mathematics and Models in Science.*

Vocabulary Skill

High-Use Academic Words High-use academic words are words that are used frequently in academic reading, writing, and discussions. These words are different from key terms because they appear in many subject areas.

Word	Definition	Example
trend	*n.* a general tendency or direction	An increase in song downloads shows a *trend* in the way people purchase music.
periodically	*adv.* at regular intervals	Scientists update their research *periodically* throughout their experiments.

2. **Quick Check** Complete each sentence with the correct high-use academic word.

- Melting glaciers show a _____ toward rising temperatures.

- Birds return to the nest _____ to tend to their chicks.

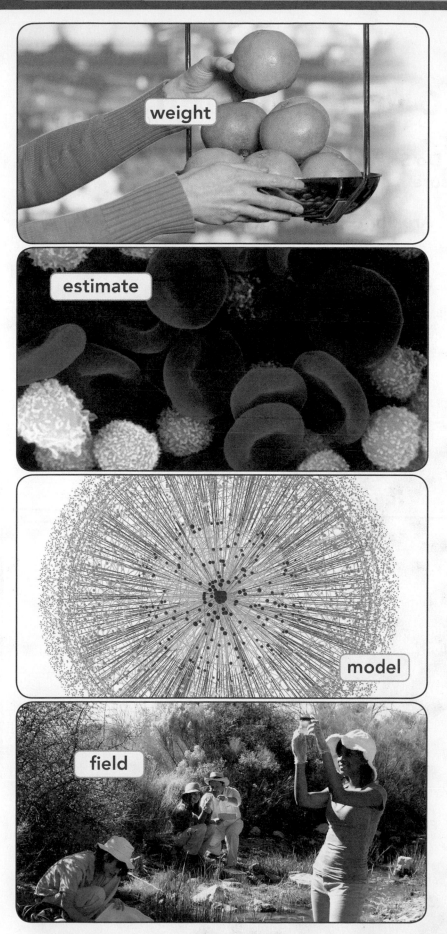

weight

estimate

model

field

Chapter Preview

LESSON 1
- metric system
- International System of Units (SI)
- mass • weight • volume
- meniscus • density

↻ **Ask Questions**
△ **Measure**

LESSON 2
- estimate • accuracy • precision
- significant figures • mean
- median • mode • range
- anomalous data • percent error

↻ **Identify the Main Idea**
△ **Interpret Data**

LESSON 3
- graph • linear graph
- nonlinear graph • outlier

↻ **Relate Cause and Effect**
△ **Graph**

LESSON 4
- model • system • input
- process • output • feedback

↻ **Identify the Main Idea**
△ **Make Models**

LESSON 5
- field

↻ **Sequence**
△ **Observe**

▶ **VOCAB FLASH CARDS** For extra help with vocabulary, visit **Vocab Flash Cards** and type in *Mathematics and Models in Science.*

Scientific Measurement

UNLOCK THE BIG ?

🔑 **Why Do Scientists Use a Standard Measurement System?**

🔑 **What Are Some SI Units of Measure?**

—— 610 meters

my planet Diary

Tallest or Deepest?

Misconception: The world's tallest structures must be built on land.

Until 2008, the world's tallest structure was the Petronius Compliant Tower, which was built on the ocean floor. This 610-meter-high tower is an oil platform in the Gulf of Mexico located 210 kilometers southeast of New Orleans. The pumps on the tower remove oil and natural gas from the Petronius oil field. Today, the 828-meter-high Burj Khalifa built on land in the city of Dubai, completed in 2010, is the tallest building in the world.

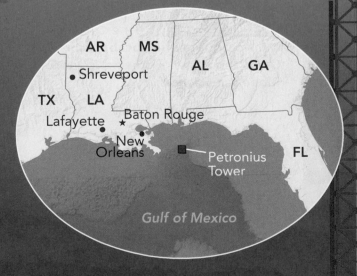

AR   MS
• Shreveport   AL   GA

TX   LA
Lafayette   Baton Rouge ★
New Orleans   ■ Petronius   FL
Tower

Gulf of Mexico

MISCONCEPTION

Communicate Discuss the questions with a partner. Then write your answers below.

1. Name one measurement you think builders had to make when they were constructing the Petronius Compliant Tower.

_____

_____

_____

_____

_____

2. What is the tallest building where you live?

_____

_____

▶ PLANET DIARY Go to **Planet Diary** to learn more about scientific measurement.

 Lab zone® Do the Inquiry Warm-Up *What Is Scientific Measurement?*

Drawing of the Petronius Compliant Tower

—— 0 meters

Vocabulary
- metric system • International System of Units (SI)
- mass • weight • volume • meniscus • density

Skills
- Reading: Ask Questions
- Inquiry: Measure

Why Do Scientists Use a Standard Measurement System?

A standard measurement system enables scientists to share information or repeat experiments done by other scientists. Modern scientists use a version of the metric system called the International System of Units (SI)—from the French *Systéme International d'Unités*. Suppose you decided to measure length using your foot. Your friend decided to measure length using her hand. How would you be able to compare the length of a 5-foot object to a 7-hand one? Without a standard measurement system, it would be hard to share information about the world.

The **metric system** is a standard measurement system based on the number 10. Modern scientists use a version of the metric system called the **International System of Units (SI)**. 🔑 **Using SI as the standard system of measurement allows scientists to compare data and communicate with each other about the results of scientific investigations.** Mass, length, and many other properties are measured using SI units. All SI units use the same set of prefixes. For example, a paper clip has a mass of about 1 gram. An object with ten times more mass than a paper clip has a mass of 10 grams, or 1 dekagram. A child could be 1 meter tall. A tree that is ten times taller than the child has a height of 10 meters, or 1 dekameter. **Figure 1** shows some common SI prefixes.

> ✎ **Ask Questions** Write a question you want to know about the SI system.
>
> _____
> _____
> _____

FIGURE 1 ·······
> VIRTUAL LAB **Prefixes of SI Units**
The man in this photo is one of the tallest men in the world at 2.46 meters, or 246 centimeters.

✎ **Name** Complete the column in the table using the meter, which is the SI unit for length, as the base.

Common SI Prefixes		
Prefix	**Meaning**	**Example**
kilo- (k)	1,000	_____
deka- (da)	10	_____
no prefix	1	meter
centi- (c)	0.01 (one hundredth)	_____
milli- (m)	0.001 (one thousandth)	_____
micro- (µ)	0.000001 (one millionth)	_____
nano- (n)	0.000000001 (one billionth)	_____

do the math!

SI prefixes show how measurements increase or decrease by powers of 10. Use the table of SI prefixes in **Figure 1** to answer the questions.

1 Calculate A picnic blanket is 1 meter across. An ant is 1 centimeter in length. How many ants of the same length would fit end-to-end across the length of the picnic blanket?

_____

2 Explain The length of the grassy park where the ant lives is 1 kilometer. How many times longer than the ant is the park? Explain your answer.

_____

_____

_____

3 CHALLENGE How could you convert the length of the ant from centimeters to kilometers? How long is the ant in kilometers?

_____

_____

_____

_____

Lab zone® Do the Quick Lab *Measuring With SI.*

🔑 Assess Your Understanding

1a. Review The International System of Units, or _____ , is based on the _____ system.

b. Apply Concepts A nickel coin weighs 5 grams. How many milligrams does it weigh?

_____

c. Calculate Suppose the mass of a dog is 90 pounds. If 1 kilogram is equal to 2.2 pounds, what is the mass of the dog in kilograms?

_____

d. Make Generalizations What might occur if the scientists in one country started to use a different system of measurement than the system used by scientists in the rest of the world?

_____

_____

_____

_____

_____

_____

_____

got it? ....

○ **I get it!** Now I know that scientists use SI to _____

_____

○ **I need extra help with** _____

Go to **MY SCIENCE ⑤ COACH** online for help with this subject.

What Are Some SI Units of Measure?

Scientists measure length, mass, volume, density, temperature, and time using SI units.

Length Length is the distance from one point to another. **The basic SI unit for measuring length is the meter (m).** One meter is about the distance from the floor to a doorknob. Metric rulers are used to measure lengths smaller than a meter, such as a centimeter (cm), or millimeter (mm). A kilometer (km) is 1,000 times longer than a meter. **Figure 2** shows two organisms that can be measured with a ruler.

Conversions for Length

1 km	= 1,000 m
1 m	= 100 cm
1 m	= 1,000 mm
1 cm	= 10 mm

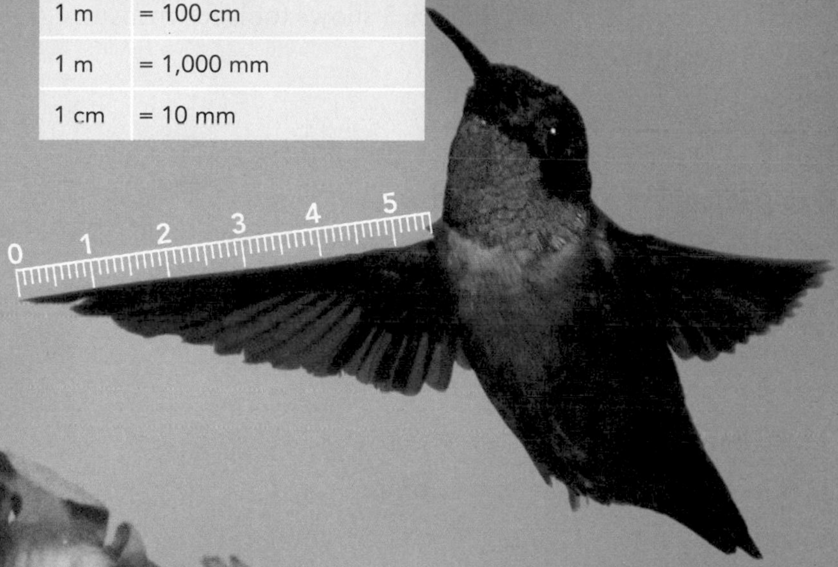

FIGURE 2 ·······································

Wing Length

You can use a metric ruler to measure the length of small objects. Line up one end of the object with the zero mark. Read the number at the other end of the object to find the length.

✎ **Use the rulers to find the lengths of the bird and butterfly wings. Then complete the activities below.**

1. **Measure** What is the length of each wing?

_____

_____

2. **Apply Concepts** Using the table in Figure 1, convert the length of each wing from centimeters to micrometers (µm).

_____

_____

Conversions for Mass

1 kg	= 1,000 g
1 g	= 1,000 mg

Mass

Mass Mass is the measure of the amount of matter in an object. 🔑 **The basic SI unit for measuring mass is the kilogram (kg).** The mass of dogs, people, cars, and other large objects is measured in kilograms. The mass of birds, cell phones, and other small objects is measured in grams (g) or milligrams (mg). The triple-beam balance shown in **Figure 3** is used to measure mass in grams.

When you step on a scale, you are measuring your weight. **Weight** is the measure of the force of gravity acting on an object. The basic SI unit for measuring weight is a measure of force called the newton (N). The pound is a non-SI unit commonly used in the United States to measure weight. When you stand on a scale, gravity pulls down on you and the springs in the scale compress. Gravity has a greater pull on objects with more mass, so these objects weigh more than objects with less mass. Weight changes as gravity changes, so you would weigh less on the moon because it has weaker gravity than Earth. However, an object's mass does not change with a change in gravity. **Figure 3** shows tools for measuring an object's mass and weight.

FIGURE 3 ··

Comparing Apples and Oranges

Triple-beam balances use weights to determine an object's mass. A spring scale is used to measure an object's weight.

1. ⚠️**Measure** Find the mass of the apple by adding the masses of each weight on the balance.

    _____

2. **Define** The spring scale measures the weight of the oranges, which is a measure of the _____

    on the oranges.

3. **Infer** Suppose the oranges weigh 16.7 newtons on Earth. How would their weight change if they were on the moon?

    _____

    _____

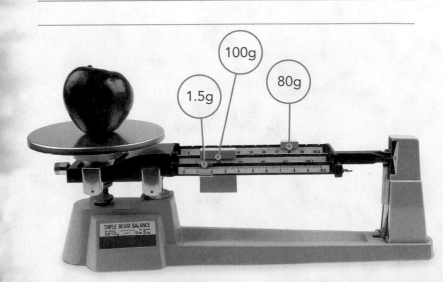

Volume

A microwave oven takes up space on a countertop. A jug of milk takes up space in the refrigerator. Air spreads out to take up space in a room. **Volume** is the amount of space taken up by an object or substance. 🔑 **The basic SI unit for measuring volume is the cubic meter (m³).** Other units include the liter (L) and cubic centimeter (cm³). Liters are used to measure liquids. Cubic meters or cubic centimeters are used to measure solid objects. Use this page to practice measuring volume.

Conversions for Volume

1 L	= 1,000 mL
1 L	= 1,000 cm³
1 mL	= 1 cm³

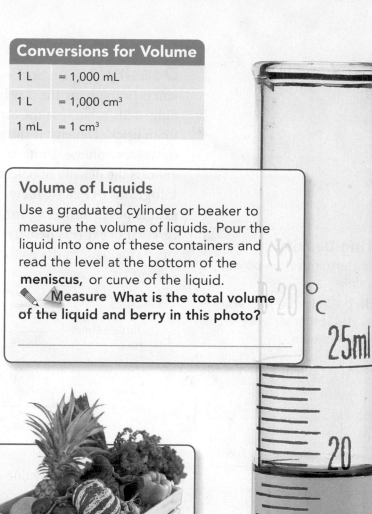

Volume of Liquids

Use a graduated cylinder or beaker to measure the volume of liquids. Pour the liquid into one of these containers and read the level at the bottom of the **meniscus,** or curve of the liquid.

✏️ **Measure** What is the total volume of the liquid and berry in this photo?

_____

Volume of Rectangular Solids

Use a ruler or meterstick to find the volume of rectangular solids. Measure the length, width, and height of the solid. Multiply these three values to get the volume.

✏️ **Calculate** What is the volume of the crate?

_____

30 cm

42 cm

28 cm

Volume of Irregular Solids

You can use the displacement of water to measure the volume of an irregular solid, like a rock or a berry. Fill a graduated cylinder partially full with water. Measure the volume of the water. Now place the berry in the water. Measure the volume of the water again. To get the volume of the berry, subtract the original volume of the water from the volume of water that included the berry.

✏️ **Infer** Why would you get a more accurate measure of the volume of an irregular solid by using displacement instead of measuring with a ruler?

_____

_____

_____

Density A foam brick and a clay brick can be the same size. If you pick them up, the clay brick feels heavy and the foam brick feels light. This is because the clay brick has a higher density than the foam brick. **Density** is the measure of how much mass is contained in a given volume. Units of mass are divided by units of volume to express the density of objects. 🔑 **The SI unit for density is kilograms per cubic meter (kg/m³), but scientists commonly use grams per milliliter (g/mL) or grams per cubic centimeter (g/cm³) to express density.** Look at **Figure 4** to compare the density of the balls in the picture.

FIGURE 4 ··································

Predicting Density

Density determines if an object floats or sinks.

✎ **Predict Circle the ball you think has the lower density. Explain your choice.**

_____

_____

_____

_____

_____

_____

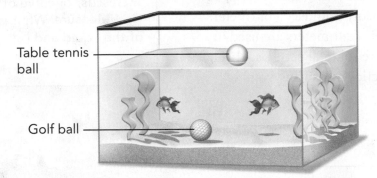

Table tennis ball

Golf ball

To find the actual value of an object's density, you can use a mathematical formula for calculating density. Once you have taken measurements to find both the mass and volume of an object, calculate its density using the following formula.

$$\text{Density} = \frac{\text{Mass}}{\text{Volume}}$$

Once you find the volume and mass of an object, calculate its density using the formula.

❶ Identify Draw a line from the word *Meniscus* to the meniscus of each graduated cylinder.

❷ Observe What is the volume of water in each graduated cylinder? What is the volume of the bolt?

_____

_____

❸ Calculate The mass of the bolt is 101 grams. Find its density.

_____

_____

_____

Meniscus

Using Density

The density of a pure substance is always the same, no matter how much of the substance you have. For example, the density of fresh water is always 1.0 g/cm³, whether you have a drop of water or a whole lake. Figure 5 shows the density of some common substances.

When you know the density of an object, you also know whether it will sink or float in water. If an object's density is less than 1.0 g/cm³, it will float. If its density is greater than 1.0 g/cm³, the object will sink. If you have an object made out of an unknown substance, you can tell whether its density is greater than or less than 1.0 g/cm³ by dropping the object in water!

FIGURE 5 ·······

Using Density

The planet Saturn could float in water because its density is less than 1.0 g/cm³.

✎ **Infer** In the table, circle the liquids or solids that would float in water. Put a star next to those that would sink in water.

Densities of Common Substances

Substance	Density (g/cm³)
Gold	19.3
Gasoline	0.7
Milk	1.03
Water	1.0
Iron	7.8
Air	0.001
Ice	0.9
Aluminum	2.7

✎ [CHALLENGE] Find the density of the surfboard and determine if the board should float. The surfboard's mass is 14 kg and its volume is 0.0875 m³. (*Hint:* The density of salt water is equal to about 1,025 kg/m³.)

_____

_____

Time How long would it take you to run 100 meters? Did you know that the fastest time recorded for running 100 meters is under 10 seconds? 🔑 **The second (s) is the SI unit used to measure time.** Seconds can be divided into smaller units, such as milliseconds (ms). Sixty seconds make up a minute. Sixty minutes make up an hour. So there are 3,600 seconds in an hour ($60 \times 60 = 3,600$).

Time is measured by clocks or stopwatches. A clock can measure time to the nearest second. Stopwatches like the one shown in **Figure 6** can measure time to the nearest hundredth of a second. The official timers used in the Olympics and other sports events can measure time to the nearest thousandth of a second!

FIGURE 6 ·······························

The Race Is On

The stopwatch shows the winning time in the last race at a school swim meet.

✎ **Answer the following questions about the race times.**

1. **Calculate** Jessica swims the last race in 22.56 seconds. By how much time did she lose the race?

   _____

   _____

2. **Analyze Sources of Error** Why would machine-operated stopwatches be used at sports events instead of hand-operated stopwatches?

   _____

   _____

   _____

   _____

   _____

   _____

Temperature

Did you need a jacket today, or could you wear shorts? You probably checked the temperature to find out. Temperature is a measure of the energy of motion of the particles in a substance. When molecules in air are moving fast and bouncing into each other, temperature is high and you feel hot. When these molecules slow down, temperature is lower and you feel cooler. Temperature affects the properties of some substances. For example, rising temperature can change a substance from a solid to a liquid to a gas.

Thermometers are instruments that measure temperature. Thermometers can have different temperature scales. Scientists commonly use thermometers with the Celsius temperature scale to measure temperature. On this scale, water freezes at 0°C and boils at 100°C. Scientists also use thermometers with the Kelvin scale to measure temperature. **Kelvin (K) is the official SI unit for temperature. The Kelvin scale starts at 0 K (absolute zero) and only goes up.** Units on the Kelvin scale are the same size as units on the Celsius scale. Use **Figure 7** to compare the Celsius and Kelvin scales.

FIGURE 7 ······························
Kelvin and Celsius Scales
Liquid in a thermometer moves up or down as temperature changes.

✎ **Use the thermometer diagrams to complete the tasks.**

1. **Identify** Color in the Celsius thermometer to show how it would look when immersed in boiling water.

2. **Predict** Color in the Kelvin thermometer to show how it would look when immersed in ice water.

3. **CHALLENGE** Use the conversion chart to label the Kelvin thermometer with temperatures that correspond to the boiling point and freezing point of water.

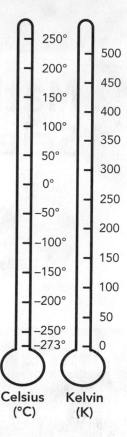

Celsius (°C)   Kelvin (K)

Conversions for Temperature

0°C	= 273 K
100°C	= 373 K

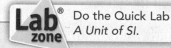
Do the Quick Lab
A Unit of SI.

🔑 Assess Your Understanding

2a. Identify A SI unit used to measure volume is the (cubic centimeter/millimeter).

b. Sequence What steps would you take to determine the density of a rubber eraser?

_____

_____

_____

_____

_____

got it?

○ **I get it!** Now I know that the SI units for length, mass, volume, density, time, and temperature are _____

_____

_____

○ **I need extra help with** _____

Go to **MY SCIENCE COACH** online for help with this subject.

Mathematics and Scientific Thinking

🔑 **What Math Skills Do Scientists Use?**

🔑 **What Math Tools Do Scientists Use?**

my PLANET DiARY

CAREER

Math in the Environment

For what job do you need to be able to solve for x and find the area of a polygon? You may be surprised to learn that people other than math teachers need to have these skills.

Rachel Sweeney is a coastal restoration project manager. Her job involves restoring barrier islands. She helps plan how to prevent erosion by building dikes. Dikes are long walls that help stop flooding.

Rachel uses math in her job every day. She uses estimation to determine the size of a grain of sand. Then she uses equations to calculate the volume of sand she needs to fill the dikes and what the mass of the sand will be. Without these math skills, Rachel's work in saving the environment would not be possible.

Answer the questions below.

1. What are two math skills Rachel uses in her job?

_____

_____

2. Think about a job that interests you. How would that job use math?

_____

_____

_____

▶ PLANET DIARY Go to **Planet Diary** to learn more about mathematics and science.

Rachel Sweeney

With the help of people like Rachel Sweeney, barrier islands such as the ones shown may be saved from erosion.

Lab zone Do the Inquiry Warm-Up *How Do Math and Science Work Together?*

Vocabulary

- estimate
- accuracy
- precision
- significant figures
- mean
- median
- mode
- range
- anomalous data
- percent error

Skills

- ↻ Reading: Identify the Main Idea
- △ Inquiry: Interpret Data

What Math Skills Do Scientists Use?

The size of a grizzly bear, the number of bees in a hive, and the distance a kangaroo can jump are just a few of the interesting things that scientists investigate. Good math skills are essential as scientists collect and analyze data about their subject. 🔑 **When collecting data, scientists use math skills that include estimation, accuracy and precision, and significant figures.**

Estimation White blood cells help the human body fight disease. When a person's blood is tested, lab technicians count the number of white blood cells in a drop of the patient's blood. Doctors then use this count in their estimate of the total number of white blood cells in all of the patient's blood. An **estimate** is an approximation of a number based on reasonable assumptions. The estimated white blood cell count helps a doctor determine if the patient has an infection. Estimates are useful when it is impossible to count every individual or object. They are also useful when the thing being estimated, such as the distance of a star, cannot be measured directly. Use **Figure 1** to practice estimation.

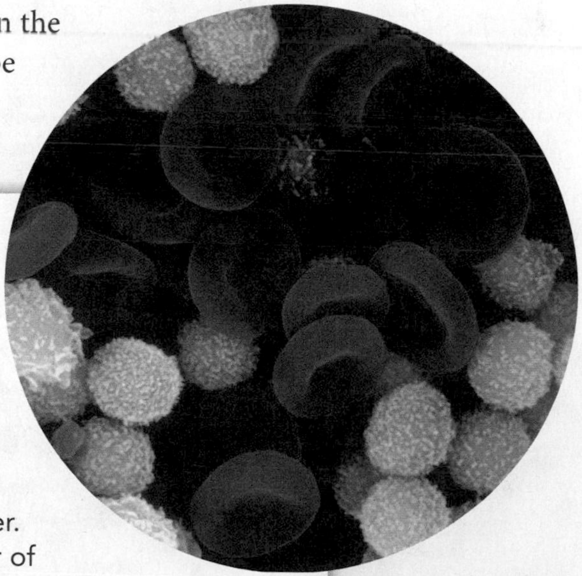

FIGURE 1 ···

Estimating

This microscopic view shows red and white blood cells.

✎ **Use the photograph to complete these tasks.**

1. **Estimate** How many white blood cells (WBC) are in the microscopic field? _____

2. **Calculate** The sample is 500 times smaller than a microliter. A microliter is one millionth of a liter. Estimate the number of white blood cells in a microliter of the patient's blood.

   Number of WBC counted × 500 = _____ WBC per microliter

3. △**Interpret Data** Patients with white blood cell counts greater than 10,500 WBC per microliter may have an infection. Could this patient have an infection? Explain.

   _____

   _____

Accuracy and Precision

When scientists make measurements, they want to be both accurate and precise. **Accuracy** refers to how close the measurement is to the true or accepted value. **Precision** refers to how close a group of measurements are to each other.

Scientists try to use the highest quality tools to take measurements. They also measure the same object more than once. By repeating measurements with high-quality tools, scientists obtain the most accurate and precise results possible. Look at **Figure 2** to determine the accuracy and precision of the measurements.

⊙ Identify the Main Idea In the text, underline the main idea that describes how scientists are accurate and precise.

FIGURE 2 ···

Accuracy and Precision

Three teams measured the mass of the turtle below.

✎ Interpret Diagrams Determine how accurate and precise each team's measurements are. Circle your answers in the boxes.

Team One	Team Two	Team Three
Measurements	**Measurements**	**Measurements**
1. 172.5 g	1. 154.5 g	1. 153.7 g
2. 172.8 g	2. 121.7 g	2. 153.6 g
3. 172.6 g	3. 177.0 g	3. 153.9 g
This team was (accurate/not accurate).	This team was (accurate/not accurate).	This team was (accurate/not accurate).
This team was (precise/not precise).	This team was (precise/not precise).	This team was (precise/not precise).

Significant Figures Measurements are never completely precise. For example, a centimeter ruler allows you to measure centimeters precisely because these units are marked evenly with lines. If you want to measure a portion of a centimeter, you have to estimate that measurement between the lines. **Significant figures** communicate how precise measurements are. The significant figures in a measurement include all digits measured exactly, plus one estimated digit. If the measurement has only one digit, you can assume that it is estimated. Look at **Figure 3.**

FIGURE 3 ···

Significant Figures

An encyclopedia is 3.2 cm across its spine. The measurement *3.2 cm* has 2 significant figures, or sig figs. The *3* is a precise measurement. The *2* is an estimate.

✎ **Calculate** Read the boxes below and answer the questions.

Adding or Subtracting Measurements

When you add or subtract measurements, the answer must have the same number of digits after the decimal point as the measurement with the fewest number of digits after the decimal point. If you add an encyclopedia to a row of books that is 42.12 cm, how long will the row be?

42.12 cm (2 places after the decimal)

+ 3.2 cm (1 place after the decimal)

45.32 cm ⟶ 45.3 cm (1 place after the decimal)

If you remove an encyclopedia from a row of books that is 42.12 cm, what will the new length of the row be?

_____

_____

Multiplying or Dividing Measurements

When you multiply or divide measurements, the answer must have the same number of significant figures as the measurement with the fewest number of significant figures. What is the area of a shelf that has a height of 33 cm and a width of 111 cm?

111 cm (3 sig figs)

× 33 cm (2 sig figs)

3,663 cm² ⟶ 3,700 cm² (2 sig figs)

Zeroes at the end of a number, but before a decimal point, are not sig figs. What is the area of a desk in the library that is 115 cm long and 45 cm wide?

_____

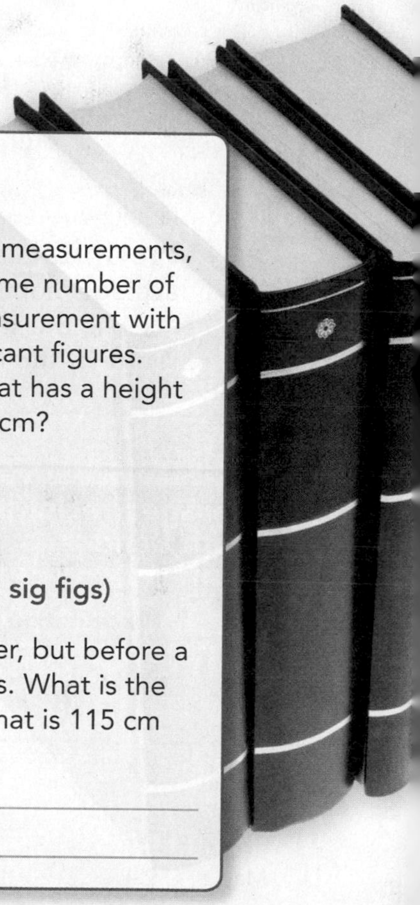

_____

Do the Quick Lab
Is It Accurate?

🔑 **Assess Your Understanding**

got it? ···

○ **I get it!** Now I know that scientists use math skills when they collect data that include_____

_____

○ **I need extra help with** _____

Go to **MY SCIENCE ⓢ COACH** *online for help with this subject.*

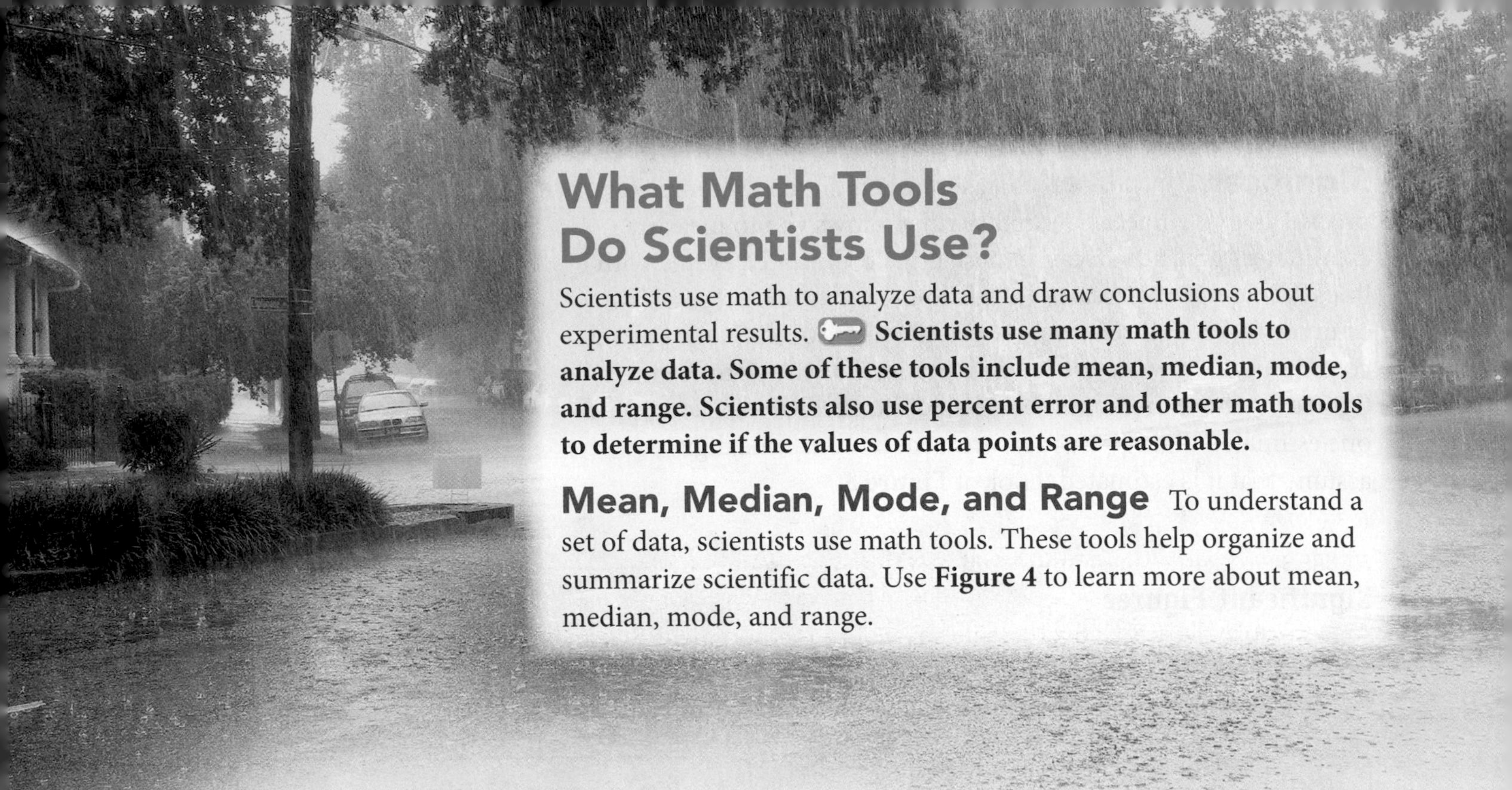

What Math Tools Do Scientists Use?

Scientists use math to analyze data and draw conclusions about experimental results. 🔑 **Scientists use many math tools to analyze data. Some of these tools include mean, median, mode, and range. Scientists also use percent error and other math tools to determine if the values of data points are reasonable.**

Mean, Median, Mode, and Range To understand a set of data, scientists use math tools. These tools help organize and summarize scientific data. Use **Figure 4** to learn more about mean, median, mode, and range.

FIGURE 4 ···

Precipitation in South Bend

The table below shows the average monthly precipitation in South Bend.

✎ **Use the table to calculate the mean, median, mode, and range of the rainfall data.**

Average Precipitation, South Bend	
Month	Average Precipitation (cm)
Jan	5.8
Feb	4.6
March	6.4
April	8.1
May	9.4
June	8.9
July	9.7
Aug	10.2
Sept	8.6
Oct	8.6
Nov	7.9
Dec	6.9

Mean The **mean** is the numerical average of a set of data. To find the mean, add all the numbers in the data set. Then divide by the total number of items that you added.

Mean of the rainfall data: _____

Median The **median** is the middle number in an ordered set of data. To find the median, list all the numbers in order from least to greatest. If the list has an odd number of entries, the median is the middle entry. If the list has an even number of entries, the median is the mean of the two middle entries.

Median of the rainfall data: _____

_____

_____

Mode The **mode** is the number that appears most often in a list of numbers.

Mode of the rainfall data: _____

Range The **range** of a data set is the difference between the greatest value in the set and the least value.

Range of the rainfall data: _____

Reasonable and Anomalous Data

Scientists must always ask themselves whether their data make sense and are reasonable. There is always an acceptable range of variation in collected data. However, some variation may not be acceptable. For example, suppose that a scientist is studying the wind speed of a hurricane that appears very strong. The scientist sees that the hurricane's wind speed has been measured at 56 km/hr, which is far lower than expected. The scientist is likely to check the equipment recording wind speed to see if it is functioning properly.

Human or equipment error can produce **anomalous data,** or data that do not fit with the data set. If a scientist sees a data point that is different from others, he or she will examine it for errors. If no errors were made, the anomalous data might be due to an unknown variable. Investigating the reason for anomalous data can lead scientists to new discoveries.

apply it!

Adult female black bears have masses from about 50 kilograms to 125 kilograms. Adult male black bears have masses from about 60 kilograms to 250 kilograms. Researchers measured the masses of five adult female black bears in their natural habitat. You can see their results in the table.

1 Identify Which mass is anomalous data?

_____

2 Solve Problems How could the researcher check the anomalous data?

_____

3 CHALLENGE What might have produced the anomalous data?

_____

_____

_____

Adult Female Black Bear Masses

Bear	Mass (in kg)
A	79
B	73
C	74
D	155
E	70

Adding It *Up*

How do scientists use measurement and mathematics?

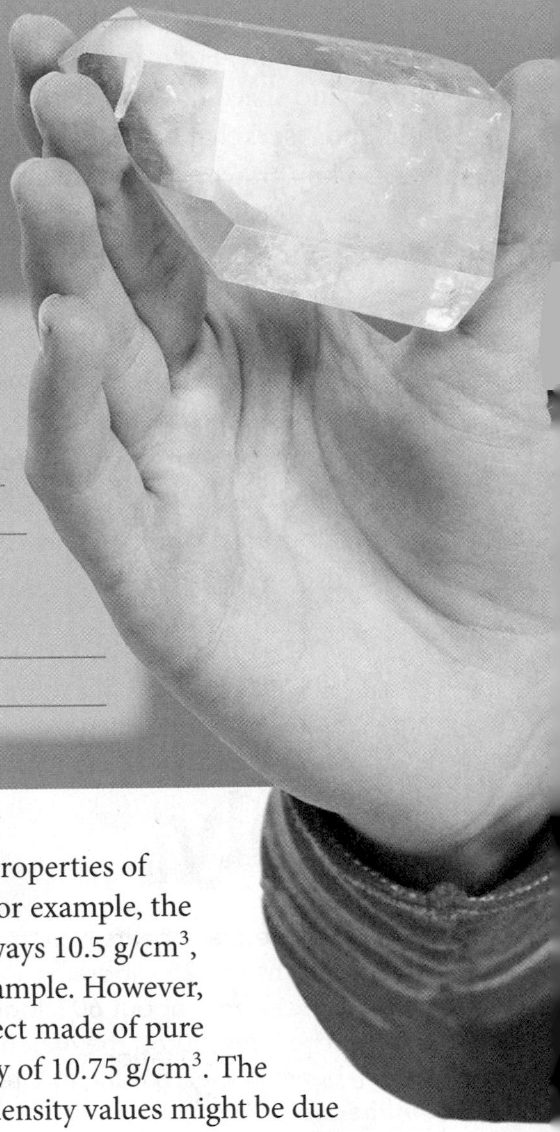

FIGURE 5 ··

> INTERACTIVE ART Two lab partners measured the mass and volume of a sample of quartz four times. They recorded their measurements in the table at the right.

✏ **Answer the questions.**

1. Draw Conclusions How do you think the partners measured the sample's mass and volume?

_____

_____

_____

2. Infer Are the students' measurements precise? Explain.

_____

_____

_____

FIGURE 6 ··················

Percent Error

A Nobel Prize medal is plated with gold. The density of gold is 19.3 g/cm³.

✏ **Calculate A worker finds the density of the Nobel medal's plating to be 20.1 g/cm³. What is the percent error of his measurement?**

_____

_____

_____

_____

Percent Error Some properties of substances never change. For example, the density of pure silver is always 10.5 g/cm³, no matter the size of the sample. However, when you measure an object made of pure silver, you may get a density of 10.75 g/cm³. The difference between the two density values might be due to an error you made when you measured the mass or volume of the silver. It could also be due to the accuracy of your measuring equipment. The percent difference between the known value of a substance and its measured value is called the **percent error**. A low percent error means that the experimental results were accurate. The formula below calculates percent error in the silver sample.

$$\text{Percent Error} = \frac{\text{experimental value} - \text{true value}}{\text{true value}} \times 100\%$$

$$\% E = \frac{10.75 \text{ g/cm}^3 - 10.5 \text{ g/cm}^3}{10.5 \text{ g/cm}^3} \times 100\%$$

$$\% E = \frac{0.25 \text{ g/cm}^3}{10.5 \text{ g/cm}^3} \times 100\% = 2.38$$

Repeated Measurements of a Piece of Quartz		
Mass	**Volume**	**Density**
130.4 g	49.6 mL	_____
131.6 g	49.5 mL	_____
129.3 g	48.6 mL	_____
130.9 g	49.4 mL	_____

3. **Calculate** Find the density for each set of quartz measurements and complete the table. What is the mean of the mass data set? Of the volume data set?

_____

_____

4. **Calculate** Use the means of the data sets to determine the density of the quartz.

_____

5. **Apply Concepts** How many significant figures should your density calculation have? Explain.

_____

_____

 Do the Quick Lab *Math Tools in Science.*

🔑 Assess Your Understanding

2a. Interpret Tables Describe any patterns of average precipitation in South Bend that the data on the table in Figure 4 indicate.

_____

_____

_____

_____

_____

b. How do scientists use measurement and mathematics?

_____

_____

_____

_____

_____

_____

_____

got it? ....

○ **I get it!** Now I know that scientists use math tools that include _____

_____

○ **I need extra help with** _____

Go to **MY SCIENCE COACH** online for help with this subject.

Using Graphs in Science

🔑 **How Do Scientists Use Graphs?**

UNLOCK
THE BIG
?

my PLANET DiaRY

Indiana Population

A census is a survey that individuals take. It provides information about the people living in the state and country. Read the facts below about Indiana's population from a 2008 estimate.

- The total population was 6,376,792 people.
- 439,999 people were under five years old.
- 1,587,821 people were under the age of 18.
- 816,229 people were over the age of 65.
- The average age was 35 years old.

SCIENCE STATS

Answer the questions below.

1. Why might it be helpful to show these data in a graph?

_____

_____

2. How might you collect data about the ages of the people in your neighborhood?

_____

_____

_____

▶ **PLANET DIARY** Go to **Planet Diary** to learn more about graphs.

Lab® Do the Inquiry Warm-Up
zone *What's in a Graph?*

Vocabulary
- graph • linear graph
- nonlinear graph • outlier

Skills
- ⟳ Reading: Relate Cause and Effect
- △ Inquiry: Graph

How Do Scientists Use Graphs?

Have you ever been to an event that started off with a jet plane flyby? If so, you probably noticed that you could see the jets before you heard the roar of their engines. That is because sound travels slower than light. The speed of sound is also affected by the temperature of the medium it's traveling through, as shown by the data in **Figure 1.** To help understand what the data mean, you can use a graph. A **graph** is a "picture" of your data.

Kinds of Data Graphs can illustrate different types of data. ⚷ **Scientists use graphs to identify trends, make predictions, and recognize anomalous, or inconsistent, data.** Graphs display categorical and numerical data. Categorical data can be grouped into categories. For example, census information can be categorized by age group. Numerical data, such as temperature and the speed of sound, are continuous, ranging from small to large amounts. Different kinds of graphs are used to display these two kinds of data.

Kinds of Graphs Line graphs are used to display numerical data, such as the data in **Figure 1.** They may show how a dependent variable changes in response to an independent variable. Scientists control changes in the independent variable. Then they collect data about how the dependent variable responded to those changes. Bar graphs can be used to display both numerical and categorical data.

⟳ **Relate Cause and Effect**
In the text, underline the cause and circle the effect of variables when scientists use them.

FIGURE 1 ••••••••••••••••••••
Graphing the Speed of Sound
As temperatures rise, so does the speed at which sound travels through the air.

✎△**Graph Make** a line graph by plotting the data from the table on the grid.

Temp. (°C)	Speed of Sound (m/s)
–15	322
0	331
15	340
30	349
45	358

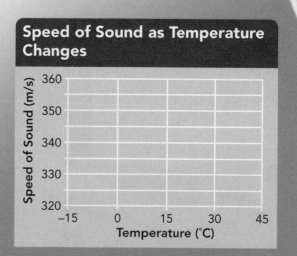

Speed of Sound as Temperature Changes

63

Linear and Nonlinear Graphs

As you saw in the line graph in **Figure 1**, temperature and the speed of sound are related. Line graphs are powerful tools because they show how different sets of data are related. The line graph shows that as temperature increases, the speed of sound increases in a predictable way.

A line graph in which the data points yield a straight line is a **linear graph.** The relationship between temperature and the speed of sound can be shown by a linear graph. A graph in which the data points do not fall along a straight line is a **nonlinear graph.** Changes in population can be shown by a nonlinear graph.

If most points do not fall exactly along a line, a graph can still show a trend. A point that is not part of the trend is an anomalous data point called an **outlier.** When a graph does not have a clear trend, it usually means the variables are not related.

Vocabulary High-Use Academic Words When a graph shows a trend, you can make predictions about data beyond the axes of the graph. Which word below is a synonym for the word *trend*?

- ○ origin
- ○ course
- ○ point

Maximum Dive Depths of Sea Animals

Animal	Dive Depths (meters)
Leatherback sea turtle (LST)	1200
Emperor penguin (EP)	565
Elephant seal (ES)	1529
King penguin (KP)	343

FIGURE 2 ·······

▶ INTERACTIVE ART **Sea Life Diving Data**

The diving depths of several sea creatures were measured and recorded in the data table.

1. **Graph** Arrange the animals in order from shallowest to deepest divers in a bar graph. Label the x-axis with the animals' initials and title the graph.

2. **Draw Conclusions** What trend does the graph show?

_____

_____

_____

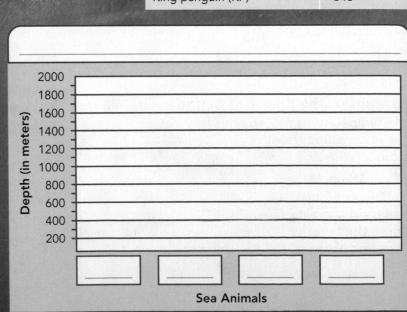

apply it!

Year	Number of Visitors (in millions)
2006	3.7
2007	7.1
2008	7.6
2009	7.9

The data table shows the number of tourists (in millions) visiting New Orleans between 2006 and 2009.

① **Graph** Plot the data on the graph and connect the points.

② **Read Graphs** The greatest increase in visitors was between _____

③ **CHALLENGE** Suppose the data for 2010 show that 4 million visitors visited New Orleans that year. How would you classify this data point? How would it be plotted on the graph?

_____

_____

_____

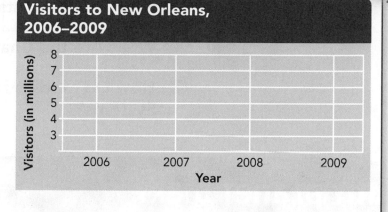

Visitors to New Orleans, 2006–2009

Y-axis: Visitors (in millions) — 8, 7, 6, 5, 4, 3

X-axis: Year — 2006, 2007, 2008, 2009

 Do the Quick Lab *Recognizing Trends.*

🗝 Assess Your Understanding

1a. Draw Conclusions What does a graph with no trend indicate about the variables?

_____

b. Compare and Contrast How are linear and nonlinear graphs alike? Different?

_____

_____

_____

_____

got it? •

○ **I get it!** Now I know that scientists use graphs _____

_____

_____

○ **I need extra help with** _____

Go to MY SCIENCE COACH online for help with this subject.

65

4 Models and Systems

UNLOCK THE BIG ?

🔑 How Do Scientists Use Models?

🔑 What Are the Characteristics of a System?

🔑 How Do Models Help Scientists Understand Systems?

MY PLANET DIARY

SCIENCE AND TECHNOLOGY

Models Used in Films

As the lights in the movie theater dim, your excitement about the latest hit movie builds. For the next two hours, a different world flashes in front of you. Monsters snatch up people, or alien robots invade Earth.

These monsters and robots are not actual objects. Instead, filmmakers develop models that they incorporate into the scenes. These models are often made on the computer. Sometimes, the models they build are very small, even though they appear huge on the movie screen. The next time you watch a movie, can you tell which things are real and which are models?

Answer the questions below.

1. How do models help filmmakers?

_____

_____

_____

2. What might you need to make a model of if you were filming a movie at your school?

_____

_____

_____

> PLANET DIARY Go to **Planet Diary** to learn more about making models.

Lab zone® Do the Inquiry Warm-Up Models in Science.

Vocabulary
- model • system • input
- process • output • feedback

Skills
- Reading: Identify the Main Idea
- Inquiry: Make Models

How Do Scientists Use Models?

Many department stores use mannequins to show customers how certain outfits might look. A mannequin is a model. A **model** is any representation of an object or a process. You use models in your daily life without even realizing it. For example, you might use a globe to find a country. A globe is a model of Earth.

Scientists work with models for a specific purpose. **Scientists use models to test their ideas about things they cannot observe directly.** Scientists often build models to create a reasonable representation of things that are either very small or very large. These kinds of models are physical models—drawings (like the one in **Figure 1**) or three-dimensional objects. But many models are not physical objects. For example, many models are models of a process. A computer program might be used to model the movement of the stars as seen from Earth.

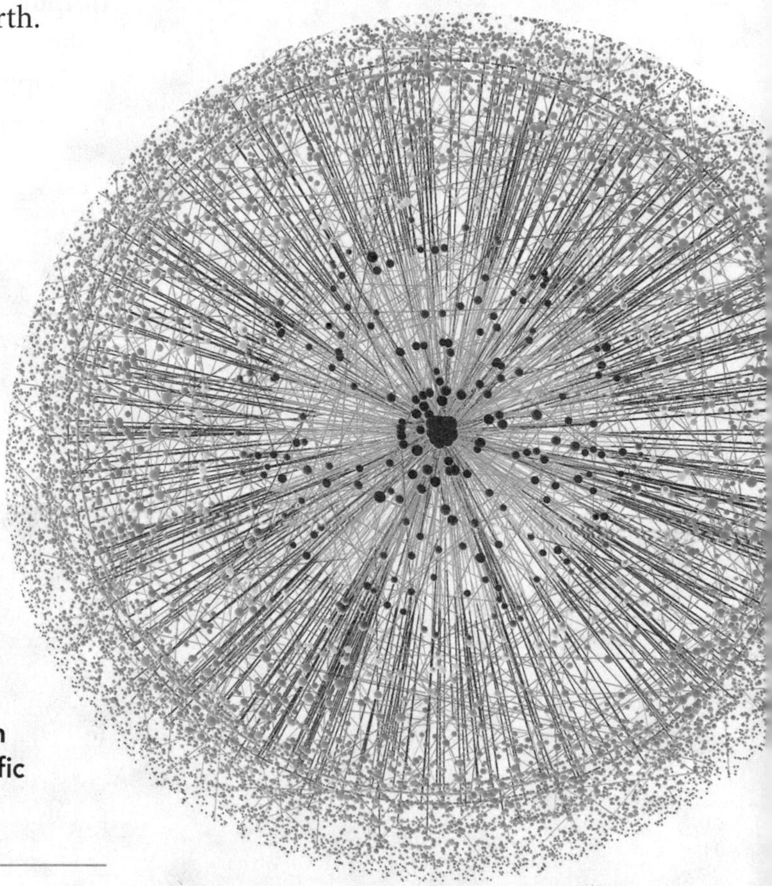

FIGURE 1 ··

Connecting the Dots

This model shows how networks (drawn as dots) connect to each other on the Internet. The bigger the dot, the more Internet traffic the network handles.

✏ **Explain** Suppose all networks in the center of the model became unavailable for 24 hours. How can scientists use this model to predict how Internet traffic will be affected?

_____

_____

_____

Lab zone® Do the Quick Lab
Working With Models

🔑 Assess Your Understanding

got it? ···

○ **I get it!** Now I know that scientists use models to _____

_____

○ **I need extra help with** _____

Go to **MY SCIENCE** 🔵 **COACH** *online for help with this subject.*

What Are the Characteristics of a System?

Models are often used to represent systems. A **system** is a group of parts that work together to carry out a function. You may recall that Earth is a system that consists of air, life, water, ice, and rock. But look at **Figure 2.** Many things you use in your daily life are systems. A bicycle pump, a toaster, and a flashlight all contain parts that work together while performing a function.

Systems have common characteristics. 🔑 **All systems have at least one input, at least one process, and at least one output.** An **input** is a material or the energy that goes into the system. A **process** is an action or series of actions that happen within the system. An **output** is the material or energy that comes out of a system. To understand input, process, and output, think of a toaster. The input is electricity. The process is heating the bread. The output is hot toast.

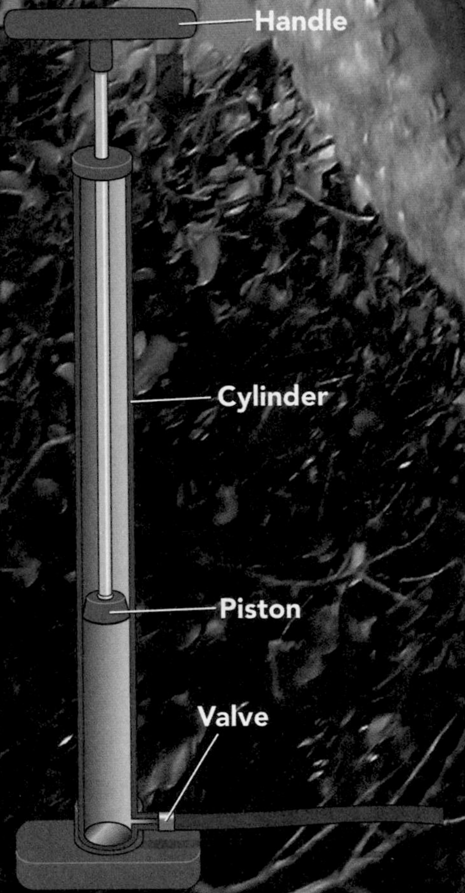

Handle

Cylinder

Piston

Valve

FIGURE 2 ···
▶ **INTERACTIVE ART** **An Everyday System**
In a bicycle pump, many parts work together as a system. ✎ Chart **Look at the pump and use what you know to fill in the chart.**

A Bicycle Pump as a System

Parts	Inputs	Outputs

Look at **Figure 3.** The harder you ride a bike, the more oxygen your muscles need. As a result, your circulatory system provides information to your heart indicating that you need more oxygen. So your heart starts beating faster. By beating faster, your heart provides more oxygen to your muscles. **Feedback** is output that changes a system in some way. When you exercise, your heart receives feedback that makes your heart pump faster.

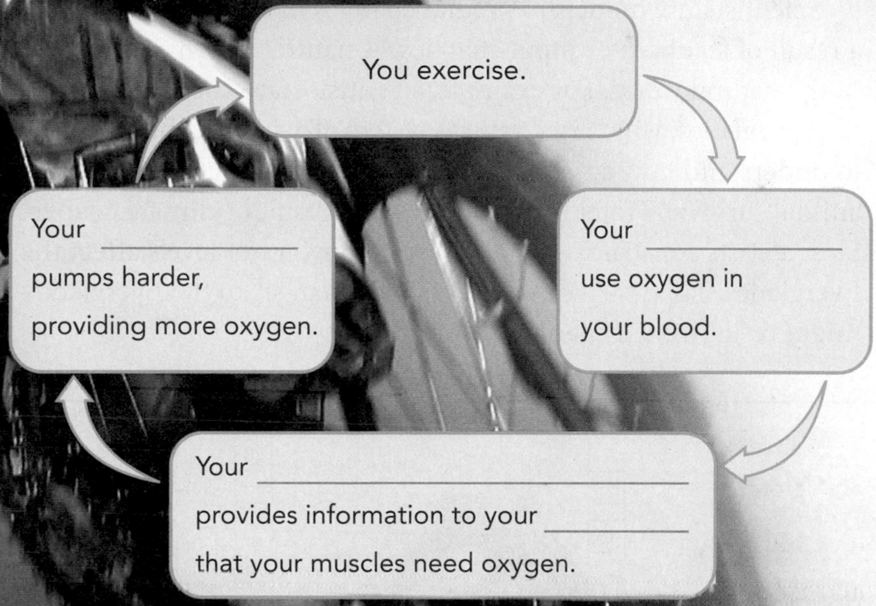

You exercise.

Your _____ pumps harder, providing more oxygen.

Your _____ use oxygen in your blood.

Your _____ provides information to your _____ that your muscles need oxygen.

FIGURE 3 ·····················

Feedback

When you exercise, your body's circulatory system feeds back information to your heart.

✎ **Fill in the blanks of the graphic organizer.**

Identify What is the input and output for this system?

_____
_____
_____
_____
_____

 Do the Quick Lab *Characteristics of Systems.*

🔑 Assess Your Understanding

1a. Identify A (model/system) is a group of parts that work together to perform a function.

b. Apply Concepts Is a handheld can opener a system? Explain.

_____
_____
_____
_____

c. Infer What is the input when you use a can opener?

_____
_____
_____
_____
_____

got it? ·····························

○ **I get it!** Now I know that all systems have _____

and some systems have feedback.

○ **I need extra help with** _____

Go to **MY SCIENCE** Ⓢ **COACH** online for help with this subject.

How Do Models Help Scientists Understand Systems?

It's easy to identify the materials and energy that make up the inputs and outputs of a system. But observing a system's process can be difficult. Models can help scientists understand a system's process. 🗝 **Scientists build models to represent a process. They test whether the input and output from the model match the input and output of the system in the natural world.**

Scientists use models to predict changes in a natural system as a result of feedback or input changes. A natural system is a system in the natural world. For example, scientists have tried to restore the Everglades, which is a natural system. To do this, they need to understand how a rise in water levels might affect plant and animal survival. Water levels can rise as a result of climate change. So scientists construct models showing how water levels affect the Everglades. Then they can predict what changes to the Everglades might result from a change in water levels.

apply it!

The Cape Sable seaside sparrow nests in certain areas of the Everglades. In one model of the sparrow's nesting habits, the sparrows start to mate when water levels drop to 5 cm. After they mate, the sparrows need approximately 43 consecutive days during which the water level is lower than 16 cm. If water levels rise to 16 cm or higher during this time, the sparrows will abandon their nest.

Nest not drawn to scale

cm

Nest not drawn to scale

cm

❶ ⚠ Make Models Shade in the water levels on each meterstick to show how Cape Sable seaside sparrow nests vary according to water levels.

❷ CHALLENGE How might scientists use the information from your model to save the species?

_____

_____

_____

_____

Modeling Simple and Complex Systems Some
systems that scientists study are simple. There may be only a few
parts in the system or a few steps in the process. A toaster is one
example of a system that is made up of only a few parts. **Figure 4**
shows another example of a simple system.

However, some systems are more complex. Many parts and
many variables, or factors that can vary, interact in these systems.
Often scientists may use a computer to keep track of the variables.
For example, weather systems are very complex. Many factors affect
weather, such as oceans, mountains and valleys, wind patterns,
and the angle of the sun's rays. These factors can interact in many
ways. As a result, scientists have a difficult time predicting when
and where rain or snow will fall. Because such systems are difficult
to model, scientists may model the specific part of the system that
they wish to study. For instance, a hurricane is a complex natural
system. To predict where a hurricane will make landfall, scientists
might try to model winds that affect the hurricane's path.

⊙ **Identify the Main Idea**
Read the text. Underline the
main idea about how scientists
model complex systems.

FIGURE 4 ··

The Mercury Cycle
Materials that contain the element mercury
can be harmful to fish that eat them.

✎ **Look at the diagram and then complete
the activities.**

1. **Identify** On the diagram, label the inputs,
   processes, and outputs of the system.

2. **Predict** Suppose you want less mercury to end
   up in fish. How might you change the inputs of
   the system?

_____

_____

_____

_____

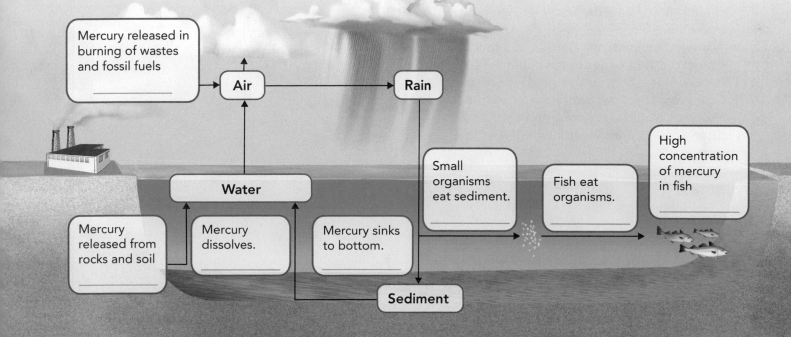

Testing Assumptions

When scientists construct a model of a system, they begin with certain assumptions. For example, an astronomer might assume that in order for a planet to support life, the planet must have water.

Scientists check their assumptions. They compare the input and output of the model to the input and output in the natural world. If they match, then the assumptions are correct. If they do not match, scientists must change one or more assumptions. The revised model more accurately represents the natural world.

Sometimes scientists make assumptions to simplify the model. A scientist who wants to study how energy flows through a certain environment might use a model called a food chain. A food chain is a series of diagrams that shows what animals eat in a certain environment. For example, in a savanna, or grassy plain, a lion eats zebras and many other animals. Zebras eat grass. But the model may assume that lions eat only zebras. So the process that is shown in the model is somewhat simpler than the process that takes place in the natural world. Yet the model still accurately shows the relationship between the parts of the system. A food web, which you can draw in **Figure 5,** is a slightly more complex model of how energy flows through an environment.

FIGURE 5 ·····················

Food Webs

Scientists use food webs to model how energy flows through a particular environment. In a food web, lines connect organisms that eat other organisms. For any two organisms, the organism that eats the other is always shown higher up on the food web. ✎ **Analyze Models and Systems** Construct a food web based on the images in the Picture Bank below. (*Hint:* Zebras and giraffes eat grass or leaves. Lions eat zebras and giraffes. Vultures eat lions, zebras, and giraffes.) Then answer the questions on the next page.

✏ **Infer** What are the assumptions of this model?

_____

_____

_____

_____

_____

[CHALLENGE] How could you test this model to see if your assumptions are correct?

_____

_____

_____

_____

_____

_____

Lab® zone Do the Lab Investigation *Selecting Models.*

🔑 Assess Your Understanding

2a. Review Scientists check _____ by comparing the inputs and outputs of a model to inputs and outputs of a natural system.

b. Explain A certain astronomer assumes that a planet must have water to support life. How does the astronomer's assumption help the astronomer search for life in the universe?

_____

_____

_____

_____

_____

c. Predict What might make the astronomer change the assumption made in the previous question?

_____

_____

_____

_____

_____

got it? ....

○ **I get it!** Now I know models help scientists understand natural systems by allowing scientists to test _____

_____

_____

and compare them to those of the natural world.

○ **I need extra help with** _____

Go to MY SCIENCE ⓢ COACH *online for help with this subject.*

Safety in the Science Laboratory

UNLOCK THE BIG ?

🔑 Why Prepare for a Scientific Investigation?

🔑 What Should You Do if an Accident Occurs?

my PLANET DiARY

Posted by: Rachel

Location: Monrovia, Indiana

Using laboratory safety is always key. My class was studying the formation of crystals, and my science teacher had us make our own! The crystals were poisonous and had to be made carefully. Our teacher said the ingredients of the crystals could be fatal. We wore goggles and aprons to protect ourselves from harmful chemicals. Listen to your teacher and follow rules.

Lab zone Do the Inquiry Warm-Up Can You Name the Safety Equipment?

BLOG

Write your answer to the question on the lines below.
What are some steps you can take to create a safe lab environment?

_____

_____

_____

▶ PLANET DIARY Go to **Planet Diary** to learn more about lab safety.

Why Prepare for a Scientific Investigation?

How do you prepare for a long trip? You probably find and reserve a place to stay weeks or months in advance. A few days before your trip, you begin to pack. You check the area's weather forecast and use the information to choose the appropriate clothes. After you make these preparations, you are ready to relax and enjoy your trip.

Vocabulary
• field

Skills
↻ Reading: Sequence
△ Inquiry: Observe

Preparing for an Investigation
Good preparation helps you have a safe, enjoyable trip. It can also help you perform a successful scientific investigation. 🔑 **Good preparation helps to keep you and your classmates safe when you perform a scientific investigation. It also keeps any living things you use safe.** To prepare for an investigation, read the procedures carefully. If you do not understand any part of the investigation, ask your teacher questions before you start. Make sure you know where all the safety equipment is located in the laboratory.

Working Safely in the Field
Although you will do many of your investigations in the laboratory, you may do some investigations in the field. The **field** is any area outside a science laboratory. The field may be a nearby forest, park, or beach. Good preparation is important in the field because there are additional safety hazards, such as wild animals, poisonous plants, or severe weather, that you may encounter. Wear appropriate clothing, including hats and sunglasses, and bring appropriate equipment, such as gloves and safety goggles. Treat plants and animals with proper care and respect. Always work in the field with another person and an adult.

These students are working in the field.

❶ △ **Observe** What clothing items protect these students?

_____

_____

❷ **CHALLENGE** Suppose the students are caught in a sudden rainstorm. How can they stay safe during the storm?

_____

75

Conducting the Investigation Safely Whenever you perform a scientific investigation, your primary concern should be your safety and the safety of others. Keep in mind this rule: *Always follow your teacher's instructions and the directions exactly.* If you have an idea that you would like to try, ask your teacher before doing it.

There are certain safety measures you should take before, during, and after an investigation. Before you do any investigation, first make sure you know its safety symbols. Safety symbols alert you to possible sources of accidents in the investigation. Familiarize yourself with any equipment you will be using. Then, clean and organize your work area. Finally, label any containers you will be using. Look at **Figure 1** to see safety symbols and learn ways to be safe during and after a scientific investigation.

FIGURE 1
Safety in the Laboratory
To be safe, there are a number of things you should do during and after a scientific investigation.

✎ **Relate Text and Visuals** For each scene shown, circle any safety equipment the students are using. Then, write in the boxes the names of four safety symbols that apply to that investigation.

During the investigation:

- Wear safety goggles to protect your eyes from chemical splashes, glass breakage, and sharp objects.

- Wear an apron to protect yourself and your clothes from chemicals.

- Wear heat-resistant gloves when handling hot objects.

- Wear plastic gloves to protect your skin when handling animals, plants, or chemicals.

- Handle live animals and plants with care.

After the investigation:

- Clean up your work area.
- Turn off and unplug any equipment, and return it to its proper place.
- Dispose of any wastes properly.
- Wash your hands thoroughly.

Safety Symbols

| Animal safety | Disposal | Breakage | Heat-Resistant Gloves | Plastic Gloves | Corrosive chemical | Sharp Object | Safety Goggles | Plant safety | Lab Apron | Hand Washing | Flames |

Caring for Plants and Animals Properly
When you are performing an investigation in the field, you are very likely to encounter plants and animals there. You may also work with plants and animals in the laboratory. Whether you are in the laboratory or in the field, you should treat living things with care and respect. Follow the animal care instructions listed in **Figure 2** when you are working with animals in the laboratory.

FIGURE 2 ·······························

Animal Care
You must treat the animals you use in an investigation properly and humanely.

✎ **Interpret Photos** What information should you know about this turtle to care for it properly?

_____

_____

_____

_____

Proper Animal Care
- Provide animals with enough space in their cage or terrarium.
- Provide proper food and clean drinking water.
- Clean the cages or terrariums regularly.
- Handle animals with care.

Lab zone® Do the Quick Lab
Be Prepared to Be Safe in the Field.

🔑 Assess Your Understanding

1a. Identify Give one safety practice you should always use at each stage of an investigation.

_____

_____

_____

b. Infer What safety symbols would you expect to see in an investigation using animals?

_____

_____

_____

got it? ··

○ **I get it!** Now I know that I should prepare for a scientific investigation because _____

_____

○ **I need extra help with** _____

Go to **MY SCIENCE COACH** online for help with this subject.

What Should You Do If an Accident Occurs?

Even with careful preparation, sometimes accidents occur during an investigation. In the event of an accident, what should you do? 🗝 **Always alert your teacher first. Then follow your teacher's directions, and carry them out quickly.** If your teacher is not available, then find and alert the nearest adult. Familiarize yourself with the location and the proper use of all the emergency equipment in your laboratory. You can use some of the equipment shown in **Figure 3.** Knowing safety and first-aid procedures beforehand will prepare you to handle accidents properly.

✏️ **Sequence** Underline the steps you should take when an accident occurs.

FIGURE 3 ·······················

Emergency Equipment

Use the emergency equipment shown in case of a fire or an injury.

✏️ **Identify** In each box, write how the equipment can help you in an emergency.

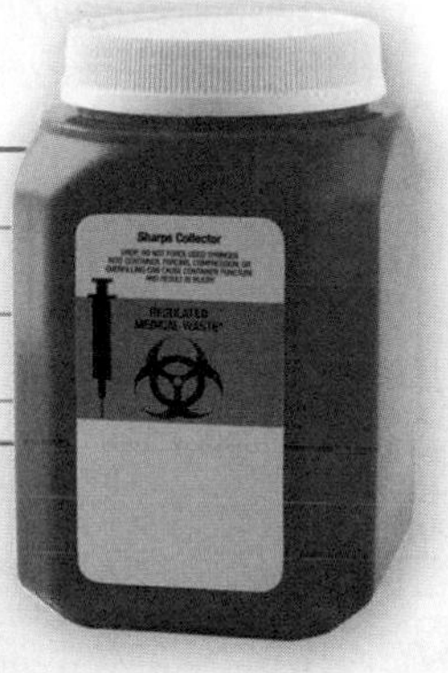

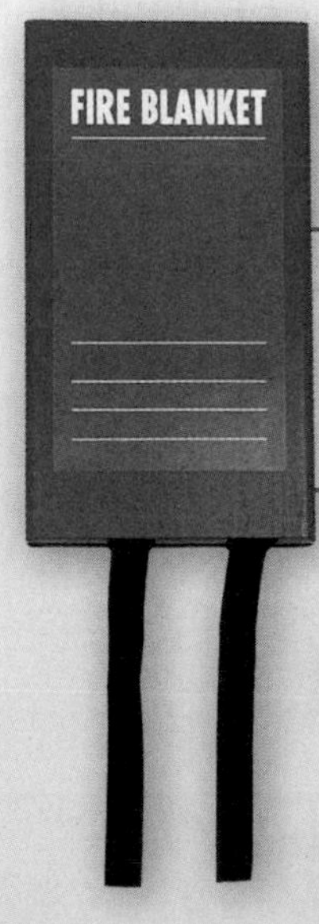

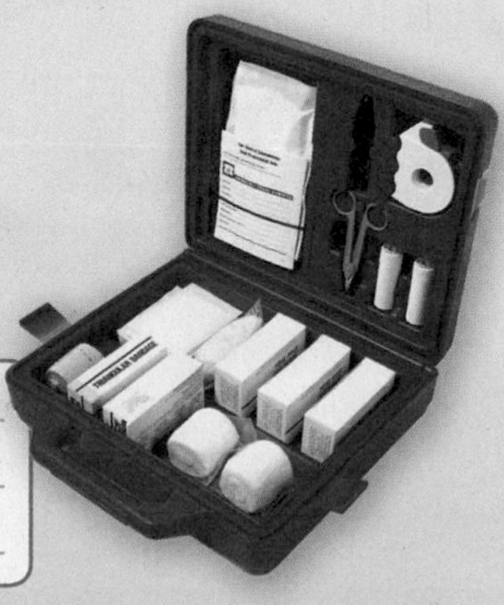

Lab zone Do the Quick Lab *How Would You Respond to These Emergencies?*

🗝 Assess Your Understanding

got it? ······················

○ I get it! Now I know that in case of an accident I should _____

_____

_____

○ I need extra help with _____

Go to MY SCIENCE COACH *online for help with this subject.*

Scientists use _____ to communicate how precise their measurements are.

LESSON 1 Scientific Measurement

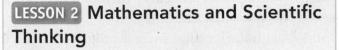

🔑 The SI system allows scientists to compare data and communicate with each other about the results of scientific investigations.

🔑 SI units for length, mass, weight, volume, density, time, and temperature include meters, kilograms, newtons, cubic meters, kilograms per cubic meter, seconds, and kelvins.

Vocabulary
• metric system • International System of Units (SI)
• mass • weight • volume • meniscus • density

LESSON 2 Mathematics and Scientific Thinking

🔑 Scientists use math skills that include estimation, accuracy and precision, and significant figures.

🔑 Scientists use math tools including mean, median, mode, range, and percent error.

Vocabulary
• estimate • accuracy • precision
• significant figures • mean • median • mode
• range • anomalous data • percent error

LESSON 3 Using Graphs in Science

🔑 Scientists use graphs to identify trends, make predictions, and recognize anomalous data.

Vocabulary
• graph
• linear graph
• nonlinear graph
• outlier

LESSON 4 Models and Systems

🔑 Scientists use models to test their ideas about things they cannot observe directly.

🔑 All systems have input, process, and output.

🔑 Scientists build models to represent a process. They test whether the input and output from the model match the input and output of the system in the natural world.

Vocabulary
• model • system • input • process • output
• feedback

LESSON 5 Safety in the Science Laboratory

🔑 Good preparation helps to keep you and your classmates safe when you perform a scientific investigation. It also keeps any living things you use safe.

🔑 In the event of an accident, always alert your teacher first. Then follow your teacher's directions, and carry them out quickly.

Vocabulary
• field

Review and Assessment

LESSON 1 **Scientific Measurement**

1. A newton is the SI unit for

a. mass.   **b.** density.

c. volume.   **d.** weight.

2. The SI system of measurement is based on the

_____

3. Calculate Find the volume of the object at the right. Explain your method.

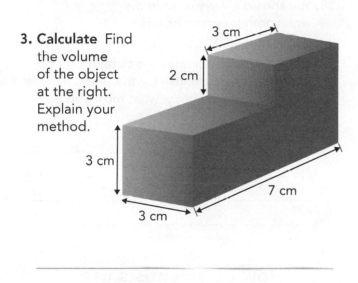

3 cm

2 cm

3 cm

3 cm

7 cm

_____

_____

_____

_____

4. Apply Concepts Will an object with a volume of 77 grams per cubic centimeter and a mass of 65 grams float or sink in water? Explain.

_____

_____

_____

5. **Write About It** Your friend sends you an e-mail about an experiment that she read about. She mentions that the results from the experiment work best at −2 K. Write an e-mail back to your friend explaining why she must be mistaken about the temperature.

LESSON 2 **Mathematics and Scientific Thinking**

6. How close a measurement is to its true or accepted value is

a. accuracy.   **b.** estimation.

c. precision.   **d.** range.

7. Nineteen is the _____ for the data set 25, 19, 18, 31, 19, 22.

8. Interpret Data How many significant figures are in the measurement 230 kg?

_____

9. Calculate You measure the mass of a model car to be 230 grams. The actual mass is 218 grams. What is your percent error?

_____

_____

Use the table below to answer Question 10.

Month and Year	Number of Ducks
Nov. 2009	356,000
Dec. 2009	656,000
Jan. 2010	976,000

10. Interpret Tables The table shows the estimated number of ducks counted in an area over several months. Why are the counts only estimates?

_____

_____

_____

_____

_____

81

LESSON 3 Using Graphs in Science

11. Anomalous data shows on a graph as a(n)

   a. nonlinear graph.   **b.** trend.

   c. linear graph.   **d.** outlier.

12. In a linear graph, data points fall along a(n)

_____

13. math! Plot a line graph using this data table from a summer science camp. Determine if the graph is linear or nonlinear and label any outliers.

Year	Number of Campers
1	52
2	60
3	63
4	41
5	70

LESSON 4 Models and Systems

14. A model is any representation of an object or

   a. an opinion.   **b.** a process.

   c. an investigation.   **d.** data.

15. A system is a group of parts that work

together to _____.

16. Explain Meteorologists use models to help them predict the weather, but their predictions are not always correct. Explain why this is so.

_____

_____

_____

_____

_____

LESSON 5 Safety in the Science Laboratory

17. What safety equipment should you use when you handle live animals?

   a. sunglasses   **b.** heat-resistant gloves

   c. plastic container   **d.** plastic gloves

18. You should always work in the _____ with another person or adult.

19. Infer You have volunteered to take care of your classroom's mouse for the week. To care for the mouse properly, what must you do?

_____

_____

_____

_____

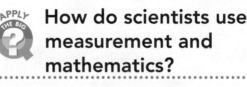

How do scientists use measurement and mathematics?

20. Suppose a scientist wants to measure the lengths of twenty queen bees from twenty different hives. How would the scientist find the mean of the data set? Why might the scientist choose to compare the queens' lengths in a bar graph?

_____

_____

_____

_____

_____

_____

_____

Ohio Benchmark Practice

Multiple Choice

Mark only one answer for each question.

1. What might be one reason scientists would build a model of Earth like the one shown here?

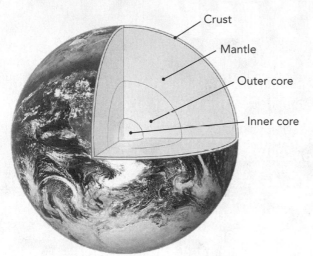

Crust
Mantle
Outer core
Inner core

   A. to show the color of the continents
   B. to show the depths of Earth's oceans
   C. to show the layers of Earth
   D. to show pressure inside Earth

2. Nicole measured the height of her locker as 39.8 cm, 42.3 cm, 42.0 cm, and 43.1 cm. The locker is actually 45.5 cm. Which *best* describes Nicole's measurements?

   A. They were accurate.
   B. They were precise.
   C. They were both accurate and precise.
   D. They were neither accurate nor precise.

3. Which SI unit would you use to measure the volume of a tomato?

   A. gram
   B. grams per cubic meter
   C. cubic centimeter
   D. newton

4. What is the median for the data set 32, 40, 38, 41, 36?

   A. 9
   B. 38
   C. 93.5
   D. 187

Short Answer

Write your answer to Question 5 on the lines below.

5. Suppose you are cleaning up after a scientific investigation in the laboratory. As you are cleaning a glass container, it slips from your hands and breaks in the sink. What should you do?

_____

_____

_____

_____

_____

Extended Response

Use the graph below to answer Question 6.

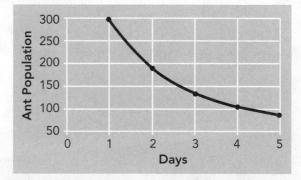

6. What kind of trend do the data show? Predict what the ant population will be at 6 days. Explain your prediction.

THE RACE TO BE FASTER

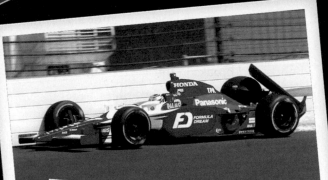

Did you know that the first Indianapolis 500 ran in 1911? The winner of the first race only averaged about 120 km/h (75 mph). Today Indy winners average more than twice that speed! What changed in all that time?

All early racecars were two-seaters. One seat was for the driver and one was for a mechanic. Ray Harroun, the winner in 1911, raced in a single-seater with a rear-view mirror. This eliminated the need for a mechanic—as well as the additional weight!

As technology progressed, the engines and exteriors of cars were manufactured from lightweight metal alloys and polymers. Engines became smaller, lighter, and more powerful. The cars became more aerodynamic. New designs decreased the resistance from air when traveling at high speeds, called drag. Race cars also switched fuels from gasoline to ethanol, allowing for smaller gas tanks. These modifications made the cars faster—and the races more exciting!

Design It Design a toy race car that is built for speed. Brainstorm potential design solutions. Document your ideas with labeled drawings and choose the best design. Build a prototype and measure how fast the car can travel on a set course without pushing it. Present your data using graphs or tables. Using this information, redesign your prototype to make the car faster. See Appendix E on page 520 for more information about the design process.

AQUANAUTS

Science has sent people to the moon and robots to Mars. But vast amounts of Earth's surface—the parts that are deep underwater—remain unexplored.

Aquarius, the world's first underwater research station, is located more than 18 meters below the ocean's surface off the southern tip of Florida. The scientists and crew who work in *Aquarius* are called aquanauts.

Aquanauts are marine biologists and oceanographers. While on board *Aquarius*, the aquanauts may study nearby coral reefs or test new technology for marine exploration. *Aquarius* has allowed scientists to study and observe undersea life in ways that were previously impossible. Aquanaut missions are also helping the National Aeronautics and Space Administration (NASA). Because the undersea habitat is similar to a space station, NASA uses *Aquarius* to explore the challenges of living in space.

Design It Find out more about *Aquarius* and the missions it supports. Then write a news article to tell the public about the underwater research station, its missions, and the people who work on it. Remember to write an attention-grabbing headline and exciting lead paragraph.

Warm and dry inside Aquarius, an aquanaut looks out at the ocean. ▽

HOW DEEP INTO EARTH CAN THIS CLIMBER GO?

What is the structure of Earth?

Descending into a canyon, this climber will get nearer to the center of Earth. But how close will he get? As climbers move down through narrow, dark passages of rock and dirt, they sometimes have to dig their way through. Some spelunkers, or cave explorers, have even descended into caves over 2,000 meters deep—the length of nearly 22 football fields!

Predict If this climber could go all the way down to Earth's center, what materials other than dirt and solid rock might he find along the way? Explain your answer.

_____

_____

_____

_____

> **UNTAMED SCIENCE** Watch the **Untamed Science** video to learn more about Earth's structure.

Introducing Earth

3 Getting Started

Check Your Understanding

1. **Background** Read the paragraph below and then answer the question.

On a field trip, Paula sees that beach cliffs near the sea have worn away. "Where do the cliffs go?" she asks. Her teacher says, "The cliffs are exposed to natural forces all year. The harsh weather breaks the cliffs into pieces. Gravity causes the pieces to fall to the sea. Waves then shape the pieces into small particles, which wash away."

A **force** is a natural power that acts on an object.

Gravity is the force that makes objects fall toward Earth's center.

A **particle** is a very small fragment of a much larger object.

• What forces change the beach cliffs each year?

_____

_____

> **MY READING WEB** If you had trouble answering the question above, visit **My Reading Web** and type in *Introducing Earth.*

Vocabulary Skill

Identify Related Word Forms You can increase your vocabulary by learning related word forms. If you know that the noun *energy* means "the ability to do work," you can figure out the meaning of the adjective *energetic.*

Verb	Noun	Adjective
destroy to reduce to pieces	**destruction** the process of reducing to pieces	**destructive** tending to cause damage or to reduce to pieces
radiate to release energy	**radiation** energy released in the form of rays or waves	**radiant** released as waves or rays

2. **Quick Check** Review the words related to *destroy.* Then circle the correct form of the word *destroy* in the following sentence.

• The (destruction/destructive) winds of a hurricane can be very dangerous.

system

hydrosphere

basalt

convection current

Chapter Preview

LESSON 1
- system
- energy
- atmosphere
- geosphere
- hydrosphere
- biosphere
- constructive force
- destructive force

↻ **Ask Questions**
△ **Draw Conclusions**

LESSON 2
- seismic wave
- pressure
- crust
- basalt
- granite
- mantle
- lithosphere
- asthenosphere
- outer core
- inner core

↻ **Identify Supporting Evidence**
△ **Interpret Data**

LESSON 3
- radiation
- convection
- conduction
- density
- convection current

↻ **Relate Cause and Effect**
△ **Communicate**

> VOCAB FLASH CARDS For extra help with vocabulary, visit **Vocab Flash Cards** and type in *Introducing Earth.*

1 The Earth System

UNLOCK THE BIG ?

🔑 **What Are the Main Parts of the Earth System?**

🔑 **How Do Constructive and Destructive Forces Change Earth?**

MY PLANET DIARY

Posted by: Nicole

Location: Medfield, Massachusetts

This past summer my family and I went to the Grand Canyon. The Grand Canyon was carved by the Colorado River. It was so cool, looking down from the edge and seeing a small line that is the river and the rock layers in all different colors. I was amazed that mules could carry you down into the canyon.

BLOG

Read the text and answer the questions.

1. How did the Colorado River change the landscape that existed before the Grand Canyon formed?

_____

_____

2. What else would you like to learn about the Colorado River?

_____

_____

_____

_____

▷ **PLANET DIARY** Go to **Planet Diary** to learn more about how natural forces change Earth's features.

 Lab® zone Do the Inquiry Warm-Up *What Is a System?*

What Are the Main Parts of the Earth System?

The Grand Canyon is made up of different parts. Rock forms the canyon walls. Water flows through the canyon in the form of a river, which carves away the rock. Animals such as deer drink the river's water. And air fills the canyon, allowing the animals to breath. All these parts work together. So the environment of the Grand Canyon can be thought of as a system. A **system** is a group of parts that work together as a whole. **Figure 1** shows how air, water, rock, and life work together in another part of Earth.

Vocabulary

- system
- energy
- atmosphere
- geosphere
- hydrosphere
- biosphere
- constructive force
- destructive force

Skills

○ Reading: Ask Questions

△ Inquiry: Draw Conclusions

Earth as a System The Earth system involves a constant flow of matter through different parts. For example, you may know that in the *water cycle,* water evaporates from the ocean, rises into the atmosphere, and then falls from the sky as rain. The rainwater then flows into and over Earth, and then back into the ocean.

You might be surprised to learn that rock, too, cycles through the Earth system. For example, new rock can form from molten material inside Earth called *magma.* This material can rise to the surface and harden on land to form new rock. The new rock can then erode into small pieces. The pieces can be washed into the ocean, where they may sink to the bottom as small particles, or *sediment.* If enough of the small particles collect, the weight of the sediment can crush all the particles together. The particles can then be cemented together to form new rock. The flow of rock through the Earth system is called the *rock cycle.*

The constant flow, or cycling, of matter through the Earth system is driven by energy. **Energy** is the ability to do work. The energy that drives the Earth system has two main sources: heat from the sun and heat flowing out of Earth as it cools.

FIGURE 1 ·····························

All Systems Go!

The many parts of the Earth system all work together.

✏ **Develop Hypotheses** Look at the photograph. Choose one part of the Earth system—rock, water, air, or life—and describe how the other parts might be affected if the first part were removed.

_____

_____

_____

_____

_____

_____

_____

_____

_____

_____

_____

_____

_____

_____

FIGURE 2 ⋅⋅⋅⋅⋅⋅⋅⋅⋅⋅⋅⋅⋅⋅⋅⋅⋅⋅⋅⋅⋅⋅⋅⋅⋅⋅⋅

> INTERACTIVE ART **The Earth System**

Earth's four spheres can affect one another.

✎ **Interpret Photos** Read the descriptions of Earth's four spheres. On the lines in each box, write the spheres that are interacting with each other in the small photograph next to the box.

Parts of the Earth System
Earth contains air, water, land, and life. Each of these parts forms its own part, or "sphere." 🔑 **The Earth system has four main spheres: the atmosphere, the hydrosphere, the geosphere, and the biosphere. As a major source of energy for Earth processes, the sun can be considered part of the Earth system as well.** Each part of the Earth system can be studied separately. But the four parts are interconnected, as shown in **Figure 2.**

One of the most important parts of the Earth system is—you! Humans greatly affect the air, water, land, and life of Earth. For instance, the amount of paved land, including roads and parking lots, in the United States is now larger than the state of Georgia.

Atmosphere
Earth's outermost layer is a mixture of gases—mostly nitrogen and oxygen. It also contains dust particles, cloud droplets, and the rain and snow that form from water vapor. It contains Earth's weather, and is the foundation for the different climates around the world. Earth's **atmosphere** (AT muh sfeer) is the relatively thin envelope of gases that forms Earth's outermost layer.

_____

_____

Geosphere
Nearly all of Earth's mass is found in Earth's solid rocks and metals, in addition to other materials. Earth's **geosphere** (GEE uh sfeer) has three main parts: a metal core, a solid middle layer, and a rocky outer layer.

_____

_____

Hydrosphere
About three quarters of Earth is covered by a relatively thin layer of water. Earth's water can take the form of oceans, glaciers, rivers, lakes, groundwater, and water vapor. Of the surface water, most is the salt water of the ocean. Only a tiny part of the hydrosphere is fresh water that is drinkable by humans. The **hydrosphere** (HY druh sfeer) contains all of Earth's water.

_____

_____

Feedback Within a System For years, the ice in glaciers at Glacier National Park in Montana has been melting. The melting is caused by rising temperatures. As the volume of ice in the glaciers has decreased, the land around the glaciers has become warmer. The warmer land melts the glaciers even faster.

Melting of the glaciers in Glacier National Park is an example of a process called *feedback*. When feedback occurs, a system returns—or feeds back—to itself data about a change in the system. In Glacier National Park, the ground around the melting glaciers feeds back warmer temperatures to the glaciers. Feedback can increase the effects of a change, as in the case of warming glaciers, or slow the effects down. Feedback demonstrates how changes in one part of the Earth system might affect the other parts. For example, the feedback of melting glaciers affects the geosphere (the ground), hydrosphere (glaciers), and atmosphere (climate).

⟲ **Ask Questions** Write a question about feedback. Then read the text and answer your question.

_____
_____
_____
_____
_____
_____
_____

 Lab zone Do the Quick Lab *Parts of Earth's System.*

🔑 **Assess Your Understanding**

1a. Review The Earth system consists of the sun and four main _____

b. Classify The sphere that contains humans is the _____

c. Evaluate the Impact on Society Give one example of how humans affect the hydrosphere. Then explain how this change impacts society.

_____
_____
_____

got it? ....

○ **I get it!** Now I know that the main parts of the Earth system are _____
_____
_____

○ **I need extra help with** _____

Go to MY SCIENCE ⓢ COACH *online for help with this subject.*

Biosphere
Life exists at the tops of mountains, deep underground, at the bottom of the ocean, and high up in the atmosphere. In fact, life exists in all kinds of conditions. But life as we know it cannot exist without water. The parts of Earth that contain living organisms make up the **biosphere** (BI uh sfeer).

_____
_____
_____

How Do Constructive and Destructive Forces Change Earth?

Suppose you left a movie camera running in one spot for the next 100 million years and then you watched the movie in fast motion. You would see lands forming and mountains rising up—but you would also see them eroding back down again. 🔑 **Lands are constantly being created and destroyed by competing forces.**

Constructive Forces The Himalayas are Earth's highest mountains. But rock in the Himalayas contains *fossils,* or remains, of ocean animals such as ammonites. How could creatures that once lived at the bottom of the sea be found at the top of the world?

The Himalayas are the result of the collision of two sections of Earth's *lithosphere,* or Earth's top layer of stiff, solid rock. This layer is broken into huge pieces, or *plates,* that move slowly over Earth. The slow movement of Earth's plates is called *plate tectonics.*

The Himalayas are the result of the collision of the plate that carries India with the plate that carries China. Over millions of years, as these plates collided, their edges were squeezed slowly upward. This process lifted up the ocean floor and formed the Himalayas, shown in **Figure 3.**

Forces that construct, or build up, mountains are called **constructive forces.** 🔑 **Constructive forces shape the land's surface by building up mountains and other landmasses.** Volcanoes build up Earth's surface by spewing lava that hardens into rock. Earthquakes build landmasses by lifting up mountains and rock.

FIGURE 3 ·······························

From Sea to Mountain
Constructive forces raised the Himalaya Mountains.

✎ **Answer the questions.**

1. **Explain** Why are ammonite fossils found in the Himalayas?

_____

_____

_____

_____

_____

_____

_____

2. **Calculate** Many peaks in the Himalayas are 7,300 meters or more above sea level. About how high above India's capital, New Delhi, are these peaks?

_____

Ammonite

CHINA

AFGHANISTAN

Eurasian Plate

HIMALAYAS

PAKISTAN

New Delhi ✪

NEPAL

BHUTAN

Indo-Australian Plate

BANGLADESH

INDIAN OCEAN

INDIA

Key
— Plate boundary
Elevation
Meters
4,500
3,000
1,800
900
300
150
0

Destructive Forces While the Himalayas are being built up, they are also being torn down. Ice, rain, wind, and changing temperatures tear the rock apart. This process is called *weathering*. After the rock is torn apart, gravity pulls it downward. Eventually, rivers and streams carry away most of the eroded material.

Because forces such as ice, rain, wind, and changing temperatures wear down, or destroy, landmasses, they are called **destructive forces.** 🔑 **Destructive forces destroy and wear away landmasses through processes like erosion and weathering.** *Erosion* is the wearing down and carrying away of land by natural forces such as water, ice, or wind.

Vocabulary Identify Related Word Forms Use the text and your knowledge of the word *weather* to write a definition of *weathering.*

_____

_____

_____

_____

**it!**

Since 1983, lava from Kilauea has covered more than 100 square kilometers of land in Hawaii. Here, lava flows into the Pacific Ocean. When it reaches the water, it cools quickly. The cooled lava hardens to form new rock.

1 ▲ **Draw Conclusions** The forces that cause lava to erupt are (constructive/destructive) forces.

2 [CHALLENGE] Other than the weather, what force wears down the new rock formed by the magma from Kilauea?

_____

_____

 Do the Quick Lab *What Forces Shape Earth?*

🔑 **Assess Your Understanding**

2a. Review Forces that erode mountains are called (constructive/destructive) forces.

b. List List the destructive forces that act on mountains to erode them.

_____

_____

c. Relate Cause and Effect How do destructive forces change Earth?

_____

_____

_____

_____

_____

got it? ....

○ **I get it!** Now I know that constructive and destructive forces change Earth by _____

_____

○ **I need extra help with** _____

Go to **my science** ⑤ **coach** *online for help with this subject.*

Earth's Interior

🔑 How Do Geologists Learn About Earth's Interior?

🔑 What Are the Features of Earth's Crust, Mantle, and Core?

UNLOCK THE BIG ?

my PLANET DiARY

Inside Earth

Deep inside Earth, our planet is constantly changing. Dr. Samuel B. Mukasa, a geochemist at the University of Michigan, studies some of these changes. He examines rocks in Antarctica that have been brought up to Earth's surface by magma. When he examines these rocks, he looks for elements that occur only in very small amounts. These elements can offer telltale signs of processes occurring near the boundary between Earth's crust and its mantle—or even at deeper levels. By studying rocks at Earth's surface, Dr. Mukasa is helping us understand Earth's interior.

CAREERS

Read the text and then answer the question.

How is Dr. Mukasa able to study Earth's interior without actually seeing it?

_____

_____

_____

_____

_____

> PLANET DIARY Go to Planet Diary to learn more about Earth's interior.

Lab zone® Do the Inquiry Warm-Up Earth's Interior.

How Do Geologists Learn About Earth's Interior?

Processes that affect Earth's surface are often a result of what's going on inside Earth. But what's inside Earth? This question is very difficult to answer, because geologists are unable to see deep inside Earth. But geologists have found other methods to study the interior of Earth. 🔑 **Geologists have used two main types of evidence to learn about Earth's interior: direct evidence from rock samples and indirect evidence from seismic waves.**

Vocabulary

- seismic wave
- pressure
- crust
- basalt
- granite
- mantle
- lithosphere
- asthenosphere
- outer core
- inner core

Skills

➔ **Reading:** Identify Supporting Evidence

△ **Inquiry:** Interpret Data

Evidence From Rock Samples Geologists have drilled holes as deep as 12.3 kilometers into Earth. The drills bring up samples of rock. These rocks give geologists clues about Earth's structure and conditions deep inside Earth, where the rocks formed. In addition, volcanoes sometimes blast rock to the surface from depths of more than 100 kilometers. These rocks provide more information about Earth's interior. Also, in laboratories, geologists have re-created conditions inside Earth to see how rock behaves. For instance, they focus laser beams on pieces of rock while squeezing the rock with great force.

Evidence From Seismic Waves To study Earth's interior, geologists use an indirect method. When earthquakes occur, they produce **seismic waves** (SYZ mik). Geologists record the seismic waves and study how they travel through Earth. The speed of seismic waves and the paths they take give geologists clues about the structure of the planet. That is, the paths of seismic waves reveal areas inside Earth where the makeup or form of material changes. To better understand how seismic waves can reveal Earth's interior, look at how the paths of ocean waves "reveal" the island shown in **Figure 1.**

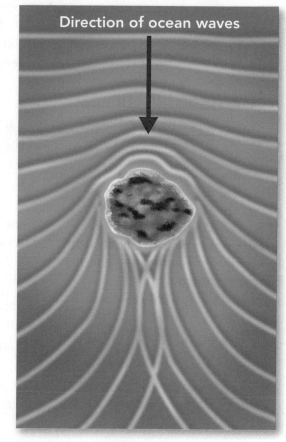

Direction of ocean waves

FIGURE 1 ·····················

Waves

Paths of ocean waves change when the waves reach an island.

✏ **Infer** Geologists have found that the paths of seismic waves change when the waves reach specific depths inside Earth. What can you infer about Earth's structure from this observation?

 Do the Quick Lab *How Do Scientists Find Out What's Inside Earth?*

🔑 Assess Your Understanding

got it? ···

○ **I get it!** Now I know that to learn about Earth's interior, geologists use two main types of evidence: _____

○ **I need extra help with** _____

Go to **my science** ⑤ **coach** online for help with this subject.

What Are the Features of Earth's Crust, Mantle, and Core?

Today, scientists know that Earth's interior is made up of three main layers. Each of Earth's layers covers the layers beneath it, much like the layers of an onion. 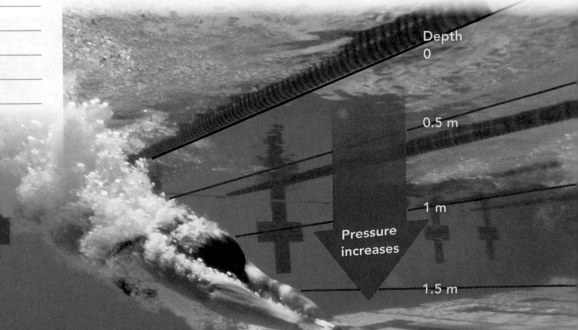 **The three main layers of Earth are the crust, the mantle, and the core. These layers vary greatly in size, composition, temperature, and pressure.**

Although each layer of Earth has its own characteristics, some properties apply throughout all of Earth. For example, the deeper inside Earth, the greater the mass of the rock that is pressing down from above. **Pressure** results from a force pressing on an area. Because of the weight of the rock above, pressure inside Earth increases with depth. **The deeper down inside Earth, the greater the pressure.** Look at **Figure 2**. Pressure inside Earth increases much like pressure in the swimming pool increases.

The mass of rock that presses down from above affects the temperature inside Earth. **The temperature inside Earth increases as depth increases.** Just beneath Earth's surface, the surrounding rock is cool. But at about 20 meters down, the rock starts to get warmer. For every 40 meters of depth from that point, the temperature typically rises 1 Celsius degree. The rapid rise in temperature continues for several tens of kilometers. Eventually, the temperature increases more slowly, but steadily. The high temperatures inside Earth are the result of the great pressures squeezing rock and the release of energy from radioactive substances. Some heat is also left over from the formation of Earth 4.6 billion years ago.

FIGURE 2 ···

Pressure and Depth

The deeper that this swimmer goes, the greater the pressure from the surrounding water.

✎ **Compare and Contrast**
How is the water in the swimming pool similar to Earth's interior? How is it different? (*Hint:* Consider both temperature and pressure in your answer.)

_____

_____

_____

_____

_____

_____

_____

_____

_____

Depth
0

0.5 m

1 m

Pressure increases

1.5 m

2 m

The Crust In the summer, you might climb a mountain or hike down into a shaded valley. During each of these activities, you are interacting with Earth's **crust,** the layer of rock that forms Earth's outer skin. 🔑 **The crust is a layer of solid rock that includes both dry land and the ocean floor.** The main elements in the crust are oxygen and silicon, as shown in **Figure 3.**

The crust is much thinner than the layer that lies beneath it. In most places, the crust is between 5 and 40 kilometers thick. It is thickest under high mountains—where it can be as thick as 80 kilometers—and thinnest beneath the ocean.

The crust that lies beneath the ocean is called oceanic crust. The composition of oceanic crust is nearly constant. Its overall composition is much like basalt, with small amounts of ocean sediment on top. **Basalt** (buh SAWLT) is a dark, fine-grained rock.

Continental crust, the crust that forms the continents, contains many types of rocks. So, unlike oceanic crust, its composition varies greatly. But overall the composition of continental crust is much like granite. **Granite** is a rock that usually is a light color and has coarse grains. Both granite and basalt have more oxygen and silicon than they have any other element.

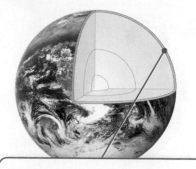

Read the text on this page and then fill in the missing information below.

Layer: _____

Thickness: _____

FIGURE 3 ⋯⋯⋯⋯⋯⋯⋯⋯⋯⋯⋯

Earth's Crust
The crust is Earth's outer layer of solid rock.

The Earth's Crust

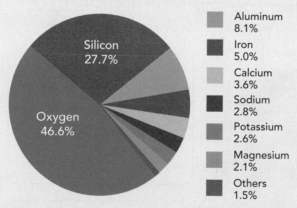

Silicon 27.7%

Oxygen 46.6%

Aluminum 8.1%

Iron 5.0%

Calcium 3.6%

Sodium 2.8%

Potassium 2.6%

Magnesium 2.1%

Others 1.5%

Note: Percentages given are by weight.

The circle graph above shows the composition of Earth's crust.

✏️ **Use the graph and the text on this page to complete the activities below.**

1. **Read Graphs** In total, how much of Earth's crust is made up of oxygen and silicon?

   _____

2. **Summarize** Fill in the missing information in the two charts at the right.

Oceanic crust

Oceanic crust

Typical rock: _____

Relative grain size: _____

Color: _____

Continental crust

Typical rock: _____

Relative grain size: _____

Color: _____

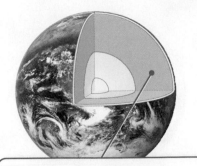

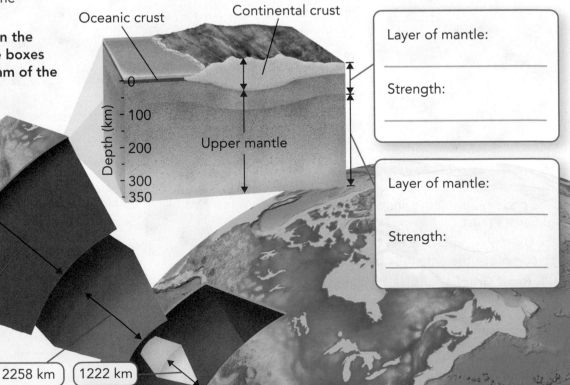

The Mantle

About 40 kilometers beneath dry land, the rock in Earth's interior changes. Rock here contains more magnesium and iron than rock above it. The rock below the boundary is the solid material of the **mantle,** a layer of hot rock. 🔑 **The mantle is made of rock that is very hot, but solid. Scientists divide the mantle into layers based on the physical characteristics of those layers. Overall, the mantle is nearly 3,000 kilometers thick.**

The Lithosphere

The uppermost part of the mantle is brittle rock, like the rock of the crust. Both the crust and the uppermost part of the mantle are strong, hard, and rigid. So geologists often group the crust and uppermost mantle into a single layer called the **lithosphere** (LITH uh sfeer). As shown in **Figure 4,** Earth's lithosphere averages about 100 kilometers thick.

The Asthenosphere

Below the lithosphere, the material is hotter and under increasing pressure. As a result, the part of the mantle just beneath the lithosphere is less rigid than the rock above. Over thousands of years this part of the mantle can bend like a metal spoon. But it's still solid. If you kicked it, you would stub your toe. This soft layer is called the **asthenosphere** (as THEN uh sfeer).

The Mesosphere

Beneath the asthenosphere, the mantle is hot but more rigid. The stiffness of the *mesosphere* is the result of increasingly high pressure. This layer includes a region called the transition zone, which lies just beneath the asthenosphere. It also includes the lower mantle, which extends down to Earth's core.

Read the text on this page and then fill in the missing information below.

Layer: _____

Thickness: _____

_____

FIGURE 4 ·······················

Mantle Piece

Earth's mantle is nearly 3,000 kilometers thick. The rigid lithosphere rests on the softer material of the asthenosphere.

✎ **Describe** Fill in the information in the boxes next to the diagram of the upper mantle.

Oceanic crust   Continental crust

Depth (km): 0 — 100 — 200 — 300 — 350

Upper mantle

Layer of mantle: _____

Strength: _____

Layer of mantle: _____

Strength: _____

2811–2886 km   2258 km   1222 km

The Core Below the mantle lies Earth's core. 🗝 **The core is made mostly of the metals iron and nickel. It consists of two parts—a liquid outer core and a solid inner core.** The outer core is 2,258 kilometers thick. The inner core is a solid ball. Its radius is 1,222 kilometers. The total radius of the core is 3,480 kilometers. Earth's core occupies the center of the planet.

Outer Core and Inner Core The **outer core** is a layer of molten metal surrounding the inner core. Despite enormous pressure, the outer core is liquid. The **inner core** is a dense ball of solid metal. In the inner core, extreme pressure squeezes the atoms of iron and nickel so much that they cannot spread out to become liquid.

Currently, most evidence suggests that both parts of the core are made of iron and nickel. But scientists have found data suggesting that the core also contains oxygen, sulfur, and silicon.

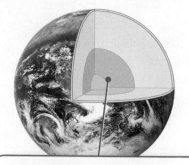

Read the text on this page and then fill in the missing information below.

Layer: _____

Radius: _____

FIGURE 5 ·······················

The Core of It
Earth's core consists of two separate layers.

✏ **Review** Put each term below in its proper place in the Venn diagram.

solid metal	molten metal
iron	nickel
dense ball	liquid layer

Outer Core   Both   Inner Core

do the math! Analyzing Data

Temperature Inside Earth
The graph shows how temperatures change between Earth's surface and the core.

❶ **Read Graphs** Between what depths does Earth's temperature increase the slowest?

_____

❷ **CHALLENGE** Why does the graph show a temperature of 16°C at 0 meters of depth?

_____

_____

❸ **Interpret Data** How does temperature change with depth in Earth's interior?

_____

_____

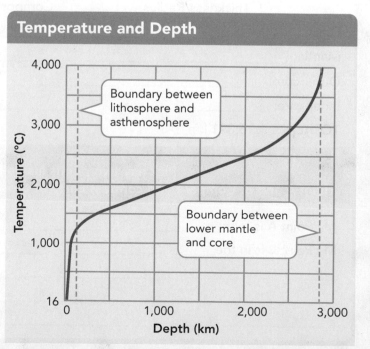

Temperature and Depth

Temperature (°C)

Boundary between lithosphere and asthenosphere

Boundary between lower mantle and core

Depth (km)

⊙ Identify Supporting
Evidence How can iron filings
provide evidence that a bar
magnet has a magnetic field?

_____

_____

_____

_____

_____

_____

The Core and Earth's Magnetic Field Scientists think that movements in the liquid outer core create Earth's magnetic field. Because Earth has a magnetic field, the planet acts like a giant bar magnet. Earth's magnetic field affects the whole planet.

To understand how a magnetic field affects an object, look at the bar magnet shown in **Figure 6.** If you place the magnet on a piece of paper and sprinkle iron filings on the paper, the iron filings line up with the bar's magnetic field. If you could surround Earth with iron filings, they would form a similar pattern.

When you use a compass, the compass needle aligns with the lines of force in Earth's magnetic field. These lines meet at Earth's magnetic poles. So the needle points to Earth's *magnetic* north pole, which is not the same location as Earth's *geographic* North Pole.

EXPLORE THE BIG ? Earth's Interior

What is the structure of Earth?

FIGURE 7 ··

▶ **REAL-WORLD INQUIRY** Earth is divided into distinct layers. Each layer has its own characteristics.

1. **Summarize** Draw each of Earth's layers. Include both the outer core and the inner core. Label each layer. Then, complete the chart below.

	Thickness/Radius	Composition	Solid/Liquid
Crust:			
Mantle:			
Outer core:			
Inner core:			
TOTAL:	6,371 km		

2. **Compare and Contrast** Pick any two points inside Earth and label them A and B. Compare and contrast Earth at those two points.

My Point A is in the _____

My Point B is in the _____

_____

_____

_____

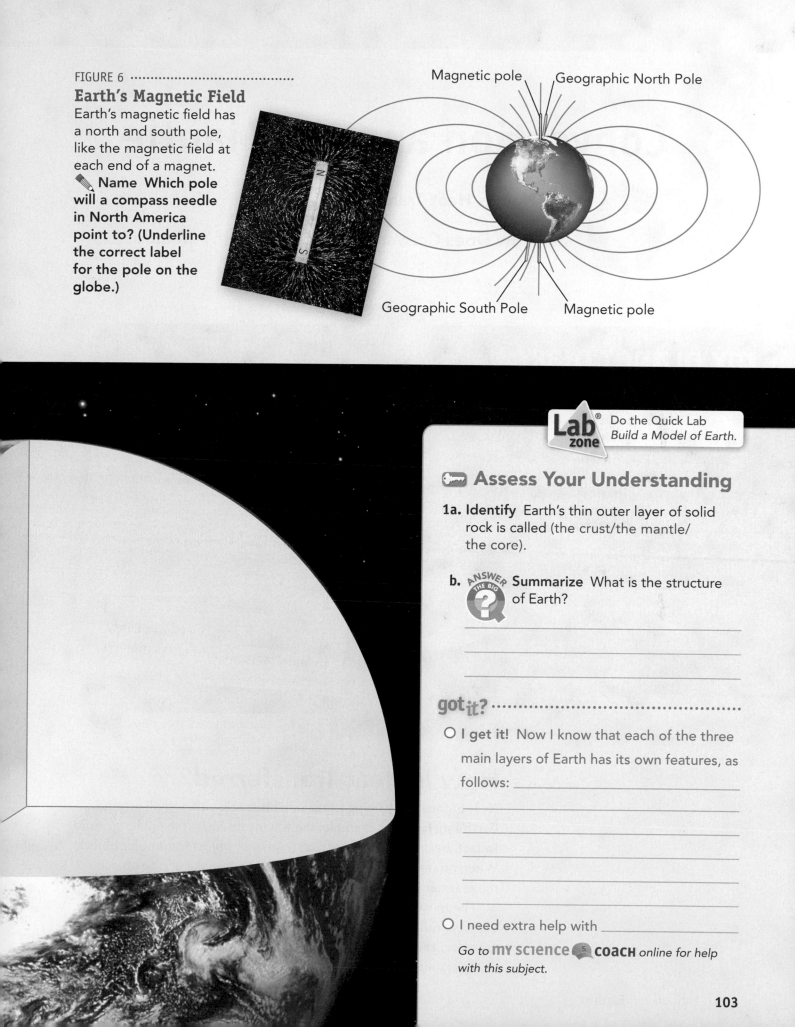

FIGURE 6 ·······················

Earth's Magnetic Field

Earth's magnetic field has a north and south pole, like the magnetic field at each end of a magnet.

✏️ **Name** Which pole will a compass needle in North America point to? (Underline the correct label for the pole on the globe.)

Magnetic pole   Geographic North Pole

Geographic South Pole   Magnetic pole

Lab ® Do the Quick Lab
zone *Build a Model of Earth.*

🔑 Assess Your Understanding

1a. Identify Earth's thin outer layer of solid rock is called (the crust/the mantle/ the core).

b. ANSWER THE BIG ? **Summarize** What is the structure of Earth?

_____

_____

_____

got it? ·······················

○ **I get it!** Now I know that each of the three main layers of Earth has its own features, as follows: _____

_____

_____

_____

_____

○ **I need extra help with** _____

Go to MY SCIENCE ⓢ COACH *online for help with this subject.*

Convection and the Mantle

UNLOCK THE BIG ?

🗝 **How Is Heat Transferred?**

🗝 **How Does Convection Occur in Earth's Mantle?**

MY PLANET DIARY

Lighting Up the Subject

Misconception: Rock cannot flow.

Did you know that the solid rock in Earth's mantle can flow like a fluid? To learn how, look at this image of a lava lamp. Heat from a bulb causes solid globs of wax at the bottom of the lamp to expand. As they expand, the globs become less dense. The globs then rise through the more dense fluid that surrounds them.

In Earth's mantle, great heat and pressure create regions of rock that are less dense than the rock around them. Over millions of years, the less dense rock slowly rises—like the solid globs in the lava lamp!

MISCONCEPTION

✏ **Compare and Contrast** Think about your own observations of liquids that flow. Then answer the question below.

How is flowing rock different from flowing water?

_____

_____

_____

_____

> **PLANET DIARY** Go to **Planet Diary** to learn more about Earth's mantle.

Lab zone® Do the Inquiry Warm-Up *Tracing Heat Flow.*

How Is Heat Transferred?

Heat is constantly being transferred inside Earth and all around Earth's surface. For example, the warm sun heats the cooler ground. In fact, heat always moves from a warmer object to a cooler object. When an object is heated, the particles that make up the object move faster. The faster-moving particles have more energy.

The movement of energy from a warmer object to a cooler object is called heat transfer. 🗝 **There are three types of heat transfer: radiation, convection, and conduction.** Look at **Figure 1** to see examples of heat transfer.

Vocabulary
- radiation • convection
- conduction • density
- convection current

Skills
↻ **Reading: Relate Cause and Effect**

△ **Inquiry: Communicate**

Radiation
The sun constantly transfers light and heat through the air, warming your skin. The transfer of energy that is carried in rays like light is called **radiation.**

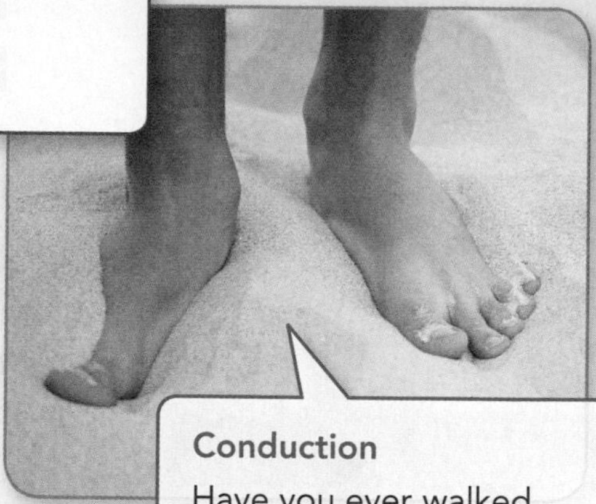

Conduction
Have you ever walked barefoot over hot sand? Your feet can feel as if they are burning! That is because the sand transfers its heat to your skin. Heat transfer between materials that are touching is called **conduction.**

Convection
Seagulls often soar on warm air currents. The currents are created as warm air rises from the ground. The warm air heats cooler air above it. Heat transfer by the movement of a fluid is called **convection.**

FIGURE 1 ·······································

⟩ **INTERACTIVE ART** **Heat Transfer**
In each type of heat transfer, heat moves from a warmer object to a colder object.

△ **Communicate** Work with a classmate to think of other examples of conduction, convection, and radiation. (*Hint:* Think of different ways to cook food.) Write your answers in the spaces provided.

Radiation

_____

_____

Conduction

_____

_____

Convection

_____

_____

 Lab zone Do the Quick Lab *How Can Heat Cause Motion in a Liquid?*

⊐ Assess Your Understanding

got it? ···

○ **I get it!** Now I know that the three types of heat transfer are _____

_____

○ **I need extra help with** _____

Go to **my science** ⑤ **coach** *online for help with this subject.*

How Does Convection Occur in Earth's Mantle?

Recall that Earth's mantle and core are extremely hot. How is heat transferred within Earth?

Convection Currents When you heat soup on a stove, convection occurs in the soup. That is, the soup at the bottom of the pot gets hot and expands. As the soup expands, its density decreases. **Density** is a measure of how much mass there is in a given volume of a substance. For example, most rock is more dense than water because a given volume of rock has more mass than the same volume of water.

The warm, less dense soup above the heat source moves upward and floats over the cooler, denser soup, as shown in **Figure 2**. Near the surface, the warm soup cools, becoming denser. Gravity then pulls the colder soup back down to the bottom of the pot. Here, it is reheated and rises again.

A constant flow begins. Cooler, denser soup sinks to the bottom of the pot. At the same time, warmer, less dense soup rises. The flow that transfers heat within a fluid is called a **convection current.** 🔑 **Heating and cooling of a fluid, changes in the fluid's density, and the force of gravity combine to set convection currents in motion.** Without heat, convection currents eventually stop.

🔁 **Relate Cause and Effect**
What three processes or forces combine to set convection currents in motion?

_____

_____

_____

_____

_____

FIGURE 2 ·······························
Convection Currents
In a pot of soup, convection currents flow as the hotter, less dense soup rises and the cooler, more dense soup sinks.

apply it!

Hot springs are common in Yellowstone National Park. Here, melted snow and rainwater seep to a depth of 3,000 meters, where a shallow magma chamber heats the rock of Earth's crust. The rock heats the water to over 200°C and keeps it under very high pressure.

❶ **Compare and Contrast** The heated water is (more/less) dense than the melted snow and rainwater.

❷ **CHALLENGE** What might cause convection currents in a hot spring?

_____

_____

Convection Currents in Earth

Inside Earth, heat from the core and the mantle act like the stove that heats the pot of soup. That is, large amounts of heat are transferred by convection currents within the core and mantle. 🗝 **Heat from the core and the mantle itself causes convection currents in the mantle.** To see how these currents work in the core and mantle, look at **Figure 3.**

How is it possible for mantle rock to flow? Over millions of years, the great heat and pressure in the mantle have caused solid mantle rock to warm and flow very slowly. Many geologists think plumes of mantle rock rise slowly from the bottom of the mantle toward the top. The hot rock eventually cools and sinks back through the mantle. Over and over, the cycle of rising and sinking takes place. Convection currents like these have been moving inside Earth for more than four billion years!

There are also convection currents in the outer core. These convection currents cause Earth's magnetic field.

FIGURE 3 ······················
› ART IN MOTION **Mantle Convection**
✏ **Interpret Diagrams** Place the following labels in the boxes for Points A and B:

| hotter | less dense | sinks |
| colder | more dense | rises |

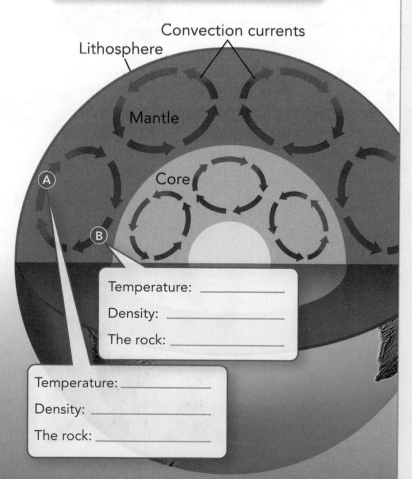

Convection currents
Lithosphere
Mantle
Core

Ⓐ
Ⓑ

Temperature: _____
Density: _____
The rock: _____

Temperature: _____
Density: _____
The rock: _____

Lab zone® Do the Lab Investigation *Modeling Mantle Convection Currents.*

🗝 Assess Your Understanding

1a. Explain A convection current transfers (heat /air) within a fluid.

b. Infer In which part of Earth's core do convection currents occur? _____

c. Predict What would happen to the convection currents in the mantle if Earth's interior eventually cooled down? Why?

_____

_____

_____

_____

_____

got it? ······································

○ **I get it!** Now I know that convection currents in the mantle are caused by_____

_____

_____

○ **I need extra help with** _____

Go to MY SCIENCE ⓢ COACH online for help with this subject.

Study Guide

Earth consists of three main layers. The _____ is the outermost layer. The _____ is made up of rock that is hot but solid. The _____ occupies Earth's center.

LESSON 1 The Earth System

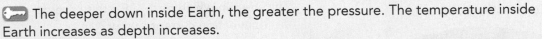

🔑 The Earth system has four main spheres: the atmosphere, the hydrosphere, the geosphere, and the biosphere. As a major source of energy for Earth processes, the sun can be considered part of the Earth system as well.

🔑 Lands are constantly being created and destroyed by competing forces. Constructive forces shape the land's surface by building up mountains and other landmasses. Destructive forces destroy and wear away landmasses through processes like erosion and weathering.

Vocabulary
• system • energy • atmosphere • geosphere • hydrosphere
• biosphere • constructive force • destructive force

LESSON 2 Earth's Interior

🔑 Geologists have used two main types of evidence to learn about Earth's interior: direct evidence from rock samples and indirect evidence from seismic waves.

🔑 The deeper down inside Earth, the greater the pressure. The temperature inside Earth increases as depth increases.

🔑 The three main layers of Earth are the crust, the mantle, and the core. The crust is a layer of solid rock that includes dry land and ocean floor. The mantle is about 3,000 km thick and is made of very hot, solid rock. The core is mostly iron and nickel. It consists of a liquid outer core and a solid inner core.

Vocabulary
• seismic wave • pressure • crust • basalt • granite • mantle
• lithosphere • asthenosphere • outer core • inner core

LESSON 3 Convection and the Mantle

🔑 There are three types of heat transfer: radiation, convection, and conduction.

🔑 Heating and cooling of a fluid, changes in the fluid's density, and the force of gravity combine to set convection currents in motion.

🔑 Heat from the core and the mantle itself causes convection currents in the mantle.

Vocabulary
• radiation • convection • conduction • density • convection current

Review and Assessment

LESSON 1 The Earth System

1. Which is part of Earth's hydrosphere?

    a. liquid outer core   **b.** solid inner core

    c. granite   **d.** ocean water

2. Earth's system has two sources of energy, which are _____

_____

_____

3. Infer Explain how the hydrosphere and biosphere interact in this swamp.

_____

_____

_____

4. Classify Are the forces that cause lava to erupt from a volcano and flow over Earth's surface constructive or destructive forces? Explain.

_____

_____

_____

5. [**Write About It**] If the amount of paved land in the United States continues to increase, how might the biosphere be affected?

LESSON 2 Earth's Interior

6. What is the relatively soft layer of the upper mantle called?

    a. continental crust   **b.** lithosphere

    c. asthenosphere   **d.** inner core

7. To learn about Earth's structure, geologists use seismic waves, which are _____

_____

_____

8. Relate Cause and Effect What do scientists think produces Earth's magnetic field?

_____

_____

_____

_____

9. Sequence Name each layer of Earth, starting from Earth's center. Include both layers of the core and all layers of the mantle.

_____

_____

_____

_____

10. Summarize What is the relationship between temperature and depth inside Earth? Is this relationship the same for pressure?

_____

_____

_____

_____

11. [**Write About It**] Compare and contrast oceanic crust with continental crust. In your answer, be sure to consider the composition and thickness of both types of crust.

LESSON 3 Convection and the Mantle

12. What is the transfer of heat by direct contact of particles of matter called?

    a. conduction   **b.** radiation

    c. convection   **d.** pressure

13. Compared to air and water, most rock has a high density, which means it has _____

_____

_____

14. Identify Name the two layers below Earth's surface in which convection takes place.

_____

15. Explain What conditions allow rock in the mantle to flow?

_____

_____

_____

16. Develop Hypotheses Suppose a certain part of the mantle is cooler than the parts surrounding it. What might happen to the cooler rock? In your answer, discuss the role of gravity.

_____

_____

_____

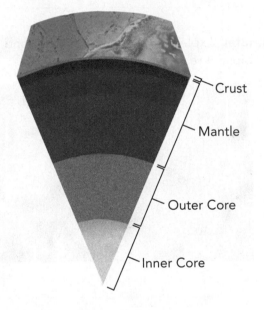 What is the structure of Earth?

17. Suppose you could travel to the center of Earth. You must design a special vehicle for your journey. What equipment should your vehicle include so that it could travel through each layer of Earth shown below? Also, what conditions should your vehicle be able to withstand? Consider temperature, pressure, and the hardness of each layer of Earth.

Crust

Mantle

Outer Core

Inner Core

_____

_____

_____

_____

_____

_____

_____

_____

_____

_____

_____

Ohio Benchmark Practice

Multiple Choice

Circle the letter of the best answer.

1. The illustration below shows a pot of boiling water.

   What process is heating the water?

   A radiation   B conduction
   C convection   D destruction

2. Which part of Earth's system is made up of plants and animals?

   A biosphere   B hydrosphere
   C atmosphere   D geosphere

3. Which part of Earth's interior is made mostly of nickel and iron and has liquid and solid parts?

   A lithosphere   B crust
   C asthenosphere D core

4. What is one result of convection currents in Earth's outer core?

   A erosion
   B Earth's magnetic field
   C melted glaciers
   D Earth's force of gravity

5. How do pressure and temperature change inside Earth as depth increases?

   A pressure and temperature decrease
   B pressure increases; temperature decreases
   C pressure decreases; temperature increases
   D pressure and temperature increase

Extended Response

Use the illustration below and your knowledge of science to help you answer Question 6. Write your answer on a separate piece of paper.

6. Describe how Earth's spheres are interacting in the scene pictured below. Also describe any notable constructive and destructive forces.

A Slice of Earth

If you could dig a hole that went straight through to the other side of the world, on your way down you'd see all of the layers underneath Earth's surface.

Of course, digging that kind of hole would be impossible. But if we want to see a slice of Earth, and all its layers, we have another tool. Seismic tomography lets us see Earth's layers as 3-D images. A computer uses data on the size and speed of seismic waves to make these images.

The sudden release of stored energy under Earth's crust sends seismic waves in all directions and causes an earthquake. The waves travel out from the center of the earthquake. Density, pressure, and temperature affect how quickly these seismic waves move through the layers of rock underground. Waves can also bend or bounce back where they meet a boundary between layers.

Scientists are able to record the speed and size of the seismic waves from thousands of earthquakes. Combining data recorded at different places allows scientists to use computers to create models of Earth's interior.

Knowing exactly what is lying beneath our feet is helping scientists learn more about tectonic processes, such as mountain building, as well as helping us find important mineral resources.

Research It Seismic tomography has been compared to CAT (computerized axial tomography) scans. How are they similar? How are they different? Research them both and create a graphic organizer outlining the similarities and differences.

This seismic tomography image shows a cross-section of Earth's crust and mantle. The colors show materials of different densities that are rising or sinking as part of convection currents in the mantle. The blue line on the map shows that this "slice" of Earth extends from the Pacific Ocean eastward to western Africa. ▶

Save the Seeds, Save the World

Bananas may be in trouble. So may some species of wheat. In fact a number of species of plants face threats to their survival. Scientists think that Earth's climate is changing. And as it changes, so does the biosphere. Some plants are becoming more vulnerable to disease or to insect pests. Human development also threatens some plants' habitats. With all these changes to the biosphere, plant species are becoming extinct at an increasing rate.

The Svalbard Global Seed Vault may be helping to preserve samples of important resources. Tucked into the permafrost in Svalbard—an island north of Norway that is farther north than almost any other landmass on Earth—the Seed Vault protects seeds that come from almost every important food crop in the world. The seeds of bananas, strawberries, rice, and beans are all preserved (along with many other species) in case they go extinct. Many seeds come from developing countries, which have a lot of biodiversity. Because the Seed Vault is in the cryosphere—the frozen portion of the hydrosphere—scientists think that Svalbard will remain frozen even if climate change continues to cause the glaciers farther south to melt.

The Seed Vault can store up to 4.5 million seeds at −18°C. Even if the power goes out, the seeds will stay frozen because the permafrost will keep the temperature of the vaults below −3.5°C.

Inside the Svalbard Global Seed Vault ▲

Write About It Scientists have observed signs of global climate change. Changes to Earth's climate are affecting many other Earth systems. For example, sea levels are rising, and sea ice is melting. Write an essay explaining how these changes might lead to the extinction of a specific plant species.

IS THIS CRACK IN EARTH GROWING?

THE BIG ?

How do moving plates change Earth's crust?

You may think that Earth's crust is one huge, solid piece. In fact, Earth's surface is broken into several pieces—like a cracked eggshell. One of the cracks runs through the middle of this lake in Iceland.

⚠ **Infer** Why do you think this crack in Earth's crust might get wider?

_____

_____

_____

_____

_____

_____

_____

_____

> **UNTAMED SCIENCE** Watch the **Untamed Science** video to learn more about Earth's crust.

Plate Tectonics

Check Your Understanding

1. **Background** Read the paragraph below and then answer the question.

Maria took a train from Oregon to Georgia. The train rode across the entire **continent** of North America. It rode up and down the Rocky Mountains, which form a **boundary** between America's east and west. The conductor said, "These mountains are part of Earth's **crust**."

A **continent** is a large landmass.

A **boundary** is the point or line where one region ends and another begins.

The **crust** is the outer layer of Earth.

• What is the crust?

_____

_____

▶ **MY READING WEB** If you had trouble answering the question above, visit **My Reading Web** and type in *Plate Tectonics.*

Vocabulary Skill

Use Prefixes A prefix is a word part that is added at the beginning of a root or base word to change its meaning. Knowing the meaning of prefixes will help you figure out new words.

Prefix	Meaning	Example
mid-	at or near the middle	mid-ocean ridge, *n.* a chain of mountains that runs along the middle of the ocean floor
sub-	below, beneath, under	subduction, *n.* a process by which part of Earth's crust sinks downward

2. **Quick Check** Choose the word from the table that best completes the sentence below.

• Oceanic crust is pushed beneath continental crust during

_____ .

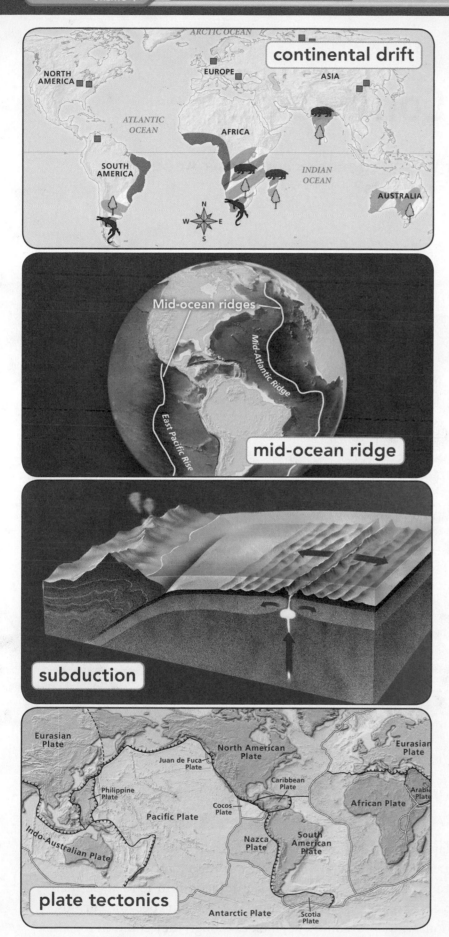

continental drift

mid-ocean ridge

subduction

plate tectonics

Chapter Preview

> **VOCAB FLASH CARDS** For extra help with vocabulary, visit **Vocab Flash Cards** and type in *Plate Tectonics.*

Drifting Continents

🔑 **What Was Wegener's Hypothesis About the Continents?**

my planeT DiaRY

A Puzzled Look

Scientists have long noticed that Earth's continents look as though they could fit together like pieces of a jigsaw puzzle. This was an idea that Alfred Wegener suggested in 1910. "Doesn't the east coast of South America fit exactly against the west coast of Africa, as if they had once been joined?" he asked. "This is an idea I'll have to pursue."

VOICES FROM HISTORY

Communicate Discuss Wegener's idea with a partner. Then answer the questions.

1. Why did Wegener think that the continents might once have been joined?

_____

_____

_____

2. If you were Wegener, what other evidence would you look for to show that the continents had once been joined?

_____

_____

▷ PLANET DIARY Go to **Planet Diary** to learn more about the continents.

 Lab Do the Inquiry Warm-Up
zone *How Are Earth's Continents Linked Together?*

What Was Wegener's Hypothesis About the Continents?

Have you ever looked at a world map and noticed how the coastlines of Africa and South America seem to match up? For many years, scientists made this same observation! In 1910, a German scientist named Alfred Wegener (VAY guh nur) became curious about why some continents look as though they could fit together.

Vocabulary
- continental drift
- Pangaea
- fossil

Skills
- ↻ Reading: Ask Questions
- △ Inquiry: Infer

According to Wegener, the continents of Earth had moved. 🔑 **Wegener's hypothesis was that all the continents were once joined together in a single landmass and have since drifted apart.** Wegener's idea that the continents slowly moved over Earth's surface became known as **continental drift.**

According to Wegener, the continents were joined together in a supercontinent, or single landmass, about 300 million years ago. Wegener called the supercontinent **Pangaea** (pan JEE uh).

Over tens of millions of years, Pangaea began to break apart. The pieces of Pangaea slowly moved to their present locations, shown in **Figure 1**. These pieces became the continents as formed today. In 1915, Wegener published his evidence for continental drift in a book called *The Origin of Continents and Oceans.*

Evidence From Land Features
Land features on the continents provided Wegener with evidence for his hypothesis. On the next page, **Figure 2** shows some of this evidence. For example, Wegener pieced together maps of Africa and South America. He noticed that mountain ranges on the continents line up. He noticed that coal fields in Europe and North America also match up.

✏️

Pangaea means "all lands" in Greek. Why is this a suitable name for a supercontinent?

_____

_____

_____

_____

FIGURE 1 ···

Piecing It All Together
The coastlines of some continents seem to fit together like a jigsaw puzzle.

✏️ **Use the map to answer the questions.**

1. **Interpret Maps** Draw an arrow to match the numbered coast with the lettered coast that seems to fit with it.

   ①   **ⓐ**
   ②   **ⓑ**
   ③   **ⓒ**
   ④   **ⓓ**

2. △ **Infer** How would a continent's climate change if it drifted closer to the equator?

   _____

   _____

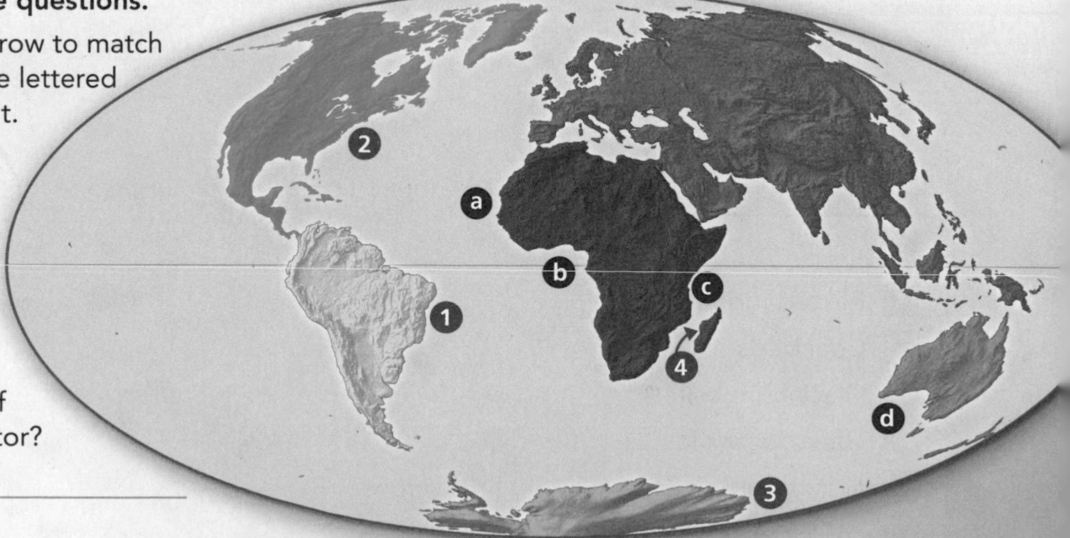

119

FIGURE 2 ··

> INTERACTIVE ART Pangaea and Continental Drift

Many types of evidence suggest that Earth's landmasses were once joined together.

⚠️ **Infer** On the top map of Pangaea, draw where each piece of evidence on the bottom map would have been found. Use a different symbol or color for each piece of evidence, and provide a key. Then label the continents.

Evidence From Fossils

Wegener also used fossils to support his hypothesis for continental drift. A **fossil** is any trace of an ancient organism that has been preserved in rock. For example, *Glossopteris* (glaw SAHP tuh ris) was a fernlike plant that lived 250 million years ago. *Glossopteris* fossils have been found in Africa, South America, Australia, India, and Antarctica, as shown in **Figure 2**. The occurrence of *Glossopteris* on landmasses that are now separated by oceans indicates that Pangaea once existed.

Other examples include fossils of the freshwater reptiles *Mesosaurus* and *Lystrosaurus*. These fossils have also been found in places now separated by oceans. Neither reptile could have swum great distances across salt water. Wegener inferred that these reptiles lived on a single landmass that had since split apart.

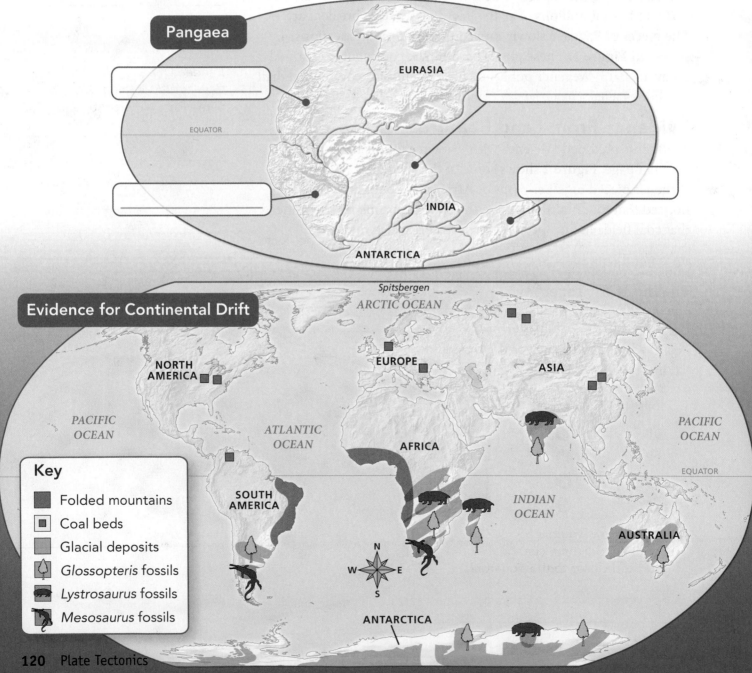

Pangaea

EURASIA

EQUATOR

INDIA

ANTARCTICA

Evidence for Continental Drift

Spitsbergen

ARCTIC OCEAN

NORTH AMERICA

EUROPE

ASIA

PACIFIC OCEAN

ATLANTIC OCEAN

AFRICA

PACIFIC OCEAN

EQUATOR

SOUTH AMERICA

INDIAN OCEAN

AUSTRALIA

N
W E
S

ANTARCTICA

Key
- ■ Folded mountains
- ▣ Coal beds
- ▢ Glacial deposits
- *Glossopteris* fossils
- *Lystrosaurus* fossils
- *Mesosaurus* fossils

Evidence From Climate

Wegener used evidence of climate change to support his hypothesis. As a continent moves toward the equator, its climate gets warmer. As a continent moves toward the poles, its climate gets colder. In either case, the continent carries along with it the fossils and rocks that formed at all of its previous locations.

For example, fossils of tropical plants are found on Spitsbergen, an island in the Arctic Ocean. When these plants lived about 300 million years ago, the island must have had a warm, mild climate. Wegener said the climate changed because the island moved.

Wegener's Hypothesis Rejected

Wegener attempted to explain how continental drift took place. He suggested that the continents plowed across the ocean floors. But Wegener could not provide a satisfactory explanation for the force that pushes or pulls the continents. Because Wegener could not identify the cause of continental drift, most geologists of his time rejected his idea.

Deep scratches have been found in rocks in South Africa. Such scratches are caused only by glaciers that move across continents. But the climate of South Africa is too mild today for glaciers to form.

1 **Infer** South Africa was once (colder/warmer) than it is today.

2 **CHALLENGE** What can you infer about South Africa's former location?

_____

_____

Ask Questions Write a question relating to climate and Wegener's hypothesis. Read the text and answer your question.

_____

_____

_____

_____

_____

_____

_____

_____

_____

 Lab zone Do the Quick Lab *Moving the Continents.*

🔑 Assess Your Understanding

1a. Review Based on evidence from land features, fossils, and climate, Wegener concluded that continents (sink/rise/move).

b. Predict Wegener said that because continents move, they can collide with each other. How could colliding continents explain the formation of mountains?

_____

_____

_____

gotit**?**

○ **I get it!** Now I know Wegener's hypothesis about the continents stated that _____

_____

_____

_____

○ **I need extra help with** _____

Go to **MY SCIENCE** 💬 **COACH** online for help with this subject.

Sea-Floor Spreading

- What Are Mid-Ocean Ridges?

- What Is Sea-Floor Spreading?

- What Happens at Deep-Ocean Trenches?

my planeT DiaRY

DISCOVERY

Marie Tharp

Have you ever tried to draw something you can't see? By 1952, geologists Marie Tharp and Bruce Heezen had set to work mapping the ocean floor. Tharp drew details of the ocean floor based on data taken from ships. The data showed how the height of the ocean floor varied. Tharp's maps, which were first published in 1957, helped to confirm the hypothesis of continental drift.

Think about what structures might lie beneath Earth's oceans. Then answer the question.

Do you think the ocean has valleys and mountains? Explain.

_____

_____

_____

_____

> PLANET DIARY Go to **Planet Diary** to learn more about the ocean floor.

 Do the Inquiry Warm-Up *What Is the Effect of a Change in Density?*

What Are Mid-Ocean Ridges?

When scientists such as Marie Tharp drew maps showing features of the ocean floor, they made a surprising discovery. In certain places, the floor of the ocean appeared to be stitched together like the seams of a baseball! The seams curved along the ocean floors for great distances, as shown in **Figure 1.**

Scientists found that the seams formed mountain ranges that ran along the middle of some ocean floors. Scientists called these mountain ranges **mid-ocean ridges.** **Mid-ocean ridges form long chains of mountains that rise up from the ocean floor.**

Vocabulary

- mid-ocean ridge
- sea-floor spreading
- deep-ocean trench
- subduction

Skills

- Reading: Relate Text and Visuals
- Inquiry: Develop Hypotheses

In the mid-1900s, scientists mapped mid-ocean ridges using *sonar*. Sonar is a device that uses sound waves to measure the distance to an object. Scientists found that mid-ocean ridges extend into all of Earth's oceans. Most mid-ocean ridges lie under thousands of meters of water. Scientists also discovered that a steep-sided valley splits the tops of some mid-ocean ridges. The ridges form the longest mountain ranges on Earth. They are longer than the Rockies in North America and longer than the Andes in South America.

FIGURE 1 ·········

Ocean Floors

Mid-ocean ridges rise from the sea floor like stitches on the seams of a baseball.

✎ **Interpret Diagrams** Look at the diagram below. Then use the scale to answer each question. Be sure to measure from the *front* of the diagram.

1. How far below sea level is the peak of the ridge?

_____

2. How high does the ridge rise from the sea floor?

_____

3. [CHALLENGE] How deep below the peak is the valley marking the center of the ridge?

_____

Vertical scale exaggerated

Depth (km)

0
1
2
3
4

Do the Quick Lab
Mid-Ocean Ridges.

🔑 Assess Your Understanding

got it? ·········

○ **I get it!** Now I know that mid-ocean ridges form _____

_____

○ **I need extra help with** _____

Go to **my science ⑤ coach** *online for help with this subject.*

What Is Sea-Floor Spreading?

By the 1960s, geologists had learned more about mid-ocean ridges. They found that mid-ocean ridges continually add new material to the ocean floor. They called this process **sea-floor spreading.**

Sea-floor spreading begins at a mid-ocean ridge, which forms along a crack in the oceanic crust. Along the ridge, new molten material from inside Earth rises, erupts, cools, and hardens to form a solid strip of rock. 🔑 **Sea-floor spreading adds more crust to the ocean floor. At the same time, older strips of rock move outward from either side of the ridge.**

Figure 2 shows evidence that geologists have found for sea-floor spreading.

Pillow lava on the ocean floor

Evidence From Ocean Material

In the central valley of mid-ocean ridges, scientists have found rocks shaped like pillows. Such rocks form only when molten material hardens quickly after erupting under water.

Ridge

Magnetic striping on both sides of the Juan de Fuca ridge

Evidence From Magnetic Stripes

Rock on the ocean floor forms from molten material. As the material erupts, cools, and hardens, magnetic minerals inside the rock line up in the direction of Earth's magnetic poles. These minerals form unseen magnetic "stripes" on the ocean floor. But the magnetic poles occasionally reverse themselves. So each stripe defines a period when molten material erupted and hardened while Earth's magnetic poles did not change.

Scientists found that the pattern of magnetic stripes on one side of a mid-ocean ridge is usually a mirror image of the pattern on the other side of the ridge. The matching patterns show that the crust on the two sides of the ridge spread from the ridge at the same time and at the same rate.

Ocean floor samples taken in 2006

Evidence From Drilling Samples

Scientists drilled into the ocean floor to obtain rock samples. They found that the farther away from a ridge a rock sample was taken, the older the rock was. The youngest rocks were always found at the center of the ridges. Recall that at the ridge center, molten material erupts and cools to form new crust. The rocks' age showed that sea-floor spreading had taken place.

FIGURE 2 ···

> INTERACTIVE ART **Sea-Floor Spreading**

Some mid-ocean ridges have a valley that runs along their center. Evidence shows that molten material erupts through this valley. The material then hardens to form the rock of the ocean floor.

✎ **Color the right half of the diagram to show magnetic striping. How does your drawing show evidence of sea-floor spreading?**

_____

_____

_____

> **Relate Text and Visuals**
How does the diagram show that new crust forms from molten material?

_____

_____

_____

_____

_____

_____

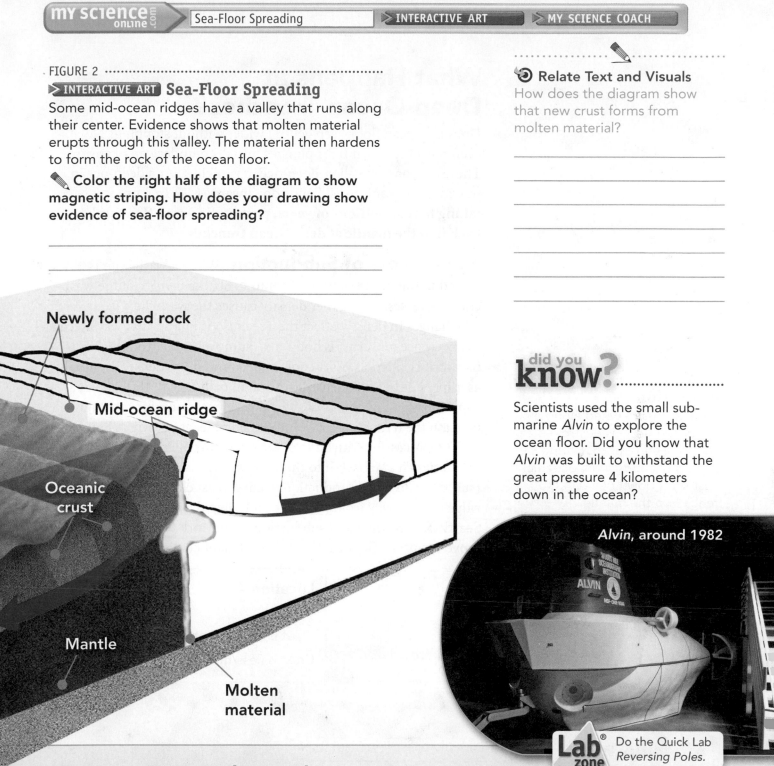

Newly formed rock

Mid-ocean ridge

Oceanic crust

Mantle

Molten material

did you know?··········

Scientists used the small submarine *Alvin* to explore the ocean floor. Did you know that *Alvin* was built to withstand the great pressure 4 kilometers down in the ocean?

Alvin, around 1982

Lab zone   Do the Quick Lab *Reversing Poles*.

⚷ **Assess Your Understanding**

1a. Review In sea-floor spreading, new crust is added at a (mid-ocean ridge/magnetic stripe).

b. Apply Concepts Suppose Earth's magnetic polarity changed many times over a short period. What pattern of striping at a mid-ocean ridge would you expect to find?

_____

_____

got it?

○ **I get it!** Now I know that sea-floor spreading is the process in which _____

_____

○ **I need extra help with** _____

Go to **my science** ⓢ **coach** online for help with this subject.

What Happens at Deep-Ocean Trenches?

Does the ocean floor keep getting wider without stopping? No, eventually the ocean floor plunges into deep underwater canyons. These canyons are called **deep-ocean trenches.** At a deep-ocean trench, the oceanic crust bends downward. 🔑 **In a process taking tens of millions of years, part of the ocean floor sinks back into the mantle at deep-ocean trenches.**

The Process of Subduction
When a washcloth is placed in water, the water soaks into it. So, the density of the washcloth increases. The higher density causes the washcloth to sink.

Changes in density affect the ocean floor in a similar way. Recall that new oceanic crust is hot. But as it moves away from the mid-ocean ridge, it cools. As it cools, it becomes more dense. Eventually, as it moves, the cool, dense crust might collide with the edge of a continent. Gravity then pulls the older, denser oceanic crust down beneath the trench and back into the mantle, as shown in **Figure 3.**

The process by which the ocean floor sinks beneath a deep-ocean trench and back into the mantle again is called **subduction** (sub DUC shun). As subduction occurs, crust closer to a mid-ocean ridge moves away from the ridge and toward a deep-ocean trench. Sea-floor spreading and subduction often work together. They move the ocean floor as if it were on a giant conveyor belt.

FIGURE 3 ·······························

Subduction
Oceanic crust created along a mid-ocean ridge is destroyed at a deep-ocean trench. During the process of subduction, oceanic crust sinks down beneath the trench into the mantle.

✏️ **Summarize** Label the mantle, the mid-ocean ridge, and the deep-ocean trench. For locations A and B, circle the correct choice for each statement.

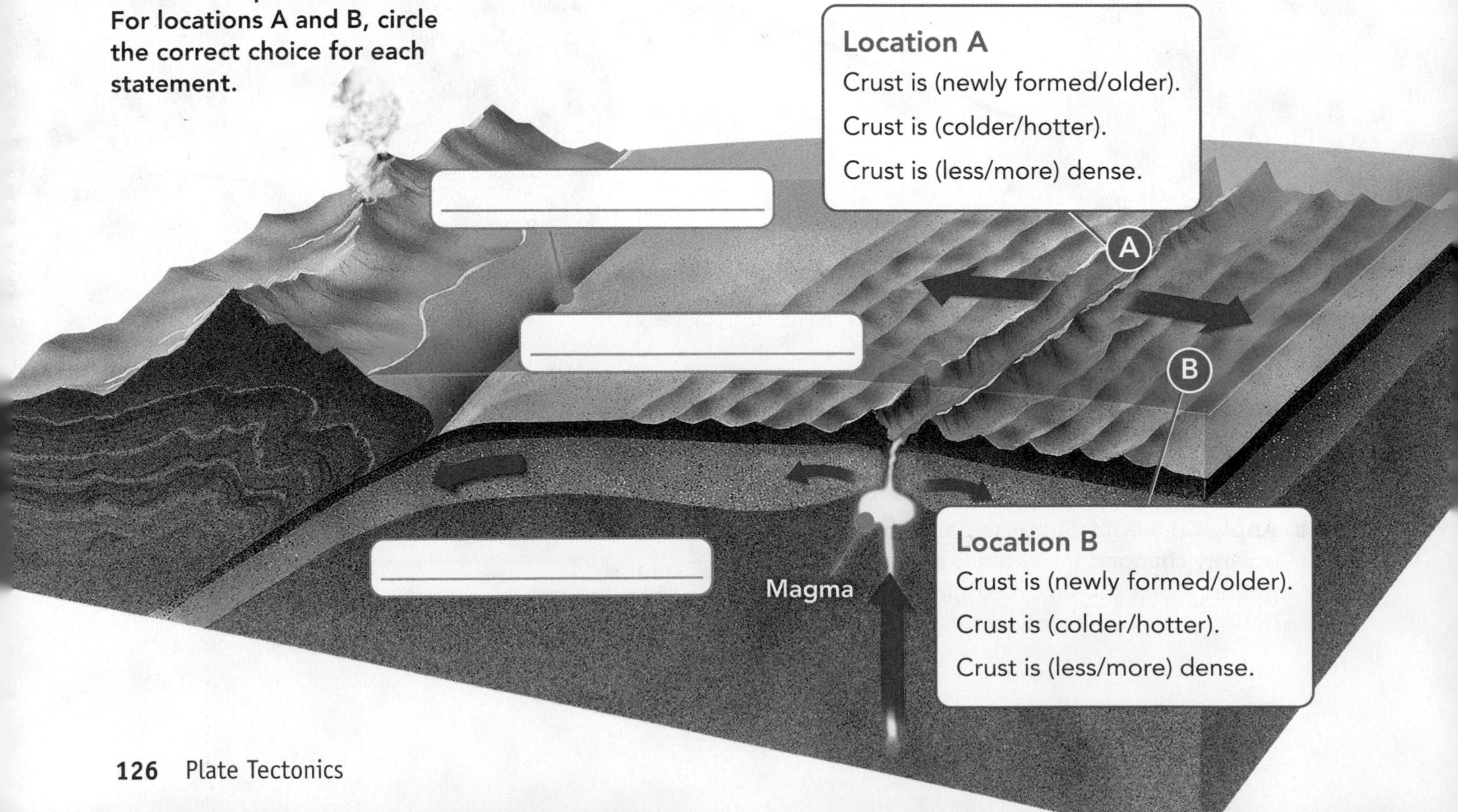

Location A

Crust is (newly formed/older).

Crust is (colder/hotter).

Crust is (less/more) dense.

Ⓐ

Ⓑ

Magma

Location B

Crust is (newly formed/older).

Crust is (colder/hotter).

Crust is (less/more) dense.

apply it!

The deepest part of the ocean is along the Mariana Trench. This trench is one of several trenches (shown in yellow) in the Pacific Ocean. After reading the main text in this lesson, answer the questions below.

1 Infer At the Pacific Ocean's deep-ocean trenches, oceanic crust is (spread/subducted).

2 Develop Hypotheses The Pacific Ocean is shrinking. Explain this fact in terms of subduction at deep-ocean trenches and spreading at mid-ocean ridges.

_____

_____

_____

_____

_____

_____

Key

— Deep-ocean trench

— Mid-ocean ridge

Subduction and Earth's Oceans

The processes of subduction and sea-floor spreading can change the size and shape of the oceans. Because of these processes, the ocean floor is renewed about every 200 million years. That is the time it takes for new rock to form at the mid-ocean ridge, move across the ocean, and sink into a trench.

The sizes of Earth's oceans are determined by how fast new crust is being created at mid-ocean ridges and how fast old crust is being swallowed up at deep-ocean trenches. An ocean surrounded by many trenches may shrink. An ocean with few trenches will probably grow larger.

For example, the Atlantic Ocean is expanding. This ocean has only a few short trenches. As a result, the spreading ocean floor has almost nowhere to go. Along the continental margins, the oceanic crust of the Atlantic Ocean floor is attached to the continental crust of the continents around the ocean. So as the Atlantic's ocean floor spreads, the continents along its edges also move. Over time, the whole ocean gets wider.

Lab zone Do the Lab Investigation *Modeling Sea-Floor Spreading.*

🔑 Assess Your Understanding

2a. Review Subduction takes place at (mid-ocean ridges/deep-ocean trenches).

b. Relate Cause and Effect Why does subduction occur?

_____

_____

_____

_____

got it? ....

○ **I get it!** Now I know that at deep-ocean

trenches _____

_____

○ I need extra help with _____

Go to **my science** ⓢ **coach** *online for help with this subject.*

127

The Theory of Plate Tectonics

UNLOCK THE BIG ?

🔑 **What Is the Theory of Plate Tectonics?**

my planet Diary

Slip-Sliding Away

In 30 million years, this airplane might take one hour longer to fly from New York to London than it takes today. That's because these two cities are moving slowly apart as they ride on pieces of Earth's crust.

THIS TRIP SEEMS TO GET A LITTLE LONGER EACH TIME!

New York

London

Atlantic Ocean

Sea-floor spreading

FUN FACT

Recall the name of your state capital. Then, answer the question below.

Will your state capital be farther from London in 30 million years? Explain.

_____

_____

_____

_____

▷ PLANET DIARY Go to **Planet Diary** to learn more about Earth's crust.

Lab ® Do the Inquiry Warm-Up
zone *Plate Interactions.*

What Is the Theory of Plate Tectonics?

Have you ever dropped a hard-boiled egg? The eggshell cracks into uneven pieces. Earth's lithosphere, its solid outer shell, is like that eggshell. It is broken into pieces separated by cracks. These pieces are called **plates.** Earth's major tectonic plates are shown in **Figure 1.**

Vocabulary

- plate • divergent boundary • convergent boundary
- transform boundary • plate tectonics • fault
- rift valley

Skills

- ⟳ Reading: Relate Cause and Effect
- △ Inquiry: Calculate

Earth's plates meet at boundaries. Along each boundary, plates move in one of three ways. Plates move apart, or diverge, from each other at a **divergent boundary** (dy VUR junt). Plates come together, or converge, at a **convergent boundary** (kun VUR junt). Plates slip past each other along a **transform boundary.**

In the mid-1960s, geologists combined what they knew about sea-floor spreading, Earth's plates, and plate motions into a single theory called **plate tectonics.** 🔑 **The theory of plate tectonics states that Earth's plates arc in slow, constant motion, driven by convection currents in the mantle.** Plate tectonics explains the formation, movement, and subduction of Earth's plates.

Mantle Convection and Plate Motions
What force is great enough to move the continents? Earth's plates move because they are the top part of the large convection currents in Earth's mantle. During subduction, gravity pulls denser plate edges downward, into the mantle. The rest of the plate also moves. The motion of the plates is like the motion of liquid in a pot of soup heating on a stove.

FIGURE 1 ··································
▶ REAL-WORLD INQUIRY
Earth's Plates
Plate boundaries divide the lithosphere into large plates.

✎ **Interpret Maps** Draw arrows at all the boundaries of the Pacific plate, showing the directions in which plates move. (*Hint:* First, study the map key.)

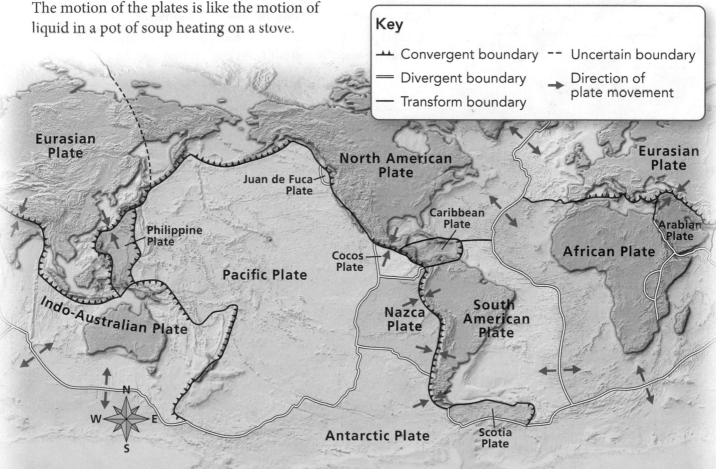

Key

⊣⊣ Convergent boundary -- Uncertain boundary
══ Divergent boundary → Direction of plate movement
── Transform boundary

Eurasian Plate

North American Plate

Juan de Fuca Plate

Eurasian Plate

Philippine Plate

Caribbean Plate

Arabian Plate

Cocos Plate

African Plate

Pacific Plate

Nazca Plate

South American Plate

Indo-Australian Plate

N
W E
S

Antarctic Plate

Scotia Plate

Plate Motions Over Time Scientists use satellites to measure plate motion precisely. The plates move very slowly—from about 1 to 12 centimeters per year. The North American and Eurasian plates move apart at a rate of 2.5 centimeters per year. Because the plates have been moving for tens to hundreds of millions of years, they have moved great distances.

Over time, the movement of Earth's plates has greatly changed the location of the continents and the size and shape of the oceans. As plates move, they change Earth's surface, producing earthquakes, volcanoes, mountain ranges, and deep-ocean trenches. Geologists have evidence that, before Pangaea existed, other supercontinents formed and split apart over the last billion years. Pangaea itself formed when Earth's landmasses moved together about 350 to 250 million years ago. Then, about 200 million years ago, Pangaea began to break apart, as shown in **Figure 2**. Earth's plates continue to move today. Scientists measure the plates' movements over time and can use these data to predict where the continents will be millions of years from now.

FIGURE 2 ·

> **INTERACTIVE ART** **Plate Motion**

Since the breakup of Pangaea, the continents have taken about 200 million years to move to their present location.

Use the maps to answer the questions.

1. **Interpret Maps** List three examples of continents that have drifted apart from each other.

_____

_____

_____

_____

2. **CHALLENGE** Which two landmasses that were not connected to each other in Pangaea have collided on Earth today?

_____

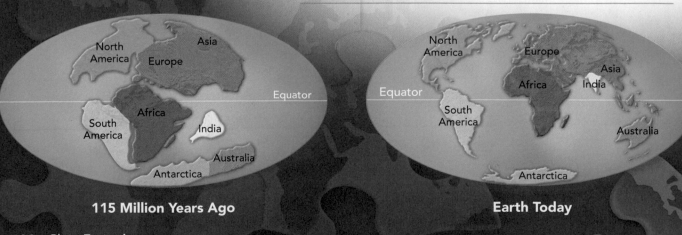

200 Million Years Ago

Pangaea
Equator

115 Million Years Ago

North America
Asia
Europe
Africa
South America
India
Australia
Antarctica
Equator

Earth Today

North America
Europe
Africa
Asia
India
South America
Australia
Antarctica
Equator

Plate Boundaries Recall that the edges of Earth's plates meet at plate boundaries. **Faults**—breaks in Earth's crust where rocks have slipped past each other—form along these boundaries. Convection currents in Earth's mantle cause the plates to move. As the plates move, they collide, pull apart, or grind past each other. These movements produce great changes in Earth's surface and on the ocean floor. These changes include the formation of volcanoes, mountain ranges, and deep-ocean trenches.

Divergent Boundaries Can a crack in Earth's crust be so wide that people can walk through it? In Iceland it can! There, two plates move slowly away from each other. **Figure 3** shows part of the crack that has formed as these two plates have moved apart over time.

Recall that plates move away from each other at a divergent boundary. Most divergent boundaries occur along the mid-ocean ridges, where new crust is added during sea-floor spreading. But in a few places, the mid-ocean ridge rises above sea level. Volcanic activity of the mid-Atlantic ridge is also seen in Iceland.

Where pieces of Earth's crust diverge on land, a deep valley called a **rift valley** forms. Several rift valleys make up the East African rift system. There, the crust is slowly pulling apart over a wide area.

FIGURE 3 ···

Breaking Up Is Hard to Do
Two plates separate to form a great crack in Iceland, marking a divergent boundary.

✎ **Interpret Diagrams** Draw arrows on the diagram to show how plates move at a divergent boundary. Then describe how the plates move.

_____

_____

_____

Vocabulary Prefixes Read the text about the three types of plate boundaries. Circle the correct meaning of each prefix given here.

Di- = (away/together/along)

Con- = (away/together/along)

Trans- = (away/together/along)

do the math!
···

Plates move at very slow rates. These rates are from about 1 to 12 cm per year. To calculate rates of motion, geologists use the following formula.

$$\text{Rate} = \frac{\text{Distance}}{\text{Time}}$$

✎ **Calculate** The Pacific plate is sliding past the North American plate. In 10 million years, the plate will move 500 km. What is the Pacific plate's rate of motion? Express your answer in centimeters per year.

131

FIGURE 4 ┄┄┄┄┄┄┄┄┄┄┄┄┄┄┄┄┄┄┄

The Andes

The Andes Mountains formed at a convergent boundary.

✎ **Interpret Diagrams** Draw arrows on the diagram to show how plates move when they converge. Then describe how the plates move.

_____

_____

Convergent Boundaries The Andes Mountains run for 8,900 kilometers along the west coast of South America. Here, two plates collide. Recall that a boundary where two plates come together, or collide, is called a convergent boundary.

What happens when two plates collide? The density of the plates determines which one comes out on top. Oceanic crust becomes cooler and denser as it spreads away from the mid-ocean ridge. Where two plates carrying oceanic crust meet at a trench, the plate that is more dense sinks under the less dense plate.

A plate carrying oceanic crust can also collide with a plate carrying continental crust. Oceanic crust is more dense than continental crust. The more dense oceanic crust can push up the less dense continental crust. This process has formed the Andes, as shown in **Figure 4.** Meanwhile, the more dense oceanic crust also sinks as subduction occurs. Water eventually leaves the sinking crust and rises into the wedge of the mantle above it. This water lowers the melting point of the mantle in the wedge. As a result, the mantle partially melts and rises up as magma to form volcanoes.

Two plates carrying continental crust can also collide. Then, neither piece of crust is dense enough to sink far into the mantle. Instead, the collision squeezes the crust into high mountain ranges.

EXPLORE THE BIG ? Earth's Changing Crust

How do moving plates change Earth's crust?

FIGURE 6 ┄┄┄┄┄┄┄┄┄┄┄┄┄┄┄┄┄┄┄┄┄┄┄┄┄┄┄┄┄┄┄┄┄┄┄┄┄┄

▶ **ART IN MOTION** As plates move, they produce mountains, volcanoes, and valleys as well as mid-ocean ridges and deep-ocean trenches.

✎ **Identify** Fill in the blanks with the correct terms from the list on the next page. (*Hint:* Some points use more than one term.)

Molten material

Molten material

Transform Boundaries Recall that a transform boundary is a place where two plates slip past each other, moving in opposite directions. Beneath the surface of a transform boundary, the sides of the plates are rocky and jagged. So, the two plates can grab hold of each other and "lock" in place. Forces inside the crust can later cause the two plates to unlock. Earthquakes often occur when the plates suddenly slip along the boundary that they form. However, crust is neither created nor destroyed at transform boundaries. The San Andreas fault, shown in **Figure 5,** is one example of a transform boundary.

FIGURE 5 ·······················
Fault Line
The San Andreas fault in California marks a transform boundary.

✎ **Interpret Diagrams** Draw arrows on the diagram to show how plates move at a transform boundary. Then describe how the plates move.

_____

_____

_____

Lab ® Do the Quick Lab *Mantle*
zone *Convection Currents.*

⚷ Assess Your Understanding

1a. Review Moving plates form convergent, divergent, or _____ boundaries.

b. ANSWER THE BIG ? **Summarize** How do moving plates change Earth's crust?

_____

_____

_____

_____

_____

_____

_____

_____

_____

got it? ·······················

○ **I get it!** Now I know that the three types of plate boundaries are _____

_____

○ **I need extra help with** _____

Go to **MY SCIENCE** ⑤ **COACH** *online for help with this subject.*

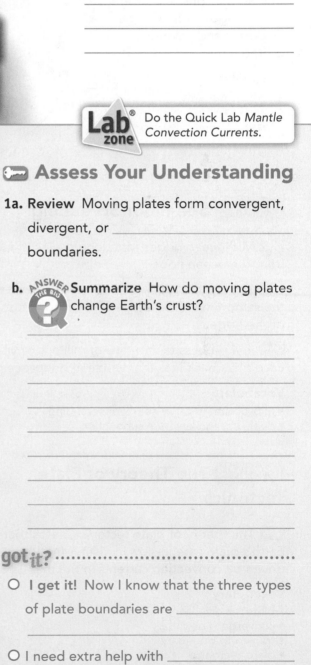

Rift valley	Mountains	Convection
Volcanoes	Subduction	Oceanic crust
Sea-floor spreading	Mid-ocean ridge	Convergent boundary
Transform boundary	Continental crust	Deep-ocean trench
Divergent boundary		

New crust forms at _____. Crust is subducted and destroyed at _____. Mountains form where plates _____.

LESSON 1 Drifting Continents

🔑 Wegener's hypothesis was that all the continents were once joined together in a single landmass and have since drifted apart.

Vocabulary
• continental drift
• Pangaea
• fossil

LESSON 2 Sea-Floor Spreading

🔑 Mid-ocean ridges form long chains of mountains that rise up from the ocean floor.

🔑 Sea-floor spreading adds more crust to the ocean floor. At the same time, older strips of rock move outward from either side of the ridge.

🔑 In a process taking tens of millions of years, part of the ocean floor sinks back into the mantle at deep-ocean trenches.

Vocabulary
• mid-ocean ridge   • sea-floor spreading
• deep-ocean trench   • subduction

LESSON 3 The Theory of Plate Tectonics

🔑 The theory of plate tectonics states that Earth's plates are in slow, constant motion, driven by convection currents in the mantle.

Vocabulary
• plate   • divergent boundary
• convergent boundary
• transform boundary
• plate tectonics   • fault
• rift valley

Review and Assessment

Drifting Continents

1. What did Wegener think happens during continental drift?

    a. Continents move.   **b.** Continents freeze.

    c. The mantle warms.   **d.** Convection stops.

2. Wegener thought that all the continents were once joined together in a supercontinent that he called _____.

3. **Draw** The drawing shows North America and Africa. Circle the parts of the coastlines of the two continents that were joined in Pangaea.

North America

Africa

4. **Make Judgments** Wegener proposed that mountains form when continents collide, crumpling up their edges. Was Wegener's idea about how mountains form consistent with his hypothesis of continental drift? Explain.

_____

_____

_____

_____

5. Write About It Michelle is a scientist working in Antarctica. She learns that fossils of *Glossopteris* have been found on Antarctica. Her colleague Joe, working in India, has also found *Glossopteris* fossils. Write a letter from Michelle to her colleague explaining how these fossils could be found in both places. Define *continental drift* in your answer and discuss how it explains the fossil findings.

Sea-Floor Spreading

6. In which areas does subduction of the ocean floor take place?

    a. rift valleys   **b.** the lower mantle

    c. mid-ocean ridges   **d.** deep-ocean trenches

7. A mid-ocean ridge is a _____

_____

that rises up from the ocean floor.

8. **Compare and Contrast** Look at the diagram. Label the area where new crust forms.

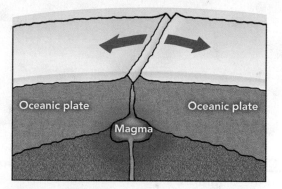

Oceanic plate   Oceanic plate

Magma

9. **Apply Concepts** Why are the oldest parts of the ocean floor no older than about 200 million years?

_____

_____

_____

10. **Sequence** Place the following steps of sea-floor spreading in their correct sequence.

    A. The molten material cools and hardens, forming a strip of rock along the ocean floor.

    B. The strip of rock moves away from the ridge.

    C. Molten material from inside Earth rises to the ocean floor at a mid-ocean ridge.

_____

11. Write About It How is pillow lava evidence of sea-floor spreading?

4 Review and Assessment

LESSON 3 The Theory of Plate Tectonics

12. At which boundary do two plates pull apart?

    a. convergent   **b.** transform

    c. divergent   **d.** mantle-crust

13. When a divergent boundary occurs on land, it forms a _____.

Use the diagram to answer Questions 14–15.

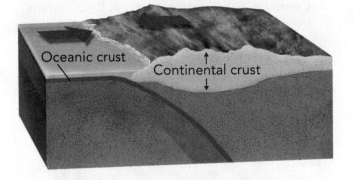

14. Classify What type of plate boundary is shown in the diagram?

_____

15. Predict What type of landforms will result from the plate movement shown in the diagram?

_____

16. Compare and Contrast How does the density of oceanic crust differ from that of continental crust? Why is this difference important?

_____

_____

_____

_____

17. math! It takes 100,000 years for a plate to move about 2 kilometers. What is the rate of motion in centimeters per year?

_____

 How do moving plates change Earth's crust?

18. Summarize Suppose Earth's landmasses someday all move together again. Describe the changes that would occur in Earth's oceans and Earth's landmasses. Use the map and the theory of plate tectonics to explain your ideas.

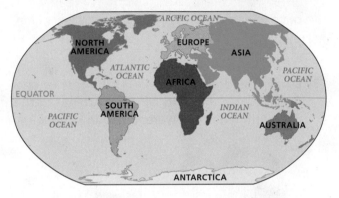

_____

_____

_____

_____

_____

_____

_____

_____

_____

_____

_____

_____

_____

_____

_____

_____

_____

_____

_____

_____

Ohio Benchmark Practice

Multiple Choice

Circle the letter of the best answer.

1. The diagram shows a process in Earth's crust.

   Which statement best describes the process in the diagram?

   A Converging plates form mountains.

   B Converging plates form volcanoes.

   C Diverging plates form mountains.

   D Diverging plates form a rift valley.

2. What is one piece of evidence that caused Wegener to think that continents moved?

   A He found an old map of the world that showed movement.

   B He found similar fossils on different continents that are separated by oceans.

   C He proved his hypothesis with an experiment that measured movement.

   D He observed the continents moving with his own eyes.

3. Which of the following is evidence for sea-floor spreading?

   A matching patterns of magnetic stripes found in the crust of the ocean floor

   B new rock found farther from mid-ocean ridges than older rock

   C pieces of different crust found on different continents

   D changes in climate on the continent of Africa

4. What happens to new oceanic crust at a mid-ocean ridge?

   A It forms new mountains under the water.

   B It climbs up the mantle to form a trench.

   C It gets hotter and sinks into a trench.

   D It is so dense that gravity pulls it into a deep-ocean trench.

5. What force causes the movement of Earth's plates?

   A convection currents

   B pressure

   C sound waves

   D cooling

Extended Response

Use the map below and your knowledge of science to help you answer Question 6. Write your answer on a separate piece of paper.

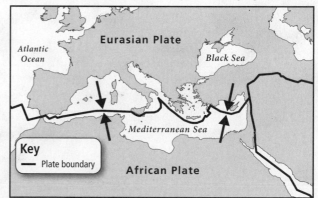

6. The African plate is moving toward the Eurasian plate at a rate of a few centimeters per year. How will this area change in 100 million years? In your answer, consider how the continents will change and how the Mediterranean Sea will change.

ALVIN:2.0
AN EXTREME MAKEOVER

For years, *Alvin*, the world's oldest research submarine, has worked hard. *Alvin* carries scientists deep into the ocean. The research submarine has made over 4,400 dives—some as deep as 4,500 meters beneath the water's surface. With the help of *Alvin*, scientists have discovered everything from tube worms to the wreck of the *Titanic*. But *Alvin* allows scientists to see only the top 63 percent of the ocean. The rest of the ocean lies even deeper than 4,500 meters, where *Alvin* can't go.

Enter *Alvin* 2.0—*Alvin's* replacement. It is bigger and faster, with more windows and improved sensors. It can go down to 6,500 meters and carry heavier samples. Even better, *Alvin* 2.0 allows scientists to see most of the ocean—only 1 percent of the ocean lies deeper than 6,500 meters!

With better and deeper access to the ocean, scientists are excited about all of the new and weird discoveries they'll make with *Alvin* 2.0.

▼ Presenting . . . the new *Alvin!*

Design It Research more about *Alvin* 2.0's features. Think about a new feature that you would like to add to *Alvin* 2.0. What needs would your feature meet? Draw or describe a design for the part, and explain how it will work on the new model.

Museum of Science

An Ocean Is Born

In one of the hottest, driest places in the world, Earth's crust is cracking.

In the Afar region of Ethiopia, Earth's tectonic plates are moving apart. Here, Earth's crust is so thin that magma has been able to break through the surface. As the plates drifted farther apart, the crust sank to form a valley that is 59 kilometers long!

Today volcanoes, earthquakes, and hydrothermal fields tell us how thin the crust is, and how the plates are pulling apart. Eventually, this valley could sink deep enough to allow salt water from the nearby Red Sea to move in and form an ocean. This ocean could split Africa apart. Although it could take millions of years for an actual ocean to form, scientists are excited to witness the steps that will lead to its birth.

Research It Research a major change in Earth's surface caused by plate movement. Try to find at least two different accounts of the event. Create a timeline or a storyboard showing when and how the change occurred.

▲ Tectonic plates are pulling apart in this dry, hot area in the Afar region of Ethiopia.

▲ Lava seeps out of a crack in the lava lake on top of Erfa Ale, the highest mountain in the Afar region. Scientists must wear protective clothing in this extremely hot, dangerous environment.

139

WHAT COULD CAUSE THIS BUILDING TO TOPPLE?

Why do earthquakes occur more often in some places than in others?

Earthquakes can strike without a moment's notice. The ground can buckle and buildings can topple, as happened to this building in Taiwan in 1999. These disasters may seem like random events. But the structure of Earth suggests a different conclusion. **Predict** **Do you think geologists can predict where and when an earthquake will occur? Explain.**

_____

_____

_____

_____

_____

> **UNTAMED SCIENCE** Watch the **Untamed Science** video to learn more about earthquakes.

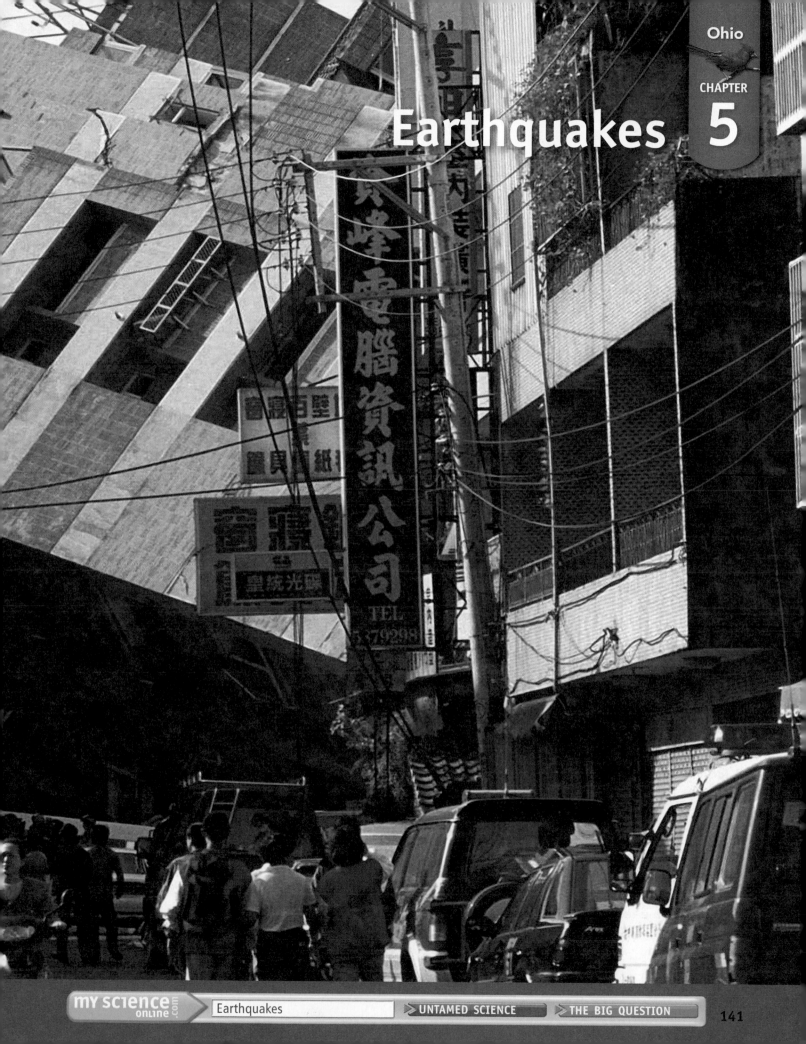

Earthquakes

5 Getting Started

Check Your Understanding

1. **Background** Read the paragraph below and then answer the question.

Ann's parents couldn't move the huge boulder from their yard. The **force** of their pushing didn't budge the rock. "Let's crush it," said Ann's mom. She went on, "Smaller pieces will each have smaller **mass** and **volume.** Then we can move the rock one piece at a time."

> A **force** is a push or pull exerted on an object.
>
> **Mass** is a measure of the amount of matter an object contains and its resistance to movement.
>
> **Volume** is the amount of space that matter occupies.

• What features of the boulder make it hard to move?

_____

> **MY READING WEB** If you had trouble completing the question above, visit **My Reading Web** and type in *Earthquakes.*

Vocabulary Skill

Identify Multiple Meanings Some familiar words have more than one meaning. Words you use every day may have different meanings in science. Look at the different meanings of the words below.

Word	Everyday Meaning	Scientific Meaning
fault	*n.* blame or responsibility Example: The team's loss was not the fault of any one person.	*n.* a crack or break in rock along which rock surfaces can slip Example: A fault ran through the cliff.
focus	*v.* to concentrate Example: Focus your attention on reading, writing, and arithmetic.	*n.* the area where rock that is under stress begins to break, causing an earthquake Example: The focus of the earthquake was 70 kilometers below Earth's surface.

2. **Quick Check** Circle the sentence below that uses the scientific meaning of the word *fault.*
   • Errors in the test were the test writer's **fault.**
   • The San Andreas **fault** runs along the coast of California.

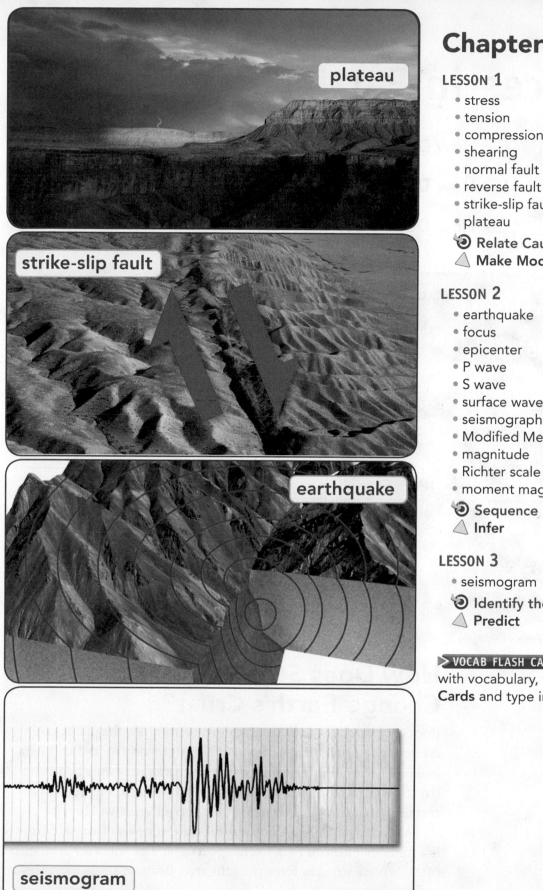

plateau

strike-slip fault

earthquake

seismogram

Chapter Preview

LESSON 1
- stress
- tension
- compression
- shearing
- normal fault
- reverse fault
- strike-slip fault
- plateau

↻ **Relate Cause and Effect**
△ **Make Models**

LESSON 2
- earthquake
- focus
- epicenter
- P wave
- S wave
- surface wave
- seismograph
- Modified Mercalli scale
- magnitude
- Richter scale
- moment magnitude scale

↻ **Sequence**
△ **Infer**

LESSON 3
- seismogram

↻ **Identify the Main Idea**
△ **Predict**

▷ **VOCAB FLASH CARDS** For extra help with vocabulary, visit **Vocab Flash Cards** and type in *Earthquakes.*

Forces in Earth's Crust

UNLOCK
THE BIG
?

🔑 **How Does Stress Change Earth's Crust?**

🔑 **How Do Faults Form?**

🔑 **How Does Plate Movement Create New Landforms?**

my PLANET DiARY

MISCONCEPTION

Still Growing!

Mount Everest in the Himalayas is the highest mountain on Earth. Climbers who reach the peak stand 8,850 meters above sea level. You might think that mountains never change. But forces inside Earth push Mount Everest at least several millimeters higher each year. Over time, Earth's forces slowly but constantly lift, stretch, bend, and break Earth's crust in dramatic ways!

✏️ **Communicate** Discuss the following question with a classmate. Write your answer below.

How long do you think it took Mount Everest to form? Hundreds of years? Thousands? Millions? Explain.

_____

_____

_____

_____

▷ PLANET DIARY Go to **Planet Diary** to learn more about forces in Earth's crust.

Lab zone® Do the Inquiry Warm-Up *How Does Stress Affect Earth's Crust?*

How Does Stress Change Earth's Crust?

Rocks are hard and stiff. But the movement of Earth's plates can create strong forces that slowly bend or fold many rocks like a caramel candy bar. Like the candy bar, some rocks may only bend and stretch when a strong force is first applied to them. But beyond a certain limit, all rocks in Earth's brittle upper crust will break.

Forces created by plate movement are examples of stress. **Stress** is a force that acts on rock to change its shape or volume. Geologists often express stress as force per unit area. Because stress increases as force increases, stress adds energy to the rock. The energy is stored in the rock until the rock changes shape or breaks.

Vocabulary

- stress
- tension
- compression
- shearing
- normal fault
- reverse fault
- strike-slip fault
- plateau

Skills

- Reading: Relate Cause and Effect
- Inquiry: Make Models

Three kinds of stress can occur in the crust—tension, compression, and shearing. 🔑 **Tension, compression, and shearing work over millions of years to change the shape and volume of rock.** Most changes in the crust occur only very slowly, so that you cannot directly observe the crust bending, stretching, or breaking. **Figure 1** shows the three types of stress.

Tension Rock in the crust can be stretched so that it becomes thinner in the middle. This process can make rock seem to act like a piece of warm bubble gum. The stress force that pulls on the crust and thins rock in the middle is called **tension.** Tension occurs where two plates pull apart.

Compression One plate pushing against another plate can squeeze rock like a giant trash compactor. The stress force that squeezes rock until it folds or breaks is called **compression.** Compression occurs where two plates come together.

Shearing Stress that pushes a mass of rock in two opposite directions is called **shearing.** Shearing can cause rock to break and slip apart or to change its shape. Shearing occurs where two plates slip past each other.

Before stress

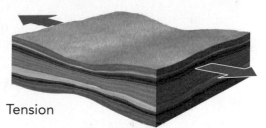
Tension

Compression

Shearing

FIGURE 1 ·······················

› **ART IN MOTION** **Stress in Earth's Crust**
Stress can push, pull, or squeeze rock in Earth's crust.
✏️ **Apply Concepts** Look at the pair of arrows in the second diagram. These arrows show how tension affects rock. Draw a pair of arrows on the third diagram to show how compression affects rock. Then, draw a pair of arrows on the bottom diagram to show how shearing acts on rock.

Lab zone® Do the Quick Lab
Effects of Stress.

🔑 Assess Your Understanding

got**it?** ··

○ **I get it!** Now I know that stress changes Earth's crust by changing the _____

_____

○ I need extra help with _____

Go to **MY SCIENCE** ⊙ **COACH** *online for help with this subject.*

How Do Faults Form?

Recall that a fault is a break in the rock of the crust where rock surfaces slip past each other. Most faults occur along plate boundaries, where the forces of plate motion push or pull the crust so much that the crust breaks. 🔑 **When enough stress builds up in rock, the rock breaks, creating a fault.** There are three main types of faults: normal faults, reverse faults, and strike-slip faults.

Normal Faults The Rio Grande River flows through a wide valley in New Mexico. Here, tension has pulled apart two pieces of Earth's crust, forming the valley. Where rock is pulled apart by tension in Earth's crust, normal faults form. In a **normal fault,** the fault cuts through rock at an angle, so one block of rock sits over the fault, while the other block lies under the fault. The block of rock that sits over the fault is called the *hanging wall.* The rock that lies under the fault is called the *footwall.* The diagram of the normal fault in **Figure 2** shows how the hanging wall sits over the footwall. When movement occurs along a normal fault, the hanging wall slips downward. Normal faults occur where two plates diverge, or pull apart.

FIGURE 2 ···

▶ ART IN MOTION **Faults**

The three main types of faults are defined by the direction in which rock moves along the fault. ✏️ **Observe In the descriptions below the first two diagrams, fill in the blanks to indicate how rock moves. In both of these diagrams, label the hanging wall and footwall.**

Key

→ Movement along the fault

→ Force deforming the crust

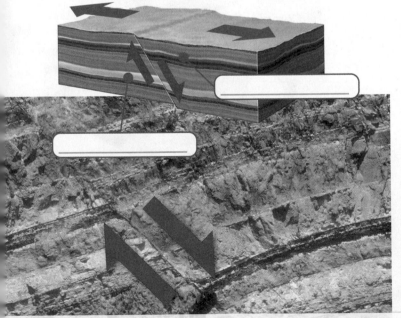

Normal fault

In a normal fault, the hanging wall _____ _____ relative to the footwall.

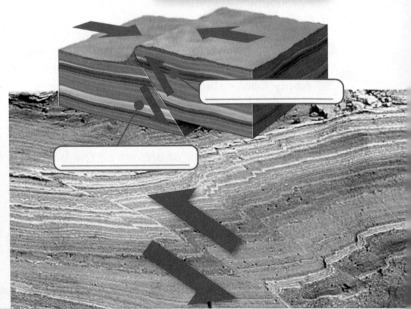

Reverse fault

In a reverse fault, the hanging wall moves _____ relative to the footwall.

Reverse Faults

The northern Rocky Mountains rise high above the western United States and Canada. These mountains were gradually lifted up over time by movement along reverse faults. A **reverse fault** has the same structure as a normal fault, but the blocks move in the reverse direction. That is, the hanging wall moves up and the footwall moves down. **Figure 2** shows a reverse fault. Reverse faults form where compression pushes the rock of the crust together.

Strike-Slip Faults

The hilly plains in southern California are split by the San Andreas fault, shown in **Figure 2**. Here, shearing has produced a strike-slip fault. In a **strike-slip fault**, the rocks on either side of the fault slip past each other sideways, with little up or down motion. A strike-slip fault that forms the boundary between two plates is called a transform boundary. The San Andreas fault is an example of a transform boundary.

Lab zone® Do the Quick Lab Modeling Faults.

apply it!

The low angle of a thrust fault allows rock in the hanging wall to be pushed great distances. For example, over millions of years, rock along the Lewis thrust fault in Glacier National Park has moved 80 kilometers.

1 **Identify** Based on the arrows showing fault movements in the diagram, a thrust fault is a type of (normal fault/reverse fault).

2 **CHALLENGE** Why might the type of rock in the hanging wall of the Lewis thrust fault be different from the type of rock in the footwall?

_____

_____

_____

_____

Strike-slip fault

Rocks on either side of a strike-slip fault move past each other.

🔑 Assess Your Understanding

1a. Review When enough stress builds up in brittle rock, the rock breaks, causing a

_____ to form.

b. Infer A geologist sees a fault along which blocks of rock in the footwall have moved higher relative to blocks of rock in the hanging wall. What type of fault is this?

_____

got it? ....

○ **I get it!** Now I know that faults form when

_____

○ **I need extra help with** _____

_____

Go to **my science** ⓢ **coach** online for help with this subject.

How Does Plate Movement Create New Landforms?

Most changes in the crust occur so slowly that they cannot be observed directly. But what if you could speed up time so that a billion years passed by in minutes? Then, you could watch the movement of Earth's plates fold, stretch, and uplift the crust over wide areas. **Over millions of years, the forces of plate movement can change a flat plain into features such as anticlines and synclines, folded mountains, fault-block mountains, and plateaus.**

Vocabulary Identify Multiple Meanings Underline the sentence that uses the scientific meaning of *fold.*

- The rock looked as crushed as my shirts if I don't fold them.
- Rock that bends without breaking may form a fold.

Folding Earth's Crust

Have you ever skidded on a rug that wrinkled up as your feet pushed it across the floor? Sometimes plate movements can cause Earth's crust to fold much like the rug. Then, rocks stressed by compression may bend without breaking.

How Folds Form Folds are bends in rock that form when compression shortens and thickens Earth's crust. A fold can be a few centimeters across or hundreds of kilometers wide. **Figure 3** shows folds in rock that were exposed when a road was cut through a hillside in California.

FIGURE 3

Folded Rock

Folds in rock shorten and thicken the Earth's crust. Over time, this process can form mountains.

Make Models Hold down the right edge of this page. Then, push the left edge toward the center of the book. Is this activity a good model for showing how folded rock forms? Explain.

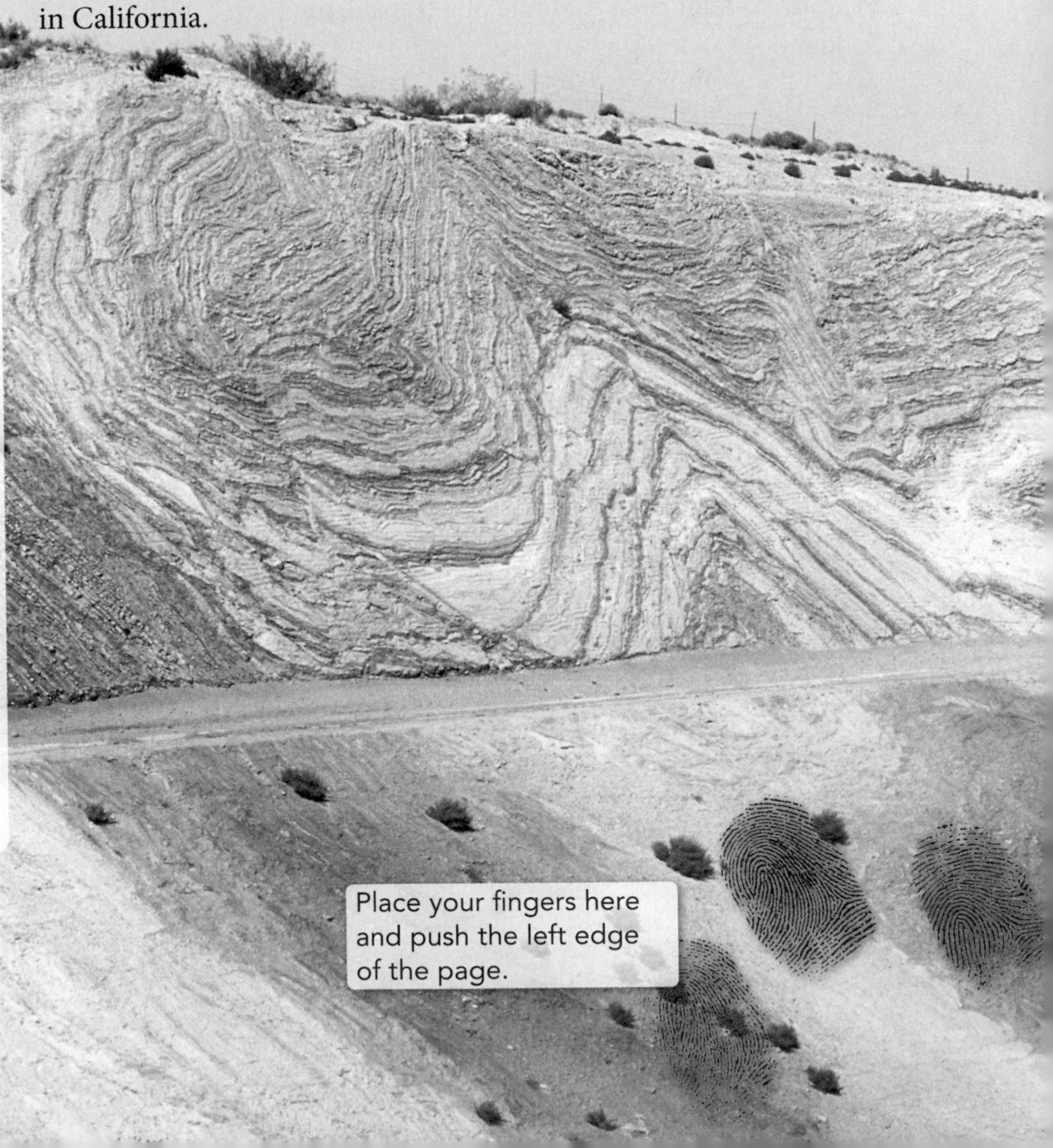
Place your fingers here and push the left edge of the page.

How Anticlines and Synclines Form Geologists use the terms *anticline* and *syncline* to describe upward and downward folds in rock. A fold in rock that bends upward into an arch is an anticline (AN tih klyn), as shown in **Figure 4.** A fold in rock that bends downward to form a **V** shape is a syncline (SIN klyn). Anticlines and synclines are found in many places where compression forces have folded the crust. The central Appalachian Mountains in Pennsylvania are folded mountains made up of anticlines and synclines.

How Folded Mountains Form The collision of two plates can cause compression and folding of the crust over a wide area. Folding produced some of the world's largest mountain ranges. The Himalayas in Asia and the Alps in Europe formed when pieces of the crust folded during the collision of two plates. These mountains formed over millions of years.

FIGURE 4 ·······························

Anticlines and Synclines
Compression can cause folds in the crust. Two types of folding are anticlines, which arch up, and synclines, which dip down.
Relate Cause and Effect Draw arrows to show the direction in which forces act to compress the crust. (*Hint:* Review the information on compression in this lesson.) Then label the anticline and the syncline.

When two normal faults cause valleys to drop down on either side of a block of rock, what type of landform results?

_____

_____

Stretching Earth's Crust

If you traveled by car from Salt Lake City to Los Angeles, you would cross the Great Basin. This region contains many mountains separated by broad valleys, or basins. The mountains form from tension in Earth's crust that causes faulting. Such mountains are called fault-block mountains.

How do fault-block mountains form? Where two plates move away from each other, tension forces create many normal faults. Suppose two normal faults cause valleys to drop down on either side of a block of rock. This process is shown in the diagram that accompanies the photograph in **Figure 5.** As the hanging wall of each normal fault slips downward, the block in between now stands above the surrounding valleys, forming a fault-block mountain.

FIGURE 5 ·······

Tension and Normal Faults

As tension forces pull the crust apart, two normal faults can form a fault-block mountain range, as you can see in the diagram below. The mountain range in the photograph is in the Great Basin. Valleys can also form as a result of two normal faults.

Predict Label the hanging wall and the two footwalls in diagram A. In diagram B, draw the new position of the hanging wall after movement occurs. Describe what happens.

_____

_____

_____

_____

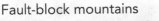

Fault-block mountains

A Before movement occurs along the faults.

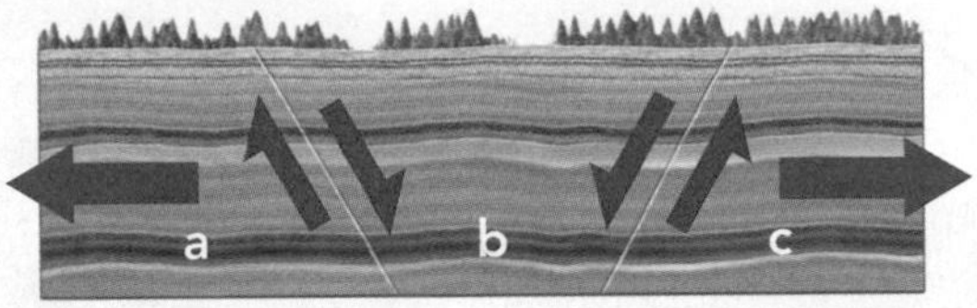

a. _____

b. _____

c. _____

B Draw the outcome after movement occurs along the faults.

Key

Movement along the fault

Force deforming the crust

Uplifting Earth's Crust The forces that raise mountains can also uplift, or raise, plateaus. A **plateau** is a large area of flat land elevated high above sea level. Some plateaus form when forces in Earth's crust push up a large, flat block of rock. Like a fancy sandwich, a plateau consists of many different flat layers, and is wider than it is tall. Forces deforming the crust uplifted the Colorado Plateau in the "Four Corners" region of Arizona, Utah, Colorado, and New Mexico. **Figure 6** shows one part of that plateau in northern Arizona.

FIGURE 6 ······························
The Kaibab Plateau
The Kaibab Plateau forms the North Rim of the Grand Canyon. The plateau is the flat-topped landform in the right half of the photograph.

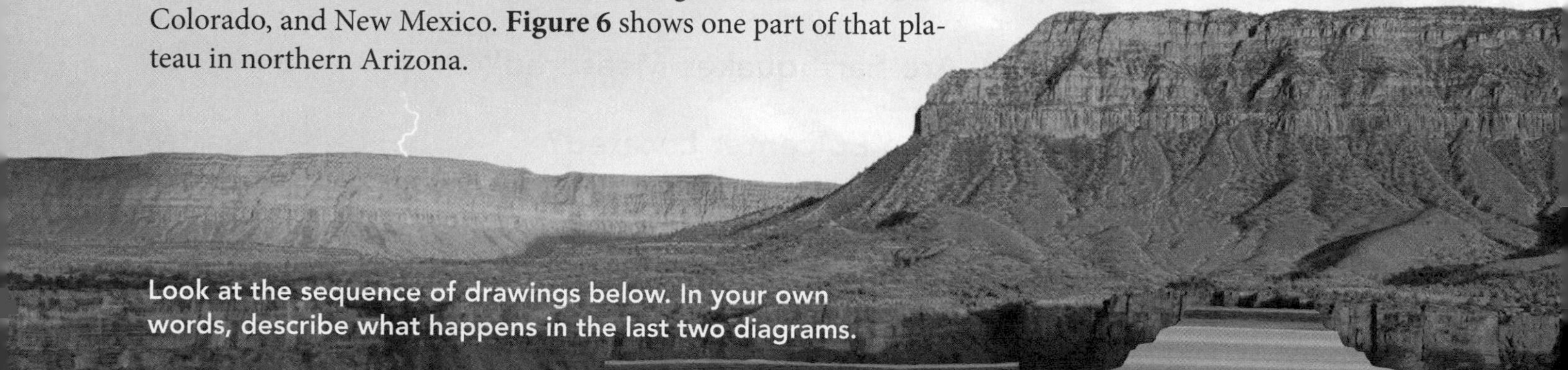

Look at the sequence of drawings below. In your own words, describe what happens in the last two diagrams.

A flat, layered block of rock lies somewhere in Earth's crust.

_____
_____
_____
_____

_____
_____
_____
_____

Lab zone   Do the Quick Lab *Modeling Stress.*

🔑 **Assess Your Understanding**

2a. Review Normal faults often occur when two plates (come together/pull apart).

b. Interpret Diagrams Look at the diagram that accompanies the photograph in **Figure 5.** Does the block of rock in the middle move up as a result of movement along the normal faults? Explain.

_____
_____
_____
_____

got it?

○ **I get it!** Now I know that plate movements create new features by _____
_____
_____
_____
_____

○ **I need extra help with** _____

Go to MY SCIENCE ⓢ COACH *online for help with this subject.*

151

Earthquakes and Seismic Waves

UNLOCK THE BIG ?

🔑 What Are Seismic Waves?

🔑 How Are Earthquakes Measured?

🔑 How Is an Epicenter Located?

my planeT DiaRY

DISASTER

Witness to Disaster

On May 12, 2008, a major earthquake struck China. American reporter Melissa Block was conducting a live radio interview in that country at the moment the earthquake struck.

"What's going on?" Block asked. She remained on the air and continued: "The whole building is shaking. The whole building is SHAKING."

Block watched as the ground moved like waves beneath her feet. The top of the church across the street started to fall down. For minutes, the ground continued to vibrate under Block's feet. The earthquake that day killed about 87,000 people.

—NPR.com

✏️ **Communicate** Discuss these questions with a group of classmates. Write your answers below.

1. What does Melissa Block's experience tell you about the way the ground can move during an earthquake?

_____

_____

2. How do you think you would react during an earthquake or other disaster?

_____

_____

_____

▶ **PLANET DIARY** Go to **Planet Diary** to learn more about earthquakes.

Lab zone ® Do the Inquiry Warm-Up *How Do Seismic Waves Travel Through Earth?*

Vocabulary
- earthquake • focus • epicenter • P wave
- S wave • surface wave • seismograph
- Modified Mercalli scale • magnitude • Richter scale
- moment magnitude scale

Skills
↻ Reading: Sequence
△ Inquiry: Infer

What Are Seismic Waves?

Earth is never still. Every day, worldwide, several thousand earth-quakes are detected. An **earthquake** is the shaking and trembling that results from movement of rock beneath Earth's surface. Most earthquakes are too small to notice. But a large earthquake can crack open the ground, shift mountains, and cause great damage.

Cause of Earthquakes The forces of plate movement cause earthquakes. Plate movements produce stress in Earth's crust, adding energy to rock and forming faults. Stress increases along a fault until the rock slips or breaks, causing an earthquake. In seconds, the earthquake releases an enormous amount of stored energy. Some of the energy released during an earthquake travels in the form of seismic waves. ⚷ **Seismic waves are vibrations that are similar to sound waves. They travel through Earth carrying energy released by an earthquake.** The speed and path of the waves in part depend on the material through which the waves travel.

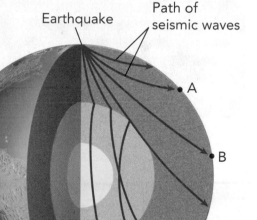

Earthquake   Path of seismic waves

• A

• B

• C

apply it!

Earthquakes start below the surface of Earth. But an earthquake's seismic waves do not carry energy only upward, toward Earth's surface. They also carry energy downward, through Earth's interior.

❶ Look at the drawing showing Earth's interior. At which point(s) can seismic waves be detected?

○ A only
○ A and B
○ A, B, and C

❷ △ **Infer** At which point do you think the seismic waves will have the most energy? Why?

_____
_____
_____
_____

Sequence Number the following in the order in which seismic waves would be felt:

__ At an earthquake's epicenter

__ At a distance of 500 km from the earthquake's focus

__ At the earthquake's focus

FIGURE 1

▶ INTERACTIVE ART Seismic Waves

The diagram shows how seismic waves traveled during an earthquake along the Denali fault.

Match the two points in the diagram to the two terms below them. Then, write a short, science-based news article that describes how, why, and where the earthquake took place. Include a headline.

Types of Seismic Waves

Like a pebble thrown into a pond, the seismic waves of an earthquake race out in every direction from the earthquake's focus. The **focus** (FOH kus) is the area beneath Earth's surface where rock that was under stress begins to break or move. This action triggers the earthquake. The point on the surface directly above the focus is called the **epicenter** (EP uh sen tur).

Most earthquakes start in the lithosphere, within about 100 kilometers beneath Earth's surface. Seismic waves carry energy from the earthquake's focus. This energy travels through Earth's interior and across Earth's surface. That happened in 2002, when a powerful earthquake ruptured the Denali fault in Alaska, shown in **Figure 1.**

There are three main categories of seismic waves. These waves are P waves, S waves, and surface waves. But an earthquake sends out only P and S waves from its focus. Surface waves can develop wherever P and S waves reach the surface.

earthBLOG

ENTRY 1

Write your headline here.

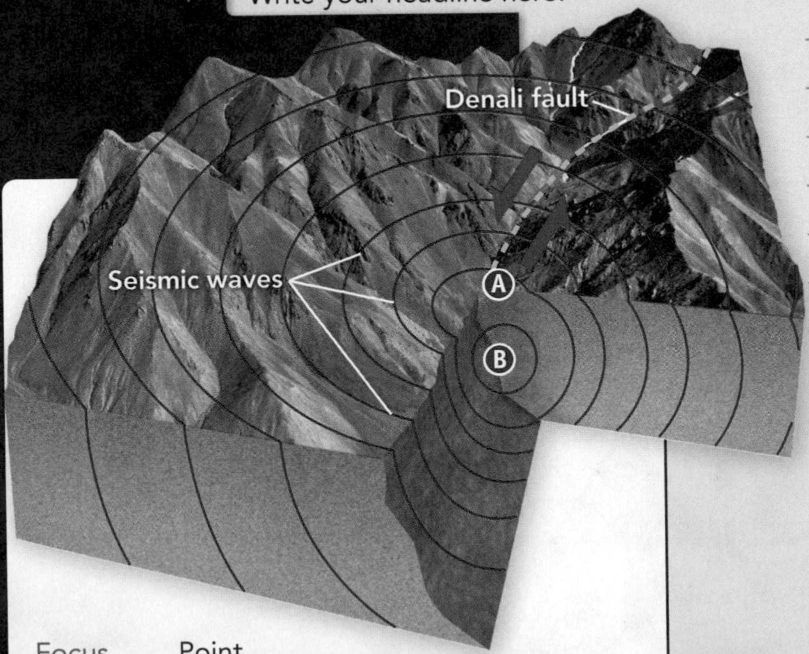

Denali fault

Seismic waves

Ⓐ

Ⓑ

Focus   Point _____

Epicenter Point _____

P Waves The first waves to arrive are primary waves, or P waves. **P waves** are seismic waves that compress and expand the ground like an accordion. Like the other types of seismic waves, P waves can damage buildings. Look at **Figure 2A** to see how P waves move.

S Waves After P waves come secondary waves, or S waves. **S waves** are seismic waves that can vibrate from side to side (as shown in **Figure 2B**) or up and down. Their vibrations are at an angle of 90° to the direction that they travel. When S waves reach the surface, they shake structures violently. While P waves travel through both solids and liquids, S waves cannot move through liquids.

Surface Waves When P waves and S waves reach the surface, some of them become surface waves. **Surface waves** move more slowly than P and S waves, but they can produce severe ground movements. These waves produce movement that is similar to waves in water, where the water's particles move in a pattern that is almost circular. Surface waves can make the ground roll like ocean waves (**Figure 2C**) or shake buildings from side to side.

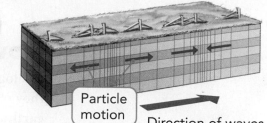

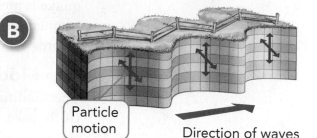

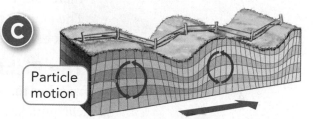

FIGURE 2 ⋯⋯⋯⋯⋯⋯⋯⋯⋯⋯⋯⋯⋯⋯

P, S, and Surface Waves
Earthquakes release stored energy as seismic waves.
✎ **Describe** Draw a line from each type of seismic wave to the movement it causes.

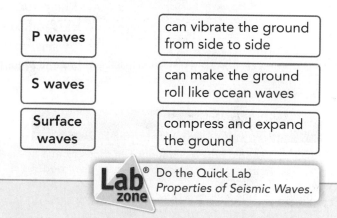

P waves	can vibrate the ground from side to side
S waves	can make the ground roll like ocean waves
Surface waves	compress and expand the ground

Lab® zone Do the Quick Lab
Properties of Seismic Waves.

🔑 **Assess Your Understanding**

1a. Review The energy released by an earthquake moves out from the earthquake's _____ in the form of seismic waves.

b. Predict Small earthquakes occur along a certain fault several times a year. Why might geologists worry if no earthquakes occur for 25 years?

_____

_____

_____

got it? ⋯⋯⋯⋯⋯⋯⋯⋯⋯⋯⋯⋯⋯⋯⋯⋯⋯⋯

○ **I get it!** Now I know that seismic waves are_____

_____

○ **I need extra help with** _____

Go to **MY SCIENCE** 🔵 **COACH** *online for help with this subject.*

How Are Earthquakes Measured?

Geologists monitor earthquakes by measuring the seismic waves they produce. This is done in two ways. 🔑 **The amount of earthquake damage or shaking that is felt is rated using the Modified Mercalli scale. The magnitude, or size, of an earthquake is measured on a seismograph using the Richter scale or moment magnitude scale.** A **seismograph** is an instrument that records and measures an earthquake's seismic waves.

The Modified Mercalli Scale

The **Modified Mercalli scale** rates the amount of shaking from an earthquake. The shaking is rated by people's observations, without the use of any instruments. This scale is useful in regions where there aren't many instruments to measure an earthquake's strength. The table in **Figure 3** describes the 12 steps of the Mercalli scale. To rank examples of damage, look at the photographs in **Figure 3.**

The Richter Scale

An earthquake's **magnitude** is a single number that geologists assign to an earthquake based on the earthquake's size. There are many magnitude scales. These scales are based on the earliest magnitude scale, called the **Richter scale.** Magnitude scales like the Richter scale rate the magnitude of small earthquakes based on the size of the earthquake's waves as recorded by seismographs. The magnitudes take into account that seismic waves get smaller the farther a seismograph is from an earthquake.

Rank	Description
I–III	People notice vibrations like those from a passing truck. Unstable objects disturbed.
IV–VI	Some windows break. Plaster may fall.
VII–IX	Moderate to heavy damage. Buildings jolted off foundations.
X–XII	Great destruction. Cracks appear in ground. Waves seen on surface.

FIGURE 3 ·································

> **INTERACTIVE ART** **Modified Mercalli Scale**
The Modified Mercalli scale uses Roman numerals to rate the damage and shaking at any given location, usually close to the earthquake. ✏️ **Classify Assign a Modified Mercalli rating to each photograph.**

The Moment Magnitude Scale

Geologists use the **moment magnitude scale** to rate the total energy an earthquake releases. News reports may mention the Richter scale, but the number quoted is almost always an earthquake's moment magnitude. To assign a magnitude to an earthquake, geologists use data from seismographs and other sources. The data allow geologists to estimate how much energy the earthquake releases. **Figure** 4 gives the magnitudes of some recent, strong earthquakes.

Comparing Magnitudes

An earthquake's moment magnitude tells geologists how much energy was released by an earthquake. Each one-point increase in magnitude represents the release of roughly 32 times more energy. For example, a magnitude 6 earthquake releases 32 times as much energy as a magnitude 5 earthquake.

An earthquake's effects increase with magnitude. Earthquakes with a magnitude below 5 are small and cause little damage. Those with a magnitude above 6 can cause great damage. The most powerful earthquakes, with a magnitude of 8 or above, are rare. In the 1900's, only three earthquakes had a magnitude of 9 or above. More recently, the 2004 Sumatra earthquake had a magnitude of 9.2.

FIGURE 4 ·······················

Earthquake Magnitude

The table gives the moment magnitudes of some recent earthquakes.

Magnitude	Location	Date
9.2	Sumatra (Indian Ocean)	December 2004
7.9	China	May 2008
7.6	Turkey	August 1999
6.6	Japan	October 2004
5.4	California	July 2008

[CHALLENGE] Approximately how many times stronger was the earthquake in Turkey than the earthquake in Japan?

_____

did you know?·······················

About 98 percent of Antarctica is covered by ice. Large shifts in the ice here can cause "ice quakes." Did you know that these "ice quakes" can be the equivalent of magnitude 7 earthquakes?

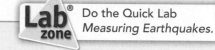

Lab zone® Do the Quick Lab *Measuring Earthquakes.*

🔑 Assess Your Understanding

2a. Identify The _____ scale rates earthquakes based on the amount of energy that is released.

b. Infer Suppose the moment magnitude of an earthquake is first thought to be 6, but is later found to be 8. Would you expect the earthquake damage to be more or less serious? Why?

_____

_____

_____

_____

got it?·······················

○ **I get it!** Now I know that to measure earthquakes, geologists use seismic waves to determine _____

_____

○ **I need extra help with** _____

Go to **my science** ⓢ **coach** *online for help with this subject.*

How Is an Epicenter Located?

When an earthquake occurs, geologists try to pinpoint the earthquake's epicenter. Why? Locating the epicenter helps geologists identify areas where earthquakes may occur in the future.

🔑 **Geologists use seismic waves to locate an earthquake's epicenter.** To do this, they use data from thousands of seismograph stations set up all over the world. However, you can use a simpler method to find an earthquake's epicenter.

Recall that seismic waves travel at different speeds. P waves arrive at a seismograph first. Then S waves follow close behind. Look at the graph, P and S Waves, below. Suppose you know when P waves arrived at a seismograph after an earthquake, and when S waves arrived. You can read the graph to find the distance from the seismograph to the epicenter. Notice that the farther away an earthquake is from a given point, the greater the time between the arrival of the P waves and the S waves.

Suppose you know the distance of three seismograph stations from an epicenter. You can then draw three circles to locate the epicenter. Look at **Figure 5.** The center of each circle is a particular seismograph's location. The radius of each circle is the distance from that seismograph to the epicenter. The point where the three circles intersect is the location of the epicenter.

do the math!

Seismic Wave Speeds

Seismographs at five observation stations recorded the arrival times of the P and S waves produced by an earthquake. These data were used to draw the graph.

1 Read Graphs What variable is shown on the x-axis of the graph? What variable is shown on the y-axis?

_____

2 Estimate How long did it take the S waves to travel 2,000 km?

_____

3 Estimate How long did it take the P waves to travel 2,000 km?

_____

4 Calculate What is the difference in the arrival times of the P waves and the S waves at 2,000 km? At 4,000 km?

_____

_____

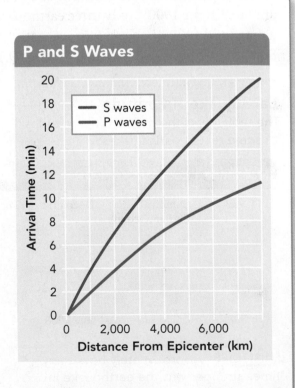

P and S Waves

- S waves
- P waves

Arrival Time (min) / Distance From Epicenter (km)

FIGURE 5 ··

Determining an Earthquake's Epicenter

The map shows how to find the epicenter of an earthquake using data from three seismographic stations. ✎ **Interpret Maps** Suppose **a fourth seismographic station is located in San Diego. What was the approximate difference in arrival times of P and S waves here?**

Hint: Use the map scale to determine how far San Diego is from the epicenter. Then, use the graph on the previous page to find your answer.

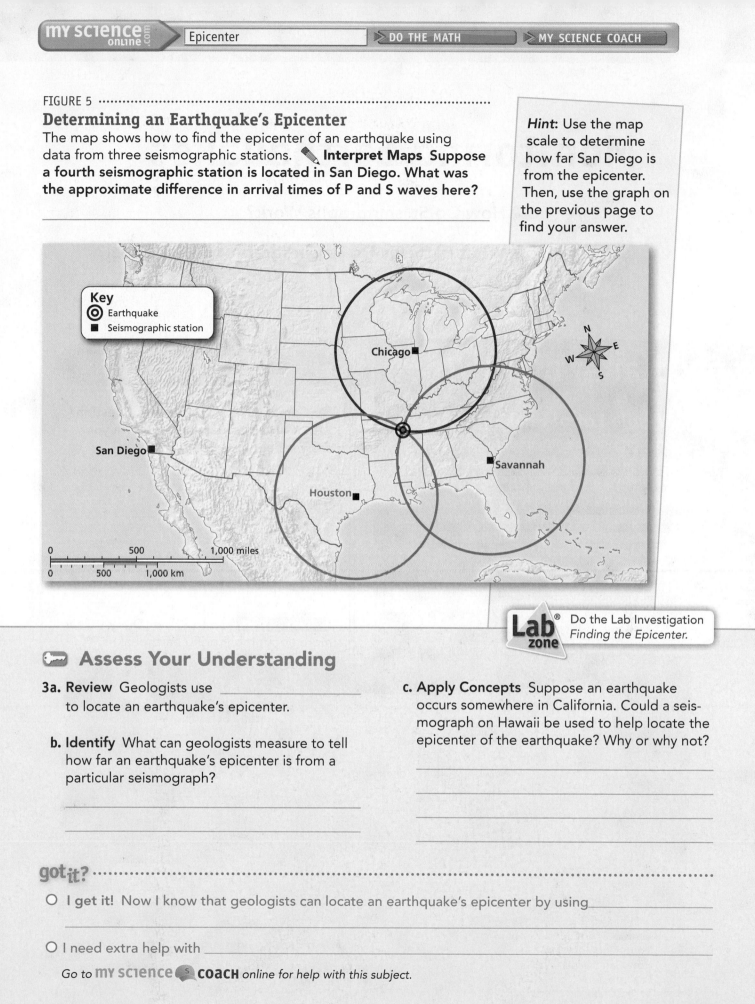

Key
⦾ Earthquake
■ Seismographic station

Chicago

San Diego

Houston

Savannah

0   500   1,000 miles
0   500   1,000 km

Lab zone ® Do the Lab Investigation *Finding the Epicenter.*

🗝 Assess Your Understanding

3a. Review Geologists use _____ to locate an earthquake's epicenter.

b. Identify What can geologists measure to tell how far an earthquake's epicenter is from a particular seismograph?

_____

_____

c. Apply Concepts Suppose an earthquake occurs somewhere in California. Could a seismograph on Hawaii be used to help locate the epicenter of the earthquake? Why or why not?

_____

_____

_____

_____

got it? ···

○ **I get it!** Now I know that geologists can locate an earthquake's epicenter by using _____

○ I need extra help with _____

Go to MY SCIENCE ⓢ COACH *online for help with this subject.*

Monitoring Earthquakes

UNLOCK THE BIG ?

🔑 How Do Seismographs Work?

🔑 What Patterns Do Seismographic Data Reveal?

my PLaneT DiaRY

Whole Lot of Shaking Going On

Is the ground moving under your school? A project that will monitor shaking underneath the entire nation might help you find out!

In 2004, scientists in the USArray project placed 400 seismographs across the western United States. Every month, 18 seismographs are picked up and moved east, "leapfrogging" the other seismographs. The map below shows one arrangement of the array. The seismic data that are obtained will help scientists learn more about our active Earth!

FUN FACT

✎ **Communicate** Discuss this question with a group of classmates. Write your answer below.

When the array arrives in your state, what information might it provide?

_____

_____

_____

_____

▷ PLANET DIARY Go to **Planet Diary** to learn more about monitoring earthquakes.

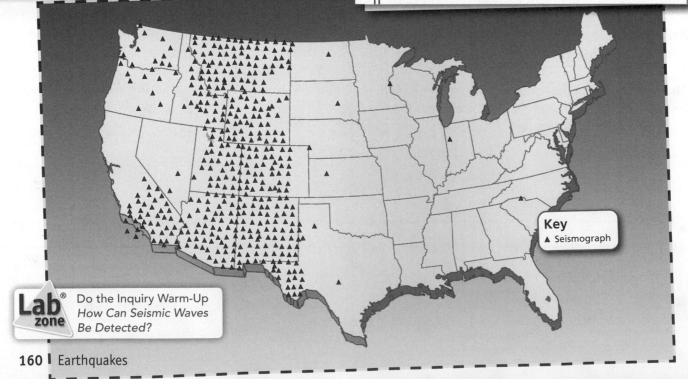

Key
▲ Seismograph

Lab zone ® Do the Inquiry Warm-Up *How Can Seismic Waves Be Detected?*

Vocabulary
- seismogram

Skills
↪ Reading: Identify the Main Idea
△ Inquiry: Predict

How Do Seismographs Work?

Today, seismographs are complex electronic devices. Some laptop computers and car air bags contain similar devices that detect shaking. But a simple seismograph, like the one in **Figure 1,** can consist of a heavy weight attached to a frame by a spring or wire. A pen connected to the weight rests its point on a drum that can rotate. As the drum rotates, the pen in effect draws a straight line on paper wrapped tightly around the drum. 🔑 **Seismic waves cause a simple seismograph's drum to vibrate, which in turn causes the pen to record the drum's vibrations.** The suspended weight with the pen attached moves very little. This allows the pen to stay in place and record the drum's vibrations.

Measuring Seismic Waves When you write a sentence, the paper stays in one place while your hand moves the pen. But in a seismograph, it's the pen that remains stationary while the paper moves. Why is this? All seismographs make use of a basic principle of physics: Whether it is moving or at rest, every object resists any change to its motion. A seismograph's heavy weight resists motion during an earthquake. But the rest of the seismograph is anchored to the ground and vibrates when seismic waves arrive.

FIGURE 1 ···

Recording Seismic Waves

In a simple seismograph, a pen attached to a suspended weight records an earthquake's seismic waves.

✏️ **Make Models** To mimic the action of a seismograph, hold the tip of a pencil on the right edge of the seismograph paper below. Have a classmate pull the right edge of the book away from your pencil while the classmate also "vibrates" the book side to side.

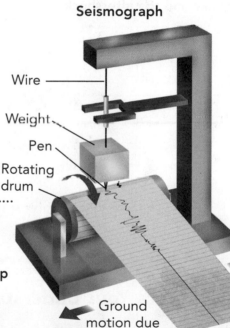

Seismograph

Wire

Weight

Pen

Rotating drum

Ground motion due to seismic waves

FIGURE 2 ········

Seismograms

When an earthquake's seismic waves reach a simple seismograph, the seismograph's drum vibrates. The vibrations are recorded by the seismograph's pen, producing a seismogram, as shown on the top diagram.

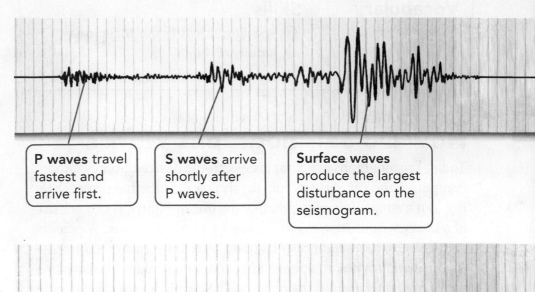

P waves travel fastest and arrive first.

S waves arrive shortly after P waves.

Surface waves produce the largest disturbance on the seismogram.

CHALLENGE An aftershock is a smaller earthquake that occurs after a larger earthquake. Draw the seismogram that might be produced by a seismograph during an earthquake and its aftershock. Label the earthquake and the aftershock.

Reading a Seismogram You have probably seen the zigzagging lines used to represent an earthquake. The pattern of lines, called a **seismogram,** is the record of an earthquake's seismic waves produced by a seismograph. Study the seismogram in **Figure 2.** Notice when the P waves, S waves, and surface waves arrive. The height of the lines drawn by the seismograph is greater for a more severe earthquake or an earthquake closer to the seismograph.

Lab zone® Do the Quick Lab *Design a Seismograph.*

🔑 Assess Your Understanding

1a. Review The height of the lines on a seismogram is (greater/less) for a stronger earthquake.

b. Interpret Diagrams What do the relatively straight, flat portions of the seismogram at the top of **Figure 2** represent?

_____

_____

_____

got it?

○ **I get it!** Now I know that a simple seismograph works when _____

_____

_____

_____

○ **I need extra help with** _____

Go to MY SCIENCE ⓢ COACH *online for help with this subject.*

What Patterns Do Seismographic Data Reveal?

Geologists use seismographs to monitor earthquakes. Other devices that geologists use detect slight motions along faults. Yet even with data from many different devices, geologists cannot yet predict when and where an earthquake might strike. ⌐○ **But from past seismographic data, geologists have created maps of where earthquakes occur around the world. The maps show that earthquakes often occur along plate boundaries.** Recall that where plates meet, plate movement stores energy in rock that makes up the crust. This energy is eventually released in an earthquake.

Earthquake Risk in North America Earthquake risk largely depends on how close a given location is to a plate boundary. In the United States, two plates meet along the Pacific coast in California, Washington state, and Alaska, causing many faults. Frequent earthquakes occur in California, where the Pacific plate and the North American plate meet along the San Andreas fault. In Washington, earthquakes result from the subduction of the Juan de Fuca plate beneath the North American plate. Recall that during subduction, one plate is forced down under another plate.

✎ ······················

↻ **Identify the Main Idea**
Underline the sentence in the second paragraph that describes the main factor in determining earthquake risk for a given location.

apply it!

The map shows areas where serious earthquakes are likely to occur, based on the location of past earthquakes across the United States.

❶ **Interpret Maps** The map indicates that serious earthquakes are most likely to occur (on the east coast/in the midsection/on the west coast) of the United States.

❷ **Predict** Based on the evidence shown in the map, predict where you think plate boundaries lie. Explain your reasoning.

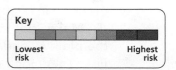

Key

Lowest risk   Highest risk

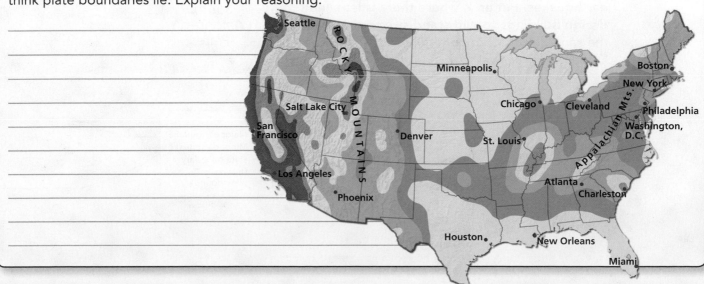

Earthquake Risk Around the World Many of the world's earthquakes occur in a vast area of geologic activity called the Ring of Fire. In this area, plate boundaries form a ring around the Pacific Ocean. Volcanoes as well as earthquakes are common along these boundaries. The Ring of Fire includes the west coast of Central America and the west coast of South America. Strong earthquakes have occurred in countries along these coasts, where plates converge. Across the Pacific Ocean, the Pacific Plate collides with several other plates. Here, Japan, Indonesia, New Zealand, and New Guinea are seismically very active.

India, China, and Pakistan also have been struck by large earthquakes. In this area of the world, the Indo-Australian Plate collides with the Eurasian Plate. Earthquakes are also common where the Eurasian Plate meets the Arabian and African plates.

Earthquakes and Plate Tectonics

Why do earthquakes occur more often in some places than in others?

FIGURE 3 ···

> REAL-WORLD INQUIRY **Earthquakes Around the World**

Earthquakes are closely linked to plate tectonics. The map shows where past earthquakes have occurred in relation to plate boundaries.

✏ **Make Judgments** Draw an outline tracing the plate boundaries that make up the Ring of Fire. Then, look at North America. Draw a star where buildings should be built to withstand earthquakes. Put an X where there is less need to design buildings to withstand strong shaking. Do the same for another continent (not Antarctica). Explain your answers.

_____

_____

_____

_____

_____

_____

_____

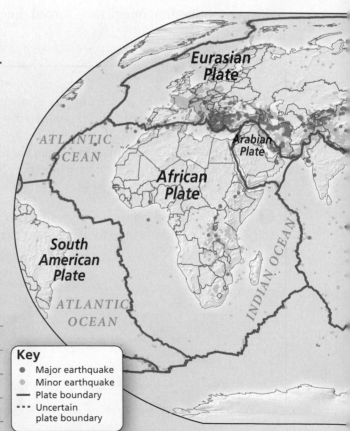

Key
- ● Major earthquake
- ● Minor earthquake
- ── Plate boundary
- ··· Uncertain plate boundary

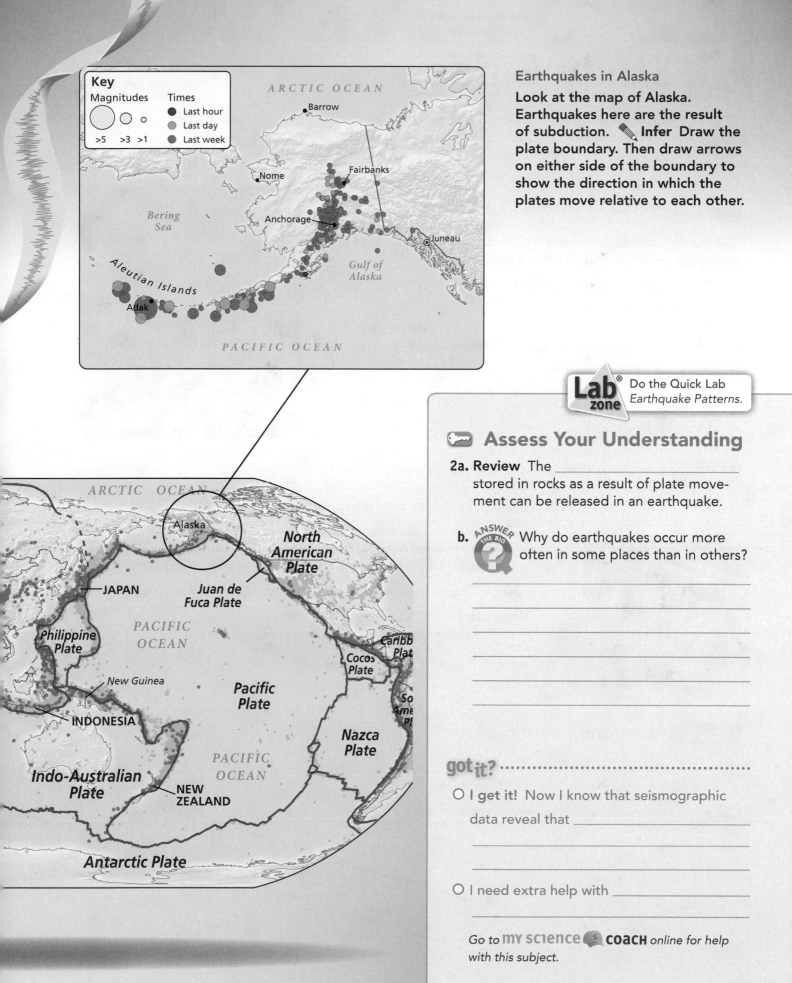

Earthquakes in Alaska

Look at the map of Alaska. Earthquakes here are the result of subduction. ✎ **Infer** Draw the plate boundary. Then draw arrows on either side of the boundary to show the direction in which the plates move relative to each other.

Key

Magnitudes

○ ○ ○
>5 >3 >1

Times
● Last hour
● Last day
● Last week

ARCTIC OCEAN

Barrow

Nome
Fairbanks

Bering
Sea
Anchorage
Juneau

Gulf of
Alaska

Aleutian Islands
Adak

PACIFIC OCEAN

ARCTIC OCEAN

Alaska

North
American
Plate

JAPAN
Juan de
Fuca Plate

Philippine
Plate

PACIFIC
OCEAN

New Guinea

Pacific
Plate

Caribb
Plat

Cocos
Plate

So
Ame
Pl

INDONESIA

Nazca
Plate

Indo-Australian
Plate

PACIFIC
OCEAN

NEW
ZEALAND

Antarctic Plate

Lab ® Do the Quick Lab
zone *Earthquake Patterns.*

🔑 Assess Your Understanding

2a. Review The _____ stored in rocks as a result of plate movement can be released in an earthquake.

b. ANSWER THE BIG **❓** Why do earthquakes occur more often in some places than in others?

_____
_____
_____
_____
_____
_____
_____

got**it?** ·····························

○ **I get it!** Now I know that seismographic data reveal that _____
_____

○ **I need extra help with** _____
_____

Go to **MY SCIENCE** Ⓢ **COACH** *online for help with this subject.*

165

Earthquakes often occur along _____ , where _____

_____ stores energy in rock that makes up the crust.

LESSON 1 Forces in Earth's Crust

🔑 Tension, compression, and shearing work over millions of years to change the shape and volume of rock.

🔑 When enough stress builds up in rock, the rock breaks, creating a fault.

🔑 Plate movement can change a flat plain into features such as folds, folded mountains, fault-block mountains, and plateaus.

Vocabulary
• stress • tension • compression • shearing
• normal fault • reverse fault • strike-slip fault • plateau

LESSON 2 Earthquakes and Seismic Waves

🔑 Seismic waves carry energy produced by an earthquake.

🔑 The amount of earthquake damage or shaking that is felt is rated using the Modified Mercalli scale. An earthquake's magnitude, or size, is measured using the Richter scale or moment magnitude scale.

🔑 Geologists use seismic waves to locate an earthquake's epicenter.

Vocabulary
• earthquake • focus • epicenter • P wave • S wave
• surface wave • seismograph • Modified Mercalli scale
• magnitude • Richter scale • moment magnitude scale

LESSON 3 Monitoring Earthquakes

🔑 Seismic waves cause a simple seismograph's drum to vibrate, which in turn causes the pen to record the drum's vibrations.

🔑 From past seismographic data, geologists have created maps of where earthquakes occur around the world. The maps show that earthquakes often occur along plate boundaries.

Vocabulary
• seismogram

Surface waves

S waves

P waves

Review and Assessment

LESSON 1 Forces in Earth's Crust

1. Which force squeezes Earth's crust to make the crust shorter and thicker?

   a. tension   **b.** normal

   c. shearing   **d.** compression

2. Rocks on either side of a _____ fault slip past each other with little up and down motion.

3. List Give two examples of mountain ranges in the world that have been caused by folding.

_____

_____

_____

4. Interpret Diagrams What type of stress is shown in the diagram below?

_____

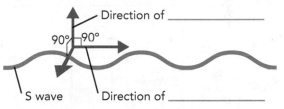

5. Relate Cause and Effect Plateaus are large, flat, elevated areas of land. What is one way plateaus can form?

_____

_____

_____

6. [Write About It] Compression causes folds called anticlines and synclines. How do these features resemble each other? How do they differ from one another?

LESSON 2 Earthquakes and Seismic Waves

7. Which of these scales rates earthquake damage at a particular location?

   a. focus   **b.** Modified Mercalli

   c. Richter   **d.** moment magnitude

8. The point on Earth's surface directly above an earthquake's focus is called _____

_____

9. Interpret Diagrams Label the diagram to show the directions an S wave travels and vibrates.

Direction of _____

90° 90°

S wave   Direction of _____

10. Explain How is the energy released by an earthquake related to its moment magnitude?

_____

_____

_____

11. Interpret Data Can geologists use data from only two seismographic stations to locate an earthquake's epicenter? Explain.

_____

_____

_____

12. math! Seismograph A records P waves at 6:05 P.M. and S waves at 6:10 P.M. Seismograph B records P waves at 6:10 P.M. and S waves at 6:25 P.M. What is the difference in the arrival times at each device? Which device is closer to the earthquake's epicenter?

_____

_____

_____

167

LESSON 3 Monitoring Earthquakes

13. In which type of location is earthquake risk the greatest?

    a. at plate centers   **b.** on big plates

    c. at plate boundaries   **d.** on small plates

14. Very high, jagged lines on a seismogram indicate that an earthquake is either _____

_____

Use the graph to answer questions 15–16.

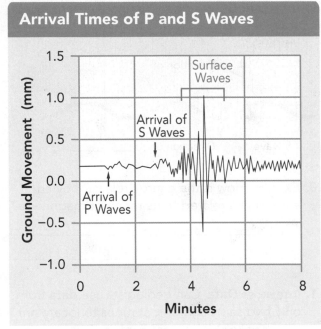

Arrival Times of P and S Waves

15. Read Graphs Which type of seismic waves produced the largest ground movement?

_____

16. Interpret Data What was the difference in arrival times for the P waves and the S waves?

_____

17. [Write About It] There is a high risk of earthquakes along the San Andreas fault in California. What is happening in Earth's crust along the fault to cause this high earthquake risk? Use the theory of plate tectonics in your answer.

APPLY THE BIG ? Why do earthquakes occur more often in some places than in others?

18. An architect is hired to design a skyscraper in the Indonesian city of Jakarta, which is near the Ring of Fire. The architect must follow special building codes that the city has written. What might those codes be for and why are they important in Jakarta?

_____

_____

_____

_____

_____

_____

_____

_____

Ohio Benchmark Practice

Multiple Choice

Circle the letter of the best answer.

1. The diagram below shows a mass of rock affected by stress.

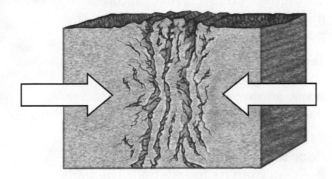

   What type of stress process is shown in this diagram?

   A   pulling apart   B   tension
   C   compression   D   shearing

2. An earthquake occurs along a fault when

   A   energy in the rock along the fault does not change for a long period of time.
   B   stress in the rock along the fault causes the rock to melt.
   C   enough energy builds up in the rock along the fault to cause the rock to break or slip.
   D   energy in the rock along the fault is changed to heat.

3. Which scale would a geologist use to estimate the total energy released by an earthquake?

   A   Modified Mercalli scale
   B   Richter scale
   C   epicenter scale
   D   moment magnitude scale

4. When an earthquake occurs, seismic waves travel

   A   only through the hanging wall.
   B   only through the footwall.
   C   outward from the focus.
   D   inward to the epicenter.

5. Where are the areas that are at greatest risk from earthquakes?

   A   in the center of plates
   B   where plates meet
   C   in the middle of the ocean
   D   where land meets water

Extended Response

Use the diagram below and your knowledge of science to help you answer Question 6. Write your answer on a separate piece of paper.

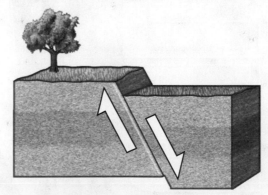

6. Explain the process that forms a normal fault and leads to an earthquake along the fault. Describe the fault, the type of stress that produces it, and events that occur before and during the earthquake.

Seismic-SAFE BUILDINGS

Suppose you are on the highest floor of a tall building in your town. An earthquake strikes. What features might help the building withstand the powerful effects of an earthquake?

Tension ties firmly "tie" the floors and ceilings of the building to the walls, and work to absorb and scatter earthquake energy.

Base isolators are pads under the first floor that separate, or isolate, the building from its foundation. The pads stop some of an earthquake's energy from entering the building.

Cross braces form a network of steel on the outside of the building to stiffen its frame.

Dampers work like shock absorbers in a car, absorbing some of the energy of seismic waves.

Design It Use cardboard, craft sticks, and modeling clay to build a model of a seismic-safe building. Place your model on a table, and drop a heavy book next to it. Then try bumping the table to shake the model sideways. How well does your building stand up? What changes could you make to improve your structure's stability?

▲ Cross braces on the outside of the building help to support the frame.

What Do the Toads Know?

On May 12, 2008, a strong earthquake struck China. Within days, bloggers claimed that many signs had predicted the earthquake. One blogger wrote that thousands of toads moved through the area just before the earthquake. Another claimed to have seen ponds that emptied and dried up.

Write About It Write an entry that you might post in a blog. Do you believe the bloggers' claims about signs that might predict an earthquake? What evidence would you look for to determine whether the bloggers' claims were scientifically accurate?

FORENSIC SEISMOLOGY

In May 2008, India tested two nuclear devices by exploding them underground. Days later, Pakistan conducted similar tests. The world learned of these tests because these explosions caused seismic waves.

How did geologists know the seismic waves were produced by nuclear explosions and not by earthquakes? Seismic waves from underground nuclear explosions produce a different seismogram pattern than earthquakes do.

Research It Research how the seismograms produced by nuclear explosions differ from those produced by earthquakes, and make a poster illustrating the differences.

▲ An underground nuclear test destroyed these test buildings at Pokaran, India, in 1998.

WHAT CAUSED THIS EXPLOSION?

How does a volcano erupt?

Vivid orange and red sparks shower the night sky. A small crowd stands by and watches this beautiful scene light up the night. Could this be a fireworks display gone crazy? You've probably guessed that it is a volcano erupting. This volcano is actually exploding, sending hot gases, ash, and lava into the air. ⟋Infer **What could cause a volcano to blow up?**

_____

_____

_____

_____

_____

▶ **UNTAMED SCIENCE** Watch the **Untamed Science** video to learn more about volcanoes.

Volcanoes

6 Getting Started

Check Your Understanding

1. **Background** Read the paragraph below and then answer the question.

Mr. Carenni said, "For today's activity, let's make a model of Earth's crust. We can think of the crust as a thin film of ice resting on top of a much thicker layer of hard, packed snow. Now let's suppose that the ice breaks into pieces. On Earth, these pieces are called plates. The edges of the plates are called boundaries."

> The **crust** is Earth's rocky, outer layer.
>
> A **plate** is one of the large pieces that Earth's crust is broken into.
>
> **Boundaries** are lines along which something ends.

- Suppose two pieces of ice are pushed slowly together. What might happen to the edges of the pieces?

_____

_____

> **MY READING WEB** If you had trouble answering the question above, visit **My Reading Web** and type in *Volcanoes.*

Vocabulary Skill

High-Use Academic Words High-use words are words that are used frequently in academic reading, writing, and discussions. These words are different from key terms because they appear in many subject areas.

Word	Definition	Example
surface	*n.* the exterior or outermost layer of an object	The *surface* of Earth is very rocky.
stage	*n.* a point in a process	Middle age is one *stage* of life.
hazard	*n.* a possible danger	Forest fires can be a *hazard* for people living near the woods.

2. **Quick Check** Choose the word from the table that best completes the sentence.

- When a volcano erupts, the lava can be a _____

  for cities and towns nearby.

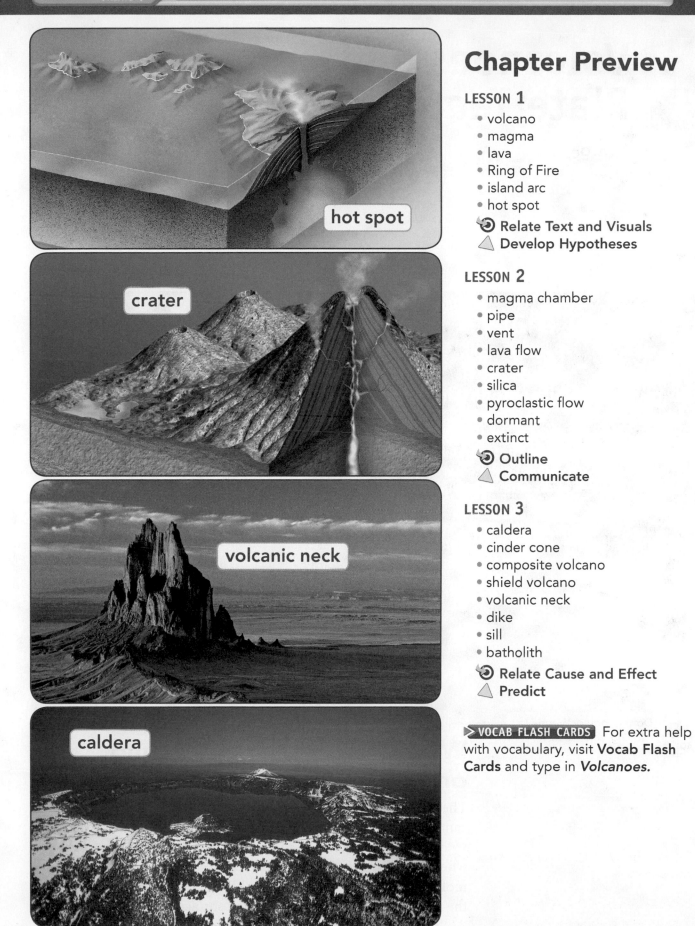

hot spot

crater

volcanic neck

caldera

Chapter Preview

LESSON 1
- volcano
- magma
- lava
- Ring of Fire
- island arc
- hot spot

⟳ **Relate Text and Visuals**
△ **Develop Hypotheses**

LESSON 2
- magma chamber
- pipe
- vent
- lava flow
- crater
- silica
- pyroclastic flow
- dormant
- extinct

⟳ **Outline**
△ **Communicate**

LESSON 3
- caldera
- cinder cone
- composite volcano
- shield volcano
- volcanic neck
- dike
- sill
- batholith

⟳ **Relate Cause and Effect**
△ **Predict**

▷ **VOCAB FLASH CARDS** For extra help with vocabulary, visit **Vocab Flash Cards** and type in **Volcanoes.**

Volcanoes and Plate Tectonics

🔑 **Where Are Volcanoes Found on Earth's Surface?**

my pLaneT DiaRY

FIELD TRIP

Mountain of Fire, Mountain of Ice

Climbers who struggle up the snow-packed slopes of Mount Erebus on Antarctica may be in for an unpleasant surprise. Balls of scorching molten rock three meters across might come hurtling out of the air and land just steps from climbers' feet! Why? Because Mount Erebus is one of Earth's southernmost volcanoes.

Scientists believe that Mount Erebus lies over an area where material from Earth's mantle rises and then melts. The melted material reaches the surface at Mount Erebus.

Read the text and then answer the question.

How did Mount Erebus form?

_____

_____

_____

_____

_____

_____

▷ PLANET DIARY Go to **Planet Diary** to learn more about volcanoes.

Lab® **zone** Do the Inquiry Warm-Up *Moving Volcanoes.*

Where Are Volcanoes Found on Earth's Surface?

The eruption of a volcano can be awe-inspiring. Molten material can be spewed high into the atmosphere. Villages can be buried in volcanic ash. A **volcano** is a mountain that forms in Earth's crust when molten material, or magma, reaches the surface. **Magma** is a molten mixture of rock-forming substances, gases, and water from the mantle. When magma reaches the surface, it is called **lava**. After magma and lava cool, they form solid rock.

Vocabulary
- volcano • magma • lava • Ring of Fire
- island arc • hot spot

Skills
↻ Reading: Relate Text and Visuals
△ Inquiry: Develop Hypotheses

Volcanoes and Plate Boundaries Are volcanoes found randomly across Earth? No, in general, volcanoes form a regular pattern on Earth. To understand why, look at the map in **Figure 1.** Notice how volcanoes occur in many great, long belts. ⚷ **Volcanic belts form along the boundaries of Earth's plates.**

Volcanoes can occur where two plates pull apart, or diverge. Here, plate movements cause the crust to fracture. The fractures in the crust allow magma to reach the surface. Volcanoes can also occur where two plates push together, or converge. As the plates push together, one plate can sink beneath the other plate. Water that is brought down with the sinking plate eventually helps to form magma, which rises to the surface.

The **Ring of Fire,** shown in **Figure 1,** is one major belt of volcanoes. It includes the many volcanoes that rim the Pacific Ocean. The Ring of Fire includes the volcanoes along the coasts of North and South America and those in Japan and the Philippines.

↻ **Relate Text and Visuals**
Volcanoes often form belts along plate boundaries. How does **Figure 1** illustrate that this statement holds true for North America?

_____
_____
_____
_____
_____
_____

FIGURE 1 ••••••••••••••••••••••••••••

The Ring of Fire
The Ring of Fire is a belt of volcanoes that circles the Pacific Ocean. As with most of Earth's volcanoes, these volcanoes form along boundaries of tectonic plates.

△ **Develop Hypotheses** Circle a volcano on the map that does not fall along a plate boundary. Why did this volcano form here? Write your answer below. Revise your answer after finishing the lesson.

Original Hypothesis: _____
_____
_____
_____
_____

Revised Hypothesis: _____
_____
_____

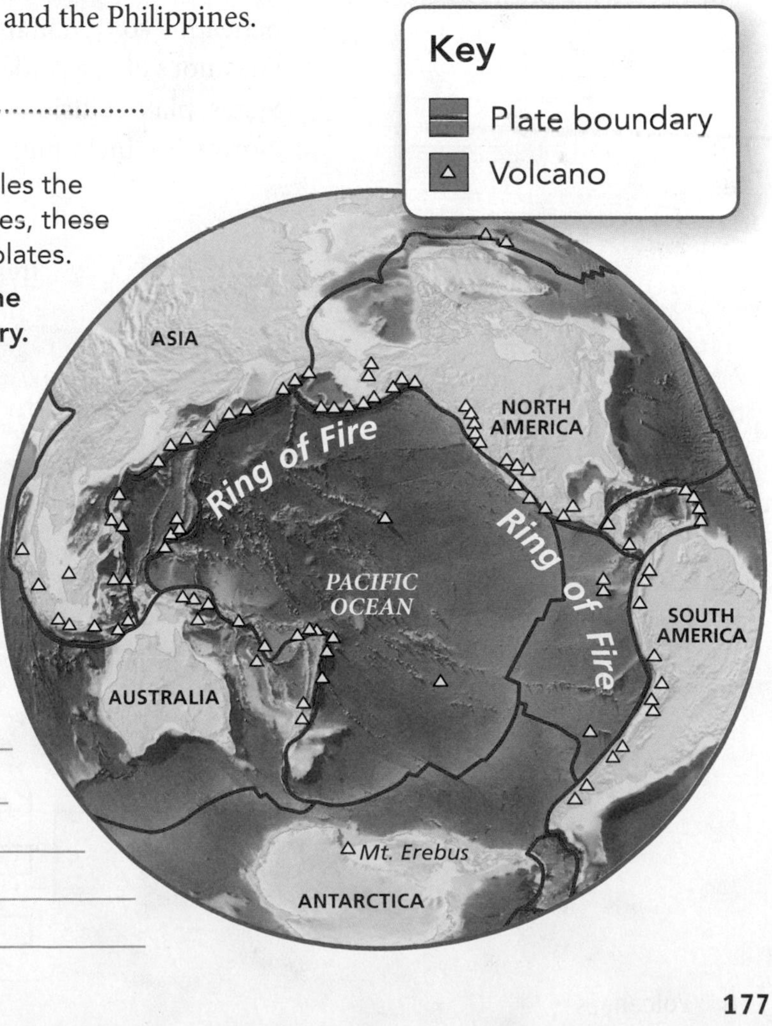

Key

■ Plate boundary
△ Volcano

177

FIGURE 2 ·····························

> **ART IN MOTION**

Volcanoes and Converging Boundaries

Volcanoes often form where two plates collide.

✎ **Compare and Contrast** Shade the arrows to show the direction of plate movement. Then compare and contrast the ways volcanoes form at A and B.

_____

_____

_____

_____

_____

_____

_____

_____

_____

_____

Diverging Boundaries Volcanoes form along the mid-ocean ridges, where two plates move apart. Mid-ocean ridges form long, underwater mountain ranges that sometimes have a rift valley down their center. Along the rift valley, lava pours out of cracks in the ocean floor. This process gradually builds new mountains. Volcanoes also form along diverging plate boundaries on land. For example, large volcanoes are found along the Great Rift Valley in East Africa.

Converging Boundaries Many volcanoes form near converging plate boundaries, where two oceanic plates collide. Through subduction, the older, denser plate sinks into the mantle and creates a deep-ocean trench. Water in the sinking plate eventually leaves the crust and rises into the wedge of the mantle above it. As a result, the melting point of the mantle in the wedge is lowered. So, the mantle partially melts. The magma that forms as a result rises up. This magma can break through the ocean floor, creating volcanoes.

The resulting volcanoes sometime create a string of islands called an **island arc.** Look at **Figure 2.** The curve of an island arc echoes the curve of its deep-ocean trench. Major island arcs include Japan, New Zealand, the Aleutians, and the Caribbean islands.

Volcanoes also occur where an oceanic plate is subducted beneath a continental plate. Collisions of this type produced the volcanoes of the Andes Mountains in South America. In the United States, plate collisions also produced the volcanoes of the Pacific Northwest, including Mount St. Helens and Mount Rainier.

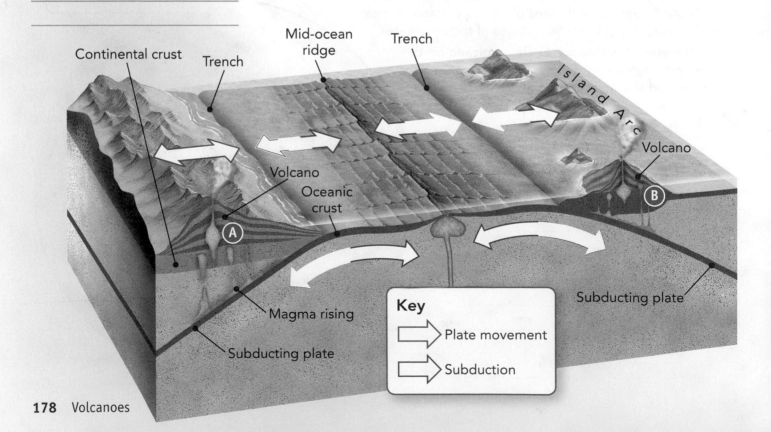

Hot Spots Not all volcanoes form along plate boundaries. Some volcanoes are the result of "hot spots" in Earth's mantle. A **hot spot** is an area where material from deep within Earth's mantle rises through the crust and melts to form magma. 🔑 **A volcano forms above a hot spot when magma erupts through the crust and reaches the surface.** Hot spots stay in one place for many millions of years while the plate moves over them. Some hot spot volcanoes lie close to plate boundaries. Others lie in the middle of plates. Yellowstone National Park in Wyoming marks a huge hot spot under the North American plate.

apply it!

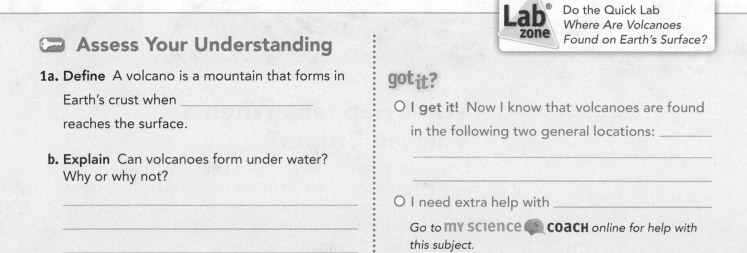

The Hawaiian Islands have formed one by one as the Pacific plate drifts slowly over a hot spot. This process has taken millions of years.

1 The hot spot is currently forming volcanic mountains on the island of (Oahu/Maui/**Hawaii**).

2 Do you think Maui will erupt again? Why or why not?

_____

_____

3 [CHALLENGE] Which island is older—Kauai or Maui? Why?

_____

_____

_____

_____

🔑 **Assess Your Understanding**

1a. Define A volcano is a mountain that forms in Earth's crust when _____ reaches the surface.

b. Explain Can volcanoes form under water? Why or why not?

_____

_____

Lab zone Do the Quick Lab *Where Are Volcanoes Found on Earth's Surface?*

got it?

○ **I get it!** Now I know that volcanoes are found in the following two general locations: _____

_____

_____

○ **I need extra help with** _____

Go to **MY SCIENCE** ⓢ **COACH** *online for help with this subject.*

Volcanic Eruptions

UNLOCK THE BIG ?

🔑 **What Happens When a Volcano Erupts?**

🔑 **What Are the Stages of Volcanic Activity?**

MY PLANET DiARY

Hotheaded!

Can lava look like hair from the top of your head? It often does in Hawaii! Here, hikers may come across thin strands of hardened material that shimmer like gold in the sunlight. These thin strands are Pele's hair (PAY layz). Pele is the Hawaiian goddess of volcanoes and fire. Her "hair" is actually volcanic glass! It forms when tiny drops of molten lava fly into the air. The wind stretches these drops into threads that are as thin as hair. The glass strands then settle in crevices in the ground, forming clumps.

Read the text. Then answer the question.

How does Pele's hair form?

_____

_____

_____

_____

▶ **PLANET DIARY** Go to **Planet Diary** to learn more about lava.

Lab zone® Do the Inquiry Warm-Up *How Fast Do Liquids Flow?*

What Happens When a Volcano Erupts?

Lava begins as magma. Magma usually forms in the somewhat soft layer of hot, solid rock that lies in the upper mantle, just below a layer of harder rock. The magma is less dense than the material that is around it. So it rises into any cracks in the rock above. If this magma reaches the surface, a volcano can form.

Vocabulary
- magma chamber • pipe • vent • lava flow • crater
- silica • pyroclastic flow • dormant • extinct

Skills
↺ Reading: Outline
△ Inquiry: Communicate

Inside a Volcano A volcano is more than a large, cone-shaped mountain. Inside a volcano is a system of passageways through which magma moves, as shown in **Figure 1.**

- **Magma chamber** All volcanoes have a pocket of magma beneath the surface. Beneath a volcano, magma collects in a **magma chamber.** During an eruption, the magma forces its way through one or more cracks in Earth's crust.

- **Pipe** Magma moves upward through a **pipe,** a long tube that extends from Earth's crust up through the top of the volcano, connecting the magma chamber to Earth's surface.

- **Vent** Molten rock and gas leave the volcano through an opening called a **vent.** Some volcanoes have a single central vent at the top. But volcanoes often have vents on the sides also.

- **Lava flow** A **lava flow** is the spread of lava as it pours out of a vent.

- **Crater** A **crater** is a bowl-shaped area that may form at the top of a volcano around the central vent.

Vocabulary High-Use Academic Words A system is a group of parts that function as a whole. Describe why a volcano might be considered a system.

_____
_____
_____
_____
_____

FIGURE 1 ....

> **INTERACTIVE ART** **Inside a Volcano**

A volcano is made up of many different parts.

✎ **Identify** Place each word in its proper place in the diagram.

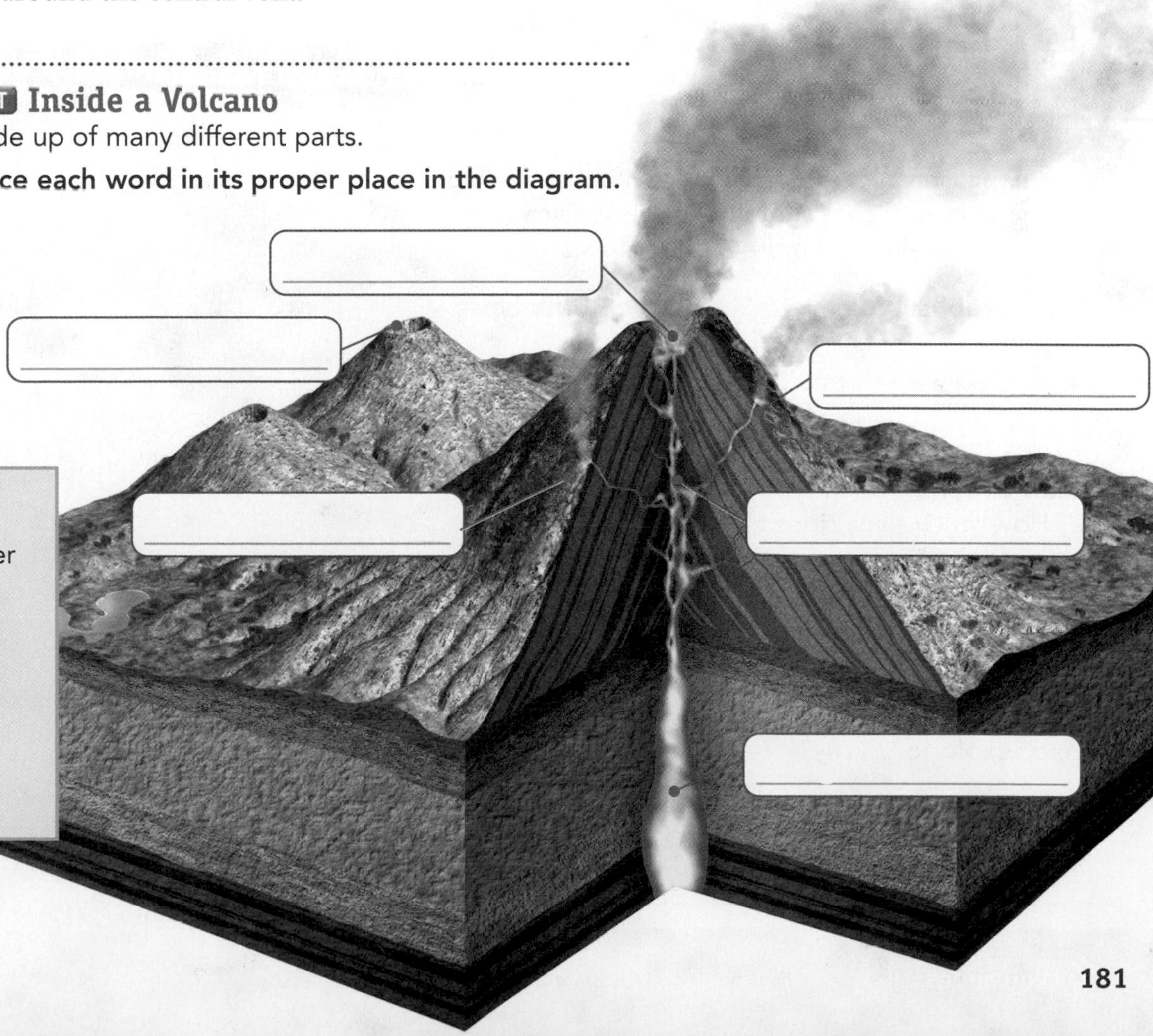

Word Bank

Magma chamber

Pipe

Central vent

Side vent

Lava flow

Crater

181

did you
know? ....

Stromboli volcano lies on an island off the coast of Italy. The volcano has been erupting almost constantly for at least 2,400 years! Expanding gases dissolved in magma cause the eruption to be nearly constant.

A Volcanic Eruption Perhaps you know that dissolved carbon dioxide gas is trapped in every can of soda. But did you know that dissolved gases are trapped in magma? These dissolved gases are under great pressure. During an eruption, as magma rises toward the surface, the pressure of the surrounding rock on the magma decreases. The dissolved gases begin to expand, forming bubbles. These bubbles are much like the bubbles in the soda can. As pressure falls within the magma, the size of the gas bubbles increases greatly. These expanding gases exert great force. **When a volcano erupts, the force of the expanding gases pushes magma from the magma chamber through the pipe until it flows or explodes out of the vent.** Once magma escapes from the volcano and becomes lava, the remaining gases bubble out.

Two Types of Volcanic Eruptions
Some volcanic eruptions occur gradually, over days, months, or even years. Others are great explosions. **Geologists classify volcanic eruptions as quiet or explosive.** Whether an eruption is quiet or explosive depends in part on the magma's silica content and whether the magma is thin and runny or thick and sticky. **Silica** is a material found in magma that forms from the elements oxygen and silicon. Temperature also helps determine how fluid, or runny, magma is.

do the
math!
Magma Composition

Magma varies in composition. It is classified according to the amount of silica it contains. The less silica that the magma contains, the more easily it flows.

1 **Read Graphs** What materials make up both types of magma?

_____

2 **Read Graphs** Which type of magma has more silica? How much silica does this magma contain?

_____

_____

3 [CHALLENGE] Which of these magmas do you think might erupt in a dramatic explosion? Why?

_____

_____

_____

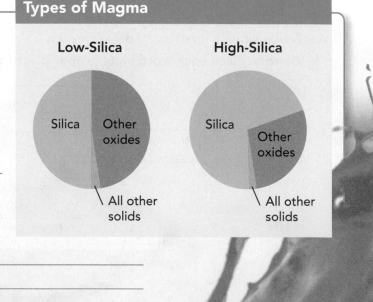

Types of Magma

Low-Silica

Silica | Other oxides

\ All other solids

High-Silica

Silica | Other oxides

\ All other solids

Quiet Eruptions A volcano erupts quietly if its magma is hot or low in silica. Hot, low-silica magma is thin and runny and flows easily. The gases in the magma bubble out gently. Low-silica lava oozes quietly from the vent and can flow for many kilometers.

Quiet eruptions can produce different types of lava, as shown in **Figure 2.** The different types of lava harden into different types of rock. Pahoehoe (pah HOH ee hoh ee) forms from fast-moving, hot lava that is thin and runny. The surface of pahoehoe looks like a solid mass of ropelike coils. Aa (AH ah) forms from lava that is cooler and thicker. The lava that aa forms from is also slower-moving. Aa has a rough surface consisting of jagged lava chunks.

Mostly quiet eruptions formed the Hawaiian Islands. On the island of Hawaii, lava pours from the crater near the top of Kilauea. Lava also flows out of long cracks on the volcano's sides. In general, the temperature of magma and lava can range from about 750°C to 1175°C—hot enough to melt copper! Quiet eruptions have built up the island of Hawaii over hundreds of thousands of years.

FIGURE 2 ···

Lava From Quiet Eruptions
Quiet eruptions can produce two different types of lava.

✏ **Interpret Photographs** Which lava is hardening to form aa? Which is hardening to form pahoehoe? Write your answers in the spaces provided. Then, in your own words, describe the texture of each type of rock.

⊙ Outline Review the text on this page and on the previous page. Then complete the following outline.

Types of Volcanic Eruptions

1. Quiet eruption

   a. Kilauea

   b. _____

2. Explosive eruption

   a. _____

   b. High-silica magma

Explosive Eruptions A volcano erupts explosively if its magma is high in silica. High-silica magma is thick and sticky. This type of magma can build up in the volcano's pipe, plugging it like a cork in a bottle. Dissolved gases, including water vapor, cannot escape from the thick magma. The trapped gases build up pressure until they explode. The erupting gases and steam push the magma out of the volcano with incredible force. That's what happened during the eruption of Mount St. Helens in Washington State. This eruption is shown in **Figure 3.**

An explosive eruption throws lava powerfully into the air where it breaks into fragments that quickly cool and harden into pieces of different sizes. The smallest pieces are volcanic ash. Volcanic ash is made up of fine, rocky particles as small as a speck of dust. Pebble-sized particles are called cinders. Larger pieces, called bombs, may range from the size of a golf ball to the size of a car.

FIGURE 3 ···

What a Blast!

The explosive eruption of Mount St. Helens in 1980 blew off the top of the mountain.

✎ **Explain** Read the text in this section. In your own words, explain how dissolved gases caused Mount St. Helens to erupt explosively.

_____

_____

_____

_____

_____

_____

_____

Before 1980 eruption

During 1980 eruption

After 1980 eruption

Volcano Hazards

Volcano Hazards Both quiet eruptions and explosive eruptions can cause damage far from a crater's rim. For example, during a quiet eruption, lava flows from vents, setting fire to, and often burying, everything in its path. A quiet eruption can cover large areas with a thick layer of lava.

During an explosive eruption, a volcano can belch out a mixture of dangerous materials such as hot rock and ash. This mixture of materials can form a fast-moving cloud that rushes down the sides of the volcano. A **pyroclastic flow** (py roh KLAS tik) is the mixture of hot gases, ash, cinders, and bombs that flow down the sides of a volcano when it erupts explosively. Landslides of mud, melted snow, and rock can also form from an explosive eruption. **Figure 4** shows one result of an explosive eruption.

FIGURE 4 ·······························

Volcano Hazards
In 1991, Mount Pinatubo in the Philippines erupted explosively.

△ **Communicate** What hazards did Mount Pinatubo present to towns near the volcano? Consider the effects of lava, ash, and gases. Work in a small group. List your answers here.

_____

_____

_____

_____

_____

_____

_____

_____

Do the Lab Investigation *Gelatin Volcanoes.*

🔑 Assess Your Understanding

1a. Review Two types of volcanic eruptions are

_____

_____

b. Infer Some volcanoes have great glaciers on their slopes. Why might these glaciers be a hazard if a volcano erupts?

_____

_____

_____

got it?

○ **I get it!** Now I know that when a volcano erupts, the force of the expanding gases

_____

_____

_____

○ **I need extra help with** _____

Go to **MY SCIENCE ⓢ COACH** online for help with this subject.

What Are the Stages of Volcanic Activity?

The activity of a volcano may last from less than a decade to more than 10 million years. But most long-lived volcanoes do not erupt continuously. You can see the pattern of activity by looking at the eruptions of volcanoes in the Cascade Range, shown in **Figure 5.** Mount Jefferson has not erupted in at least 15,000 years. Will it ever erupt again? 🔑 **Geologists often use the terms active, dormant, or extinct to describe a volcano's stage of activity.**

An active, or live, volcano is one that is erupting or has shown signs that it may erupt in the near future. A **dormant,** or sleeping, volcano is a volcano that scientists expect to awaken in the future and become active. An **extinct,** or dead, volcano is a volcano that is unlikely to ever erupt again. For example, hot-spot volcanoes may become extinct after they drift away from the hot spot.

Changes in activity in and around a volcano may give warning shortly before a volcano erupts. Geologists use special instruments to detect these changes. For example, tiltmeters can detect slight surface changes in elevation and tilt caused by magma moving underground. Geologists can also monitor gases escaping from the volcano. They monitor the many small earthquakes that occur around a volcano before an eruption. The upward movement of magma triggers these earthquakes. Also, rising temperatures in underground water may signal that magma is nearing the surface.

Key

→ Direction of plate movement

— Plate boundary

FIGURE 5 ···

Cascade Volcanoes

The Cascade volcanoes have formed as the Juan de Fuca plate sinks beneath the North American plate.

✏️ **Develop Hypotheses** Answer the questions.

1. Circle the three volcanoes that appear to be the most active.

2. Why might geologists still consider Mount Jefferson to be an active volcano?

_____

_____

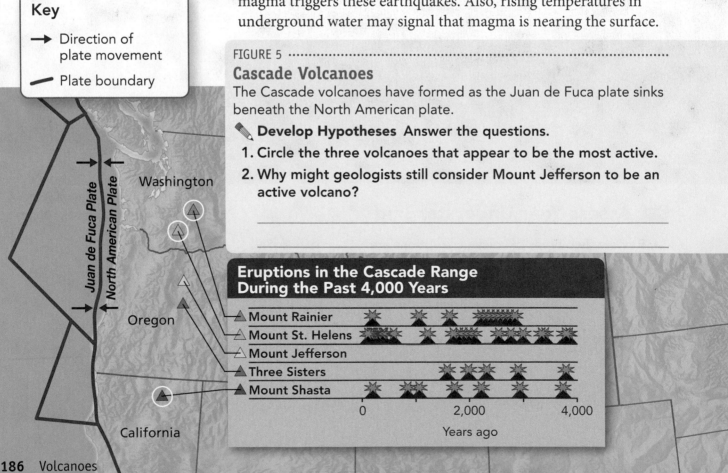

Eruptions in the Cascade Range During the Past 4,000 Years

Mount Rainier
Mount St. Helens
Mount Jefferson
Three Sisters
Mount Shasta

0   2,000   4,000

Years ago

Juan de Fuca Plate

North American Plate

Washington

Oregon

California

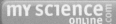
EXPLORE THE BIG ?

MT. RAINIER

How does a volcano erupt?

FIGURE 6 ···

> **REAL-WORLD INQUIRY** Mount Rainier is part of the Cascade volcanoes. All past eruptions of Mount Rainier have included ash and lava.

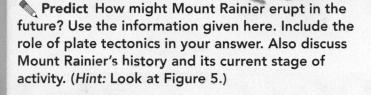

Magma at Mount Rainier

60% Silica   **40%** Other material

North American plate

Juan de Fuca plate

Seattle

Mount Rainier

✎ **Predict** How might Mount Rainier erupt in the future? Use the information given here. Include the role of plate tectonics in your answer. Also discuss Mount Rainier's history and its current stage of activity. (*Hint:* Look at Figure 5.)

_____

_____

_____

_____

_____

_____

_____

_____

_____

_____

_____

_____

_____

 Lab zone® Do the Quick Lab *Volcanic Stages.*

🔑 Assess Your Understanding

2a. Identify A volcano that is currently erupting is called an (active/dormant/extinct) volcano.

b. **ANSWER THE BIG ?** How does a volcano erupt?

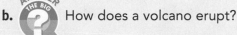

_____

_____

_____

got it?

○ **I get it!** Now I know that the three stages in

the life cycle of a volcano are _____

_____

_____

○ **I need extra help with** _____

Go to **my science** 🅢 **COACH** *online for help with this subject.*

Volcanic Landforms

UNLOCK THE BIG ?

🔑 **What Landforms Do Lava and Ash Create?**

🔑 **What Landforms Does Magma Create?**

my planeT DiaRY

BLOG

Posted by: Jackson

Location: West Hills, California

I was subjected to the sight of an active, dangerous volcano. We were on Hawaii, in a small aircraft over the Big Island.

The volcano was quite large—maybe a few miles in diameter. Out of the top of this volcano, there was an immense pillar of smoke, being blown out to sea by the Hawaiian winds. Judging by the patterns of the hardened lava on the slopes of the volcano, it was a shield volcano. The whole area was literally oozing with volcanic activity. Quite a few large depressions had formed where presumably there had been a magma pocket that collapsed in on itself.

Answer the questions below.

1. What landforms were created by the volcano that Jackson saw?

_____

_____

_____

2. If you had a chance to visit Hawaii, would you prefer to see a volcano from an airplane or from the ground? Explain.

_____

_____

_____

_____

▶ **PLANET DIARY** Go to **Planet Diary** to learn more about volcanic landforms.

Lab ® Do the Inquiry Warm-Up
zone *How Do Volcanoes Change Land?*

Vocabulary

- caldera
- cinder cone
- composite volcano
- shield volcano
- volcanic neck
- dike
- sill
- batholith

Skills

↻ **Reading:** Relate Cause and Effect

△ **Inquiry:** Predict

What Landforms Do Lava and Ash Create?

Lava has built up much of the islands of Hawaii. In fact, for much of Earth's history, volcanic activity on and beneath Earth's surface has built up Earth's land areas and formed much of the ocean crust. **Volcanic eruptions create landforms made of lava, ash, and other materials. These landforms include shield volcanoes, cinder cone volcanoes, composite volcanoes, and lava plateaus. Other landforms include calderas, which are the huge holes left by the collapse of volcanoes.** A caldera is shown in **Figure 1**.

FIGURE 1 ·····················

How a Caldera Forms

Crater Lake in Oregon fills an almost circular caldera.

✎ **Interpret Diagrams** In your own words, describe what is happening in the sequence of diagrams below.

Calderas

Large eruptions can empty the main vent and magma chamber beneath a volcano. With nothing to support it, the mountain top may collapse inward. A **caldera** (kal DAIR uh) is the hole left when a volcano collapses. A lake can form, filling the hole. If the volcano erupts again, a steep-walled cone may form in the middle.

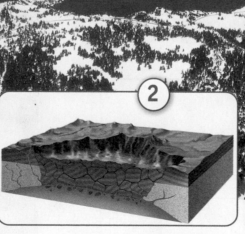

① ②

③

_____

_____

_____

_____

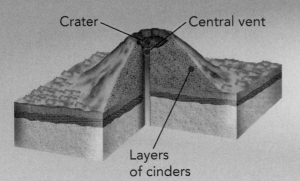

Crater — Central vent

Layers of cinders

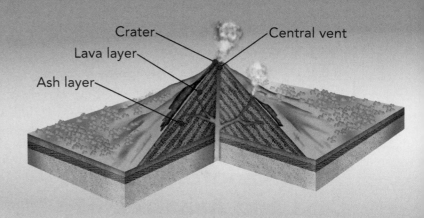

Crater — Central vent
Lava layer
Ash layer

Cinder Cone Volcanoes

If a volcano's magma has high silica content, it will be thick and sticky. So the volcano can erupt explosively, producing ash, cinders, and bombs. These materials can build up around the vent in a steep, cone-shaped hill or small mountain that is called a **cinder cone.** For example, Paricutín in Mexico erupted in 1943 in a farmer's cornfield. The volcano built up a cinder cone that was about 400 meters high.

Composite Volcanoes

Sometimes, the silica content of magma can vary. So eruptions of lava flows alternate with explosive eruptions of ash, cinder, and bombs. The result is a composite volcano. **Composite volcanoes** are tall, cone-shaped mountains in which layers of lava alternate with layers of ash. Mount Fuji in Japan and Mount St. Helens in Washington State are composite volcanoes. Composite volcanoes can be more than 4,800 meters tall.

FIGURE 2 ···

Volcanic Mountains

Lava from volcanoes cools and hardens to form lava plateaus and three types of mountains.

✎ **Read the text at the top of these two pages. Then answer the questions.**

1. **Classify** Identify the type of volcanic landform shown in each of the two photographs at the right.
2. **CHALLENGE** Use the graphic organizer to compare and contrast two types of volcanoes.

	Volcano Type: ___	Volcano Type: ___
Typical size		
Shape		
How the volcano forms		

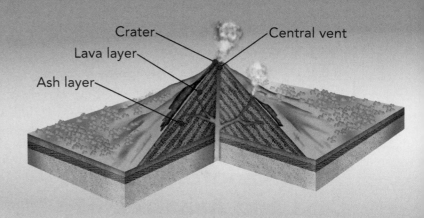

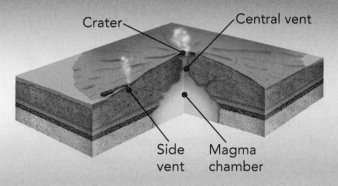

Crater Central vent

Side vent Magma chamber

Fissures New lava layer

Lava layers

Shield Volcanoes

At some spots on Earth's surface, thin layers of lava pour out of a vent and harden on top of previous layers. Such lava flows slowly build a wide, gently sloping mountain called a **shield volcano.** Hot spot volcanoes that form on the ocean floor are usually shield volcanoes. For example, in Hawaii, Mauna Loa rises 9,000 meters from the ocean floor!

Lava Plateaus

Lava can flow out of several long cracks in an area. The thin, runny lava floods the area and travels far before cooling and solidifying. After millions of years, repeated floods of lava can form high, level plateaus. These plateaus are called lava plateaus. The Columbia Plateau is a lava plateau that covers parts of Washington State, Oregon, and Idaho.

The Hawaiian Islands are very fertile, or able to support plant growth. In fact, many areas near volcanoes have rich, fertile soil. The rich soil forms after hard lava and ash break down. The ash releases substances that plants need to grow.

1 ⚠ **Predict** What type of industry might you expect to find on land near volcanoes?

_____

2 **Analyze Costs and Benefits** Lava flows could force people to flee their homes on the island of Hawaii. But in 2006, sales from crops on the island totaled over $153 million. Are the risks worth the rewards? Explain.

_____

_____

_____

Do the Quick Lab *Identifying Volcanic Landforms.*

🔑 Assess Your Understanding

1a. Review Volcanic landforms can be built up by (lava only/ash only/both lava and ash).

b. Explain Suppose lava from a certain volcano has built up a steep, cone-shaped hill around a central vent. What can you conclude about the kind of lava that formed the volcano?

_____

_____

_____

got it?

○ **I get it!** Now I know that lava and ash can create the following landforms: _____

_____

_____

○ **I need extra help with** _____

Go to **MY SCIENCE** 🅂 **COACH** *online for help with this subject.*

What Landforms Does Magma Create?

Sometimes magma cools and hardens into rock before reaching the surface. Over time, forces such as flowing water, ice, or wind may strip away the layers above the hardened magma and expose it. 🔑 **Features formed by magma include volcanic necks, dikes, and sills, as well as dome mountains and batholiths.**

Volcanic Necks

Look at **Figure 3**. The landform that looks like a giant tooth stuck in the ground is Shiprock in New Mexico. Shiprock formed when magma hardened in an ancient volcano's pipe. Later, the softer rock around the pipe wore away, exposing the harder rock inside. A **volcanic neck** forms when magma hardens in a volcano's pipe and the surrounding rock later wears away.

Dikes and Sills

Magma that forces itself across rock layers hardens into a **dike.** Magma that squeezes between horizontal rock layers hardens to form a **sill.**

✏️ **Relate Cause and Effect**
What type of landform can be created when magma hardens in a volcano's pipe?

○ Sill
○ Dike
○ Volcanic neck

FIGURE 3 ··················

▶ **INTERACTIVE ART** **Volcanic Necks, Dikes, and Sills**
A dike extends outward from Shiprock, a volcanic neck in New Mexico.

✏️ **Identify** Label the formations. How can you tell which is which?

_____
_____
_____

Volcanic neck

Dike

Sill

CANADA
British Columbia batholith
Idaho batholith
PACIFIC OCEAN
UNITED STATES
Sierra Nevada batholith
Baja batholith

Key
Batholith
0   200 mi
0   200 km

Dome Mountains

Dome Mountains Bodies of hardened magma can create dome mountains. A dome mountain forms when uplift pushes a large body of hardened magma toward the surface. The hardened magma forces the layers of rock to bend upward into a dome shape. Eventually, the rock above the dome mountain wears away, leaving it exposed. This process formed the Black Hills in South Dakota.

Batholiths How large can landforms created by magma be? Look at the map in **Figure 4**. A **batholith** (BATH uh lith) is a mass of rock formed when a large body of magma cools inside the crust. Batholiths form the core of many mountain ranges. Over millions of years, the overlying rock wears away, allowing the batholith to move upward. Flowing water and grinding ice slowly carve the batholith into mountains.

FIGURE 4 ···

Batholiths

Batholiths are common in the western United States. The mountains shown here are part of the Sierra Nevada batholith.

✎ **Measure** About how long is the Sierra Nevada batholith? (*Hint:* Use the map and map key.)

_____

Lab zone Do the Quick Lab
How Can Volcanic Activity Change Earth's Surface?

🔑 Assess Your Understanding

2a. Review Dikes and sills are two examples of landforms created when (magma/lava) forces its way through cracks in the upper crust.

b. Identify What feature forms when magma cuts across rock layers?

_____

c. Infer Which is older—a dike or the rock layers the dike cuts across? Explain.

_____

_____

_____

_____

got **it?** ··

○ **I get it!** Now I know that magma creates landforms such as _____

_____

○ **I need extra help with** _____

Go to **my science** ⑤ **coach** *online for help with this subject.*

A volcano erupts when the force of expanding gases pushes _____ from the magma chamber through the _____ until it flows or explodes out of the _____ .

LESSON 1 Volcanoes and Plate Tectonics

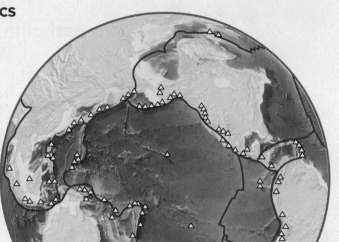

🔑 Volcanic belts form along the boundaries of Earth's plates.

🔑 A volcano forms above a hot spot when magma erupts through the crust and reaches the surface.

Vocabulary
- volcano • magma • lava
- Ring of Fire • island arc
- hot spot

LESSON 2 Volcanic Eruptions

🔑 When a volcano erupts, the force of the expanding gases pushes magma from the magma chamber through the pipe until it flows or explodes out of the vent.

🔑 Geologists classify volcanic eruptions as quiet or explosive.

🔑 Geologists often use the terms active, dormant, or extinct to describe a volcano's stage of activity.

Vocabulary
- magma chamber • pipe • vent • lava flow
- crater • silica • pyroclastic flow • dormant • extinct

LESSON 3 Volcanic Landforms

🔑 Volcanic eruptions create landforms made of lava, ash, and other materials. These landforms include shield volcanoes, cinder cone volcanoes, composite volcanoes, and lava plateaus. Other landforms include calderas, or the huge holes left by the collapse of volcanoes.

🔑 Features formed by magma include volcanic necks, dikes, and sills, as well as dome mountains and batholiths.

Vocabulary
- caldera • cinder cone • composite volcano
- shield volcano • volcanic neck • dike • sill
- batholith

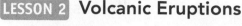
Review and Assessment

LESSON 1 Volcanoes and Plate Tectonics

1. At what point does magma become lava?

  a. below a vent   **b.** inside a pipe

  c. at Earth's surface   **d.** in Earth's mantle

2. Magma reaches the surface by erupting through a volcano, which is a _____

_____

3. Explain Does magma consist only of rock-forming materials? Explain.

_____

_____

_____

4. Relate Cause and Effect What causes volcanoes to form along a mid-ocean ridge?

_____

_____

_____

_____

5. Interpret Diagrams Look at the diagram below. Draw an arrow to indicate the direction of plate movement.

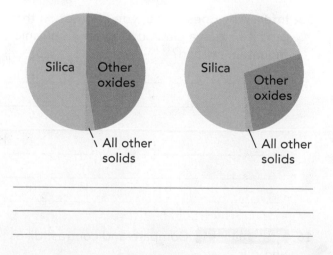

Oceanic plate

Hot spot

6. **Write About It** What role do converging plates play in the formation of volcanoes?

LESSON 2 Volcanic Eruptions

7. What type of rock forms from thin and runny, fast-moving lava?

  a. pyroclastic   **b.** silica

  c. aa   **d.** pahoehoe

8. As magma rises to the surface during an eruption, pressure on the magma decreases, allowing gas bubbles to _____

9. Define What is an extinct volcano?

_____

_____

10. Predict How might a volcano be hazardous for plants and animals that live nearby?

_____

_____

_____

_____

11. A certain volcano has erupted only explosively in the past. Another volcano has erupted only quietly. The magma composition for both volcanoes is shown below. Circle the chart showing the magma composition for the volcano that erupted quietly. Explain.

Silica — Other oxides — All other solids

Silica — Other oxides — All other solids

_____

_____

_____

_____

12. What type of volcanic mountain is composed of layers of lava that alternate with layers of ash?

   a. cinder cone   **b.** composite volcano

   c. shield volcano   **d.** caldera

13. Sometimes magma creates batholiths, which

are _____

_____

_____

14. Name What type of volcano forms when thin layers of lava pour out of a vent and harden on top of previous layers?

_____

Use the illustration to answer the question below.

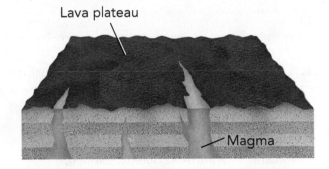

Lava plateau

Magma

15. Infer Why doesn't the type of eruption that produces a lava plateau produce a volcanic mountain instead?

_____

_____

_____

_____

_____

16. **Write About It** Compare and contrast dikes and sills.

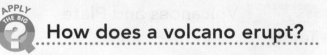

How does a volcano erupt?

17. You are a blogger who interviews geologists. A certain geologist has just returned from studying a nearby volcano. The geologist tells you that the volcano may soon erupt. Write three questions you would ask the geologist about her evidence, her prediction about the type of eruption that will occur, and about the role of plate tectonics in the eruption. Write an answer for each of your questions.

_____

_____

_____

_____

_____

_____

_____

_____

_____

_____

_____

_____

_____

_____

_____

Ohio Benchmark Practice

Multiple Choice

Circle the letter of the best answer.

1. What volcanic feature is forming in the diagram below?

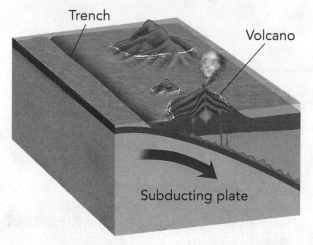

Trench

Volcano

Subducting plate

A island arc B mid-ocean ridge
C caldera D diverging boundary

2. Which of the following landforms is formed by magma?

A caldera

B dome mountain

C cinder cone volcano

D composite volcano

3. What type of feature can form when magma hardens between horizontal layers of rock?

A volcanic neck B dike
C cinder cone D sill

4. Which is the first step in the formation of a hot-spot volcano?

A Material in the mantle rises and melts.
B Lava erupts and forms an island.
C Two plates move apart.
D Magma flows through a pipe.

5. What do we call a volcano that has not erupted in a long time but that scientists believe may erupt sometime in the future?

A dormant B active
C extinct D island arc

Extended Response

Use the diagram below and your knowledge of science to help you answer Question 6. Write your answer on a separate piece of paper.

6. A geologist observes the area around a large volcano. She decides that this volcano must once have had an explosive eruption. What evidence might have led her to this conclusion? Discuss the type of magma that produces an explosive eruption and the rocks that would result from an explosive eruption.

197

Congratulations, It's an Island!

On November 15, 1963, a fiery eruption shot out from the icy sea, off the south coast of Iceland, spewing gigantic clouds of ash.

A new island, Surtsey, formed. A volcanic eruption began 130 meters under the sea and forced volcanic ash to the surface. Eventually, the layers of lava and ash formed a volcanic cone that rose above sea level—the birth of Surtsey.

Eruptions continued for nearly four years as steady flows of lava moved outward and cooled in the sea. By the end, Surtsey had an area of 2.7 square kilometers.

It takes a long time for a new island to cool down! At the very base of the island, water flows through layers of loose rocks. When it makes contact with the extremely hot magma chamber deep under the sea, the water evaporates. Steam travels through the layers of porous rock at the base of the island, heating the island up.

To protect Surtsey's environment, the government of Iceland allows only a handful of scientists to visit the delicate new environment. Surtsey is a natural laboratory that gives scientists valuable information on how plant and animal populations begin on a volcanic island.

Research It The arrival of living things on Surtsey is an example of primary succession. Research the organisms that live on Surtsey, or in another area of newly formed lava rock. Make a storyboard showing primary succession on Surtsey or on the area you have researched.

▲ Island of Surtsey today. People are not allowed to live on the island, but scientists who have permission to research there have built a research station.

Volcanologists have a seriously hot job. They investigate how, where, and when volcanoes all over the world erupt. You might find a volcanologist studying on the slopes of Mount St. Helens in Washington State, or investigating the crater of Krakatoa in Indonesia. They also try to predict eruptions.

Volcanologists have to take safety very seriously—after all, they work around actively erupting volcanoes! They have to watch out for volcanic gases and landslides. Volcanology is not all about adventures in the field, though. Volcanologists study Earth sciences, math, and physics in order to understand what they observe in the field. They also spend time writing about what they learn, so that other people can learn from their research.

Research It Research the history of a volcano that has been studied by volcanologists. Based on your research, describe how the volcano has erupted and try to predict if and when it might erupt again.

A Dangerous Job

AN EXPLOSIVE SECRET

Scientists once believed that explosive volcanic eruptions could not happen deep under water. Instead, they thought, lava seeped slowly from undersea volcanoes.

But in 2008, scientists found jagged pieces of glassy volcanic rock around undersea volcanoes in the Arctic Ocean. Seeping lava does not cause jagged glassy rocks. Explosive eruptions do.

The Gakkel Ridge is a long crack in the floor of the Arctic Ocean. The two sides of the crack are spreading apart slowly. As a result, gas builds up in pockets of magma beneath the ridge. Eventually the pressure of this gas causes explosive volcanic eruptions. The eruptions release lava, heat, gases, and trace metals into the ocean water. The jagged rocks that scientists found came from these explosions.

Ice cap covering North Pole

▲ The Gakkel Ridge (in red) is located under the Arctic Ocean.

Research It Research volcanic activity along another mid-ocean ridge, such as the Juan de Fuca Ridge. Prepare a graphic organizer comparing the timing, intensity, and volcanic activities along the two mid-ocean ridges.

WHAT CAN YOU LEARN FROM A BUG?

How do scientists study Earth's past?

Long ago, a fly got stuck in resin from a tree. Today, that fly is a fossil that scientists can study. It's a clue to what Earth was like on the day the fly got stuck. **Develop Hypotheses** What do you think scientists can learn from fossils like this?

_____

_____

_____

_____

_____

_____

_____

> **UNTAMED SCIENCE** Watch the **Untamed Science** video to learn more about fossils.

A Trip Through Geologic Time

Check Your Understanding

1. Background Read the paragraph below and then answer the question.

Forces inside Earth move large pieces, or plates, of Earth's crust very slowly over long periods of time. These forces are explained by plate tectonics. Where these plates meet, volcanic eruptions can produce igneous rocks. Over time, rivers, wind, and ice can break down the rocks and carry sediment to new places.

> The theory of **plate tectonics** states that pieces of Earth's upper layers move slowly, carried by convection currents inside Earth.
>
> An **igneous rock** forms when melted material hardens inside Earth or on the surface.
>
> **Sediment** is made up of small pieces of rock and other material.

• How do volcanic eruptions produce rocks?

_____

_____

> **MY READING WEB** If you had trouble answering the question above, visit **My Reading Web** and type in *A Trip Through Geologic Time.*

Vocabulary Skill

Prefixes The root of a word is the part of the word that carries the basic meaning. A prefix is a word part placed in front of the root to change the meaning of the root or to form a new word. Look at the examples in the table below.

Prefix	Meaning	Example
in-	inside, inward	intrusion, *n.*
ex-	outside, outward	extrusion, *n.*
super-	over, above	superposition, *n.*

2. Quick Check The root *–trusion* means "pushing." What might *extrusion* mean?_____

fossil

intrusion

law of superposition

vertebrate

Chapter Preview

LESSON 1
- fossil • mold • cast
- petrified fossil • carbon film
- trace fossil • paleontologist
- evolution • extinct

↻ **Compare and Contrast**
△ **Pose Questions**

LESSON 2
- relative age • absolute age
- law of superposition • extrusion
- intrusion • fault • index fossil
- unconformity

↻ **Relate Text and Visuals**
△ **Infer**

LESSON 3
- radioactive decay • half-life

↻ **Identify the Main Idea**
△ **Calculate**

LESSON 4
- geologic time scale • era
- period

↻ **Summarize**
△ **Make Models**

LESSON 5
- comet

↻ **Sequence**
△ **Communicate**

LESSON 6
- invertebrate • vertebrate
- amphibian • reptile
- mass extinction • mammal

↻ **Identify Supporting Evidence**
△ **Classify**

▸ **VOCAB FLASH CARDS** For extra help with vocabulary, visit **Vocab Flash Cards** and type in *A Trip Through Geologic Time.*

Fossils

UNLOCK THE BIG ?

🔑 **What Are Fossils?**

🔑 **What Are the Kinds of Fossils?**

🔑 **What Do Fossils Show?**

MY PLANET DIARY

DISCOVERY

A Dinosaur Named Sue

On a hot day in August 1990, Sue Hendrickson was hunting for fossils near the town of Faith, South Dakota. She found some little pieces of bone below a cliff. When she looked up at the cliff, she saw more bones. These bones weren't little. They were enormous! She and other scientists determined that they were the bones of a *Tyrannosaurus rex.* In fact, she'd found the largest and most complete skeleton of a *Tyrannosaurus* ever discovered. Today, the skeleton, nicknamed "Sue," is on display at the Field Museum in Chicago.

✎ **Communicate** Write your answer to each question below. Then discuss your answers with a partner.

1. What science skills did Sue Hendrickson use when she discovered Sue?

_____

_____

2. What do you think scientists can learn by studying dinosaur skeletons?

_____

_____

▶ **PLANET DIARY** Go to **Planet Diary** to learn more about fossils.

Lab zone® Do the Inquiry Warm-Up *What's in a Rock?*

Vocabulary
- fossil • mold • cast • petrified fossil • carbon film
- trace fossil • paleontologist • evolution • extinct

Skills
↻ Reading: Compare and Contrast
△ Inquiry: Pose Questions

What Are Fossils?

Sue is one of the most nearly complete dinosaur fossils ever found. **Fossils** are the preserved remains or traces of living things. ⊶ **Most fossils form when living things die and are buried by sediment. The sediment slowly hardens into rock and preserves the shapes of the organisms.** Sediment is made up of rock particles or the remains of living things. Most fossils form from animals or plants that once lived in or near quiet water such as swamps, lakes, or shallow seas where sediment builds up. In **Figure 1,** you can see how a fossil might form.

When an organism dies, its soft parts often decay quickly or are eaten by animals. That is why only hard parts of an organism generally leave fossils. These hard parts include bones, shells, teeth, seeds, and woody stems. It is rare for the soft parts of an organism to become a fossil.

FIGURE 1 ·······························
> **INTERACTIVE ART** **How a Fossil Forms**
A fossil may form when sediment quickly covers an organism's body.

An organism dies and sinks to the bottom of a lake.

The organism is covered by sediment.

✎ **Sequence** What happens next?

_____

_____

Do the Quick Lab
Sweet Fossils.

⊶ **Assess Your Understanding**

got it? ··

○ I get it! Now I know that fossils are_____

_____

○ I need extra help with _____

Go to **my science** ⬤ **COACH** *online for help with this subject.*

What Are the Kinds of Fossils?

🔑 **Fossils found in rock include molds and casts, petrified fossils, carbon films, and trace fossils. Other fossils form when the remains of organisms are preserved in substances such as tar, amber, or ice.** Look at examples of the kinds of fossils in **Figure 2**.

Molds and Casts The most common fossils are molds and casts. A **mold** is a hollow area in sediment in the shape of an organism or part of an organism. A mold forms when the organism is buried in sediment. Later, water may deposit minerals and sediment into a mold, forming a cast. A **cast** is a solid copy of the shape of an organism. Molds and casts can preserve fine details.

Petrified Fossils A fossil may form when the remains of an organism become petrified. The term *petrified* means "turned into stone." **Petrified fossils** are fossils in which minerals replace all of an organism, or a part, such as a dinosaur bone. This can also happen to wood, such as tree trunks. Water carrying minerals seeps into spaces in the plant's cells. Over time, the water evaporates, leaving the minerals behind.

Carbon Films Another type of fossil is a **carbon film,** an extremely thin coating of carbon on rock. When sediment buries an organism, some gases escape from the sediment, leaving carbon behind. Eventually, only a thin film of carbon remains. This process can preserve the delicate parts of plant leaves and insects.

🌀 **Compare and Contrast** How are carbon films and preserved remains different?

_____

_____

_____

_____

_____

_____

FIGURE 2 ⋯⋯⋯⋯⋯⋯⋯⋯⋯⋯⋯⋯
Types of Fossils
In addition to petrified fossils, fossils may be molds and casts, carbon films, trace fossils, or preserved remains.

✏️ **Classify Identify each fossil shown here by its type.**

Raised Fern
This fossil shows the texture of a leaf. Fossil type:

_____

Hollow Fern
Can you see the veins in this plant leaf? Fossil type:

_____

Where They Walked
This footprint shows how a dinosaur walked. Fossil type:

_____

Fine Details
This fossil preserves a thin layer that shows the details of an ancient insect. Fossil type:

_____

apply it!

This fossil is of an ancient organism called *Archaeopteryx*. Study the photograph and then answer the questions.

1 What type of fossil is this?

_____

2 **Pose Questions** List two questions about the organism that studying this fossil could help you answer.

_____

_____

Trace Fossils

Trace fossils provide evidence of the activities of ancient organisms. A fossilized footprint is one example. In such a fossil, a print is buried by sediment, which slowly becomes solid rock. Trails and burrows can also become trace fossils.

Preserved Remains

Some processes can preserve entire organisms. For example, some organisms become trapped in sticky tar or tree resin. When the resin hardens, it becomes a substance called amber. Freezing can also preserve remains.

Frozen in Time

Ice preserved even the fur and skin of this woolly mammoth for thousands of years. Fossil type:

_____

From Wood to Stone

Minerals replaced other materials inside this tree, producing the colors shown here. Fossil type:

_____

Lab zone | Do the Quick Lab *Modeling Trace Fossils.*

🔑 Assess Your Understanding

1a. Identify A (mold/trace fossil) can form when sediment buries the hard part of an organism.

b. Explain A petrified fossil forms when

_____ replace parts of

a(n) _____ .

c. Make Generalizations What might you learn from a carbon film that you could not learn from a cast?

_____

_____

got it? ....

○ **I get it!** Now I know that the kinds of fossils are _____

_____

_____

○ **I need extra help with** _____

Go to **my science** **COACH** *online for help with this subject.*

What Do Fossils Show?

Would you like to hunt for fossils all over the world? And what could you learn from them? Scientists who study fossils are called **paleontologists** (pay lee un TAHL uh jists). Together, all the information that paleontologists have gathered about past life is called the fossil record. ⬚ **The fossil record provides evidence about the history of life and past environments on Earth. The fossil record also shows how different groups of organisms have changed over time.**

Fossils and Past Environments Paleontologists use fossils to build up a picture of Earth's past environments. The fossils found in an area tell whether the area was a shallow bay, an ocean bottom, or a freshwater swamp.

Fossils also provide evidence about the past climate of a region. For example, coal has been found in Antarctica. But coal forms only from the remains of plants that grow in warm, swampy regions. The presence of coal shows that the climate of Antarctica was once much warmer than it is today. **Figure 3** shows another example of how fossils show change in an environment.

FIGURE 3 ··············
> INTERACTIVE ART **Wyoming, 50 Million Years Ago**
Today, as you can see in the postcard, Wyoming has areas of dry plateaus. But 50 million years ago, the area was very different. ✏ **Infer Identify the organism or kind of organism shown by fossils a, b, and c.**

Palms

a

b

c

Crocodilian

Bat

CHALLENGE What features of *Hyracotherium* show that it is related to horses?

_____

_____

_____

_____

Gar

Change and the Fossil Record

The fossil record also reveals changes in organisms. Older rocks contain fossils of simpler organisms. Younger rocks contain fossils of both simple and more complex organisms. In other words, the fossil record shows that life on Earth has evolved, or changed over time. **Evolution** is the change in living things over time.

The fossil record shows that millions of types of organisms have evolved. But many others, including the dinosaurs, have become extinct. A type of organism is **extinct** if it no longer exists and will never again live on Earth.

Scientists use fossils to reconstruct extinct organisms and determine how they may be related to living organisms. For example, the animals called *Hyracotherium* in **Figure 3** are related to modern horses.

Sequoia

Uintatherium

Hyracotherium

Coryphodon

Greetings FROM WYOMING

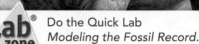

Lab zone ® | Do the Quick Lab
Modeling the Fossil Record.

🔑 Assess Your Understanding

2a. Explain What does the fossil record show about how life has changed over time?

_____

_____

_____

b. Apply Concepts Give an example of a question you could ask about a fossil of an extinct organism.

_____

_____

_____

got it? ....

○ **I get it!** Now I know that the fossil record shows _____

_____

○ **I need extra help with** _____

Go to **MY SCIENCE** ⓢ **COACH** online for help with this subject.

The Relative Age of Rocks

🔑 How Old Are Rock Layers?

🔑 How Can Rock Layers Change?

MY PLANET DIARY

Posted by Owen

Location Tacoma, WA

A couple of summers ago, my dad took me rock climbing for the first time. I went to a place called Frenchman Coulee in central Washington. It was really cool because the rock was basalt, which forms in giant pillars. It starts as lava, and then cools and you can see the different lava flows in the rock. Another cool thing is that Frenchman Coulee, which is a canyon, was gouged out by huge Ice Age floods.

✏️ **Communicate** Discuss the question below with a partner. Then answer it on your own.

How do you think scientists figure out the age of the basalt layers at Frenchman Coulee?

_____

_____

_____

_____

▶ PLANET DIARY Go to **Planet Diary** to learn more about the age of rock layers.

Lab zone Do the Inquiry Warm-Up *Which Layer Is the Oldest?*

How Old Are Rock Layers?

If you found a fossil in a rock, you might start by asking, "What is it?" Your next question would probably be, "How old is it?" The first step is to find the age of the rock.

Relative and Absolute Age Geologists have two ways to express the age of a rock. The **relative age** of a rock is its age compared to the ages of other rocks. You have probably used the idea of relative age when comparing your age with someone else's. For example, if you say that you are older than your brother but younger than your sister, you are describing your relative age.

Vocabulary

- relative age • absolute age • law of superposition
- extrusion • intrusion • fault • index fossil
- unconformity

Skills

- Reading: Relate Text and Visuals
- Inquiry: Infer

The relative age of a rock does not provide its absolute age. The **absolute age** of a rock is the number of years that have passed since the rock formed. It may be impossible to know a rock's absolute age exactly, so geologists often use both absolute and relative ages.

Rock Layers Fossils are most often found in layers of sedimentary rock. Geologists use the **law of superposition** to determine the relative ages of sedimentary rock layers. **According to the law of superposition, in undisturbed horizontal sedimentary rock layers the oldest layer is at the bottom. Each higher layer is younger than the layers below it.** The deeper you go, the older the rocks are.

Figure 1 shows rock layers in the Grand Canyon. Rock layers like these form a record of Earth's history. Scientists can study this record to understand how Earth and life on Earth have changed.

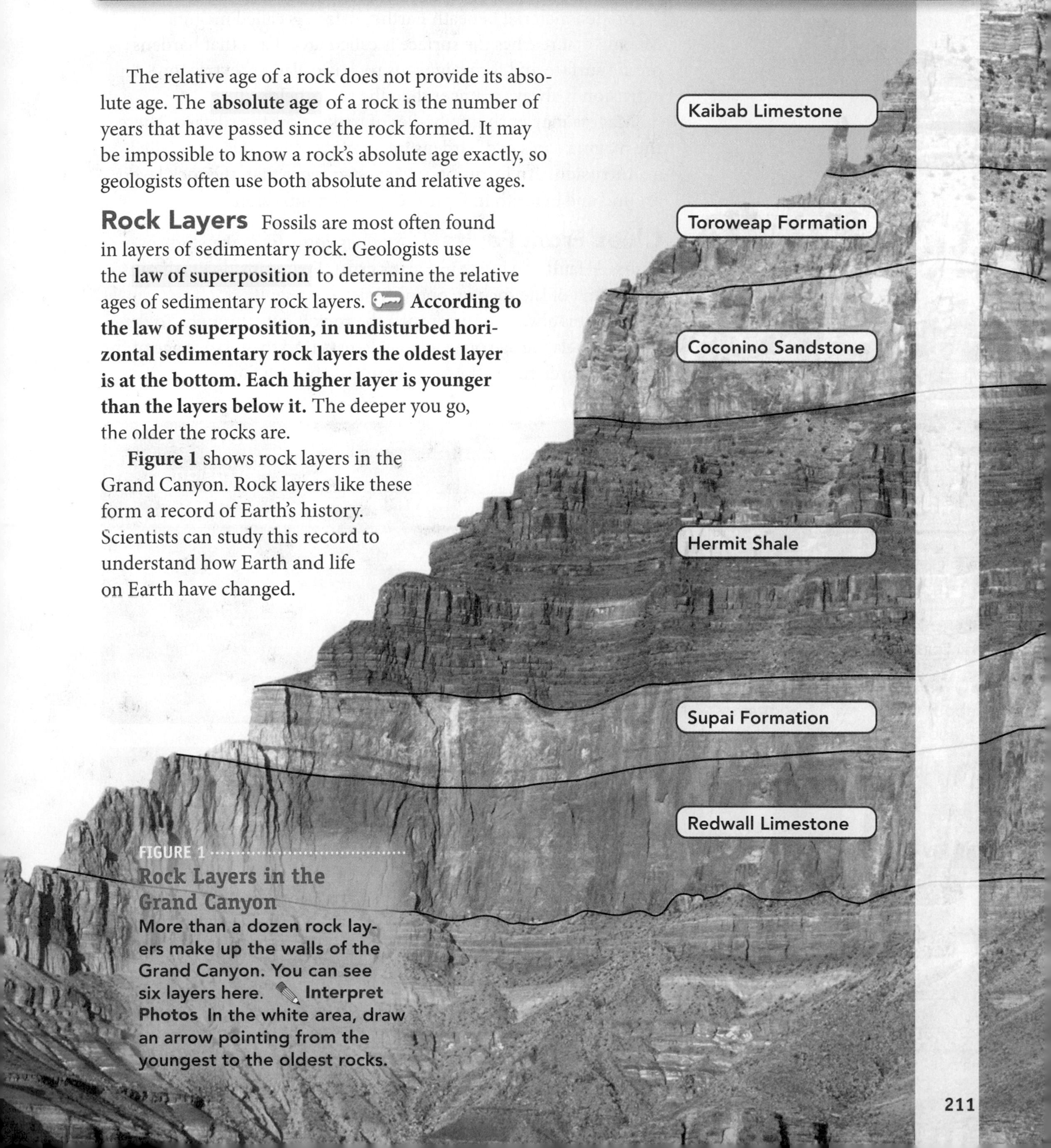

Kaibab Limestone

Toroweap Formation

Coconino Sandstone

Hermit Shale

Supai Formation

Redwall Limestone

FIGURE 1 ·······························

Rock Layers in the Grand Canyon
More than a dozen rock layers make up the walls of the Grand Canyon. You can see six layers here. ✎ **Interpret Photos** In the white area, draw an arrow pointing from the youngest to the oldest rocks.

211

_____

_____

_____

_____

_____

_____

apply it!

The diagram below shows rock layers found at a site.

❶ Circle the area on the diagram that shows an intrusion.

❷ Shade the oldest layer on the diagram.

❸ **Infer** What can you infer about the relative ages of areas B and E?

_____

_____

_____

_____

_____

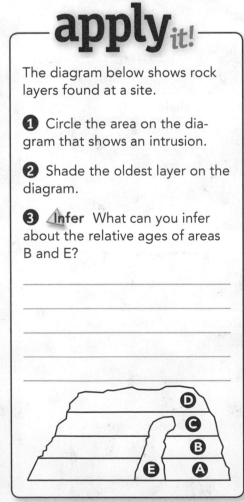

Clues From Igneous Rock

There are other clues to the relative ages of rocks besides the position of rock layers. To determine relative age, geologists also study extrusions and intrusions of igneous rock, faults, and index fossils.

Molten material beneath Earth's surface is called magma. Magma that reaches the surface is called lava. Lava that hardens on the surface and forms igneous rock is called an **extrusion.** An extrusion is always younger than the rocks below it.

Magma may push into bodies of rock below the surface. There, the magma cools and hardens into a mass of igneous rock called an **intrusion.** An intrusion is always younger than the rock layers around and beneath it. **Figure 2** shows an intrusion.

Clues From Faults

More clues come from the study of faults. A **fault** is a break in Earth's crust. Forces inside Earth cause movement of the rock on opposite sides of a fault.

A fault is always younger than the rock it cuts through. To determine the relative age of a fault, geologists find the relative age of the youngest layer cut by the fault. **Figure 3** shows a fault.

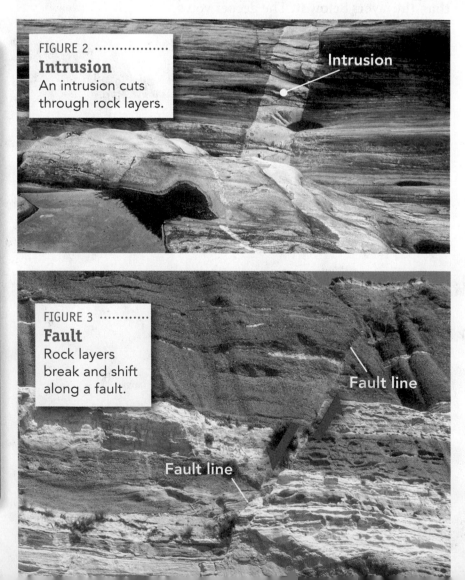

FIGURE 2 ·················
Intrusion
An intrusion cuts through rock layers.

Intrusion

FIGURE 3 ···········
Fault
Rock layers break and shift along a fault.

Fault line

Fault line

How Do Fossils Show Age? To date rock layers, geologists first find the relative age of a layer of rock at one location. Then they can match layers in other locations to that layer.

Certain fossils, called index fossils, help geologists match rock layers. To be useful as an **index fossil**, a fossil must be widely distributed and represent an organism that existed for a geologically short period of time. 🔑 **Index fossils are useful because they tell the relative ages of the rock layers in which they occur.** Scientists infer that layers with matching index fossils are the same age.

You can use index fossils to match rock layers. Look at **Figure 4,** which shows rock layers from four different locations. Notice that two of the fossils are found in only one of these rock layers. These are the index fossils.

FIGURE 4 ·································
> INTERACTIVE ART Index Fossils
Scientists use index fossils to match rock layers.

✏ **Interpret Diagrams** Label the layers to match the first area shown. Circle the fossil or fossils that you can use as index fossils. What can you infer about the history of Location 4?

_____

_____

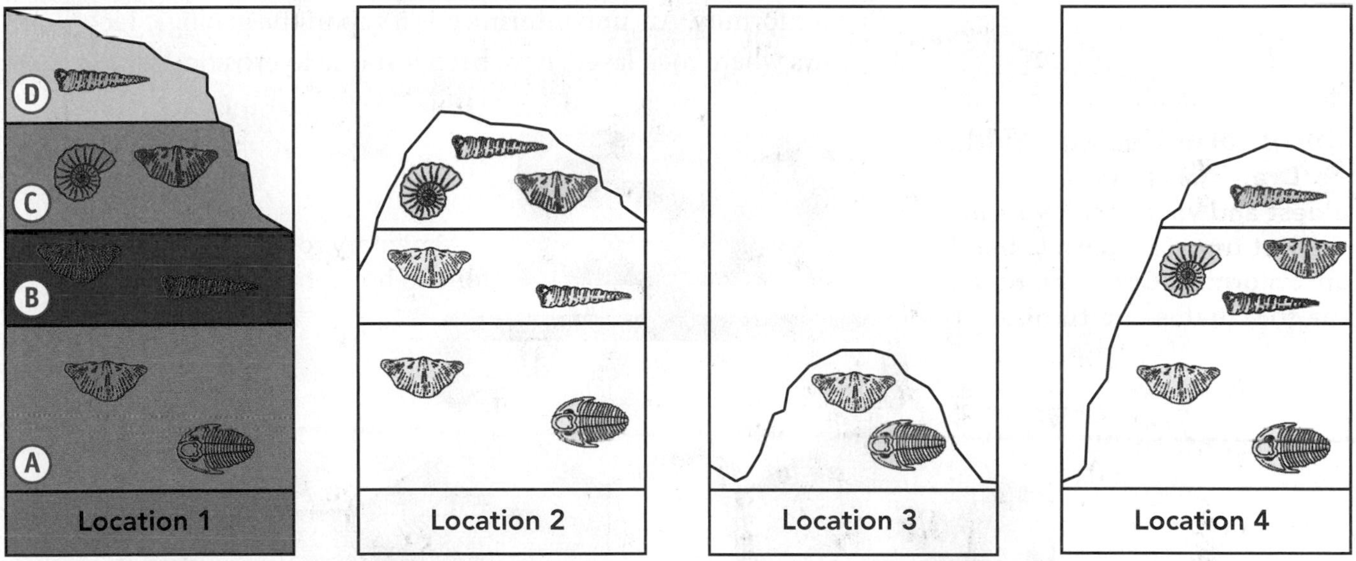

Location 1   Location 2   Location 3   Location 4

Do the Lab Investigation
Exploring Geologic Time Through Core Samples.

🔑 **Assess Your Understanding**

1a. Explain In an area with several different rock layers, which is oldest? Explain.

_____

_____

b. Infer How could a geologist match the rock layers in one area to rock layers found in another area?

_____

_____

_____

_____

got it? ···

○ **I get it!** Now I know that you can find the relative age of rocks by_____

○ **I need extra help with**_____

Go to MY SCIENCE 🔵 COACH online for help with this subject.

How Can Rock Layers Change?

The geologic record of sedimentary rock layers is not complete. In fact, most of Earth's geologic record has been lost to erosion. 🔑 **Gaps in the geologic record and folding can change the position in which rock layers appear.** Motion along faults can also change how rock layers line up. These changes make it harder for scientists to reconstruct Earth's history. **Figure 5** shows how the order of rock layers may change.

Gaps in the Geologic Record When rock layers erode away, an older rock surface may be exposed. Then deposition begins again, building new rock layers. The surface where new rock layers meet a much older rock surface beneath them is called an unconformity. An **unconformity** is a gap in the geologic record. It shows where rock layers have been lost due to erosion.

·············· ✏ ··············

🔁 **Relate Text and Visuals**
Underline the sentences that explain how the rock layers in **Figure 5** changed.

FIGURE 5 ··························

Unconformities and Folding
✏ **Draw Conclusions** Shade the oldest and youngest layers in the last two diagrams. Label the unconformity. Circle the part of the fold that is overturned.

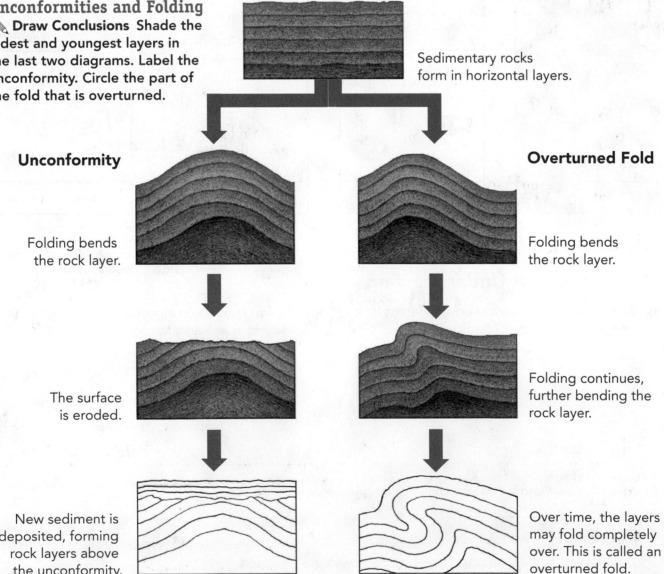

Sedimentary rocks form in horizontal layers.

Unconformity

Folding bends the rock layer.

The surface is eroded.

New sediment is deposited, forming rock layers above the unconformity.

Overturned Fold

Folding bends the rock layer.

Folding continues, further bending the rock layer.

Over time, the layers may fold completely over. This is called an overturned fold.

Folding Sometimes, forces inside Earth fold rock layers so much that the layers are turned over completely. In this case, the youngest rock layers may be on the bottom!

No one place holds a complete geologic record. Geologists compare rock layers in many places to piece together as complete a sequence as possible.

Study the photo. Then answer the questions.

❶ What does the photo show? (an unconformity/folding)

❷ What evidence do you see for your answer to Question 1?

_____

❸ **CHALLENGE** What can you infer about the history of this area?

_____

_____

_____

Lab zone® Do the Quick Lab *How Did It Form?*

🔑 Assess Your Understanding

2a. List Name two ways rock layers can change.

_____

b. Explain How does folding change rock layers?

_____

_____

_____

c. Draw Conclusions Two locations include a layer of rock with a particular index fossil. In one location, the layer occurs in a higher position than in the other. What can you conclude about the history of the two areas?

_____

_____

_____

got**it?**..

○ I get it! Now I know that rock layers can change due to _____

_____

○ I need extra help with_____

    Go to **MY SCIENCE** ⓢ **COACH** online for help with this subject.

215

Radioactive Dating

UNLOCK THE BIG Q?

🔑 What Is Radioactive Decay?

🔑 What Is Radioactive Dating?

MY PLANET DiARY

VOICES FROM HISTORY

Marie Curie

In 1896, French scientists named Marie and Pierre Curie heard about experiments that had been done by another scientist, Henri Becquerel (bek uh REL). Marie Curie later described what happened:

> Becquerel had shown that by placing some uranium salt on a photographic plate, covered with black paper, the plate would be affected as if light had fallen on it. The effect is produced by special rays which are emitted by the uranium salt…. My determinations showed that the emission of the rays is an atomic property of the uranium.

The property that Becquerel and the Curies discovered was called radioactivity. Today, radioactivity is used for many purposes—including finding the age of rocks!

After you read Marie Curie's description, answer the following questions.

1. What did Marie and Pierre Curie discover about radioactivity?

_____

_____

_____

2. What does the discovery of radioactivity tell you about how scientists work together?

_____

_____

_____

> PLANET DIARY Go to **Planet Diary** to learn more about the uses of radioactivity.

 Lab zone Do the Inquiry Warm-Up *How Long Till It's Gone?*

Vocabulary
- radioactive decay
- half-life

Skills
- ↻ Reading: Identify the Main Idea
- △ Inquiry: Calculate

What Is Radioactive Decay?

Most elements usually do not change. But some elements can break down, or decay, over time. These elements release particles and energy in a process called **radioactive decay.** These elements are said to be radioactive. ⌐ **During radioactive decay, the atoms of one element break down to form atoms of another element.**

Half-Life   The rate of decay of each radioactive element never changes. The **half-life** of a radioactive element is the time it takes for half of the radioactive atoms to decay. You can see in **Figure 1** how a radioactive element decays over time.

FIGURE 1 ·······························

Half-Life
The half-life of a radioactive element is the amount of time it takes for half of the radioactive atoms to decay.

✎ **Graph** What pattern do you see in the graph? Use the pattern to complete the last bar.

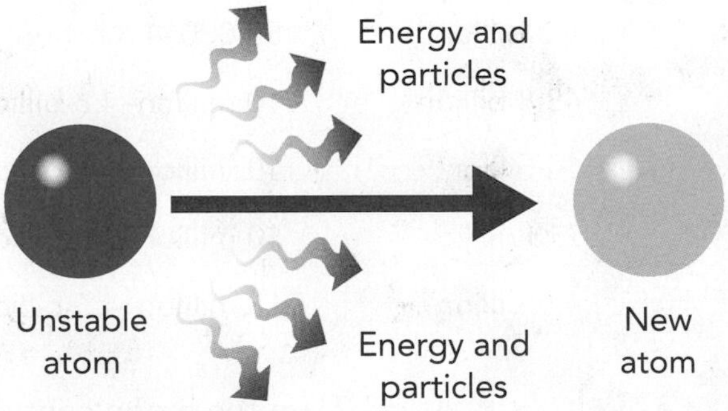

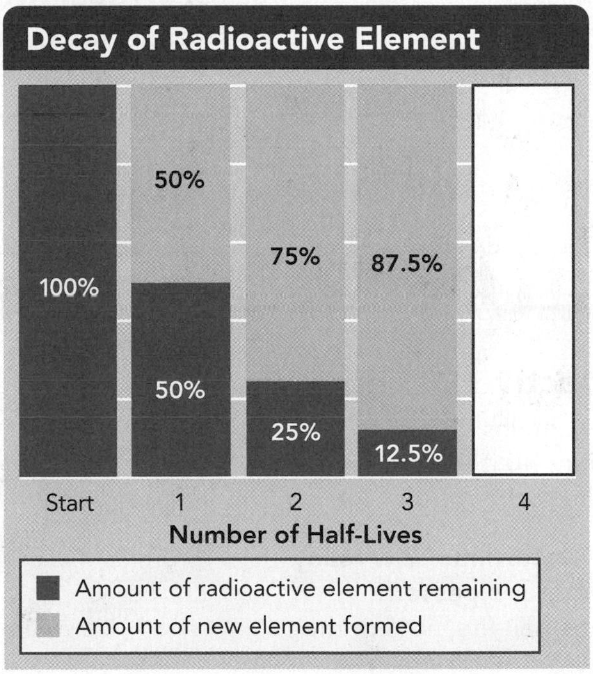

Energy and particles

Unstable atom → New atom

Energy and particles

Decay of Radioactive Element

100%   50%   75%   87.5%
       50%   25%   12.5%

Start   1   2   3   4
Number of Half-Lives

■ Amount of radioactive element remaining
■ Amount of new element formed

Lab zone®   Do the Quick Lab
The Dating Game.

⌐ Assess Your Understanding

got it? ···

○ I get it! Now I know that radioactive decay occurs when _____

_____

○ I need extra help with _____

Go to MY SCIENCE ⓢ COACH online for help with this subject.

What Is Radioactive Dating?

Radioactive elements occur naturally in igneous rocks. Scientists use the rate at which these elements decay to calculate the rock's age. As a radioactive element within the igneous rock decays, it changes into another element. So the composition of the rock changes slowly over time. The amount of the radioactive element decreases. But the amount of the new element increases.

Determining Absolute Ages Geologists use radioactive dating to determine the absolute ages of rocks. ⚷ **In radioactive dating, scientists first determine the amount of a radioactive element in a rock. Then they compare that amount with the amount of the stable element into which the radioactive element decays.** They use this information and the half-life of the element to calculate the age of the rock.

Potassium-Argon Dating Scientists often date rocks using potassium-40. This form of potassium decays to stable argon-40 and has a half-life of 1.3 billion years. Potassium-40 is useful in dating the most ancient rocks because of its long half-life.

do the math!

Radioactive Dating

A rock contains 25% of the potassium-40 it started with. How old is the rock?

STEP ① Determine how many half-lives have passed.
After one half-life, 50% of the potassium would remain. After two half-lives, 25% of the potassium would remain. So two half-lives have passed.

STEP ② Find the half-life of potassium-40.
The half-life of potassium-40 is 1.3 billion years.

STEP ③ Multiply the half-life by the number of half-lives that have passed.
1.3 billion years/half-life × 2 half-lives = 2.6 billion years, so the rock is about 2.6 billion years old.

Elements Used in Radioactive Dating

Radioactive Element	Half-life (years)	Dating Range (years)
Carbon-14	5,730	500–50,000
Potassium-40	1.3 billion	50,000–4.6 billion
Rubidium-87	48.8 billion	10 million–4.6 billion
Thorium-232	14 billion	10 million–4.6 billion
Uranium-235	713 million	10 million–4.6 billion
Uranium-238	4.5 billion	10 million–4.6 billion

1 **Calculate** A rock from the moon contains 12.5% of the potassium-40 it began with. How old is the rock? (*Hint:* 12.5% = $\frac{1}{8}$)

_____

_____

2 **Calculate** A fossil contains $\frac{1}{16}$ of the carbon-14 it began with. How old is the fossil?

_____

_____

Carbon-14 Dating

Carbon-14 is a radioactive form of carbon. All plants and animals contain carbon, including some carbon-14. After an organism dies, the carbon-14 in the organism's body decays. It changes to stable nitrogen-14. To determine the age of a sample, scientists measure the amount of carbon-14 that is left in the organism's remains. Carbon-14 has been used to date fossils such as frozen mammoths and the skeletons of prehistoric humans.

Carbon-14 has a half-life of only 5,730 years. For this reason, it generally can't be used to date fossils or rocks older than about 50,000 years. The amount of carbon-14 left would be too small to measure accurately. Also, most rocks do not contain much carbon.

➔ **Identify the Main Idea**
Underline the main idea in the first paragraph to the left.

FIGURE 2 ·······························

> **REAL-WORLD INQUIRY** **Using Carbon-14 Dating**

Scientists have dated these skeletons to 5,000–6,000 years ago. But they do not use radioactive dating to find the age of stone artifacts made by people.

✎ **Make Generalizations** Why not?

_____

_____

_____

_____

Lab® **zone** Do the Quick Lab *How Old Is It?*

🔑 Assess Your Understanding

1a. Identify Scientists use the method of (radioactive dating/relative dating) to find the absolute age of a rock.

b. Apply Concepts The half-life of thorium-232 is 14 billion years. A rock with 25% of its thorium-232 remaining is _____ years old.

c. **CHALLENGE** A scientist finds stone tools in the ruins of an ancient house. The house also has ashes in a fireplace. How could the scientist estimate the age of the stone tools?

_____

_____

_____

_____

got it? ···

○ **I get it!** Now I know that radioactive dating is done by _____

_____

○ **I need extra help with** _____

Go to **my science** ⬤ⁱ **coach** online for help with this subject.

The Geologic Time Scale

UNLOCK THE BIG ?

🔑 **What Is the Geologic Time Scale?**

my planet diary

SCIENCE STATS

Earth's History in a Day

Suppose you could squeeze all of Earth's 4.6-billion-year history into one 24-hour day. The table shows the times at which some major events would take place.

	Time	First Appearance
A	Midnight	Earth
B	3:00 A.M.	Rocks
C	4:00 A.M.	Bacteria
D	2:00 P.M.	Algae
E	8:30–9:00 P.M.	Seaweeds and jellyfish
F	10:00 P.M.	Land plants
G	10:50 P.M.	Dinosaurs
H	11:39 P.M.	Mammals
I	11:58:43 P.M.	Humans

Use the data in the table to answer these questions.

1. ✏️ **Sequence** Write the letter for each event on the clock diagram.

2. Did anything surprise you about the data? If so, what?

_____

_____

▶ PLANET DIARY Go to **Planet Diary** to learn more about Earth's history.

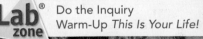
Lab zone® Do the Inquiry Warm-Up *This Is Your Life!*

Vocabulary

- geologic time scale
- era • period

Skills

↻ Reading: Summarize
△ Inquiry: Make Models

What Is the Geologic Time Scale?

When you speak of the past, what names do you use for different spans of time? You probably use names such as century, decade, year, month, week, and day. But these units aren't very helpful for thinking about much longer periods of time. Scientists needed to develop a way to talk about Earth's history.

🔑 **Because the time span of Earth's past is so great, geologists use the geologic time scale to show Earth's history.** The **geologic time scale** is a record of the geologic events and the evolution of life forms as shown in the fossil record. Scientists make inferences about Earth's history based on the principle of uniformitarianism (yoon uh fawrm uh TAYR ee un iz um). This principle states that the processes that operate today also operated in the past.

Scientists first developed the geologic time scale by studying rock layers and index fossils worldwide. With this information, scientists placed Earth's rocks in order by relative age. Later, radioactive dating helped determine the absolute age of the divisions in the geologic time scale. **Figure 1** shows some of the earliest known rocks.

↻ **Summarize** Write two or three sentences to summarize the information on this page.

_____

_____

_____

_____

_____

_____

FIGURE 1 ·····························

Ancient Rocks

The Isua rocks in Greenland are among the oldest rocks on Earth. They formed after heat and pressure changed sedimentary rocks that formed under early oceans.

FIGURE 2 ·····················

The Geologic Time Scale

The divisions of the geologic time scale are used to date events in Earth's history.

✎ **Calculate** After you read the next page, calculate and fill in the duration of each period. Then use the time scale to identify the period in which each organism below lived.

Organism: *Wiwaxia*

Age: about 500 million years

Period: _____

Organism: *Velociraptor*

Age: about 80 million years

Period: _____

Organism: *Smilodon*

Age: about 12,000 years

Period: _____

	PERIOD	MILLIONS OF YEARS AGO	DURATION (MILLIONS OF YEARS)
Cenozoic Era	QUATERNARY	1.6	
	NEOGENE	23	
	PALEOGENE	66	
Mesozoic Era	CRETACEOUS	146	
	JURASSIC	200	
	TRIASSIC	251	
Paleozoic Era	PERMIAN	299	
	CARBONIFEROUS	359	
	DEVONIAN	416	
	SILURIAN	444	
	ORDOVICIAN	488	
	CAMBRIAN	542	
Precambrian Time		4,600	

Dividing Geologic Time As geologists studied the fossil record, they found major changes in life forms at certain times. They used these changes to mark where one unit of geologic time ends and the next begins. Therefore, the divisions of the geologic time scale depend on events in the history of life on Earth. **Figure 2** shows the major divisions of the geologic time scale.

Precambrian Time Geologic time begins with a long span of time called Precambrian Time (pree KAM bree un). Precambrian Time, which covers about 88 percent of Earth's history, ended 542 million years ago. Few fossils survive from this time period.

Eras Geologists divide the time between Precambrian Time and the present into three long units of time called **eras.** They are the Paleozoic Era, the Mesozoic Era, and the Cenozoic Era.

Periods Eras are subdivided into units of geologic time called **periods.** You can see in **Figure 2** that the Mesozoic Era includes three periods: the Triassic Period, the Jurassic Period, and the Cretaceous Period.

The names of many of the geologic periods come from places around the world where geologists first described the rocks and fossils of that period. For example, the name *Cambrian* refers to Cambria, a Latin name for Wales. The rocks shown below are in Wales. The dark bottom layer dates from the Cambrian period.

Refer to the geologic time scale shown in **Figure 2** to answer the questions below.

Suppose you want to make a model of the geologic time scale. You decide to use a scale of 1 cm = 1 million years.

1 Not counting Precambrian time, which era would take up the most space? _____

2 **Make Models** How long would the Mesozoic Era be in your model? _____

3 [CHALLENGE] Suppose you used a different scale: 1 m = 1 million years. What would be one advantage and one disadvantage of this scale?

_____
_____
_____
_____
_____
_____

 Do the Quick Lab
Going Back in Time.

🔑 Assess Your Understanding

1a. Define The geologic time scale is a record of _____ and _____.

b. Sequence Number the following periods in order from earliest to latest.

Neogene _____   Jurassic _____
Quaternary _____   Triassic _____
Cretaceous _____

c. Draw Conclusions Refer to My Planet Diary and **Figure 2.** During which period did modern humans arise?

_____

got it? ....

○ **I get it!** Now I know that geologic time _____
_____

○ **I need extra help with** _____

Go to MY SCIENCE COACH online for help with this subject.

Early Earth

UNLOCK THE BIG 🔑 **How Did Earth Form?**

MY PLANET DIARY

CAREERS

Exploring Life Under Water

Dr. Anna-Louise Reysenbach always loved water sports. She was also interested in organisms that live in strange, extreme environments. Now, as a biology professor at Portland State University in Oregon, she gets to combine her two loves—and learn about early life on Earth!

Dr. Reysenbach uses submersibles, or submarines, to study bacteria that live deep under the ocean. No sunlight reaches these depths. There, hot water carrying dissolved minerals from inside Earth flows out through vents. Some kinds of bacteria use chemical energy from this material to make food, much as plants use the energy from sunlight. Scientists think that these bacteria are very similar to some of the earliest forms of life on Earth.

✏️ **Communicate** Discuss the work of Dr. Reysenbach with a partner. Then answer these questions on your own.

1. How are the bacteria near ocean vents different from many other organisms on Earth?

_____

_____

_____

2. Would you like to work under water in a submersible? Why, or why not?

_____

_____

_____

_____

> **PLANET DIARY** Go to **Planet Diary** to learn more about deep ocean vents.

Lab zone® Do the Inquiry Warm-Up *How Could Planet Earth Form in Space?*

Vocabulary
- comet

Skills
- Reading: Sequence
- Inquiry: Communicate

How Did Earth Form?

Using radioactive dating, scientists have determined that the oldest rocks ever found on Earth are about 4 billion years old. But scientists think Earth formed even earlier than that.

The Age of Earth According to these scientists' hypothesis, the moon formed from material knocked loose when a very young Earth collided with another object. This means Earth and the moon are about the same age. Scientists have used radioactive dating to find the age of moon rocks that astronauts brought back to Earth. The oldest moon rocks are about 4.6 billion years old. Scientists infer that Earth is also roughly 4.6 billion years old—only a little older than those moon rocks.

Earth Takes Shape **Scientists think that Earth began as a ball of dust, rock, and ice in space. Gravity pulled this mass together.** As Earth grew larger, its gravity increased, pulling in more dust, rock, and ice nearby.

The energy from collisions with these materials raised Earth's temperature until the planet was very hot. Scientists think that Earth may have become so hot that it melted. Denser materials sank toward the center, forming Earth's dense, iron core. Less dense, molten material hardened over time to form Earth's outer layers—the solid crust and mantle.

FIGURE 1 ·····················
Early Earth
This artist's illustration shows Earth shortly after the moon formed. Earth was hot and volcanic, and contained no liquid water. The moon was much closer to Earth than it is today. Over time, Earth's surface began to cool, forming solid land.

✎ **Make Generalizations**
Could life have existed on Earth at the time shown in the illustration? Why, or why not?

_____

_____

_____

_____

FIGURE 2 ········:···········

Development of the Atmosphere

The illustration shows the difference between Earth's first and second atmospheres.

✎ **Relate Text and Visuals**
Fill in the missing information for each atmosphere.

First atmosphere
Gases included:

_____

Blown away by:

_____

Ultraviolet light

✎ **Sequence** How did Earth's oceans develop over time?

1. _____
_____
_____

2. _____
_____
_____

3. _____
_____
_____

The Atmosphere Early Earth may have included light gases such as hydrogen and helium. Then the sun released strong bursts of particles called the solar wind. Earth's gravity could not hold the light gases, and the solar wind blew away Earth's first atmosphere.

After Earth lost its first atmosphere, a second atmosphere formed. Volcanic eruptions and collisions with comets added carbon dioxide, water vapor, nitrogen, and other gases to the atmosphere. A **comet** is a ball of dust, gas, and ice that orbits the sun. **Figure 2** shows the first and second atmospheres.

The Oceans At first, Earth's surface was too hot for water to remain a liquid. All water remained as water vapor. As Earth's surface cooled, the water vapor began to condense to form rain. The rainwater gradually accumulated and formed oceans. The oceans absorbed much of the carbon dioxide from the atmosphere.

The Continents During early Precambrian Time, much of Earth's rock cooled and hardened. Less than 500 million years after Earth formed, the rock at the surface formed continents.

Scientists have found that the continents move very slowly over Earth's surface because of forces inside Earth. Over billions of years, Earth's landmasses have repeatedly formed, broken apart, and then crashed together again.

apply it!

❶ Draw a diagram showing Earth's structure after oceans began to form.

❷ ⚠ Communicate Write a caption for your diagram explaining how Earth changed over time.

_____

_____

_____

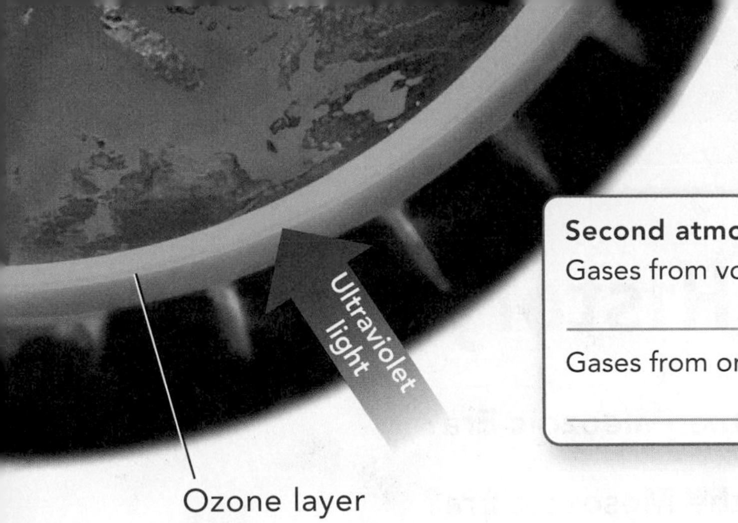

Ultraviolet light

Ozone layer

Second atmosphere
Gases from volcanoes and comets:

_____

Gases from organisms:

_____

Early Organisms Scientists cannot pinpoint when or where life began on Earth. But scientists have found fossils of single-celled organisms in rocks that formed about 3.5 billion years ago. Scientists think that all other forms of life on Earth arose from these simple organisms. **Figure 3** shows remains of organisms similar to these early life forms. The bacteria Dr. Reysenbach studies are probably similar to these early organisms.

About 2.5 billion years ago, many organisms began using energy from the sun to make food. This process is called photosynthesis. One waste product of photosynthesis is oxygen. As organisms released oxygen, the amount of oxygen in the atmosphere slowly grew. Some oxygen changed into a form called ozone. The atmosphere developed an ozone layer that blocked the ultraviolet rays of the sun. Shielded from these rays, organisms could live on land.

FIGURE 3 ···

Stromatolites
These stromatolite fossils (stroh MAT uh lyt) from Australia are the remains of reefs built by early organisms. Some similar fossils are more than three billion years old.

Do the Quick Lab
Learning From Fossils.

Assess Your Understanding

1a. **Identify** Earth formed _____ years ago.

b. **Sequence** Write the numbers 1, 2, and 3 to show the correct order of the events below.

_____ Ozone layer forms.

_____ Earth loses its first atmosphere.

_____ Volcanoes and collisions with comets add water vapor to the atmosphere.

c. CHALLENGE How would Earth's atmosphere be different if organisms capable of photosynthesis had not evolved?

_____

_____

got it? ··

O **I get it!** Now I know that key features of early Earth were _____

_____

_____

_____

_____

O I need extra help with _____

Go to **MY SCIENCE COACH** online for help with this subject.

Eras of Earth's History

🔑 **What Happened in the Paleozoic Era?**

🔑 **What Happened in the Mesozoic Era?**

🔑 **What Happened in the Cenozoic Era?**

my planet Diary

Mystery Metal

The rock layers in the photo hold evidence in one of the great mysteries of science: What killed the dinosaurs?

Find the thin, pale layer of rock marked by the ruler. This layer formed at the end of the Cretaceous period. It contains unusually high amounts of the metal iridium. At first, scientists could not explain the amount of iridium in this layer.

Iridium is more common in asteroids than on Earth. Many scientists now infer that an asteroid struck Earth. The impact threw dust into the air, blocking sunlight for years. About half the plant and animal species on Earth—including the dinosaurs—died out.

FUN FACT

Think about what you know about fossils and Earth's history as you answer these questions.

1. What have many scientists inferred from the iridium found at the Cretaceous boundary?

_____

_____

_____

2. What are some questions you have about the history of life on Earth?

_____

_____

_____

▷ **PLANET DIARY** Go to **Planet Diary** to learn more about mass extinctions.

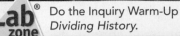

Lab zone® Do the Inquiry Warm-Up *Dividing History.*

Vocabulary
- invertebrate
- vertebrate
- amphibian
- reptile
- mass extinction
- mammal

Skills
- ⟳ Reading: Identify Supporting Evidence
- △ Inquiry: Classify

What Happened in the Paleozoic Era?

The extinction of the dinosaurs is one of the most famous events in Earth's history, but it is just one example of the changes that have taken place. Through most of Earth's history, the only living things were single-celled organisms.

Near the end of Precambrian time, more complex living things evolved. Feathery, plantlike organisms anchored themselves to the seafloor. Jellyfish-like organisms floated in the oceans. Scientists have found fossils of such organisms in Australia, Russia, China, and southern Africa. But a much greater variety of living things evolved during the next phase of geologic time—the Paleozoic Era.

The Cambrian Explosion During the Cambrian Period, life took a big leap forward. ⬤━ **At the beginning of the Paleozoic Era, a great number of different kinds of organisms evolved. For the first time, many organisms had hard parts, including shells and outer skeletons.** Paleontologists call this event the Cambrian Explosion because so many new life forms appeared within a relatively short time.

FIGURE 1 ···

Cambrian Life
The photo below shows a fossil of a Cambrian organism called *Anomalocaris*. The illustration shows one artist's idea of what *Anomalocaris* (the large organism) and other organisms looked like.

✏ **Interpret Photos** What does the fossil tell you about what *Anomalocaris* looked like?

_____

_____

229

FIGURE 2

Changing Landscapes

✎ **Summarize** Based on the text and illustrations, describe the organisms in each period and how they differed from those in the previous period.

Silurian _____

_____

_____

_____

_____

Invertebrates Develop At this time, all animals lived in the sea. Many were animals without backbones, or **invertebrates.** Invertebrates such as jellyfish, worms, and sponges made their home in the Cambrian ocean.

Brachiopods and trilobites were also common in the Cambrian seas. Brachiopods resembled modern clams, but are only distantly related to them. Trilobites were a huge and varied group of arthropods (AR thru pahds), animals with jointed legs and many body segments.

New Organisms Arise Invertebrates soon shared the seas with a new type of organism. During the Ordovician (awr duh VISH ee un) Period, the first vertebrates evolved. A **vertebrate** is an animal with a backbone. Jawless fishes with suckerlike mouths were the first vertebrates.

The First Land Plants Until the Silurian (sih LOOR ee un) Period, only one-celled organisms lived on the land. But during the Silurian Period, plants became abundant. These first, simple plants grew low to the ground in damp areas. By the Devonian Period (dih VOH nee un), plants that could grow in drier areas had evolved. Among these plants were the earliest ferns.

Early Fishes Both invertebrates and vertebrates lived in the Devonian seas. Even though the invertebrates were more numerous, the Devonian Period is often called the Age of Fishes. Every main group of fishes was present in the oceans at this time. Most fishes now had jaws, bony skeletons, and scales on their bodies. Sharks appeared in the late Devonian Period.

Silurian

Devonian

Animals Reach Land

The Devonian Period was also when animals began to spread widely on land. The first insects evolved during the Silurian Period, but vertebrates reached land during the Devonian. The first land vertebrates were lungfish with strong, muscular fins. The first amphibians evolved from these lungfish. An **amphibian** (am FIB ee un) is an animal that lives part of its life on land and part of its life in water.

The Carboniferous Period

Throughout the rest of the Paleozoic, other vertebrates evolved from amphibians. For example, small reptiles developed during the Carboniferous Period. **Reptiles** have scaly skin and lay eggs that have tough, leathery shells.

During the Carboniferous Period, winged insects evolved into many forms, including huge dragonflies and cockroaches. Giant ferns and cone-bearing plants formed vast swampy forests called coal forests. The remains of the coal-forest plants formed thick deposits of sediment that changed into coal over hundreds of millions of years.

○ **Identify Supporting Evidence** Underline the evidence that supports the statement, "The Devonian Period was also when animals began to spread widely on land."

Devonian _____

_____

_____

_____

_____

Carboniferous _____

Carboniferous

What two effects did the formation of Pangaea have?

_____

_____

_____

_____

Pangaea During the Permian Period, between 299 and 250 million years ago, Earth's continents moved together to form a great landmass, or supercontinent, called Pangaea (pan JEE uh). The formation of Pangaea caused deserts to expand in the tropics. At the same time, sheets of ice covered land closer to the South Pole.

Mass Extinction **At the end of the Permian Period, most species of life on Earth died out.** This was a **mass extinction,** in which many types of living things became extinct at the same time. Scientists estimate that about 90 percent of all ocean species died out. So did about 70 percent of species on land. Even widespread organisms like trilobites became extinct.

Scientists aren't sure what caused this extinction. Some think an asteroid struck Earth, creating huge dust clouds. Massive volcanic eruptions spewed carbon dioxide and sulfur dioxide into the atmosphere. Temperatures all over Earth rose during this time, too. The amount of carbon dioxide in the oceans increased and the amount of oxygen declined, though scientists aren't sure why. All these factors may have contributed to the mass extinction.

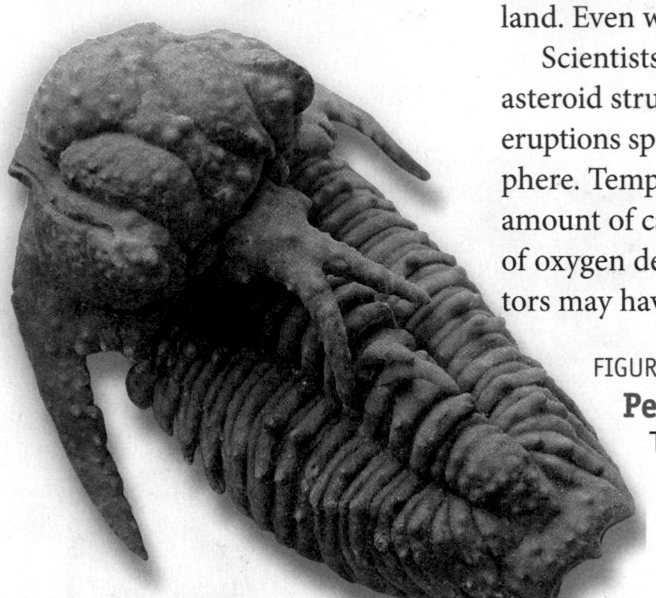

FIGURE 3 ···

Permian Trilobite

Throughout the Paleozoic, trilobites such as this Permian example were one of the most successful groups of organisms. But no species of trilobites survived the Permian mass extinction.

Lab zone® Do the Quick Lab _Graphing the Fossil Record._

Assess Your Understanding

1a. List What are the periods of the Paleozoic Era?

_____

_____

_____

b. Sequence Number the following organisms in order from earliest to latest appearance.

amphibians _____   jawless fishes _____

trilobites _____   bony fishes _____

c. Relate Cause and Effect Name two possible causes of the mass extinction at the end of the Paleozoic.

_____

_____

_____

_____

_____

_____

_____

got it? ···

○ **I get it!** Now I know that the main events in the Paleozoic Era were _____

_____

○ **I need extra help with** _____

Go to **MY SCIENCE** 🔵 **COACH** _online for help with this subject._

What Happened in the Mesozoic Era?

When you think of prehistoric life, do you think of dinosaurs? If so, you're thinking of the Mesozoic Era.

The Triassic Period Some living things managed to survive the Permian mass extinction. Plants and animals that survived included fish, insects, reptiles, and cone-bearing plants called conifers. 🔑 **Reptiles were so successful during the Mesozoic Era that this time is often called the Age of Reptiles.** The first dinosaurs appeared about 225 million years ago, during the Triassic (tri AS ik) Period.

Mammals also first appeared during the Triassic Period. A **mammal** is a vertebrate that can control its body temperature and feeds milk to its young. Mammals in the Triassic Period were very small, about the size of a mouse.

The Jurassic Period During the Jurassic Period (joo RAS ik), dinosaurs became common on land. Other kinds of reptiles evolved to live in the ocean and in the air. Scientists have identified several hundred different kinds of dinosaurs.

One of the first birds, called *Archaeopteryx,* appeared during the Jurassic Period. The name *Archaeopteryx* means "ancient winged one." Many paleontologists now think that birds evolved from dinosaurs.

apply it!

The illustrations show a flying reptile called *Dimorphodon* and one of the earliest birds, *Archaeopteryx.*

❶ Identify two features the two animals have in common.

_____

_____

❷ Identify one major difference between the two animals.

_____

_____

❸ ◢ Classify Which animal is *Archaeopteryx*? How do you know it is related to birds?

_____

_____

FIGURE 4 ·····························

The End of the Dinosaurs
Many scientists hypothesize that an asteroid hit Earth near the present-day Yucatán Peninsula, in southeastern Mexico.

✏️ CHALLENGE Write a short story summarizing the events shown in the illustration.

_____
_____
_____
_____
_____
_____
_____
_____
_____
_____

The Cretaceous Period Reptiles, including dinosaurs, were still widespread throughout the Cretaceous Period (krih TAY shus). Birds began to replace flying reptiles during this period. Their hollow bones made them better adapted to their environment than the flying reptiles, which became extinct.

Flowering plants first evolved during the Cretaceous. Unlike conifers, flowering plants produce seeds that are inside a fruit. The fruit helps the seeds spread.

Another Mass Extinction 🔑 **At the close of the Cretaceous Period, about 65 million years ago, another mass extinction occurred. Scientists hypothesize that this mass extinction occurred when an asteroid from space struck Earth.** This mass extinction wiped out more than half of all plant and animal groups, including the dinosaurs.

When the asteroid hit Earth, the impact threw huge amounts of dust and water vapor into the atmosphere. Dust and heavy clouds blocked sunlight around the world for years. Without sunlight, plants died, and plant-eating animals starved. The dust later formed the iridium-rich rock layer you read about at the beginning of the lesson. Some scientists think that climate changes caused by increased volcanic activity also helped cause the mass extinction.

THE DEATH OF THE DINOSAURS

BY TERRY DACTYL

 ® Do the Quick Lab
Modeling an Asteroid Impact.

🔑 **Assess Your Understanding**

got it? ·······························

○ **I get it!** Now I know that the main developments in the Mesozoic Era were _____

_____

○ I need extra help with _____

Go to MY SCIENCE 🔵 COACH *online for help with this subject.*

What Happened in the Cenozoic Era?

During the Mesozoic Era, mammals had to compete with dinosaurs for food and places to live. 🔑 **The extinction of dinosaurs created an opportunity for mammals. During the Cenozoic Era, mammals evolved to live in many different environments—on land, in water, and even in the air.**

The Paleogene and Neogene Periods

During the Paleogene and Neogene periods, Earth's climates were generally warm and mild, though they generally cooled over time. In the oceans, mammals such as whales and dolphins evolved. On land, flowering plants, insects, and mammals flourished. Grasses first began to spread widely. Some mammals became very large, as did some birds.

The Quaternary Period

Earth's climate cooled and warmed in cycles during the Quaternary Period, causing a series of ice ages. Thick glaciers covered parts of Europe and North America. The latest warm period began between 10,000 and 20,000 years ago. Over thousands of years, most of the glaciers melted.

In the oceans, algae, coral, mollusks, fish, and mammals thrived. Insects and birds shared the skies. Flowering plants and mammals such as bats, cats, dogs, cattle, and humans became common. The fossil record suggests that modern humans may have evolved as early as 190,000 years ago. By about 12,000 to 15,000 years ago, humans had migrated to every continent except Antarctica.

FIGURE 5 ·······························

Giant Mammals

Many giant mammals evolved in the Cenozoic Era. This *Megatherium* is related to the modern sloth shown to the right, but was up to six meters tall.

✏️ **Measure About how many times taller was *Megatherium* than a modern sloth?** _____

Geologic History

EXPLORE THE BIG ?

> ART IN MOTION How do scientists study Earth's past?

FIGURE 6 ···
This timeline shows key events in Earth's history. Use
what you have learned to fill in the missing information.

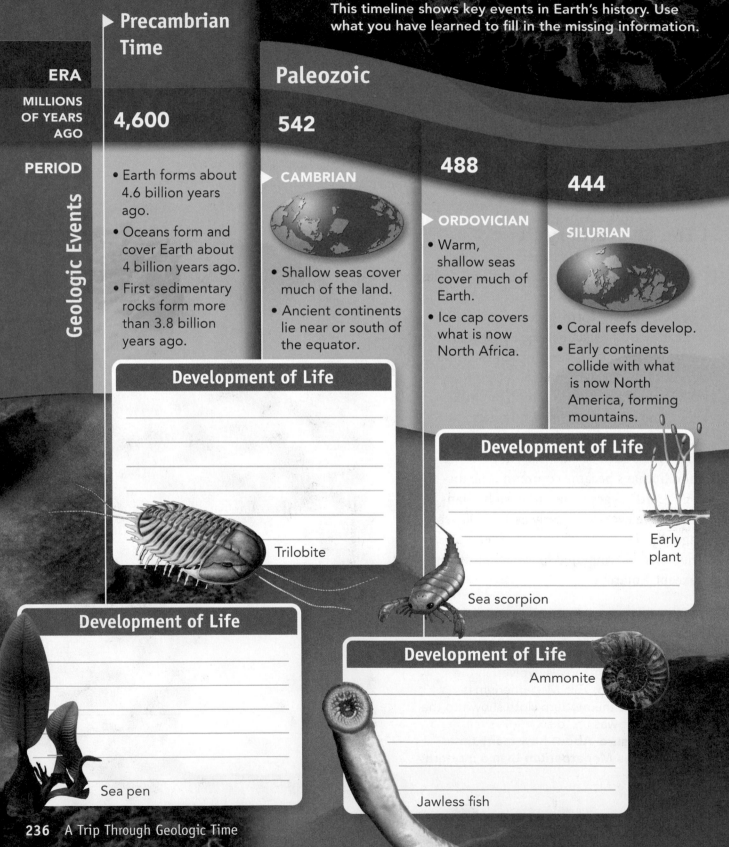

Precambrian Time

Paleozoic

ERA		
MILLIONS OF YEARS AGO	4,600	542

PERIOD

Geologic Events

- Earth forms about 4.6 billion years ago.
- Oceans form and cover Earth about 4 billion years ago.
- First sedimentary rocks form more than 3.8 billion years ago.

CAMBRIAN

- Shallow seas cover much of the land.
- Ancient continents lie near or south of the equator.

488

ORDOVICIAN

- Warm, shallow seas cover much of Earth.
- Ice cap covers what is now North Africa.

444

SILURIAN

- Coral reefs develop.
- Early continents collide with what is now North America, forming mountains.

Development of Life

Trilobite

Development of Life

Early plant

Sea scorpion

Development of Life

Sea pen

Development of Life

Ammonite

Jawless fish

236 A Trip Through Geologic Time

Note: To make the timeline easier to read, periods are shown at the about the same size, though some were longer than others. They are not drawn to scale.

Giant dragonfly (Carboniferous)

359

299

416

DEVONIAN

- Seas rise and fall over what is now North America.

CARBONIFEROUS

- Early Appalachian Mountains form.
- North America and northern Europe lie in warm, tropical region.

PERMIAN

- Deserts become larger in tropical regions.
- The supercontinent Pangaea forms as all continents join together.

Development of Life

Club moss

Development of Life

Bony fish

Early amphibian

Development of Life

Dimetrodon

Geologic History

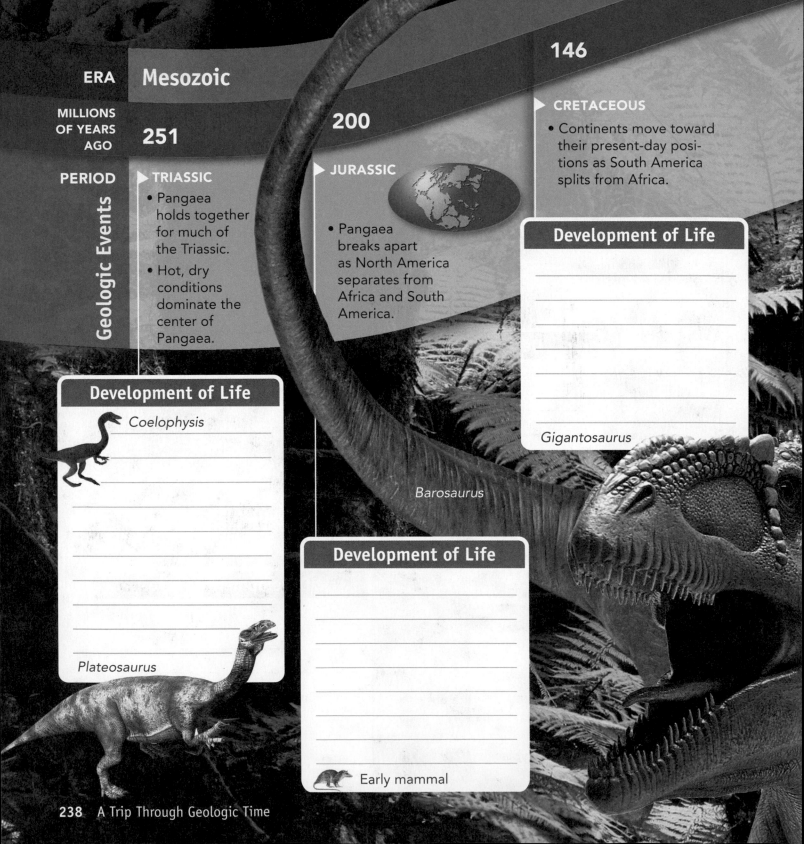

ERA Mesozoic

MILLIONS OF YEARS AGO 251

146

PERIOD

▶ TRIASSIC

Geologic Events

- Pangaea holds together for much of the Triassic.
- Hot, dry conditions dominate the center of Pangaea.

▶ JURASSIC

- Pangaea breaks apart as North America separates from Africa and South America.

▶ CRETACEOUS

- Continents move toward their present-day positions as South America splits from Africa.

Development of Life

Coelophysis

Plateosaurus

Development of Life

Early mammal

Barosaurus

Development of Life

Gigantosaurus

Cenozoic

66

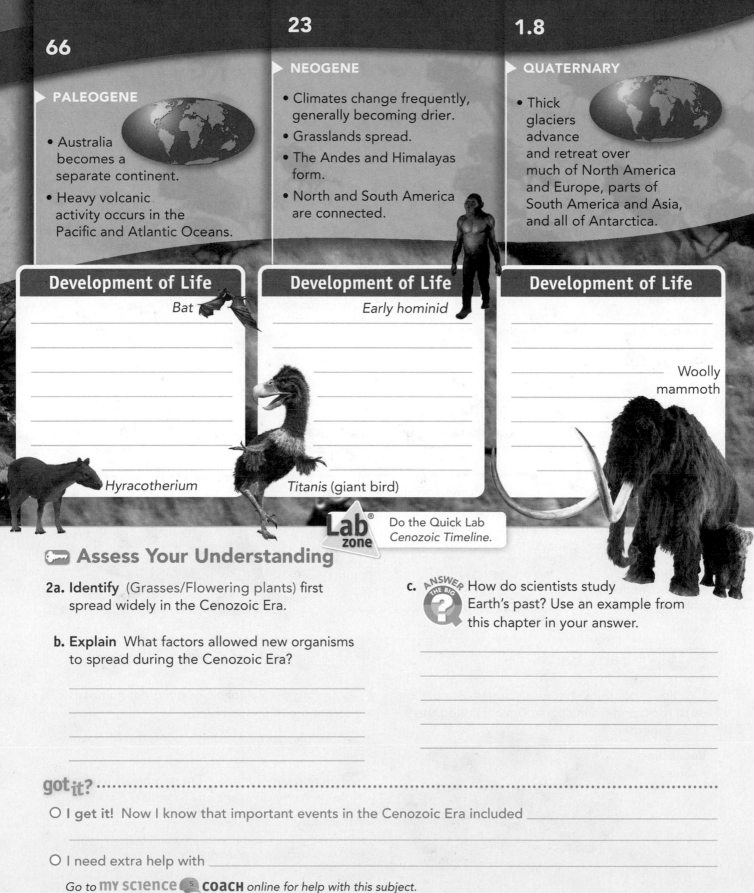

PALEOGENE

- Australia becomes a separate continent.
- Heavy volcanic activity occurs in the Pacific and Atlantic Oceans.

23

NEOGENE

- Climates change frequently, generally becoming drier.
- Grasslands spread.
- The Andes and Himalayas form.
- North and South America are connected.

1.8

QUATERNARY

- Thick glaciers advance and retreat over much of North America and Europe, parts of South America and Asia, and all of Antarctica.

Development of Life

Bat

Hyracotherium

Development of Life

Early hominid

Titanis (giant bird)

Development of Life

Woolly mammoth

Lab zone Do the Quick Lab *Cenozoic Timeline.*

🔑 Assess Your Understanding

2a. Identify (Grasses/Flowering plants) first spread widely in the Cenozoic Era.

b. Explain What factors allowed new organisms to spread during the Cenozoic Era?

_____

_____

_____

c. ANSWER THE BIG **❓** How do scientists study Earth's past? Use an example from this chapter in your answer.

_____

_____

_____

_____

got it? ....

○ **I get it!** Now I know that important events in the Cenozoic Era included _____

_____

○ **I need extra help with** _____

Go to **my science 🟢 coach** online for help with this subject.

Study Guide

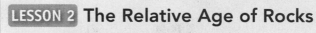

Scientists study _____ in order to draw inferences about how
_____ have changed over time.

LESSON 1 Fossils

🗝 Most fossils form when sediment hardens into rock, preserving the shapes of organisms.

🗝 Fossils include molds, casts, petrified fossils, carbon films, trace fossils, and preserved remains.

🗝 Fossils provide evidence about Earth's history.

Vocabulary
• fossil • mold • cast • petrified fossil
• carbon film • trace fossil • paleontologist
• evolution • extinct

LESSON 2 The Relative Age of Rocks

🗝 In horizontal sedimentary rock layers, the oldest layer is generally at the bottom. Each layer is younger than the layers below it.

🗝 Gaps in the geologic record and folding can change the position in which rock layers appear.

Vocabulary
• relative age • absolute age
• law of superposition • extrusion • intrusion
• fault • index fossil • unconformity

LESSON 3 Radioactive Dating

🗝 During radioactive decay, the atoms of one element break down to form atoms of another element.

🗝 In radioactive dating, scientists compare the amount of a radioactive element in a rock with the amount of the stable element into which the radioactive element decays.

Vocabulary
• radioactive decay
• half-life

LESSON 4 The Geologic Time Scale

🗝 Because the time span of Earth's past is so great, geologists use the geologic time scale to show Earth's history.

Vocabulary
• geologic time scale
• era
• period

LESSON 5 Early Earth

🗝 Scientists think that Earth began as a ball of dust, rock, and ice in space. Gravity pulled this mass together.

Vocabulary
• comet

LESSON 6 Eras of Earth's History

🗝 During the Paleozoic Era, a great number of different organisms evolved.

🗝 Reptiles spread widely during the Mesozoic Era.

🗝 During the Cenozoic Era, mammals evolved to live in many different environments.

Vocabulary
• invertebrate • vertebrate • amphibian • reptile
• mass extinction • mammal

Review and Assessment

LESSON 1 Fossils

1. A hollow area in sediment in the shape of all or part of an organism is called a

  a. mold.   **b.** cast.

  c. trace fossil.   **d.** carbon film.

2. A series of dinosaur footprints in rock are an example of a(n) _____ fossil.

3. Develop Hypotheses Which organism has a better chance of leaving a fossil: a jellyfish or a bony fish? Explain.

_____

_____

_____

Use the picture below to answer Questions 4–5.

4. Classify What type of fossil is shown?

_____

5. Infer This fossil was found in a dry, mountainous area. What can you infer about how the area has changed over time?

_____

_____

_____

_____

6. **Write About It** Suppose you are developing a museum exhibit about fossils. Write a guide for visitors to your exhibit explaining how fossils form and what scientists can learn from them.

LESSON 2 The Relative Age of Rocks

7. A gap in the geologic record that occurs when sedimentary rocks cover an eroded surface is called a(n)

  a. intrusion.   **b.** unconformity.

  c. fault.   **d.** extrusion.

8. A geologist finds an area of undisturbed sedimentary rock. The _____ layer is most likely the oldest.

9. Apply Concepts A geologist finds identical index fossils in a rock layer in the Grand Canyon in Arizona and in a rock layer in northern Utah, more than 675 kilometers away. What can she infer about the ages of the two rock layers?

_____

_____

LESSON 3 Radioactive Dating

10. The time it takes for half of a radioactive element's atoms to decay is its

  a. era.   **b.** half-life.

  c. relative age.   **d.** absolute age.

11. Calculate The half-life of carbon-14 is 5,730 years. A basket has 25% of its carbon-14 remaining. About how old is the basket?

_____

_____

12. Solve Problems Uranium-235 has a half-life of 713 million years. Would uranium-235 or carbon-14 be more useful for dating a fossil from Precambrian time? Explain.

_____

_____

_____

_____

241

LESSON 4 The Geologic Time Scale

13. The geologic time scale is subdivided into

    a. relative ages.   **b.** absolute ages.

    c. unconformities.   **d.** eras and periods.

14. Scientists developed the geologic time scale by studying _____

_____

15. Sequence Which major division of geologic time came first?

_____

Which period of geologic time occurred most recently?

_____

LESSON 5 Early Earth

16. Which of the following was found in Earth's first atmosphere?

    a. carbon dioxide   **b.** hydrogen

    c. oxygen   **d.** ozone

17. Over time, Earth's rock hardened and formed land called _____

18. Explain How do scientists think that Earth's oceans formed?

_____

_____

_____

19. Write About It Do you agree or disagree with the following statement? "Without photosynthesis, land animals and plants could not have evolved." Use evidence to justify your answer.

LESSON 6 Eras of Earth's History

20. The earliest multicelled organisms were

    a. invertebrates.   **b.** land plants.

    c. vertebrates.   **d.** bacteria.

21. Explain How did Earth's environments change from the Neogene to the Quaternary Period?

_____

_____

22. Evaluate Science in the Media If you see a movie in which early humans fight dinosaurs, how would you judge the scientific accuracy of that movie? Give reasons for your judgment.

_____

_____

_____

_____

_____

APPLY THE BIG Q How do scientists study Earth's past?

23. Look at the fossil below. What can you infer about the organism and its environment? Be sure to give evidence for your inferences.

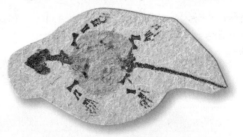

_____

_____

_____

_____

_____

_____

Ohio Benchmark Practice

Multiple Choice

Circle the letter of the correct answer.

1. Use the table to answer the question.

Geologic Time Scale	
Time Period	**Duration (Millions of Years)**
Cenozoic Era	66
Mesozoic Era	185
Paleozoic Era	291
Precambrian Time	about 4,058

A class is designing an outdoor model to show the geologic time scale from Precambrian Time through the present. If they use a scale of 1 m = 100 million years, how long will their model be?

A 46,000 m   **B** 460 m

C 46 m   **D** 4.6 m

2. A leaf falls into a shallow lake and is rapidly buried in the sediment. The sediment changes to rock over millions of years. Which type of fossil would **most likely** be formed?

A carbon film

B cast

C preserved remains

D trace fossil

3. What change in Earth's atmosphere allowed organisms to live on land?

A a collision with a comet

B the development of the ozone layer

C a strong burst of particles from the sun

D the absorption of carbon dioxide by oceans

4. Which of the following organisms lived during the Paleozoic Era?

A dinosaurs

B flowering plants

C grasses

D trilobites

5. Scientists can determine the absolute age of rocks using

A fault lines.

B index fossils.

C radioactive dating.

D the law of superposition.

Short Answer

Use the diagram below and your knowledge of science to answer Question 6. Write your answer on a separate sheet of paper.

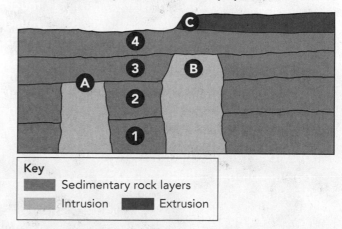

Key
- Sedimentary rock layers
- Intrusion
- Extrusion

6. Write the order in which the rock areas shown formed. Justify your answer using evidence from the diagram.

PUTTING THE PUZZLE TOGETHER

Imagine you are putting together a puzzle, but you don't have all the pieces. That's the problem for scientists trying to determine exactly what an animal looked like. Paleontologists may find only some of the bones of a prehistoric animal. They may find bones from more than one of the same kind of animal.

Scientists build reconstructions of the animals based on the fossils they have and observations of living relatives of the animal. Computed tomography (CT) scans help scientists make virtual fossils. They start with the pieces they have and then fill in the rest of the puzzle virtually. For example, if the scientists have found a fossil of the right jaw bone, the computers are able to help them model the left jaw bone, and build virtual models of the entire head.

Bones tell a story that scientists can understand. It's much harder to figure out the size and shape of the muscles or the color of the animal. Different scientists will build slightly different reconstructions of the same kind of animal. Because so many pieces of the puzzle are missing, it may be impossible to have a perfectly accurate reconstruction. Because the organisms are extinct, scientists may never know for sure.

Write About It Research the different ways in which paleontologists have reconstructed *Tyrannosaurus rex*. Choose one change and explain how it differed from a previous reconstruction. Why did paleontologists think this was a good change?

Paleontologist Jack Horner can use CT scans to create a 3-D model of this Lambeosaur skull. ▶

Teen Finds Fossils

In early 2007, sixteen-year-old Sierra Sarti-Sweeney went for a walk at Boca Ciega Millenium Park in Seminole, Florida. She wanted to take some nature pictures. She did not expect to stumble on a mammoth!

During her walk, Sierra noticed bones in a stream bed. With her older brother, Sean, she brought the bones to local scientists. The bone Sierra found was the tooth of a prehistoric Columbian mammoth. Archaeologists say that the tooth and other fossils Sierra found could be as much as 100,000 years old!

Since Sierra's find, digging at the site has uncovered even more bones, including those from prehistoric camels, 2-meter turtles, and saber-toothed cats. According to scientists, the findings suggest that this part of Florida was once like the African savanna region.

For Sierra, the experience was exciting. She even had a call from a late-night television host. Finding the tooth confirmed Sierra's desire to be a zoologist and to keep looking at the world around her.

Design It Plan an exhibit of Sierra's findings. What would people want to know and see? Make a brochure advertising your exhibit and develop a presentation of the fossils found at Boca Ciega Millenium Park.

FROZEN EVIDENCE

In the giant ice cap at the South Pole, a continuous record of snow exists reaching back more than 800,000 years. Scientists have drilled 3.2 kilometers down into the ice. From the cores they pull up, scientists learn about the temperature and the different gases in the air when each layer was formed.

These cores show that temperatures go up and down in cycles. Long ice ages (about 90,000 years) follow short warm periods (about 10,000 years). The climate record also shows that temperatures and amounts of carbon dioxide change together. If carbon dioxide levels rise, temperatures also rise.

Research It Find at least three sources that explain the ice cores project. Write an essay critiquing the explanations provided. Note any bias, misinformation, or missing information.

Researchers extract samples from the ice at the South Pole. ▲

WHAT COULD THIS BLACK WIDOW SPIDER BE DOING?

How do plants and animals reproduce and grow?

The large spider with the red hourglass shape on its abdomen is a female black widow spider. The smaller, orange and brown spider is a full-grown male black widow. The black widow spider gets its name from the fact that the female sometimes kills and eats the male after mating. In the center of the web is an egg sac. An average of 460 spiderlings will hatch from the eggs inside.

△Infer What do you think the female black widow spider could be doing?

_____

_____

_____

_____

▶ UNTAMED SCIENCE Watch the **Untamed Science** video to learn more about life cycles.

Plant and Animal Life Cycles

8 Getting Started

Check Your Understanding

1. **Background** Read the paragraph below and then answer the question.

Sal and Kai are at the zoo, trying to decide where to go. Sal wants to see the birds, reptiles, and **mammals.** Kai has a completely different plan. She doesn't understand why Sal only wants to see **vertebrates.** Kai would rather go directly to the **invertebrate** exhibit.

> **Mammals** are vertebrates whose body temperatures are regulated by their internal heat, and that have skin covered with hair or fur and glands that produce milk to feed their young.
>
> **Vertebrates** are animals with backbones.
>
> **Invertebrates** are animals without backbones.

- Circle the correct word to complete the following sentence. A bird is an example of a (vertebrate/invertebrate).

> MY READING WEB If you had trouble completing the question above, visit **My Reading Web** and type in *Plant and Animal Life Cycles.*

Vocabulary Skill

Greek Word Origins Many science words come to English from ancient Greek. Learning the Greek word parts can help you understand some of the terms in this chapter.

Greek Word Part	Meaning	Example Word
chloros	pale green	chloroplast, *n.* green cellular structure in which photosynthesis occurs
petalon	leaf	petal, *n.* colorful, leaflike flower structure

2. **Quick Check** *Chlorophyll* is a pigment found in plants. Which part of the word *chlorophyll* tells you that it is a green pigment?

_____

sepal

fruit

external fertilization

amniotic egg

Chapter Preview

LESSON 1

- root cap • cambium • stoma
- transpiration • embryo
- germination • flower
- pollination • sepal • petal
- stamen • pistil • ovary

↻ **Relate Cause and Effect**

△ **Observe**

LESSON 2

- sporophyte • gametophyte
- annual • biennial • perennial
- fertilization • zygote
- cone • ovule • fruit

↻ **Summarize**

△ **Infer**

LESSON 3

- larva • polyp • medusa
- external fertilization
- internal fertilization
- gestation period

↻ **Compare and Contrast**

△ **Calculate**

LESSON 4

- amniotic egg • placenta
- metamorphosis
- complete metamorphosis
- pupa
- incomplete metamorphosis
- nymph • tadpole

↻ **Identify the Main Idea**

△ **Interpret Data**

▷ **VOCAB FLASH CARDS** For extra help with vocabulary, visit **Vocab Flash Cards** and type in *Plant and Animal Life Cycles.*

Plant Structures

UNLOCK THE BIG ?

🔑 **What Are the Functions of Roots, Stems, and Leaves?**

🔑 **How Do Seeds Become New Plants?**

🔑 **What Are the Structures of a Flower?**

MY PLANET DIARY

SCIENCE STATS

Plant Giants

- The aroid plant (as shown here) on the island of Borneo in Asia has leaves that can grow three meters long! These are the largest undivided leaves on Earth!

- The rafflesia flower can grow up to one meter wide and weigh seven kilograms.

- The jackfruit can weigh up to 36 kilograms. That's the world's largest fruit that grows on trees!

Write your answer below.

Why do you think the aroid plant has such big leaves?

_____

_____

_____

▶ **PLANET DIARY** Go to **Planet Diary** to learn more about plant structures.

Lab® zone Do the Inquiry Warm-Up *Which Plant Part Is It?*

What Are the Functions of Roots, Stems, and Leaves?

Each part of a plant plays an important role in its structure and function. Roots, stems, and leaves are just three structures we will look into further.

Roots Have you ever tried to pull a dandelion out of the soil? It's not easy, is it? That is because most roots are good anchors. Roots have three main functions. 🔑 **Roots anchor a plant in the ground, absorb water and minerals from the soil, and sometimes store food.** The more root area a plant has, the more water and minerals it can absorb.

Vocabulary

- root cap • cambium • stoma • transpiration
- embryo • germination • flower • pollination
- sepal • petal • stamen • pistil • ovary

Skills

↪ **Reading:** Relate Cause and Effect

△ **Inquiry:** Observe

Types of Roots The two main types of root systems are shown in **Figure 1.** A fibrous root system consists of many similarly sized roots that form a dense, tangled mass. Plants with fibrous roots take a lot of soil with them when you pull them out of the ground. Lawn grass, corn, and onions have fibrous root systems. In contrast, a taproot system has one long, thick main root. Many smaller roots branch off the main root. A plant with a taproot system is hard to pull out of the ground. Carrots, dandelions, and cacti have taproots.

FIGURE 1 ·······

Root Systems and Structure

There are two main root systems with many structures.

✎ **Interpret Photos** Label the taproot *T* and the fibrous roots *F*.

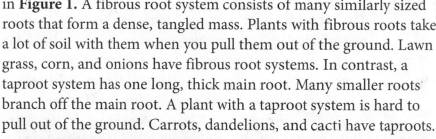

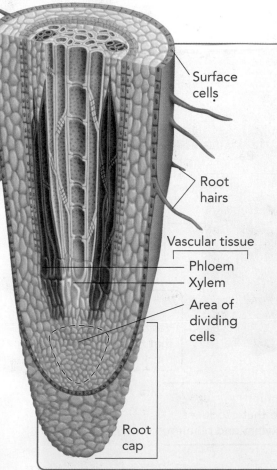

Surface cells

Root hairs

Vascular tissue

Phloem
Xylem

Area of dividing cells

Root cap

Root Structure

In **Figure 2,** you can see the structure of a typical root. The tip of the root is rounded and is covered by the root cap. The **root cap** protects the root from injury as the root grows through the soil. Behind the root cap are the cells that divide to form new root cells.

Root hairs grow out of the root's surface. These tiny hairs can enter the spaces between soil particles, where they absorb water and minerals. The root hairs also help to anchor the plant in the soil.

Locate the vascular tissue in the center of the root. The water and nutrients that are absorbed from the soil quickly move into the xylem. From there, these substances are transported upward to the plant's stems and leaves. Phloem transports food manufactured in the leaves to the root. The root tissues then use the food for growth or store it for future use by the plant.

FIGURE 2 ·······

Root Structure

Roots have many structures.

✎ **Define** What is the function of the root cap?

_____

_____

Stems

The stem of a plant has two main functions. 🔑 **The stem carries substances between the plant's roots and leaves. The stem also provides support for the plant and holds up the leaves so they are exposed to the sun.** In addition, some stems, such as those of asparagus, store food.

The Structure of a Stem Stems can be either woody or herbaceous (hur BAY shus). Woody stems are hard and rigid, such as in maple trees. Herbaceous stems contain no wood and are often soft. Plants with herbaceous stems include daisies, ivy, and asparagus (pictured left).

Herbaceous and woody stems consist of phloem and xylem tissue as well as many other supporting cells. As you can see in **Figure 3,** a woody stem contains many layers of tissue. The outermost layer is bark. Bark includes an outer protective layer and an inner layer of living phloem, which transports food through the stem. Next is a layer of cells called the **cambium** (KAM bee um), which divides to produce new phloem and xylem. It is xylem that makes up most of what you call "wood." Sapwood is active xylem that transports water and minerals through the stem. The older, darker, heartwood is inactive but provides support.

FIGURE 3 ···

Stem Structure

The woody stem of a tree contains many different structures.

✎ **Interpret Diagrams** Label the active xylem and phloem on the tree trunk below.

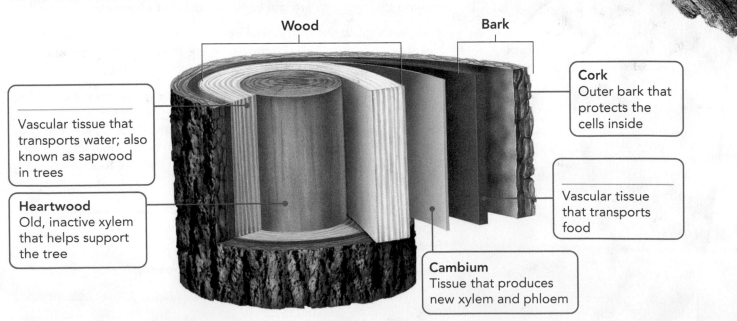

Wood

Bark

Cork
Outer bark that protects the cells inside

_____
Vascular tissue that transports water; also known as sapwood in trees

Heartwood
Old, inactive xylem that helps support the tree

Cambium
Tissue that produces new xylem and phloem

_____
Vascular tissue that transports food

Annual Rings Have you ever looked at a tree stump and seen a pattern of circles that looks something like a target? These circles are called annual rings. They represent a tree's yearly growth. Annual rings are made of xylem. Xylem cells that form in the spring are large and have thin walls because they grow rapidly. They produce a wide, light brown ring. Xylem cells that form in the summer grow slowly and, therefore, are small and have thick walls. They produce a thin, dark ring. One pair of light and dark rings represents one year's growth. You can estimate a tree's age by counting its annual rings.

The width of a tree's annual rings can provide important clues about past weather conditions, such as rainfall. In rainy years, more xylem is produced, so the tree's annual rings are wide. In dry years, rings are narrow. By examining annual rings from some trees in the southwestern United States, scientists were able to infer that severe droughts occurred in the years 840, 1067, 1379, and 1632.

◀ **The annual rings in a tree reveal the tree's history.**

apply it!

❶ Calculate How old was the tree when it was cut down?

_____

❷ Observe The area at Area C is blackened from a fire that affected one side of the tree. Describe how the tree grew after the fire.

_____
_____
_____
_____

❸ CHALLENGE Areas A and B both represent four years of growth. What might account for their difference in size?

_____
_____
_____
_____
_____
_____
_____

Vocabulary Greek Word Origins The Greek word *stoma* means "mouth." How are the stomata of a plant like mouths?

_____

_____

_____

_____

_____

_____

Leaves

Leaves vary greatly in size and shape. Pine trees have needle-shaped leaves. Birch trees have small rounded leaves with jagged edges. Regardless of their shape, leaves play an important role in a plant. **Leaves capture the sun's energy and carry out the food-making process of photosynthesis.**

The Structure of a Leaf If you were to cut through a leaf and look at the edge under a microscope, you would see the structures in **Figure 4.** The leaf's top and bottom surface layers protect the cells inside. Between the layers of cells are veins that contain xylem and phloem.

The surface layers of the leaf have small openings, or pores, called **stomata** (stoh MAH tuh; *singular* stoma). The stomata open and close to control when gases enter and leave the leaf. When the stomata are open, carbon dioxide enters the leaf, and oxygen and water vapor exit.

Upper Leaf Cells
Tightly packed cells trap the energy in sunlight.

Lower Leaf Cells
Widely spaced cells allow carbon dioxide to reach cells for photosynthesis and oxygen to escape into the air.

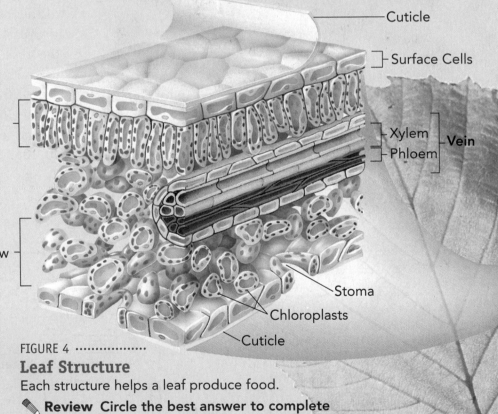

Cuticle

Surface Cells

Xylem — **Vein**
Phloem

Stoma

Chloroplasts

Cuticle

FIGURE 4 ·················
Leaf Structure
Each structure helps a leaf produce food.

Review Circle the best answer to complete the sentences.

(Cuticles/Chloroplasts) are the structures in which food is made. (Cuticles/Chloroplasts) are the waxy layers that help plants reduce water loss.

The Leaf and Photosynthesis The structure of a leaf is ideal for carrying out photosynthesis. The cells that contain the most chloroplasts are located near the leaf's upper surface, where they get the most light. The chlorophyll in the chloroplasts traps the sun's energy.

Carbon dioxide enters the leaf through open stomata. Water, which is absorbed by the plant's roots, travels up the stem to the leaf through the xylem. During photosynthesis, sugar and oxygen are produced from the carbon dioxide and water. Oxygen passes out of the leaf through the open stomata. The sugar enters the phloem and then travels throughout the plant.

Controlling Water Loss Because such a large area of a leaf is exposed to the air, water can quickly evaporate from a leaf into the air. The process by which water evaporates from a plant's leaves is called **transpiration.** A plant can lose a lot of water through transpiration. A corn plant, for example, can lose almost 4 liters of water on a hot summer day. Without a way to slow down the process of transpiration, a plant would shrivel up and die.

Fortunately, plants have ways to slow down transpiration. One way plants retain water is by closing the stomata. The stomata often close when leaves start to dry out.

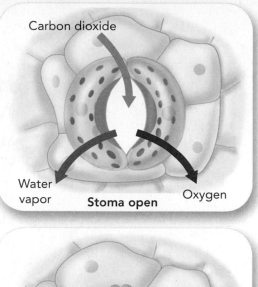

Carbon dioxide

Water vapor · **Stoma open** · Oxygen

Stoma closed

FIGURE 5 ·······································

Stomata
Stomata can slow water loss.

✏ **Name** What three substances enter and leave a plant through stomata?

_____

_____

 Do the Lab Investigation
Investigating Stomata.

🔑 Assess Your Understanding

1a. List What are the functions of a stem?

_____

_____

_____

_____

_____

b. Infer If you forget to water a houseplant for a few days, would its stomata be open or closed? Why?

_____

_____

_____

_____

got**it?** ··

○ **I get it!** Now I know that roots, stems, and leaves perform functions like _____

_____

○ **I need extra help with** _____

Go to **MY SCIENCE ⓢ COACH** *online for help with this subject.*

How Do Seeds Become New Plants?

Many plants begin their life cycle as a seed. You can follow the cycle from seed to plant in **Figure 6.** All seeds share important similarities. 🔑 **Inside a seed is a partially developed plant. If a seed lands in an area where conditions are favorable, the plant sprouts out of the seed and begins to grow.**

Seed Structure A seed has three main parts—an embryo, stored food, and a seed coat. The young plant that develops from the zygote, or fertilized egg, is called the **embryo.** The embryo already has the beginnings of roots, stems, and leaves. In the seeds of most plants, the embryo stops growing when it is quite small. When the embryo begins to grow again, it uses the food stored in the seed until it can make its own food by photosynthesis. In all seeds, the embryo has one or more seed leaves, or cotyledons. In some seeds, food is stored in the cotyledons. In others, food is stored outside the embryo.

The outer covering of a seed is called the seed coat. The seed coat acts like plastic wrap, protecting the embryo and its food from drying out. This allows a seed to remain inactive for a long time. In many plants, the seeds are surrounded by a structure called a fruit.

FIGURE 6 ·······················

> INTERACTIVE ART **Story of a Seed**

Read the text on this page and the next page. Then complete the activities about seeds becoming new plants.

✎ **Complete each task.**

1. **Review** On the diagram, label the seed's embryo, cotyledons, and seed coat.

Stem and root

Stored food

Seed Dispersal

After seeds form, they are usually scattered. The scattering of seeds is called seed dispersal. Seeds can be dispersed in many different ways. When animals eat fruit, the seeds inside the fruit pass through the animal's digestive system and are deposited in new areas. Other seeds are enclosed in barblike structures that hook onto fur or clothing. The seeds fall off in a new area. Water also disperses seeds that fall into oceans and rivers. Wind disperses lightweight seeds, such as those of dandelions and maple trees. Some plants eject their seeds. The force scatters the seeds in many directions. A seed that is dispersed far from its parent plant has a better chance of survival. Far away, a seed does not have to compete with its parent for light, water, and nutrients.

Germination

After a seed is dispersed, it may remain inactive for a while before it germinates. **Germination** (jur muh NAY shun) occurs when the embryo begins to grow again and pushes out of the seed. Germination begins when the seed absorbs water. Then the embryo uses stored food to begin to grow. The roots first grow downward. Then its stem and leaves grow upward.

> **Relate Cause and Effect**
> Underline a cause of seed dispersal and circle its effect in the text on this page.

2. Explain Give two reasons why this seed can be successfully dispersed by wind.

_____

_____

_____

_____

B

A

3. CHALLENGE Which young plant, A or B, is more likely to grow into an adult plant? Why?

_____

_____

_____

 Lab zone Do the Quick Lab *The In-Seed Story.*

⚷ Assess Your Understanding

got it?

○ **I get it!** Now I know that a seed becomes a new plant when _____

_____

○ **I need extra help with** _____

Go to **my science COACH** online for help with this subject.

What Are the Structures of a Flower?

Flowers come in all sorts of shapes, sizes, and colors. But, despite their differences, all flowers have the same function—reproduction. A **flower** is the reproductive structure of an angiosperm. 🔑 **A typical flower contains sepals, petals, stamens, and pistils.**

The colors and shapes of most flower structures and the scents produced by most flowers attract insects and other animals. These organisms ensure that pollination occurs. **Pollination** is the transfer of pollen from male reproductive structures to female reproductive structures. Pollinators, such as those shown in **Figure 7,** include birds, bats, and insects such as bees and flies. As you read, keep in mind that some flowers lack one or more of the parts. For example, some flowers have only male reproductive parts, and some flowers do not have petals.

Sepals and Petals
When a flower is still a bud, it is enclosed by leaflike structures called **sepals** (SEE pulz). Sepals protect the developing flower and are often green in color. When the sepals fold back, they reveal the flower's colorful, leaflike **petals.** The petals are generally the most colorful parts of a flower. The shapes, sizes, and number of petals vary greatly between flowers.

Stamens
Within the petals are the flower's male and female reproductive parts. The **stamens** (STAY munz) are the male reproductive parts. Locate the stamens inside the flower in **Figure 8.** The thin stalk of the stamen is called the filament. Pollen is made in the anther, at the top of the filament.

FIGURE 7 ·······································

Pollinator Matchup
Some pollinators are well adapted to the plants they pollinate. For example, the long tongue of the nectar bat helps the bat reach inside the agave plant, as shown below.

✎ **Apply Concepts** Write the letter of the pollinator on the plant it is adapted to pollinate.

Pistils The female parts, or **pistils** (PIS tulz), are found in the center of most flowers, as shown in **Figure 8.** Some flowers have two or more pistils; others have only one. The sticky tip of the pistil is called the stigma. A slender tube, called a style, connects the stigma to a hollow structure at the base of the flower. This hollow structure is the **ovary,** which protects the seeds as they develop. An ovary contains one or more ovules.

FIGURE 8 ·······························

> INTERACTIVE ART Structures of a Typical Flower
Flowers have many structures.

✎ **Relate Text and Visuals**
Use the word bank to fill in the missing labels.

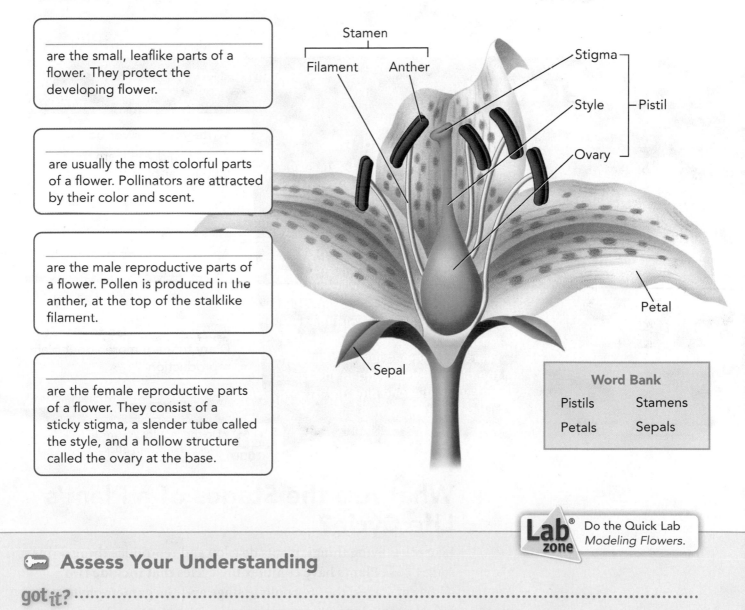

_____ are the small, leaflike parts of a flower. They protect the developing flower.

_____ are usually the most colorful parts of a flower. Pollinators are attracted by their color and scent.

_____ are the male reproductive parts of a flower. Pollen is produced in the anther, at the top of the stalklike filament.

_____ are the female reproductive parts of a flower. They consist of a sticky stigma, a slender tube called the style, and a hollow structure called the ovary at the base.

Word Bank

Pistils	Stamens
Petals	Sepals

Lab zone ® Do the Quick Lab *Modeling Flowers.*

🔑 Assess Your Understanding

got it? ··

○ **I get it!** Now I know that the structures of a flower include _____

_____

○ **I need extra help with** _____

Go to **MY SCIENCE** 🔵 **COACH** *online for help with this subject.*

Plant Reproduction

🔑 **What Are the Stages of a Plant Life Cycle?**

🔑 **How Do Plants Reproduce?**

MY PLANET DiARY

FUN FACT

If Trees Could Talk

Suppose you had been alive during the ancient Egyptian Empire, the Middle Ages, the American Revolution, and both World Wars. Think of the stories you could tell! Bristlecone pine trees can be this old. In 1964, a student got permission to cut down one of these trees. He counted the tree rings to see how old the tree was, and discovered it was 4,900 years old. He had just cut down the oldest living thing in the world! Today, Bristlecone pine forests are protected.

Write your answer below.
What could you learn from a 5,000-year-old tree?

_____

_____

_____

_____

_____

▶ PLANET DIARY Go to **Planet Diary** to learn more about plant reproduction.

Lab zone® Do the Inquiry Warm-Up
Make the Pollen Stick.

What Are the Stages of a Plant's Life Cycle?

Like other living things, plants develop and reproduce through life stages. 🔑 **Plants have complex life cycles that include two different stages, the sporophyte stage and the gametophyte stage.** In the **sporophyte** (SPOH ruh fyt) stage, the plant produces spores or seeds, tiny cells that can grow into new organisms. The spore develops into the plant's other stage, called the gametophyte. In the **gametophyte** (guh MEE tuh fyt) stage, the plant produces two kinds of sex cells: sperm cells and egg cells. See **Figure 1.**

Vocabulary
- sporophyte • gametophyte • annual • biennial
- perennial • fertilization • zygote • cone
- ovule • fruit

Skills
- ⟳ Reading: Summarize
- △ Inquiry: Infer

FIGURE 1 ···

Plant Life Cycle

All plants go through two stages in their life cycle.

✎ **Interpret Diagrams** Label the sporophyte and gametophyte stages.

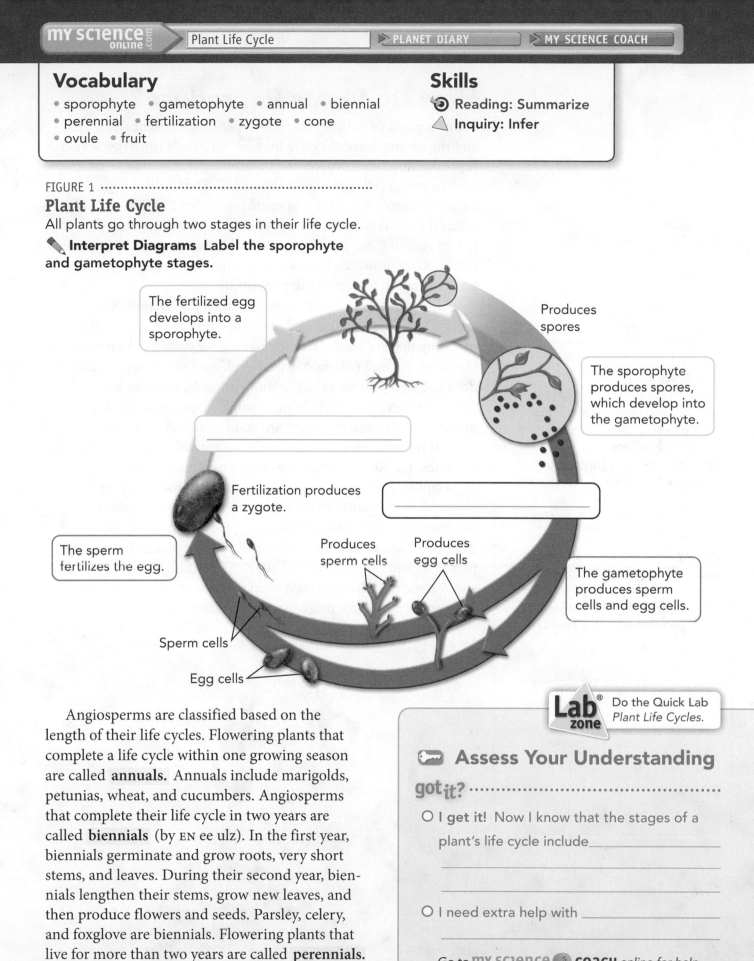

The fertilized egg develops into a sporophyte.

Produces spores

The sporophyte produces spores, which develop into the gametophyte.

Fertilization produces a zygote.

The sperm fertilizes the egg.

Produces sperm cells

Produces egg cells

The gametophyte produces sperm cells and egg cells.

Sperm cells

Egg cells

Angiosperms are classified based on the length of their life cycles. Flowering plants that complete a life cycle within one growing season are called **annuals.** Annuals include marigolds, petunias, wheat, and cucumbers. Angiosperms that complete their life cycle in two years are called **biennials** (by EN ee ulz). In the first year, biennials germinate and grow roots, very short stems, and leaves. During their second year, biennials lengthen their stems, grow new leaves, and then produce flowers and seeds. Parsley, celery, and foxglove are biennials. Flowering plants that live for more than two years are called **perennials.** Most perennials flower every year.

Lab zone® Do the Quick Lab *Plant Life Cycles.*

🔑 **Assess Your Understanding**

got it? ···

○ **I get it!** Now I know that the stages of a plant's life cycle include _____

_____

_____

○ **I need extra help with** _____

_____

Go to **my science** ⑤ **COACH** *online for help with this subject.*

How Do Plants Reproduce?

Plants reproduce in different ways depending on their structures and the environment they live in. 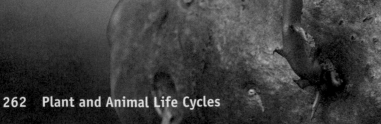 **All plants undergo sexual reproduction that involves fertilization.** **Fertilization** occurs when a sperm cell unites with an egg cell. The fertilized egg is called a **zygote.** For algae and some plants, fertilization can only occur if there is water in the environment. This is because the sperm cells of these plants swim through the water to the egg cells. Other plants, however, have an adaptation that makes it possible for fertilization to occur in dry environments.

Many plants can also undergo asexual reproduction. Recall that asexual reproduction includes only one parent and produces offspring that are identical to the parent. New plants can grow from the roots, leaves, or stems of a parent plant. Asexual reproduction does not involve flowers, pollination, or seeds, so it can happen faster than sexual reproduction. A single plant can quickly spread out in an environment if there are good conditions. However, asexual reproduction can reproduce unfavorable traits since there is no new genetic information being passed to offspring.

Scientists can take advantage of asexual reproduction in plants. A single plant can be used to create identical plants for experiments. Scientists can also copy plants with favorable characteristics. Grafting is one way of copying plants. In grafting, part of a plant's stem is cut and attached to another related plant species, such as a lemon tree and an orange tree. The plant matures and can then produce more than one kind of fruit.

FIGURE 2 ·······················

Eyes on Potatoes

Did you know that a potato is actually the underground stem of the potato plant? If you have ever left a potato out long enough, you may have noticed it beginning to sprout. A potato can grow new potato plants from buds called eyes, as seen in this photo.

✎ **Apply Concepts** Potato plants also produce flowers and reproduce sexually. How does being able to reproduce asexually benefit the plant?

_____

_____

_____

_____

_____

_____

_____

apply it!

A citrus farmer was able to graft a lemon tree branch onto an orange tree. Now the same tree produces lemons and oranges! The farmer plans to use branches from the same lemon trees to create other combined fruit trees.

1 Review The farmer used the lemon tree's ability to (sexually/asexually) reproduce.

2 Infer Name at least one negative effect of using the same lemon tree to create new trees the farmer should know about.

_____

_____

3 CHALLENGE Why might the public be opposed to using this method to create new fruit trees?

_____

_____

Nonvascular and Seedless Vascular
Plants Mosses, liverworts, hornworts, ferns, club mosses, and horsetails need to grow in moist environments. This is because the plants release spores into their surroundings, where they grow into gametophytes. When the gametophytes produce egg cells and sperm cells, there must be enough water available for the sperm to swim toward the eggs.

For example, the familiar fern, with its visible fronds, is the sporophyte stage of the plant. On the underside of mature fronds, spores develop in tiny spore cases. Wind and water can carry the spores great distances. If a spore lands in moist, shaded soil, it develops into a gametophyte. Fern gametophytes are tiny plants that grow low to the ground.

Spore cases on the fronds of a fern

263

Gymnosperms You can follow the process of gymnosperm reproduction in **Figure 3.**

1 **Cone Production**

Most gymnosperms have reproductive structures called **cones.** Cones are covered with scales. Most gymnosperms produce two types of cones: male cones and female cones. Usually, a single plant produces both male and female cones. In some types of gymnosperms, however, individual trees produce either male cones or female cones. A few gymnosperms produce no cones.

2 **Pollen Production and Ovule Development**

(A) Male cones produce pollen grains. Cells in the pollen will mature into sperm cells. (B) The female gametophyte develops in structures called ovules. An **ovule** (OH vyool) is a structure that contains an egg cell. Female cones contain at least one ovule at the base of each scale. The ovule later develops into the seed.

3 **Egg Production**

Two egg cells form inside each ovule on the female cone.

4 **Pollination**

The transfer of pollen from a male reproductive structure to a female reproductive structure is called pollination. In gymnosperms, wind often carries the pollen from the male cones to the female cones. The pollen collect in a sticky substance produced by each ovule.

5 **Fertilization**

Once pollination has occurred, the ovule closes and seals in the pollen. The scales also close, and a sperm cell fertilizes an egg cell inside each ovule. The zygote then develops into the embryo part of the seed.

6 **Seed Development**

Female cones remain on the tree while the seeds mature. As the seeds develop, the female cone increases in size. It can take up to two years for the seeds of some gymnosperms to mature. Male cones, however, usually fall off the tree after they have shed their pollen.

7 **Seed Dispersal**

When the seeds are mature, the scales open. The wind shakes the seeds out of the cone and carries them away. Only a few seeds will land in suitable places and grow into new plants.

FIGURE 3 ·······························

Gymnosperm Reproduction Cycle

The reproduction cycle of a gymnosperm is shown at right.

✎ **Complete each task.**

1. **Identify** Underline the sentence(s) on this page that use the vocabulary terms *cone* and *ovule*.

2. **Describe** What is the relationship between cones and ovules?

_____

_____

_____

_____

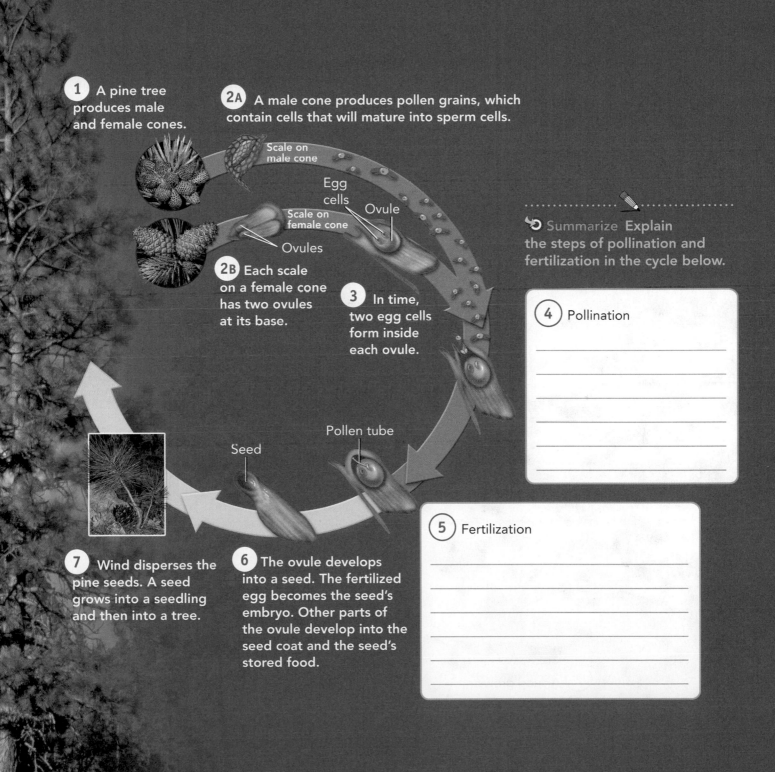

1 A pine tree produces male and female cones.

2A A male cone produces pollen grains, which contain cells that will mature into sperm cells.

Scale on male cone

Egg cells

Ovule

Scale on female cone

Ovules

2B Each scale on a female cone has two ovules at its base.

3 In time, two egg cells form inside each ovule.

Pollen tube

Seed

7 Wind disperses the pine seeds. A seed grows into a seedling and then into a tree.

6 The ovule develops into a seed. The fertilized egg becomes the seed's embryo. Other parts of the ovule develop into the seed coat and the seed's stored food.

Summarize Explain the steps of pollination and fertilization in the cycle below.

4 Pollination

_____
_____
_____
_____
_____

5 Fertilization

_____
_____
_____
_____
_____
_____

FIGURE 4 ·····································

Angiosperm Reproduction

Reproduction in angiosperms begins with flowers.

✎ **Relate Text and Visuals**
Look back at the plant life and gymnosperm reproduction cycles in this lesson. What do the yellow and purple colors of the arrows represent?

_____

_____

_____

_____

_____

Angiosperms

You can follow angiosperm reproduction in **Figure 4.** First, pollen fall on a flower's stigma. In time, the sperm cell and egg cell join together in the flower's ovule. The zygote develops into the embryo part of the seed.

Pollination A flower is pollinated when a grain of pollen falls on the stigma. Some angiosperms are pollinated by the wind, but most rely on other organisms. When an organism enters a flower to obtain food, it becomes coated with pollen. Some of the pollen can drop onto the flower's stigma as the animal leaves. The pollen can also be brushed onto the stigma of the next flower the animal visits.

Fertilization If the pollen fall on the stigma of a similar plant, fertilization can occur. A sperm cell joins with an egg cell inside an ovule within the ovary at the base of the flower. The zygote then begins to develop into the seed's embryo. Other parts of the ovule develop into the rest of the seed.

1 An apple tree produces flowers.

2A The cells in the anther produce pollen grains.

Anther

Ovary

Ovule

Egg cells

2B Inside the ovary, an egg cell is produced in each ovule.

3 Pollen grains are trapped on the stigma.

Stigma

Pollen tube

Sperm cell

Embryo

Seed

7 A seed grows into a new plant.

6 The ovary develops into a fruit.

4 The pollen grain produces a pollen tube that grows into the ovule. A sperm cell moves through the pollen tube and fertilizes the egg cell.

5 The ovule develops into a seed. The fertilized egg becomes the seed's embryo.

Fruit Development and Seed Dispersal As the seed develops, the ovary changes into a **fruit**. A fruit is the ripened ovary and other structures that enclose one or more seeds. Fruits include apples, cherries, tomatoes, squash, and many others. Fruits are the means by which angiosperm seeds are dispersed. Animals that eat fruits help to disperse their seeds by depositing them in new areas.

FIGURE 5

Flower to Fruit

Flowers eventually develop into fruit.

✎ **Sequence** Write the numbers 1 through 4 in the blank circles to show the progression from flower to fruit.

Lab zone® Do the Quick Lab *Where Are the Seeds?*

🔑 Assess Your Understanding

1a. Review (Fertilization/Asexual reproduction) occurs when a sperm cell unites with an egg cell.

b. Explain Why do plants like liverworts need to live in moist environments?

_____

_____

c. Relate Cause and Effect Underline the cause and circle the effect in the sentences below.

Pollination can occur when pollen on an insect is dropped onto the stigma.

Animals eating fruit is one way seeds are dispersed.

got it?

○ **I get it!** Now I know that all of the major plant groups reproduce _____

○ **I need extra help with** _____

Go to **MY SCIENCE ⓢ COACH** online for help with this subject.

Animal Reproduction and Fertilization

UNLOCK THE BIG ?

🔑 **How Do Animals Reproduce?**

🔑 **How Do External and Internal Fertilization Differ?**

MY PLANET DIARY

A Nutty Experiment

Did you know that moths have favorite foods? The navel orangeworm moth lays its eggs inside of nuts, such as pistachios, walnuts, and almonds. The young that hatch out of the eggs look like worms, and eat their way out of the nuts. This causes damage to crops on nut farms.

Navel orangeworm moths were thought to prefer almonds over other nuts—that is, until California middle school student Gabriel Leal found evidence to the contrary. Gabriel conducted a science project to investigate whether the young of navel orangeworm moths preferred pistachios, walnuts, or almonds. He put equal amounts of each type of nut into three different traps. A fourth trap was left empty. All four traps were placed into a cage with young navel orangeworms. Most worms went to the pistachio trap. No worms went to the empty trap. Gabriel's research could help scientists control worm damage to walnut and almond crops.

Control Variables Read the paragraphs and answer the questions below.

1. Write a one-sentence conclusion of Gabriel's research.

_____

_____

_____

2. What was the purpose of the empty trap in Gabriel's experiment?

_____

_____

_____

> **PLANET DIARY** Go to **Planet Diary** to learn more about animal reproduction and fertilization.

 Lab zone Do the Inquiry Warm-Up *Making More.*

Vocabulary
- larva • polyp • medusa • external fertilization
- internal fertilization • gestation period

Skills
↻ Reading: Compare and Contrast
△ Inquiry: Calculate

How Do Animals Reproduce?

Whether they wiggle, hop, fly, or run, have backbones or no backbones—all animal species reproduce. Elephants make more elephants, grasshoppers make more grasshoppers, and sea stars make more sea stars. Some animals produce offspring that are identical to the parent. Most animals, including humans, produce offspring that are different from the parents. 🔑 **Animals undergo either asexual or sexual reproduction to make more of their own kind or species.** Because no animal lives forever, reproduction is essential to the survival of a species.

Asexual Reproduction Imagine you are digging in the soil with a shovel, and accidentally cut a worm into two pieces. Most animals wouldn't survive getting cut in two—but the worm might. Certain kinds of worms can form whole new worms from each cut piece. This is one form of asexual reproduction. Another example of asexual reproduction is called budding. In budding, a new animal grows out of the parent and breaks off. In asexual reproduction, one parent produces a new organism identical to itself. This new organism receives an exact copy of the parent's set of genetic material, or DNA. Some animals, including sponges, jellyfish, sea anemones, worms, and the hydra in **Figure 1,** can reproduce asexually.

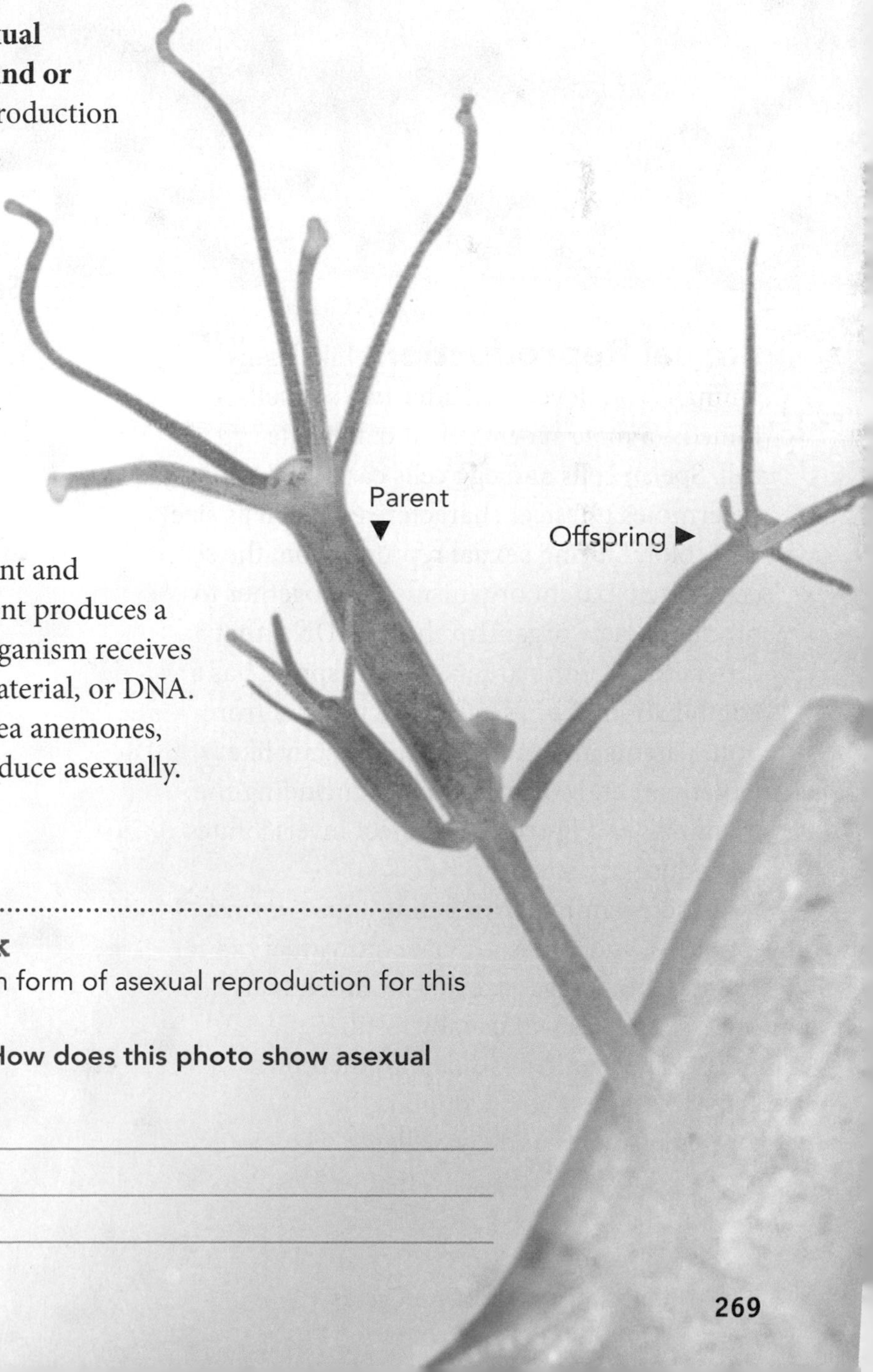

Parent ▼

Offspring ▶

FIGURE 1 ·······························

A Chip off the Old Block
Budding is the most common form of asexual reproduction for this hydra, a type of cnidarian.

✏ **Relate Text to Visuals** How does this photo show asexual reproduction?

_____

_____

_____

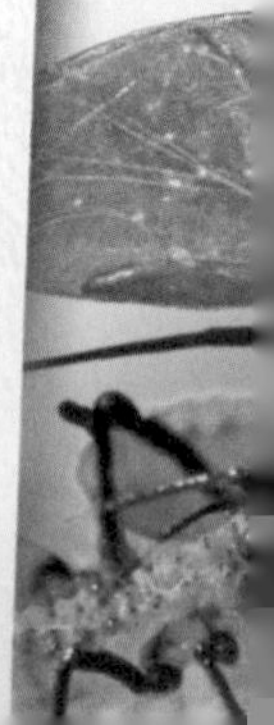

Sexual Reproduction Like many animals, you developed after two sex cells joined—a male sperm cell and a female egg cell. Sperm cells and egg cells carry DNA that determines physical characteristics such as size and color. During sexual reproduction, the sex cells of two parent organisms join together to produce a new organism that has DNA that differs from both parents. The offspring has a combination of physical characteristics from both parents and may not look exactly like either parent. Most vertebrates, including the mammals in **Figure 2,** and most invertebrates reproduce sexually.

In some animals, including some worms, mollusks, and fishes, a single individual may produce both eggs and sperm. Individuals of these species will usually fertilize the eggs of another individual, not their own eggs. Recall that fertilization is the joining of sperm and egg cells.

FIGURE 2 ....

Sexual Reproduction
These wolf cubs and guinea pig pups are products of sexual reproduction.

✎ **Use the photos to answer the questions.**

1. Interpret Photos How do the offspring in each photo differ from their parent?

_____

_____

_____

2. Explain Why do the parent and the offspring look different?

_____

_____

_____

_____

_____

Comparing Asexual and Sexual Reproduction

Asexual and sexual reproduction are different survival methods. Each method has advantages and disadvantages. An advantage of asexual reproduction is that one parent can quickly produce many identical offspring. But a major disadvantage is that the offspring have the same DNA as the parent. The offspring have no variation from the parent and may not survive changes in the environment. In contrast, sexual reproduction has the advantage of producing offspring with new combinations of DNA. These offspring may have characteristics that help them adapt and survive changes in the environment. However, a disadvantage of sexual reproduction is that it requires finding a mate, and the development of offspring takes a longer time.

did you know?

Some fishes, such as this anemone clownfish, can change from male to female during their lifetime!

FIGURE 3 ···

Asexual and Sexual Reproduction

Compare and Contrast Write an advantage and a disadvantage of each type of reproduction in the table.

	Asexual Reproduction	Sexual Reproduction
Advantage		
Disadvantage		

These aphids can reproduce asexually and sexually. They reproduce asexually when environmental conditions are favorable. If conditions worsen, they reproduce sexually.

▼

Reproductive Cycles Several aquatic invertebrates, such as sponges and cnidarians, have life cycles that alternate between asexual and sexual reproduction.

A Sponges

Sponges reproduce both asexually and sexually. Sponges reproduce asexually through budding. Small new sponges grow, or bud, from the sides of an adult sponge. Eventually, the buds break free and begin life on their own. Sponges reproduce sexually, too, but they do not have separate sexes. A sponge can produce both sperm cells and egg cells. After a sponge egg is fertilized by a sperm, a larva develops. A larva (plural larvae) is an immature form of an animal that looks very different from the adult. **Figure 4** shows sponge reproduction.

B Cnidarians

Many cnidarians alternate between two body forms: a polyp (PAHL ip) that looks like an upright vase and a medusa (muh DOO suh) that looks like an open umbrella. Some polyps reproduce asexually by budding. Other polyps just pull apart, forming two new polyps. Both kinds of asexual reproduction rapidly increase the number of polyps in a short time. Cnidarians reproduce sexually when in the medusa stage. The medusas release sperm and eggs into the water. A fertilized egg develops into a swimming larva. In time, the larva attaches to a hard surface and develops into a polyp that may continue the cycle. The moon jelly in **Figure 5** undergoes both asexual and sexual reproduction.

1. An adult sponge releases sperm.

5. The larva settles on a hard surface. It develops into an adult sponge.

2. Sperm enter another sponge and fertilize an egg.

4. Water currents carry the larva away.

3. A larva develops.

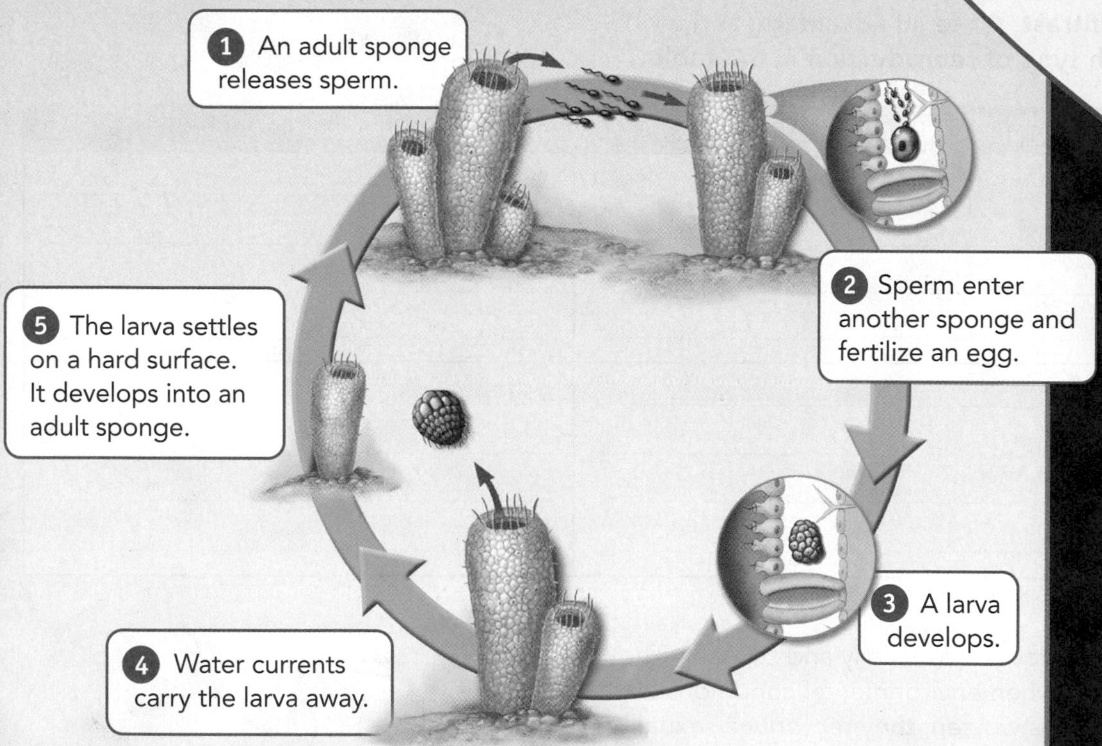

FIGURE 4 ···

Reproduction of a Sponge
These sponges are reproducing sexually. ✎ **Complete these tasks.**

1. **Identify** A budded sponge is a product of (asexual/sexual) reproduction and a larva is a product of (asexual/sexual) reproduction.

2. **Interpret Diagrams** How do the sponge larva and adult differ?

_____

_____

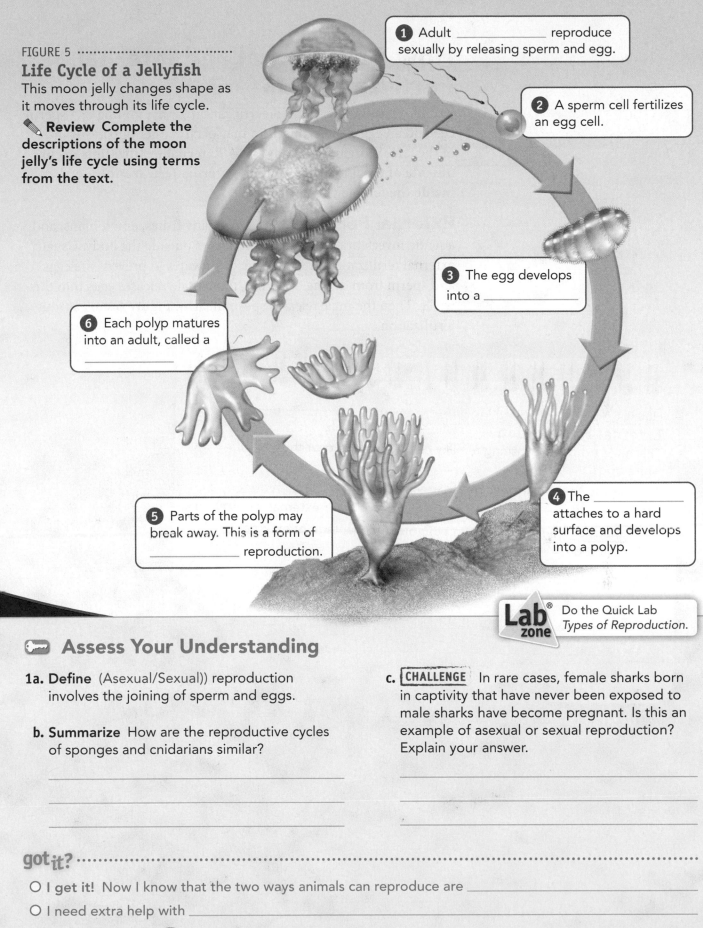

FIGURE 5 ··········

Life Cycle of a Jellyfish

This moon jelly changes shape as it moves through its life cycle.

✎ **Review** Complete the descriptions of the moon jelly's life cycle using terms from the text.

1 Adult _____ reproduce sexually by releasing sperm and egg.

2 A sperm cell fertilizes an egg cell.

3 The egg develops into a _____

4 The _____ attaches to a hard surface and develops into a polyp.

5 Parts of the polyp may break away. This is a form of _____ reproduction.

6 Each polyp matures into an adult, called a _____

Lab zone® Do the Quick Lab *Types of Reproduction.*

🔑 Assess Your Understanding

1a. Define (Asexual/Sexual)) reproduction involves the joining of sperm and eggs.

b. Summarize How are the reproductive cycles of sponges and cnidarians similar?

_____

_____

_____

c. [CHALLENGE] In rare cases, female sharks born in captivity that have never been exposed to male sharks have become pregnant. Is this an example of asexual or sexual reproduction? Explain your answer.

_____

_____

_____

got it? ···

○ **I get it!** Now I know that the two ways animals can reproduce are _____

○ **I need extra help with** _____

Go to **MY SCIENCE ⓢ COACH** online for help with this subject.

How Do External and Internal Fertilization Differ?

Sexual reproduction involves fertilization, or the joining of a sperm cell and an egg cell. Fertilization may occur either outside or inside of the female organism's body. 🔑 **External fertilization occurs outside of the female's body, and internal fertilization occurs inside the female's body.**

External Fertilization For many fishes, amphibians, and aquatic invertebrates, fertilization occurs outside the body. Usually external fertilization must take place in water to prevent the eggs and sperm from drying out. First, the female releases eggs into the water. Then the male releases sperm nearby. **Figure 6** shows trout fertilization.

FIGURE 6 ·····················

External Fertilization

This male trout is depositing a milky cloud of sperm over the round, white eggs.

✏️ **Use the text to answer the following questions.**

1. **Identify** (Land/Water) is the best environment for external fertilization.

2. **CHALLENGE** What might be a possible disadvantage of external fertilization?

_____

_____

_____

Internal Fertilization Fertilization occurs inside the body in many aquatic animals and all land animals. The male releases sperm directly into the female's body, where the eggs are located.

Most invertebrates and many fishes, amphibians, reptiles, and birds lay eggs outside the parent's body. The offspring continue to develop inside the eggs. For other animals, including most mammals, fertilized eggs develop inside the female animal. The female then gives birth to live young. The length of time between fertilization and birth is called the **gestation period.** Opossums have the shortest gestation period—around 13 days. African elephants have the longest gestation period—up to 22 months.

⊃ Compare and Contrast
Describe how external and internal fertilization are alike and different.

_____

_____

_____

_____

_____

_____

_____

do the math!

Study the graph and answer the questions below.

1 **Calculate** About how many days longer is the giraffe's gestation period than the fox's?

_____

2 **Make Generalizations** How do you think an animal's size relates to the length of its gestation period?

_____

_____

_____

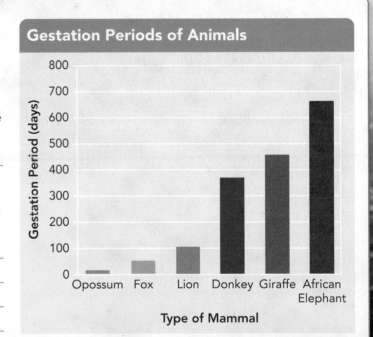

Gestation Periods of Animals

Gestation Period (days) — Type of Mammal: Opossum, Fox, Lion, Donkey, Giraffe, African Elephant

Lab zone® Do the Quick Lab
Types of Fertilization.

🔑 Assess Your Understanding

got it? ....

○ **I get it!** Now I know that external fertilization occurs _____

and internal fertilization occurs _____

○ **I need extra help with** _____

Go to MY SCIENCE ⓢ COACH online for help with this subject.

Development and Growth

UNLOCK THE BIG ?

🔑 Where Do Embryos Develop?

🔑 How Do Young Animals Develop?

🔑 How Do Animals Care for Their Young?

MY PLANET DIARY

DISCOVERY

Beware of Glass

Is that a beetle or a bottle? Australian jewel beetles seem to have trouble figuring out the difference. These large insects live in certain dry regions of Australia. Male beetles can fly, but the larger females cannot. As males fly around, they look for females. Males recognize females by the color and pattern of the female beetle's body. Researchers have discovered that male beetles are also attracted to something else with a similar color and pattern: glass bottles. Many beetles have been seen trying to mate with discarded glass bottles. Scientists are concerned that the jewel beetle population may be harmed—because mating with bottles does not produce jewel beetle offspring!

Read the paragraph and answer the questions below.

1. Why would the male's attempt to mate with bottles harm the jewel beetle population?

_____

_____

_____

_____

2. What is one way that this problem could be prevented?

_____

_____

> PLANET DIARY Go to **Planet Diary** to learn more about development and growth.

 Lab zone® Do the Inquiry Warm-Up "Eggs-amination."

Vocabulary
- amniotic egg
- placenta
- metamorphosis
- complete metamorphosis
- pupa
- incomplete metamorphosis
- nymph
- tadpole

Skills
- Reading: Identify the Main Idea
- Inquiry: Interpret Data

Where Do Embryos Develop?

Turtles, sharks, and mice all reproduce sexually. But after fertilization occurs, the offspring of these animals develop in different ways. **The growing offspring, or embryo, may develop outside or inside of the parent's body.**

Egg-Laying Animals The offspring of some animals develop inside an egg laid outside of the parent's body. Most animals without backbones, including worms and insects, lay eggs. Many fishes, reptiles, and birds lay eggs, too. The contents of the egg provide all the nutrients that the developing embryo needs. The eggs of land vertebrates, such as reptiles and birds, are called **amniotic eggs.** Amniotic eggs are covered with membranes and a leathery shell while still inside the parent's body. **Figure 1** shows some of the structures of an amniotic egg.

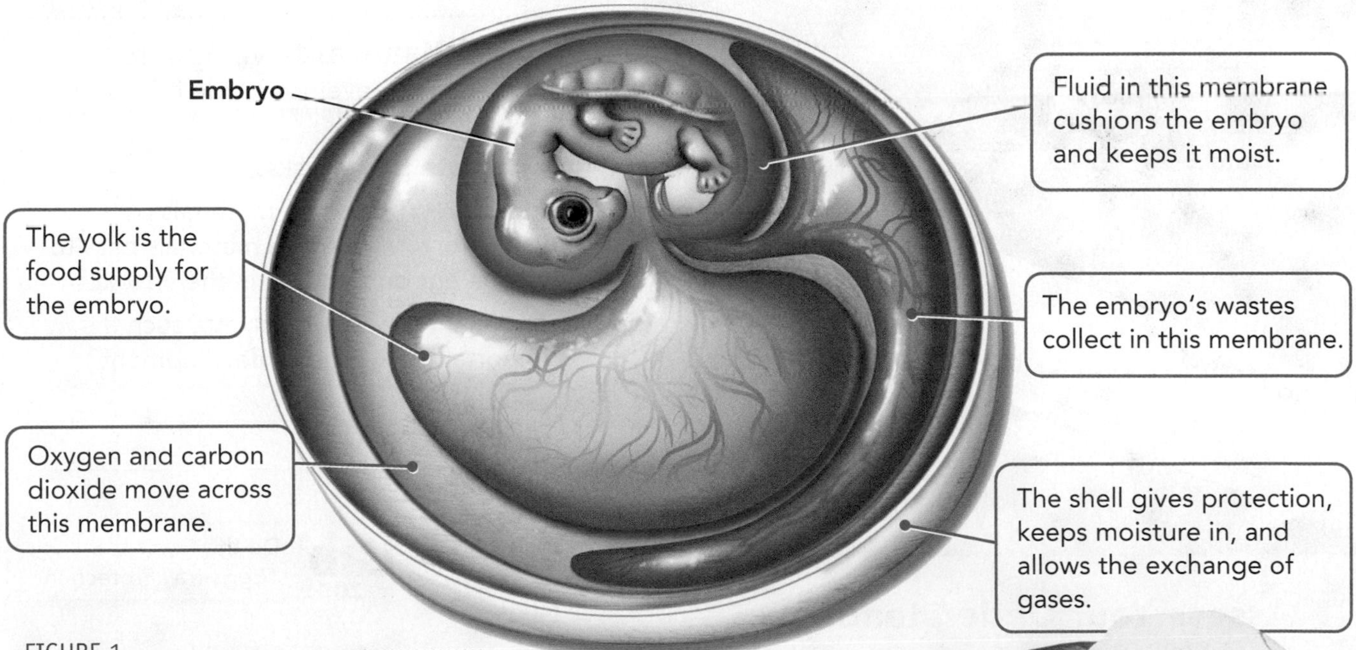

Embryo

Fluid in this membrane cushions the embryo and keeps it moist.

The yolk is the food supply for the embryo.

The embryo's wastes collect in this membrane.

Oxygen and carbon dioxide move across this membrane.

The shell gives protection, keeps moisture in, and allows the exchange of gases.

FIGURE 1 ·····················
Amniotic Egg
Reptiles, such as this tortoise, develop inside an amniotic egg. The amniotic egg is a unique adaptation for life on land.

✏ **Relate Text to Visuals** Circle the descriptions of the structures that keep the embryo from drying out.

Egg-Retaining Animals

In certain animals, an embryo develops inside an egg that is kept, or retained, within the parent's body. The developing embryo gets all its nutrients from the egg's yolk, just like the offspring of egg-laying animals. The young do not receive any extra nutrients from the parent. The egg hatches either before or after being released from the parent's body. This type of development is found in fishes, amphibians, and reptiles.

Placental Mammals

In dogs, horses, humans, and other placental mammals, the embryo develops inside the mother's body. The mother provides the embryo with everything it needs during development. Materials are exchanged between the embryo and the mother through an organ called the **placenta,** shown in **Figure 2.** Blood carrying food and oxygen from the mother flows to the placenta and then to the embryo. Blood carrying wastes and carbon dioxide from the embryo flows to the placenta and then to the mother. The mother's blood does not mix with the embryo's blood. A placental mammal develops inside its mother's body until its body systems can function on their own.

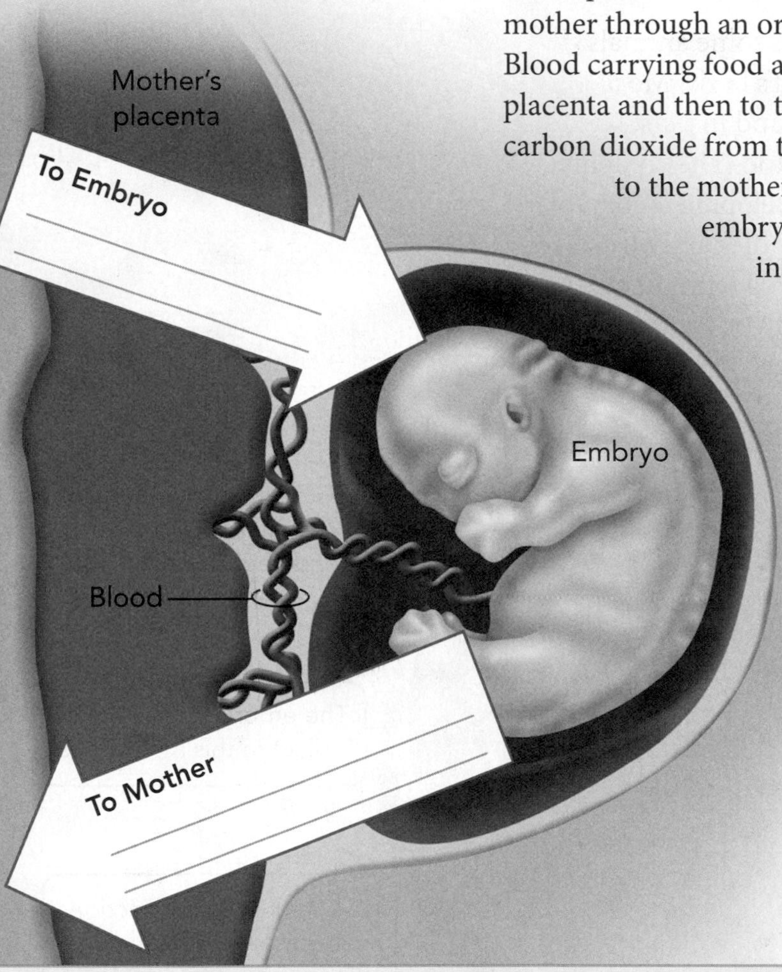

Mother's placenta

To Embryo

Embryo

Blood

To Mother

FIGURE 2 ···

Placental Mammal Development
This cat embryo develops inside its mother for about two months.

✎ **Complete these tasks.**

1. **Identify** Write which materials pass to the embryo and which materials pass to the parent on the lines in the arrows.

2. **Explain** Why is the placenta such an important structure in development?

_____

_____

 Do the Quick Lab "Eggs-tra" Protection.

⚷ Assess Your Understanding

got it? ···

○ **I get it!** Now I know that the places embryos can develop are _____

_____

○ **I need extra help with**_____

Go to **MY SCIENCE ⓢ COACH** online for help with this subject.

How Do Young Animals Develop?

Living things grow, change, and reproduce during their lifetimes. Some young animals, including most vertebrates, look like small versions of adults. Other animals go through the process of **metamorphosis,** or major body changes, as they develop from young organisms into adults. 🔑 **Young animals undergo changes in their bodies between birth and maturity, when they are able to reproduce.** As you read, notice the similarities and differences among the life cycles of crustaceans, insects, and amphibians.

Crustaceans Most crustaceans, such as lobsters, crabs, and shrimp, begin their lives as tiny, swimming larvae. The bodies of these larvae do not resemble those of adults. Larvae may swim or drift in the water as they grow and change. Eventually, through metamorphosis, crustacean larvae develop into adults. **Figure 3** shows three stages of a lobster's life cycle.

FIGURE 3 ....

Lobster Metamorphosis
Lobster larvae are only 8 millimeters long. Adults can reach lengths of 1 meter!

✏️ **Use the photos to help you complete the tasks.**

1. **Sequence** Write the correct order of the lobster's development in the circles above each photo.

2. **Interpret Photos** Which structures changed as the lobster developed and grew?

_____

_____

_____

279

Insects Have you ever seen an insect egg? You might find one on the underside of a leaf. After an insect hatches from the egg, it begins metamorphosis as it develops into an adult. Insects such as butterflies, beetles, and grasshoppers undergo complete metamorphosis or incomplete metamorphosis.

Complete Metamorphosis The cycle to the right shows a ladybug going through **complete metamorphosis,** which has four different stages: egg, larva, pupa, and adult. An egg hatches into a larva. A larva usually looks something like a worm. It is specialized for eating and growing. After a time, a larva enters the next stage of the process and becomes a **pupa** (PYOO puh). As a pupa, the insect is enclosed in a protective covering. Although the pupa does not eat and moves very little, it is not resting. Major changes in body structure take place in this stage, as the pupa becomes an adult.

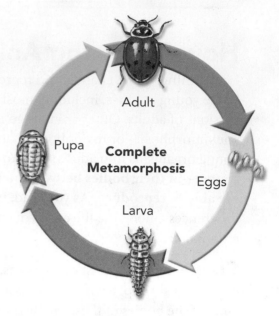

Adult

Pupa

Complete Metamorphosis

Eggs

Larva

Inside the pupa case, adult structures such as wings, antennae, and legs form.

A monarch butterfly egg develops on a milkweed plant.

A larva, or a caterpillar, hatches from the egg. The caterpillar grows larger as it feeds on plants. Then it enters the pupa stage.

Incomplete Metamorphosis In contrast, a second type of metamorphosis, called **incomplete metamorphosis,** has no distinct larval stage. Incomplete metamorphosis has three stages: egg, nymph, and adult. An egg hatches into a stage called a **nymph** (nimf), which usually looks like the adult insect without wings. As the nymph grows, it may shed its outgrown exoskeleton several times before becoming an adult. The chinch bug to the right is going through incomplete metamorphosis.

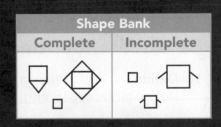

Adult

Nymph

Incomplete Metamorphosis

Eggs

Nymph

The adult butterfly comes out of the pupa case and the butterfly's wings expand as the blood flows into them.

FIGURE 4 ·······················

▷ INTERACTIVE ART

Insect Metamorphosis
The photos show a monarch butterfly going through complete metamorphosis.

✎ Sequence In the cycles below, the shapes represent stages of complete or incomplete metamorphosis. Using the shape bank, draw the shapes that you think best represent the missing stages in each type of metamorphosis.

▲
An adult monarch butterfly

Shape Bank	
Complete	**Incomplete**

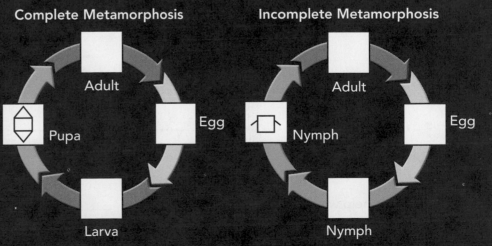

Complete Metamorphosis

Adult

Egg

Pupa

Larva

Incomplete Metamorphosis

Adult

Egg

Nymph

Nymph

Amphibians Frogs begin their life cycle as fertilized eggs in water. After a few days, larvae wriggle out of the eggs and begin swimming. The larva of a frog is called a **tadpole.** Tadpoles look very different from adult frogs. You can follow the process of frog metamorphosis in **Figure 5.**

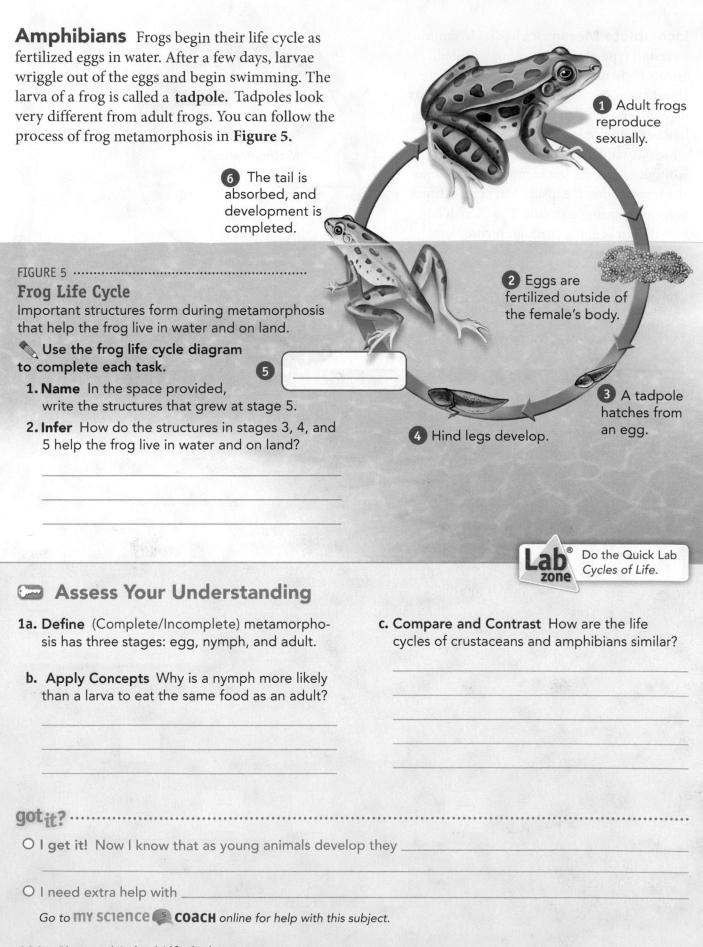

FIGURE 5 ·······················
Frog Life Cycle
Important structures form during metamorphosis that help the frog live in water and on land.

✎ **Use the frog life cycle diagram to complete each task.**

1. **Name** In the space provided, write the structures that grew at stage 5.

2. **Infer** How do the structures in stages 3, 4, and 5 help the frog live in water and on land?

_____

_____

_____

1 Adult frogs reproduce sexually.

6 The tail is absorbed, and development is completed.

2 Eggs are fertilized outside of the female's body.

5 _____

3 A tadpole hatches from an egg.

4 Hind legs develop.

Lab ® Do the Quick Lab
zone *Cycles of Life.*

🔑 Assess Your Understanding

1a. Define (Complete/Incomplete) metamorphosis has three stages: egg, nymph, and adult.

b. Apply Concepts Why is a nymph more likely than a larva to eat the same food as an adult?

_____

_____

_____

c. Compare and Contrast How are the life cycles of crustaceans and amphibians similar?

_____

_____

_____

_____

_____

got it? ···

○ **I get it!** Now I know that as young animals develop they _____

_____

○ I need extra help with _____

Go to **MY SCIENCE** ⓢ **COACH** online for help with this subject.

How Do Animals Care for Their Young?

Have you seen a caterpillar, tadpole, puppy, duckling, or other baby animal recently? You may have noticed that different animals care for their offspring in different ways. **Most amphibians and reptiles do not provide parental care, while most birds and mammals typically care for their offspring.**

No Parental Care Not all animals take care of their young. Most aquatic invertebrates, fishes, and amphibians release many eggs into water and then completely ignore them! Most amphibian larvae, or tadpoles, develop into adults without parental help. Similarly, the offspring of most reptiles, such as the snakes in **Figure 6,** are independent from the time they hatch. Offspring that do not receive parental care must be able to care for themselves from the time of birth.

FIGURE 6 ....

Checklist for Survival

These hognose snakes have just hatched from their eggs. They may stay inside the shell for several days for safety.

✏ **List** Make a list of what you think these snakes must be able to do to survive their first few days of life.

Parental Care You've probably never seen a duckling walking by itself. That's because most birds and all mammals typically spend weeks to years under the care and protection of a parent.

Birds Most bird species lay their eggs in nests that one or both parents build. Then one or both parents sit on the eggs, keeping them warm until they hatch. Some species of birds can move around and find food right after they hatch. Others are helpless and must be fed by the parent, as shown in **Figure 7.** Most parent birds feed and protect their young until they are able to care for themselves.

Mammals Whether a monotreme, a marsupial, or a placental mammal, young mammals are usually quite helpless for a long time after they are born. After birth, all young mammals are fed with milk from the mother's body. One or both parents may continue caring for their offspring until the young animals are independent.

FIGURE 7 ···

Parental Care

The parent bird shown above cares for its hungry offspring until they are ready to fly. The mother polar bear at the right stays with her cubs for up to two years.

✎ **Answer each question.**

1. **Interpret Photos** How are the parents in these two photos caring for their young?

_____

_____

_____

_____

2. **Communicate** What is one way that a family member cares for you?

_____

_____

_____

do the math! Analyzing Data

Suppose that you are a scientist researching how many fox and turtle offspring survive the first year of life. Foxes provide parental care, but turtles do not.

Type of Animal	Number of Offspring	Number That Survive the First Year	Percentage That Survive the First Year
Fox	5	_____	60%
Turtle	20	_____	20%

1 Calculate Using the information in the second and fourth columns of the table, calculate the number of offspring that survive the first year. Put your answer in the third column of the table.

2 Graph Use the data from the table to construct a double bar graph in the space provided. Label the vertical axis. Then provide a key for the data in the graph.

3 Interpret Data How do you think parental care is related to the percentage of offspring that survive the first year of life?

_____

_____

_____

_____

4 CHALLENGE Why do you think animals that provide parental care have fewer offspring?

_____

_____

_____

_____

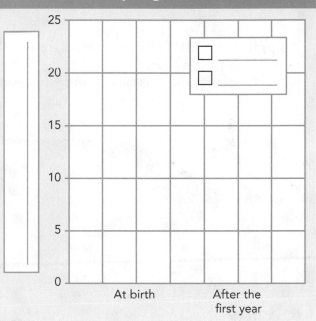

Survival of Offspring

25

20

15

10

5

0

At birth   After the first year

EXPLORE THE BIG Q

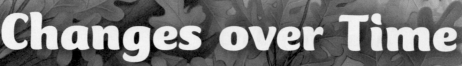

Changes over Time

How do plants and animals reproduce and grow?

FIGURE 8

REAL-WORLD INQUIRY The plants and animals that live in and near a pond reproduce and grow in different ways during different seasons.

Complete the tasks in the boxes.

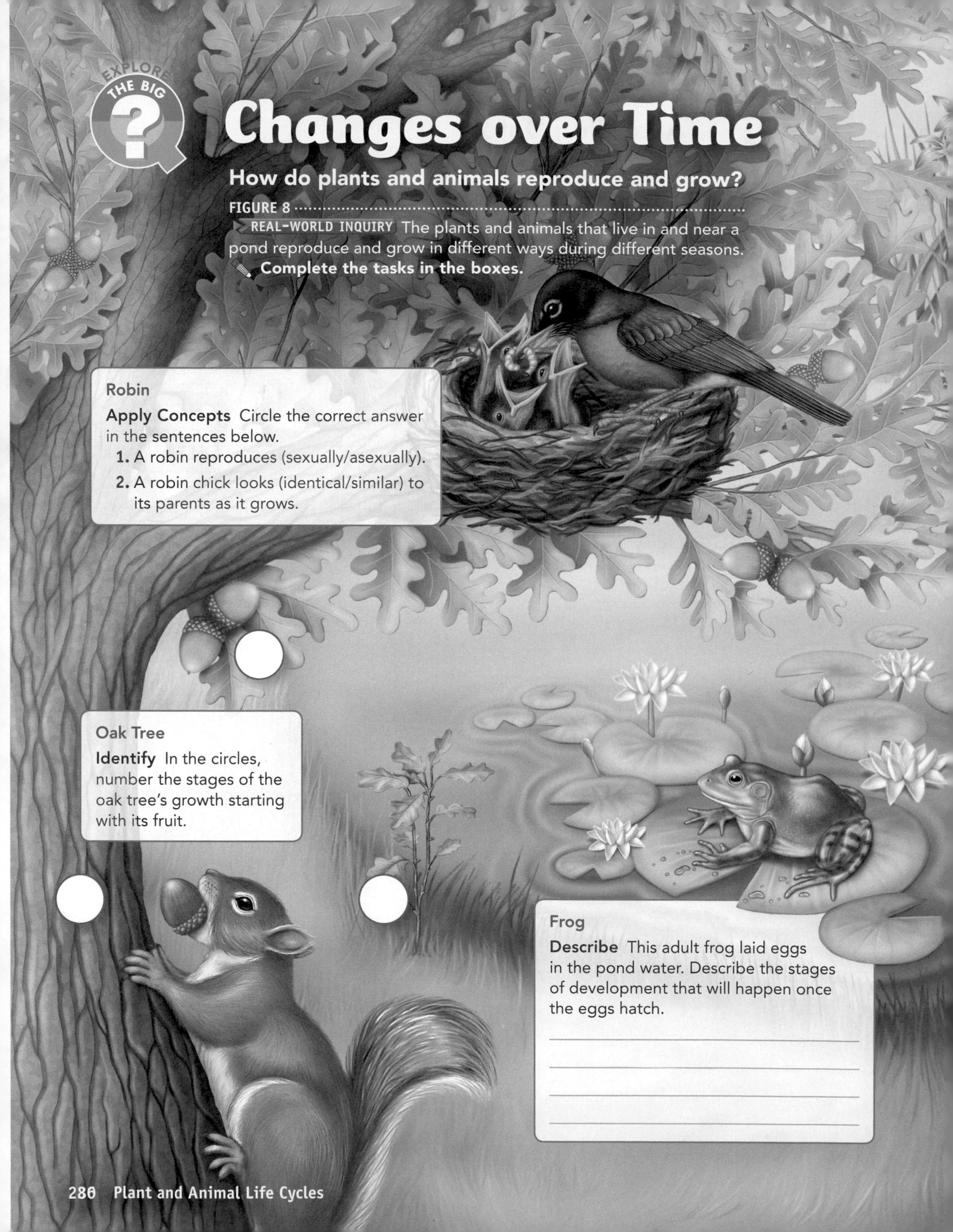

Robin

Apply Concepts Circle the correct answer in the sentences below.

1. A robin reproduces (sexually/asexually).
2. A robin chick looks (identical/similar) to its parents as it grows.

Oak Tree

Identify In the circles, number the stages of the oak tree's growth starting with its fruit.

Frog

Describe This adult frog laid eggs in the pond water. Describe the stages of development that will happen once the eggs hatch.

____

____

____

____

Fern

Review Circle the correct answer in the sentences below.
1. Ferns reproduce by releasing (seeds/spores) into their environment.
2. The ferns shown in the picture are in the (sporophyte/gametophyte) stage of growth.

Daylily

Sequence First, a daylily flower's anther produces pollen and its ovule produces egg cells. Order the rest of the daylily's reproductive stages.

___ Pollen is trapped on the stigma.

___ The ovary develops into a fruit.

___ The ovule develops into a seed.

___ A seed grows into a new plant.

___ Pollen produces a pollen tube into the ovule. A sperm cell moves through the tube and fertilizes the egg cell.

Lab zone® Do the Quick Lab *To Care or Not to Care.*

Assess Your Understanding

a. Explain Is a bird or a snake more likely to have fewer offspring? Why?

_____

_____

_____

_____

b. ANSWER THE BIG ? How do plants and animals reproduce and grow?

_____

_____

_____

_____

got it? ....

O **I get it!** Now I know that animals care for their young by_____

_____

O **I need extra help with** _____

Go to **MY SCIENCE COACH** online for help with this subject.

Plants reproduce _____. Animals reproduce either _____. Plants and animals undergo changes as they grow.

LESSON 1 Plant Structures

🔑 A plant's roots, stems, and leaves anchor the plant, absorb water and minerals, capture the sun's energy, and make food.

🔑 A seed contains a partially developed plant.

🔑 A typical flower contains sepals, petals, stamens, and pistils.

Vocabulary
- root cap • cambium • stoma • transpiration
- embryo • germination • flower • pollination
- sepal • petal • stamen • pistil • ovary

LESSON 2 Plant Reproduction

🔑 Plants have complex life cycles that include a sporophyte stage and a gametophyte stage.

🔑 All plants undergo sexual reproduction that involves fertilization.

Vocabulary
- sporophyte • gametophyte • annual • biennial
- perennial • fertilization • zygote • cone
- ovule • fruit

LESSON 3 Animal Reproduction and Fertilization

🔑 Animals undergo either asexual or sexual reproduction to make more of their own kind or species.

🔑 External fertilization occurs outside of the female's body, and internal fertilization occurs inside the female's body.

Vocabulary
- larva • polyp • medusa
- external fertilization • internal fertilization
- gestation period

LESSON 4 Development and Growth

🔑 The growing offspring, or embryo, may develop outside or inside of the parent's body.

🔑 Young animals undergo changes in their bodies between birth and maturity.

🔑 Most amphibians and reptiles do not provide parental care. Most birds and mammals do.

Vocabulary
- amniotic egg • placenta • metamorphosis
- complete metamorphosis • pupa
- incomplete metamorphosis • nymph • tadpole

Review and Assessment

LESSON 1 Plant Structures

1. A plant absorbs water and minerals through

a. roots.   b. stems.

c. leaves.   d. stomata.

2. Transpiration slows down when

_____ are closed.

3. Relate Cause and Effect When a strip of bark is removed all the way around the trunk of a tree, the tree dies. Explain why.

_____

_____

_____

4. Write About It Plant structures do not look the same among all plants. For example, some leaves are short and others long. Explain why you think there is so much variation.

LESSON 2 Plant Reproduction

5. A zygote is the direct result of

a. pollination.

b. fertilization.

c. biennial growth.

d. the sporophyte stage.

6. _____ complete their life cycles

within one growing season.

7. Sequence Describe the major events in the plant life cycle. Use the terms *zygote, sperm, sporophyte, spores, gametophyte,* and *egg.*

_____

_____

_____

_____

_____

LESSON 3 Animal Reproduction and Fertilization

8. External fertilization is common for organisms that live in

a. trees.   b. water.

c. deserts.   d. open fields.

9. The _____ is an immature

form of an organism that looks very different

from the adult.

10. Classify Label each body form of the moon jelly. Then on the lines below identify whether each form represents an asexual or sexual stage.

_____

_____

_____

11. Compare and Contrast How are the ways a trout and a bird undergo fertilization alike and different?

_____

_____

_____

_____

12. Write About It Consider the following statement: *Organisms that reproduce asexually are at a higher risk of extinction than organisms that reproduce sexually.* Do you agree or disagree? Explain your answer.

289

LESSON 4 Development and Growth

13. Which of the following organisms lays amniotic eggs?

   a. fish   **b.** insect

   c. turtle   **d.** rabbit

14. Both _____ and _____ care for their young.

15. List What stages do insects go through during complete and incomplete metamorphosis?

_____

_____

_____

16. Sequence Label each stage of complete metamorphosis. Then number each stage to put it in the correct order.

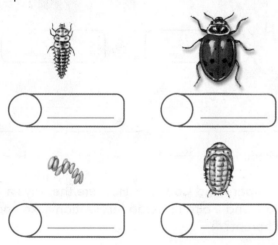

17. Compare and Contrast How is the development of an embryo in an amniotic egg and in a placental mammal different?

_____

_____

_____

_____

How do plants and animals reproduce and grow?

18. Compare and contrast the life cycles of a pine tree, a gymnosperm, and the Louisiana black bear, a mammal. Include how the organisms reproduce. Use vocabulary terms from the chapter.

_____

_____

_____

_____

_____

_____

_____

_____

_____

_____

_____

_____

_____

_____

_____

_____

_____

_____

_____

_____

_____

_____

_____

_____

_____

_____

Ohio Benchmark Practice

Multiple Choice

Mark only one answer for each question.

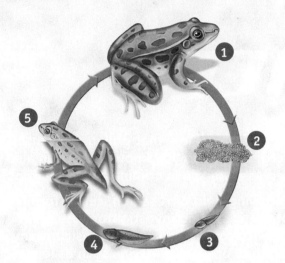

1. The larval form of the frog shown in stage 3 is called a

   A. nymph.
   B. pupa.
   C. tadpole.
   D. adult.

2. An amniotic egg is the result of _____ and _____.

   A. asexual reproduction; external fertilization
   B. asexual reproduction; internal fertilization
   C. sexual reproduction; external fertilization
   D. sexual reproduction; internal fertilization

3. Most gymnosperms produce _____, while most angiosperms produce _____.

   A. sperm, eggs
   B. pollen, cones
   C. cones, flowers
   D. flowers, fruits

4. What are the stages of incomplete metamorphosis?

   A. egg, nymph, adult
   B. egg, nymph, pupa, adult
   C. egg, larva, pupa, adult
   D. egg, larva, adult

Short Answer

Write your answers to questions 5 and 6 on another sheet of paper.

5. A grasshopper undergoes complete metamorphosis. A dragonfly undergoes incomplete metamorphosis. Compare and contrast the stages of their development.

Use the diagram below to answer question 6.

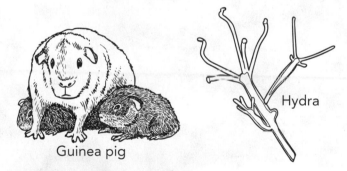

Guinea pig   Hydra

6. Identify what type of reproduction occurs in the guinea pig and the hydra. Then, compare and contrast the two types of reproduction.

Everyday Science

GRAINS
OF EVIDENCE

You probably know that pollen can cause allergies, but did you know that it can also be used as evidence in criminal investigations?

A growing field of research, called forensic botany, is helping investigators use plant evidence to solve crimes. Forensic botany is the study of plant material, such as leaves, pollen, wood, or seeds, to investigate a crime. Because certain plants grow in specific areas and flower at specific times, plant material can help identify the time or place that a crime occurred.

Seeds or pollen found on a suspect's clothing can be used to link a suspect to a crime scene. Botanical evidence can also be found in a victim's stomach. Because certain plant parts cannot be digested, forensic botanists can even determine a victim's last meal!

Write About It Find out more about the life cycle of a plant described in this chapter. Draw a life cycle for the plant. Then describe how investigators could use knowledge of the plant's life cycle to solve a crime.

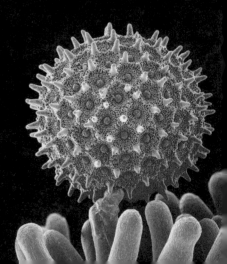

◄ Back in 1997 in New Zealand, pollen grains such as this one were used as the evidence to prove that a suspect was involved in a struggle at the crime scene.

PLANTING
ROOTS IN OUTER
SPACE

Far from farms and greenhouses on Earth, future space explorers will need to grow their own food, and recycle and purify their air and water. Astronauts from the National Aeronautics and Space Administration (NASA) have been experimenting with plants in space for many years.

Which Way Is Up?

On Earth, plant roots grow downward and outward in response to Earth's gravity, while plant shoots grow upward. In space, where there is no clear up or down, roots and shoots both grow toward the light! In order to grow with the roots at the bottom and the stems at the top, plants need gravity. So space stations need special plant chambers that rotate continuously to create artificial gravity for plants.

Tomatoes From Outer Space

To study whether radiation in space will affect the ability of seeds to grow, NASA scientists placed 12.5 million tomato seeds in a satellite that orbited Earth for six years! Students around the world then planted the seeds, which grew normally and produced normal tomatoes. So scientists now know that seeds will survive for a long time in orbit.

Design It Scientists are still learning about how to grow plants to support space travel. Find out about current NASA research on plants in space. Identify one question you have about plant growth in space. Then write a proposal for an experiment to investigate your question.

A researcher holds tiny *Arabidopsis* seedlings. *Arabidopsis* plants are related to the cabbage plant, and are often used as model plants in research projects.

WHAT MAKES THIS BABY KOALA DIFFERENT?

THE BIG ?

Why don't offspring always look like their parents?

Even though this young koala, or joey, has two fuzzy ears, a long nose, and a body shaped like its mom's, you can see that the two are different. You might expect a young animal to look exactly like its parents, but think about how varied a litter of kittens or puppies can look. This joey is an albino—an animal that lacks the usual coloring in its eyes, fur, and skin.

△ **Observe** Describe how this joey looks different from its mom.

_____

_____

_____

_____

▶ **UNTAMED SCIENCE** Watch the **Untamed Science** video to learn more about heredity.

Genetics: The Science of Heredity

9 Getting Started

Check Your Understanding

1. Background Read the paragraph below and then answer the question.

Kent's cat just had six kittens. All six kittens look different from one another—and from their two parents! Kent knows each kitten is unique because cats reproduce through **sexual reproduction,** not **asexual reproduction.** Before long, the kittens will grow bigger and bigger as their cells divide through **mitosis.**

- In what way are the two daughter cells that form by mitosis and cell division identical?

_____

> **MY READING WEB** If you had trouble completing the question above, visit **My Reading Web** and type in *Genetics: The Science of Heredity.*

Sexual reproduction involves two parents and combines their genetic material to produce a new organism that differs from both parents.

Asexual reproduction involves only one parent and produces offspring that are identical to the parent.

During **mitosis,** a cell's nucleus divides into two new nuclei, and one copy of DNA is distributed into each daughter cell.

Vocabulary Skill

Suffixes A suffix is a word part that is added to the end of a word to change its meaning. For example, the suffix *-tion* means "process of." If you add the suffix *-tion* to the verb *fertilize,* you get the noun *fertilization. Fertilization* means "the process of fertilizing." The table below lists some other common suffixes and their meanings.

Suffix	Meaning	Example
-ive	performing a particular action	recessive allele, *n.* an allele that is masked when a dominant allele is present
-ance or *-ant*	state, condition of	codominance, *n.* occurs when both alleles are expressed equally

2. Quick Check Fill in the blank with the correct suffix.

- A domin_____ allele can mask a recessive allele.

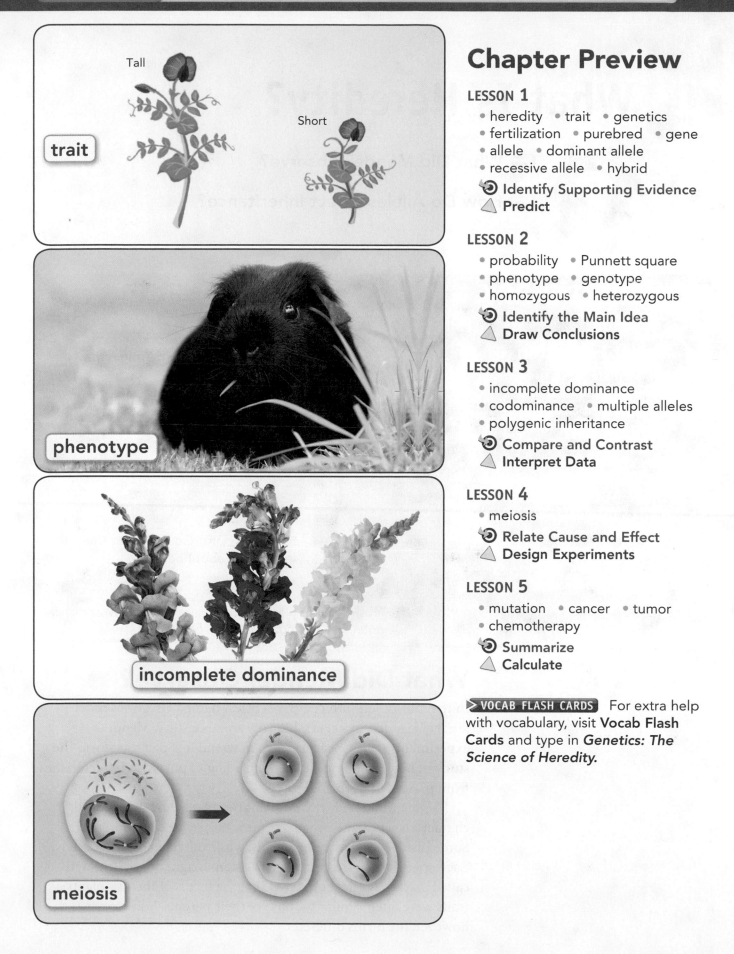

trait

Tall

Short

phenotype

incomplete dominance

meiosis

Chapter Preview

LESSON 1
- heredity • trait • genetics
- fertilization • purebred • gene
- allele • dominant allele
- recessive allele • hybrid

⊙ **Identify Supporting Evidence**
△ **Predict**

LESSON 2
- probability • Punnett square
- phenotype • genotype
- homozygous • heterozygous

⊙ **Identify the Main Idea**
△ **Draw Conclusions**

LESSON 3
- incomplete dominance
- codominance • multiple alleles
- polygenic inheritance

⊙ **Compare and Contrast**
△ **Interpret Data**

LESSON 4
- meiosis

⊙ **Relate Cause and Effect**
△ **Design Experiments**

LESSON 5
- mutation • cancer • tumor
- chemotherapy

⊙ **Summarize**
△ **Calculate**

▶ VOCAB FLASH CARDS   For extra help with vocabulary, visit **Vocab Flash Cards** and type in *Genetics: The Science of Heredity.*

What Is Heredity?

UNLOCK THE BIG ?

🔑 **What Did Mendel Observe?**

🔑 **How Do Alleles Affect Inheritance?**

my planet DiaRY

Almost Forgotten

When scientists make great discoveries, sometimes their work is praised, criticized, or even forgotten. Gregor Mendel was almost forgotten. He spent eight years studying pea plants, and he discovered patterns in the way characteristics pass from one generation to the next. For almost 40 years, people overlooked Mendel's work. When it was finally rediscovered, it unlocked the key to understanding heredity.

BIOGRAPHY

Communicate Discuss the question below with a partner. Then write your answer.

Did you ever rediscover something of yours that you had forgotten? How did you react?

_____

_____

_____

▶ **PLANET DIARY** Go to **Planet Diary** to learn more about heredity.

Lab zone Do the Inquiry Warm-Up *What Does the Father Look Like?*

What Did Mendel Observe?

In the mid-nineteenth century, a priest named Gregor Mendel tended a garden in a central European monastery. Mendel's experiments in that peaceful garden would one day transform the study of heredity. **Heredity** is the passing of physical characteristics from parents to offspring.

Mendel wondered why different pea plants had different characteristics. Some pea plants grew tall, while others were short. Some plants produced green seeds, while others had yellow seeds. Each specific characteristic, such as stem height or seed color, is called a **trait.** Mendel observed that the forms of the pea plants' traits were often similar to those of their parents. Sometimes, however, the forms differed.

Vocabulary

- heredity • trait • genetics • fertilization
- purebred • gene • allele • dominant allele
- recessive allele • hybrid

Skills

- Reading: Identify Supporting Evidence
- Inquiry: Predict

Mendel's Experiments Mendel experimented with thousands of pea plants. Today, Mendel's discoveries form the foundation of **genetics,** the scientific study of heredity. **Figure 1** shows the parts of a pea plant's flower. The pistil produces female sex cells, or eggs. The stamens produce pollen, which contains the male sex cells, or sperm. A new organism begins to form when egg and sperm cells join in the process called **fertilization.** Before fertilization can happen in pea plants, pollen must reach the pistil of a pea flower. This process is called pollination.

Pea plants are usually self-pollinating. In self-pollination, pollen from a flower lands on the pistil of the same flower. Mendel developed a method by which he cross-pollinated, or "crossed," pea plants. **Figure 1** shows his method.

Mendel decided to cross plants that had contrasting forms of a trait—for example, tall plants and short plants. He started with purebred plants. A **purebred** organism is the offspring of many generations that have the same form of a trait. For example, purebred tall pea plants always come from tall parent plants.

FIGURE 1 ·······················

Crossing Pea Plants

Mendel devised a way to cross-pollinate pea plants.

✎ Use the diagram to answer the questions about Mendel's procedure.

1. **Observe** How does flower B differ from flower A?

_____

_____

2. **Infer** Describe how Mendel cross-pollinated pea plants.

_____

_____

_____

_____

Pistil

Stamens

Pollen

299

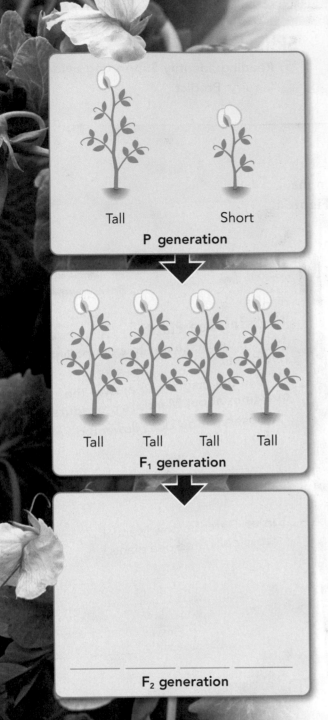

Tall   Short
P generation

Tall   Tall   Tall   Tall
F₁ generation

F₂ generation

The F₁ and F₂ Offspring

Mendel crossed purebred tall plants with purebred short plants. Today, scientists call these plants the parental, or P, generation. The resulting offspring are the first filial (FIL ee ul), or F₁, generation. The word *filial* comes from *filia* and *filius*, the Latin words for "daughter" and "son."

Look at **Figure 2** to see the surprise Mendel found in the F₁ generation. All the offspring were tall. The shortness trait seemed to have disappeared!

When these plants were full-grown, Mendel allowed them to self-pollinate. The F₂ (second filial) generation that followed surprised Mendel even more. He counted the plants of the F₂ generation. About three fourths were tall, while one fourth were short.

Experiments With Other Traits

Mendel repeated his experiments, studying other pea-plant traits, such as flower color and seed shape. **In all of his crosses, Mendel found that only one form of the trait appeared in the F₁ generation. However, in the F₂ generation, the "lost" form of the trait always reappeared in about one fourth of the plants.**

FIGURE 2 ·······························

Results of a Cross

In Mendel's crosses, some forms of a trait were hidden in one generation but reappeared in the next.

✎ **Interpret Diagrams** Draw and label the offspring in the F₂ generation.

 Do the Quick Lab *Observing Pistils and Stamens.*

🔑 Assess Your Understanding

1a. Define What happens during fertilization?

_____

_____

b. Compare and Contrast In Mendel's cross for stem height, how did the plants in the F₂ generations differ from the F₁ plants?

_____

got it?

○ **I get it!** Now I know that Mendel found that one form of a trait _____

_____

○ **I need extra help with** _____

Go to **MY SCIENCE ⓢ COACH** online for help with this subject.

How Do Alleles Affect Inheritance?

Mendel reached several conclusions from his experimental results. He reasoned that individual factors, or sets of genetic "information," must control the inheritance of traits in peas. The factors that control each trait exist in pairs. The female parent contributes one factor, while the male parent contributes the other factor. Finally, one factor in a pair can mask, or hide, the other factor. The tallness factor, for example, masked the shortness factor.

Genes and Alleles Today, scientists use the word **gene** to describe the factors that control a trait. **Alleles** (uh LEELZ) are the different forms of a gene. The gene that controls stem height in peas has one allele for tall stems and one allele for short stems. Each pea plant inherits two alleles—one from the egg and the other from the sperm. A plant may inherit two alleles for tall stems, two alleles for short stems, or one of each.

🔑 **An organism's traits are controlled by the alleles it inherits from its parents. Some alleles are dominant, while other alleles are recessive.** A **dominant allele** is one whose trait always shows up in the organism when the allele is present. A **recessive allele,** on the other hand, is hidden whenever the dominant allele is present. **Figure 3** shows dominant and recessive alleles of the traits in Mendel's crosses.

FIGURE 3 ·······················

Alleles in Pea Plants

Mendel studied the inheritance of seven different traits in pea plants.

✏️ **Use the table to answer the questions.**

1. **Draw Conclusions** Circle the picture of each dominant form of the trait in the P generation.

2. **Predict** Under what conditions would the recessive form of one of these traits reappear?

_____

_____

Inheritance of Pea Plants Studied by Mendel

	Seed Shape	Seed Color	Pod Shape	Pod Color	Flower Color	Flower Position	Stem Height
P	Wrinkled  X  Round	Yellow  X  Green	Pinched 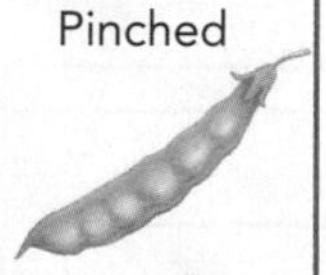 X  Smooth	Green  X  Yellow	Purple  X  White	Tip of stem  X  Side of stem	Tall  X  Short
F₁	 Round	 Yellow	 Smooth	 Green	 Purple	 Side of stem	 Tall

Alleles in Mendel's Crosses

In Mendel's cross for stem height, the purebred tall plants in the P generation had two alleles for tall stems. The purebred short plants had two alleles for short stems. But each F_1 plant inherited one allele for tall stems and one allele for short stems. The F_1 plants are called hybrids. A **hybrid** (HY brid) organism has two different alleles for a trait. All the F_1 plants are tall because the dominant allele for tall stems masks the recessive allele for short stems.

Symbols for Alleles

Geneticists, scientists who study genetics, often use letters to represent alleles. A dominant allele is symbolized by a capital letter. A recessive allele is symbolized by the lowercase version of the same letter. For example, T stands for the allele for tall stems, and t stands for the allele for short stems. When a plant has two dominant alleles for tall stems, its alleles are written as TT. When a plant has two recessive alleles for short stems, its alleles are written as tt. These plants are the P generation shown in **Figure 4.** Think about the symbols that would be used for F_1 plants that all inherit one allele for tall stems and one for short stems.

FIGURE 4 ·····························

▷ **VIRTUAL LAB** **Dominant and Recessive Alleles**

Symbols serve as a shorthand way to identify alleles.

✎ **Complete each row of the diagram.**

1. **Identify** Fill in the missing allele symbols and descriptions.

2. **Summarize** Use the word bank to complete the statements. (Terms will be used more than once.)

3. **Relate Cause and Effect** Draw the two possible ways the F_2 offspring could look.

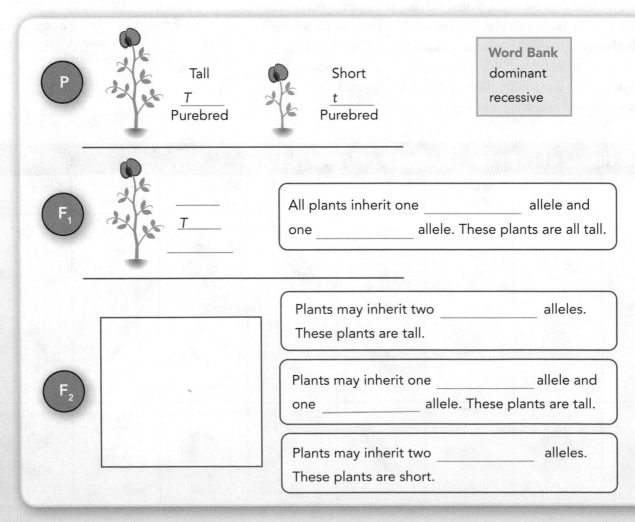

| P | Tall $\underline{T}$ Purebred | Short $\underline{t}$ Purebred | **Word Bank** dominant recessive |

F_1 _____ $\underline{T}$ _____

All plants inherit one _____ allele and one _____ allele. These plants are all tall.

F_2

Plants may inherit two _____ alleles. These plants are tall.

Plants may inherit one _____ allele and one _____ allele. These plants are tall.

Plants may inherit two _____ alleles. These plants are short.

apply it!

In fruit flies, long wings are dominant over short wings. A scientist crossed a purebred long-winged fruit fly with a purebred short-winged fruit fly.

1 If *W* stands for long wings, write the symbols for the alleles of each parent fly.

_____

2 △ **Predict** What will be the wing length of the F$_1$ offspring?

_____

3 △ **Predict** If the scientist crosses a hybrid male F$_1$ fruit fly with a hybrid F$_1$ female, what will their offspring probably be like?

_____

_____

_____

Significance of Mendel's Contribution

Mendel's discovery of genes and alleles eventually changed scientists' ideas about heredity. Before Mendel, most people thought that the traits of an individual organism were simply a blend of the parents' characteristics. Mendel showed that offspring traits are determined by individual, separate alleles inherited from each parent. Unfortunately, the value of Mendel's discovery was not known during his lifetime. But when scientists in the early 1900s rediscovered Mendel's work, they quickly realized its importance. Because of his work, Mendel is often called the Father of Genetics.

✐ **Identify Supporting Evidence** What evidence showed Mendel that traits are determined by separate alleles?

_____

_____

_____

_____

 Lab® zone Do the Quick Lab *Inferring the Parent Generation.*

🔑 Assess Your Understanding

2a. Relate Cause and Effect Why is a pea plant that is a hybrid for stem height tall?

_____

_____

_____

b. CHALLENGE Can a short pea plant be a hybrid for the trait of stem height? Why or why not?

_____

_____

_____

got it?

○ **I get it!** Now I know that an organism's traits are controlled by _____

_____

_____

_____

○ **I need extra help with** _____

Go to MY SCIENCE ⓢ COACH *online for help with this subject.*

Probability and Heredity

🔑 How Is Probability Related to Inheritance?

🔑 What Are Phenotype and Genotype?

MY PLANET DIARY

FIELD TRIP

Storm on the Way?

Have you ever watched a hurricane form? Weather forecasters at the National Hurricane Center (NHC) in Miami, Florida, have. From May 15 to November 30, the NHC Operations Area is staffed around the clock with forecasters. They study data from aircraft, ocean buoys, and satellites to develop computer models. These models predict the probable paths of a storm. If the probability of a certain path is high, the NHC issues a warning that helps save lives and reduce damage.

Communicate Answer the question below. Then discuss your answer with a partner.

Local weather forecasters often talk about the percent chance for rainfall. What do you think they mean?

_____

_____

_____

_____

_____

▷ **PLANET DIARY** Go to **Planet Diary** to learn more about probability and weather.

🔺 **Lab zone** Do the Inquiry Warm-Up *What's the Chance?*

How Is Probability Related to Inheritance?

Before the start of a football game, the team captains stand with the referee for a coin toss. The team that wins the toss chooses whether to kick or receive the ball. As the referee tosses the coin, the visiting team captain calls "heads." What is the chance that the visitors will win the toss? To answer this question, you need to understand the principles of probability.

Vocabulary
- probability
- Punnett square
- phenotype
- genotype
- homozygous
- heterozygous

Skills
- Reading: Identify the Main Idea
- Inquiry: Draw Conclusions

What Is Probability?

Each time you toss a coin, there are two possible ways it can land—heads up or tails up. **Probability** is a number that describes how likely it is that an event will occur. In mathematical terms, you can say the probability that a tossed coin will land heads up is 1 in 2. There's also a 1 in 2 probability that the coin will land tails up. A 1 in 2 probability is expressed as the fraction $\frac{1}{2}$ or as 50 percent.

The laws of probability predict what is *likely* to occur, not what *will* occur. If you toss a coin 20 times, you may expect it to land heads up 10 times and tails up 10 times. But you may get 11 heads and 9 tails, or 8 heads and 12 tails. The more tosses you make, the closer your actual results will be to those predicted by probability.

Do you think the result of one toss affects the result of the next toss? Not at all. Each event occurs independently. Suppose you toss a coin five times and it lands heads up each time. What is the probability that it will land heads up on the next toss? If you said the probability is still 1 in 2, or 50 percent, you're right. The results of the first five tosses do not affect the result of the sixth toss.

do the math!

Percentage

One way to express probability is as a percentage. A percentage is a number compared to 100. For example, 50 percent, or 50%, means 50 out of 100. Suppose you want to calculate percentage from the results of a series of basketball free throws in which 3 out of 5 free throws go through the hoop.

STEP 1 Write the comparison as a fraction.

$$3 \text{ out of } 5 = \frac{3}{5}$$

STEP 2 Calculate the number value of the fraction.

$$3 \div 5 = 0.6$$

STEP 3 Multiply this number by 100%.

$$0.6 \times 100\% = 60\%$$

.... Practice! ....

1 Calculate Suppose 5 out of 25 free throws go through the hoop. Write this result as a fraction.

_____

2 Calculate Express your answer in Question 1 as a percentage.

_____

_____

_____

_____

Probability and Genetics How is probability related to genetics? Think back to Mendel's experiments. He carefully counted the offspring from every cross. When he crossed two plants that were hybrid for stem height (*Tt*), about three fourths of the F₁ plants had tall stems. About one fourth had short stems.

Each time Mendel repeated the cross, he observed similar results. He realized that the principles of probability applied to his work. He found that the probability of a hybrid cross producing a tall plant was 3 in 4. The probability of producing a short plant was 1 in 4. Mendel was the first scientist to recognize that the principles of probability can predict the results of genetic crosses.

Punnett Squares

A tool that can help you grasp how the laws of probability apply to genetics is called a Punnett square. A **Punnett square** is a chart that shows all the possible ways alleles can combine in a genetic cross. Geneticists use Punnett squares to see these combinations and to determine the probability of a particular outcome, or result. 🔑 **In a genetic cross, the combination of alleles that parents can pass to an offspring is based on probability.**

Figure 1 shows how to make a Punnett square. In this case, the cross is between two hybrid pea plants with round seeds (*Rr*). The allele for round seeds (*R*) is dominant over the allele for wrinkled seeds (*r*). Each parent can pass either one allele or the other to an offspring. The boxes in the Punnett square show the possible combinations of alleles that the offspring can inherit.

FIGURE 1 ···
▶ INTERACTIVE ART **How to Make a Punnett Square**
You can use a Punnett square to find the probabilities of a genetic cross.

✏️ **Follow the steps in the figure to fill in the Punnett square.**

1. **Predict** What is the probability that an offspring will have wrinkled seeds?

_____

2. **Interpret Tables** What is the probability that an offspring will have round seeds? Explain your answer.

_____

_____

_____

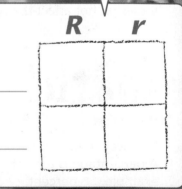

1 Start by drawing a box and dividing it into four squares.

2 The male parent's alleles are written along the top of the square. Fill in the female parent's alleles along the left side.

R   r

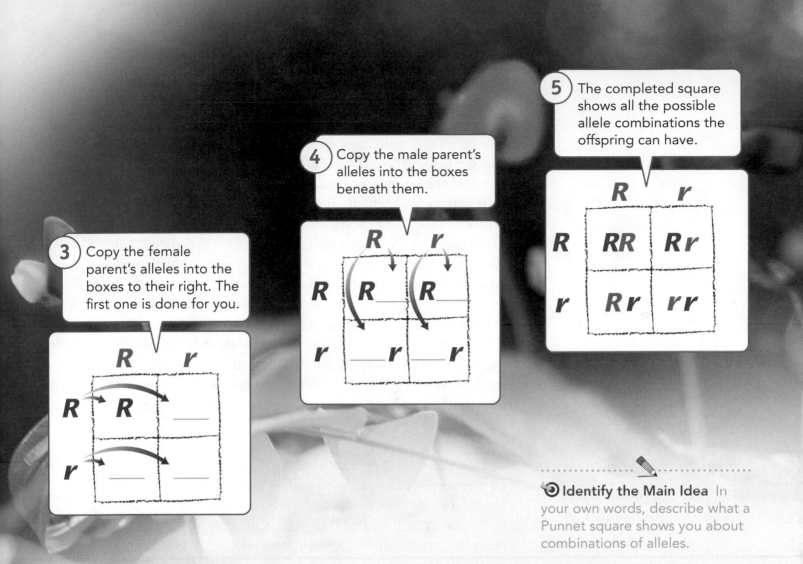

3 Copy the female parent's alleles into the boxes to their right. The first one is done for you.

4 Copy the male parent's alleles into the boxes beneath them.

5 The completed square shows all the possible allele combinations the offspring can have.

Relating Punnett Squares to Mendel Mendel did not know about alleles. But a Punnett square shows why he got the results he saw in the F₂ generations. Plants with alleles *RR* would have round seeds. So would plants with alleles *Rr*. Only plants with alleles *rr* would have wrinkled seeds.

✎ **Identify the Main Idea** In your own words, describe what a Punnet square shows you about combinations of alleles.

_____

_____

_____

_____

_____

 Do the Quick Lab *Coin Crosses.*

⚷ **Assess Your Understanding**

1a. Review What is probability?

_____

_____

b. Apply Concepts What is the probability that a cross between a hybrid pea plant with round seeds and one with wrinkled seeds will produce offspring with wrinkled seeds? (Draw a Punnett square on other paper to find the answer.)

_____

got it?

○ **I get it!** Now I know that the combination of alleles parents can pass to offspring _____

_____

○ **I need extra help with** _____

Go to MY SCIENCE ⓢ COACH *online for help with this subject.*

What Are Phenotype and Genotype?

Two terms that geneticists use are **phenotype** (FEE noh typ) and **genotype** (JEN uh typ). **An organism's phenotype is its physical appearance, or visible traits. An organism's genotype is its genetic makeup, or alleles.** In other words, genotype is an organism's alleles. Phenotype is how a trait looks or is expressed.

To compare phenotype and genotype, look at **Figure 2.** The allele for smooth pea pods (*S*) is dominant over the allele for pinched pea pods (*s*). All the plants with at least one *S* allele have the same phenotype. That is, they all produce smooth pods. However, these plants can have two different genotypes—*SS* or *Ss*. If you were to look at the plants with smooth pods, you would not be able to tell the difference between those that have the genotype *SS* and those with the genotype *Ss*. The plants with pinched pods, on the other hand, would all have the same phenotype—pinched pods—as well as the same genotype—*ss*.

Geneticists use two additional terms to describe an organism's genotype. An organism that has two identical alleles for a trait is said to be **homozygous** (hoh moh ZY gus) for that trait. A smooth-pod plant that has the alleles *SS* and a pinched-pod plant with the alleles *ss* are both homozygous. An organism that has two different alleles for a trait is **heterozygous** (het ur oh ZY gus) for that trait. A smooth-pod plant with the alleles *Ss* is heterozygous. Recall that Mendel used the term *hybrid* to describe heterozygous pea plants.

Vocabulary Suffixes The suffix *-ous* means "having." Circle this suffix in the highlighted terms *homozygous* and *heterozygous* in the paragraph at the right. These terms describe the organism as having

_____

_____

_____

FIGURE 2

Describing Inheritance

An organism's phenotype is its physical appearance. Its genotype is its genetic makeup.

✎ **Based on what you have read, answer these questions.**

1. **Classify** Fill in the missing information in the table.

2. **Interpret Tables** How many genotypes are there for the smooth-pod phenotype?

_____

Phenotypes and Genotypes

Phenotype	Genotype	Homozygous or Heterozygous
Smooth pods 	_____	_____
Smooth pods 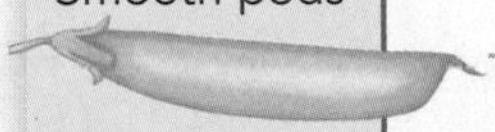	_____	_____
Pinched pods 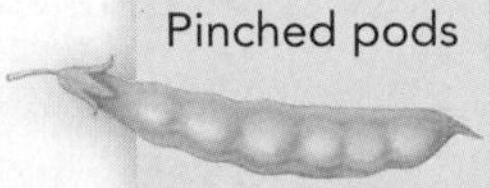	_____	_____

apply it!

Mendel's principles of heredity apply to many other organisms. For example, in guinea pigs, black fur color (*B*) is dominant over white fur color (*b*). Suppose a pair of black guinea pigs produces several litters of pups during their lifetimes. The graph shows the phenotypes of the pups. Write a title for the graph.

1 Read Graphs How many black pups were produced? How many white pups were produced?

_____

2 Infer What are the possible genotypes of the offspring?

_____

3 Draw Conclusions What can you conclude about the genotypes of the parent guinea pigs? Explain your answer.

_____

_____

_____

_____

_____

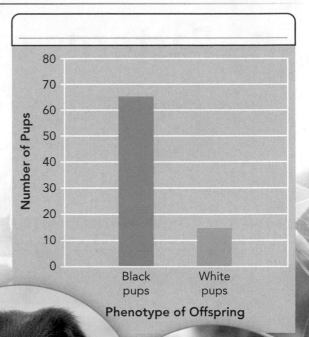

Phenotype of Offspring

Lab zone® Do the Lab Investigation *Make the Right Call!*

⚷ Assess Your Understanding

2a. Relate Cause and Effect Explain how two organisms can have the same phenotype but different genotypes.

_____

_____

_____

b. CHALLENGE In their lifetimes, two guinea pigs produce 40 black pups and 40 white pups. On a separate paper, make a Punnett square and find the likely genotypes of these parents.

_____

got it?

○ **I get it!** Now I know that phenotype and genotype are terms that describe _____

_____

_____

_____

_____

○ **I need extra help with** _____

Go to my science ⊙ coach *online for help with this subject.*

Patterns of Inheritance

UNLOCK THE BIG ?

🔑 **How Are Most Traits Inherited?**

🔑 **How Do Genes and the Environment Interact?**

MY PLANET DIARY

DISCOVERY

Cold, With a Chance of Males

Is it a male or a female? If you're a red-eared slider turtle, the answer might depend on the temperature! These slider turtles live in the calm, fresh, warm waters of the southeastern United States. For these turtles and some other reptiles, the temperature of the environment determines the sex of their offspring. At 26°C, the eggs of red-eared slider turtles all hatch as males. But at 31°C, the eggs all hatch as females. Only at about 29°C is there a 50% chance of hatching turtles of either sex.

Predict Discuss the question below with a partner. Then write your answer.

What do you think might happen to a population of red-eared slider turtles in a place where the temperature remains near or at 26°C?

_____

_____

_____

_____

▶ **PLANET DIARY** Go to **Planet Diary** to learn more about patterns of inheritance.

Lab zone® Do the Inquiry Warm-Up *Observing Traits.*

How Are Most Traits Inherited?

The traits that Mendel studied are controlled by genes with only two possible alleles. These alleles are either dominant or recessive. Pea flower color is either purple or white. Peas are either yellow or green. Can you imagine if all traits were like this? If people were either short or tall? If cats were either black or yellow?

Studying two-allele traits is a good place to begin learning about genetics. But take a look around at the variety of living things in your surroundings. As you might guess, most traits do not follow such a simple pattern of inheritance. 🔑 **Most traits are the result of complex patterns of inheritance.** Four complex patterns of inheritance are described in this lesson.

Vocabulary

- incomplete dominance
- codominance • multiple alleles
- polygenic inheritance

Skills

- Reading: Compare and Contrast
- Inquiry: Interpret Data

Incomplete Dominance

Some traits result from a pattern of inheritance known as incomplete dominance. **Incomplete dominance** occurs when one allele is only partially dominant. For example, look at **Figure 1.** The flowers shown are called snapdragons. A cross between a plant with red flowers and one with white flowers produces pink offspring.

Snapdragons with alleles *RR* produce a lot of red color in their flowers. It's no surprise that their flowers are red. A plant with two white alleles (*WW*) produces no red color. Its flowers are white. Both types of alleles are written as capital letters because neither is totally dominant. If a plant has alleles *RW*, only enough color is produced to make the flowers just a little red. So they look pink.

Codominance

The chickens in **Figure 1** show a different pattern of inheritance. **Codominance** occurs when both alleles for a gene are expressed equally. In the chickens shown, neither black feathers nor white feathers are dominant. All the offspring of a black hen and a white rooster have both black and white feathers.

Here, F^B stands for the allele for black feathers. F^W stands for the allele for white feathers. The letter *F* tells you the trait is feathers. The superscripts *B* for black and *W* for white tell you the color.

FIGURE 1 ······························
Other Patterns of Inheritance

Many crosses do not follow the patterns Mendel discovered.

✎ **Apply Concepts** Fill in the missing pairs of alleles.

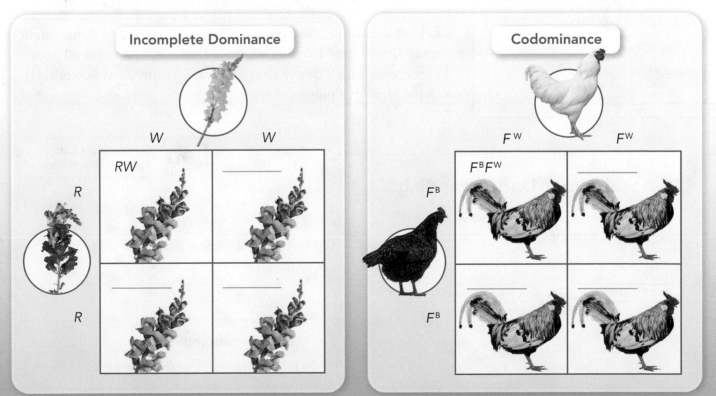

Multiple Alleles

Some genes have **multiple alleles,** which means that three or more possible alleles determine the trait. Remember that an organism can only inherit two alleles for a gene—one from each parent. Even if there are four, five, or more possible alleles, an individual can only have two. However, more genotypes can occur with multiple alleles than with just two alleles. For example, four alleles control the color of fur in some rabbits. Depending on which two alleles a rabbit inherits, its coat color can range from brownish gray to all white.

Polygenic Inheritance

The traits that Mendel studied were each controlled by a single gene. **Polygenic inheritance** occurs when more than one gene affects a trait. The alleles of the different genes work together to produce these traits.

Polygenic inheritance results in a broad range of phenotypes, like human height or the time it takes for a plant to flower. Imagine a field of sunflowers that were all planted the same day. Some might start to flower after 45 days. Most will flower after around 60 days. The last ones might flower after 75 days. The timing of flowering is a characteristic of polygenic traits.

---

apply it!

An imaginary insect called the blingwing has three alleles for wing color: *R* (red), *B* (blue), and *Y* (yellow).

1 List If an organism can inherit only two alleles for a gene, what are the six possible allele pairs for wing color in blingwings? One answer is given.

RB, _____

_____

2 ⚠ **Interpret Data** Suppose the three alleles are codominant. What wing color would each pair of alleles produce? One answer is given.

RB: purple _____

_____

_____

_____

_____

_____

Lab zone   Do the Quick Lab
Patterns of Inheritance.

🔑 Assess Your Understanding

1a. Describe How are the symbols written for alleles that share incomplete dominance?

_____

_____

b. [CHALLENGE] How is polygenic inheritance different from the patterns described by Mendel?

_____

_____

got it?

○ **I get it!** Now I know that most traits are

produced by _____

_____

_____

○ **I need extra help with** _____

Go to MY SCIENCE ⓢ COACH online for help with this subject.

312 Genetics: The Science of Heredity

How Do Genes and the Environment Interact?

You were not born knowing how to skateboard, but maybe you can skateboard now. Many traits are learned, or acquired. Unlike inherited traits, acquired traits are not carried by genes or passed to offspring. Although inherited traits are determined by genes, they also can be affected by factors in the environment. The phenotypes you observe in an organism result both from genes and from interactions of the organism with its environment.

Inherited and Acquired Traits Humans are born with inherited traits, such as vocal cords and tongues that allow for speech. But humans are not born speaking Spanish, or Mandarin, or English. The languages that a person speaks are acquired traits. Do you have a callus on your finger from writing with your pencil? That is an acquired trait. Skills you learn and physical changes that occur, such as calluses and haircuts, are aquired traits. See if you can tell the inherited traits from the acquired traits in **Figure 2**.

FIGURE 2 ···

Inherited or Acquired?

Which traits shown are carried in the genes, and which are not?

✎ **Classify** Identify each trait shown as inherited or acquired.

Their heights

Dyed hair color

Fish body color

These hedge shapes

Her freckles

313

Genes and the Environment Think again about sunflowers. Genes control when the plants flower. But sunlight, temperature, soil nutrients, and water also affect a plant's flowering time. **Environmental factors can influence the way genes are expressed.** Like sunflowers, you have factors in your environment that can affect how your genes are expressed. For example, you may have inherited the ability to play a musical instrument. But without an opportunity to learn, you may never develop the skill.

Some environmental factors can change an organism's genes. For example, tobacco smoke and other pollutants can affect genes in a person's body cells in a way that may result in lung cancer and other cancers. Still other genetic changes happen by chance.

Changes in body cells cannot be passed to offspring. Only changes in the sex cells—eggs and sperm—can be passed to offspring. Not all genetic changes have negative effects. Genetic change in sex cells is an important source of life's variety.

◑ Compare and Contrast
Underline two sentences that tell how changes to genes in body cells differ from changes to genes in egg and sperm cells.

Patterns of Inheritance

EXPLORE THE BIG ?

Why don't offspring always look like their parents?

FIGURE 3 ....

> **INTERACTIVE ART** The traits you see in organisms result from their genes and from interactions of genes with the environment.

✎ **Summarize** Match the terms in the word bank with the examples shown.

Word Bank	
Incomplete dominance	Dominant and recessive traits
Environmental factors	Polygenic inheritance
Multiple alleles	Codominance
Acquired traits	

_____

_____

_____

_____

_____

_____

Lab zone® Do the Quick Lab
Is It All in the Genes?

Assess Your Understanding

2a. Review Only genetic changes in (sex cells/ body cells) can be passed to offspring.

b. Describe Give one example of how environmental factors affect gene expression.

_____

_____

_____

c. ANSWER THE BIG ? Why don't offspring always look like their parents?

_____

_____

_____

_____

_____

got it? ....

○ **I get it!** Now I know that the environment can affect _____

_____

○ **I need extra help with** _____

Go to MY SCIENCE COACH online for help with this subject.

Ohio

LESSON

4

Chromosomes and Inheritance

UNLOCK THE BIG ?

🔑 **How Are Chromosomes, Genes, and Inheritance Related?**

🔑 **What Happens During Meiosis?**

🔑 **How Do Sexual and Asexual Reproduction Compare?**

my planet Diary

Chromosome Sleuth

Finding answers about how chromosomes relate to disease is one job of genetic technologists. These scientists analyze chromosomes from cells. The analysis may pinpoint genetic information that can cause disease or other health problems. In their work, genetic technologists use microscopes, computer-imaging photography, and lab skills. They report data that are used in research and in treating patients affected by genetic diseases.

CAREER

1. Describe a method that genetic technologists use to pursue a scientific explanation.

_____

_____

_____

_____

2. If you were a genetic technologist, what would you like to research?

_____

_____

_____

_____

▶ PLANET DIARY Go to **Planet Diary** to learn more about genetic technologists.

Lab zone® Do the Inquiry Warm-Up *Which Chromosome Is Which?*

Vocabulary
• meiosis

Skills
↻ Reading: Relate Cause and Effect
△ Inquiry: Design Experiments

How Are Chromosomes, Genes, and Inheritance Related?

Mendel's work showed that genes exist. (Remember that he called them "factors.") But scientists in the early twentieth century did not know what structures in cells contained genes. The search for the answer was something like a mystery story. The story could be called "The Clue in the Grasshopper's Cells."

At the start of the 1900s, Walter Sutton, an American geneticist, studied the cells of grasshoppers. He wanted to understand how sex cells (sperm and eggs) form. Sutton focused on how the chromosomes moved within cells during the formation of sperm and eggs. He hypothesized that chromosomes are the key to learning how offspring have traits similar to those of their parents.

apply it!

△Design Experiments Different types of organisms have different numbers of chromosomes, and some organisms are easier to study than others. Suppose you are a scientist studying chromosomes and you have to pick an organism from those shown below to do your work. Which one would you pick and why?

_____

_____

_____

_____

_____

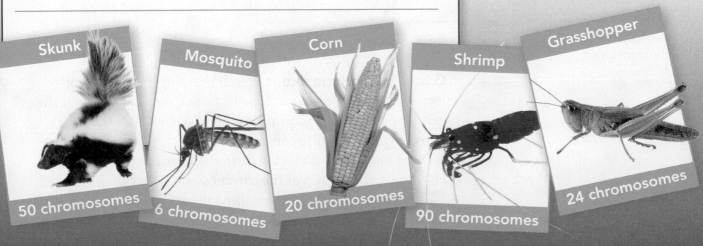

Skunk — 50 chromosomes

Mosquito — 6 chromosomes

Corn — 20 chromosomes

Shrimp — 90 chromosomes

Grasshopper — 24 chromosomes

Chromosomes and Inheritance

Sutton needed evidence to support his hypothesis. Look at **Figure 1** to see how he found this evidence in grasshopper cells. To his surprise, he discovered that grasshopper sex cells have exactly half the number of chromosomes found in grasshopper body cells.

Chromosome Pairs Sutton observed what happened when a sperm cell and an egg cell joined. The fertilized egg that formed had 24 chromosomes. It had the same number of chromosomes as each parent. These 24 chromosomes existed as 12 pairs. One chromosome in each pair came from the male parent. The other chromosome came from the female parent.

FIGURE 1 ·····················

Paired Up

Sutton studied grasshopper cells through a microscope. He concluded that genes are carried on chromosomes.

✎ **Relate Text and Visuals**
Answer the questions in the spaces provided.

① Body Cell

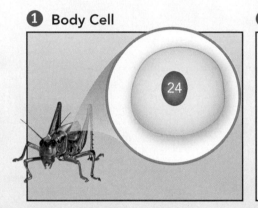

Each grasshopper body cell has 24 chromosomes.

② Sex Cells

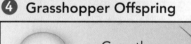

Sutton found that grasshopper sex cells each have 12 chromosomes.

1. How does the number of chromosomes in grasshopper sex cells compare to the number in body cells?

_____

_____

_____

_____

③ Fertilization

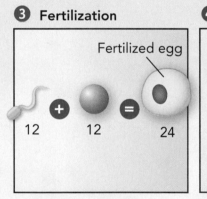

The fertilized egg cell has 24 chromosomes.

④ Grasshopper Offspring

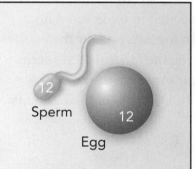

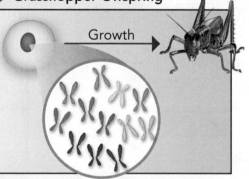

The 24 chromosomes exist as 12 pairs.

2. How is the inheritance of chromosomes similar to what you know about alleles?

_____

_____

_____

_____

Genes on Chromosomes Recall that alleles are different forms of a gene. Because of Mendel's work, Sutton knew that alleles exist in pairs in an organism. One allele comes from the female parent. The other allele comes from the male parent. Sutton realized that paired alleles are carried on paired chromosomes. His idea is now known as the chromosome theory of inheritance.

🔑 **According to the chromosome theory of inheritance, genes pass from parents to their offspring on chromosomes.**

A Lineup of Genes The body cells of humans contain 46 chromosomes that form 23 pairs. Chromosomes are made up of many genes joined together like beads on a string. Although you have only 23 pairs of chromosomes, your body cells each contain between 20,000 and 25,000 genes. Genes control traits.

Figure 2 shows a pair of chromosomes from an organism. One chromosome is from the female parent. The other chromosome is from the male parent. Notice that each chromosome has the same genes. The genes are lined up in the same order on both chromosomes. However, the alleles for some of the genes are not identical. For example, one chromosome has allele *A,* and the other chromosome has allele *a.* As you can see, this organism is heterozygous for some traits and homozygous for others.

✏️ **Relate Cause and Effect**
Suppose gene A on the left chromosome is damaged and no longer functions. What form of the trait would show? Why?

_____

_____

_____

_____

FIGURE 2 ·············

A Pair of Chromosomes
Chromosomes in a pair may have different alleles for some genes and the same alleles for others.

✏️ **Interpret Diagrams** For each pair of alleles, tell whether the organism is homozygous or heterozygous. The first two answers are shown.

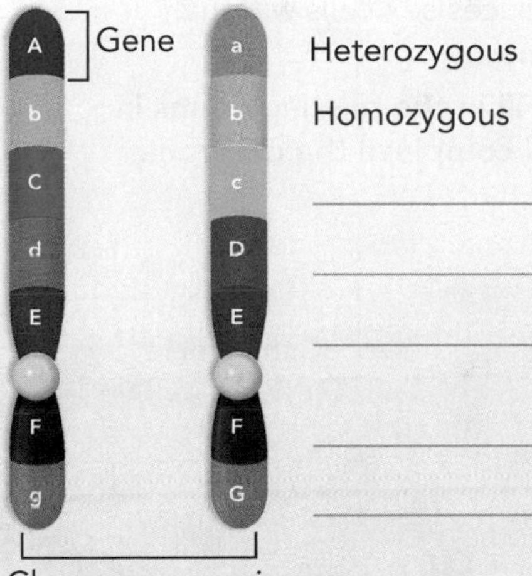

Gene

Heterozygous

Homozygous

_____

_____

_____

_____

_____

Chromosome pair

Lab zone® Do the Quick Lab *Chromosomes and Inheritance.*

🔑 Assess Your Understanding

1a. Describe When two grasshopper sex cells join, the chromosome number in the new cell is (half/double) the number in the sex cells.

b. Summarize Describe the arrangement of genes on a pair of chromosomes.

_____

_____

c. Relate Evidence and Explanation How do Sutton's observations support the chromosome theory of inheritance?

_____

_____

_____

_____

got it? ·······················

○ **I get it!** Now I know that genes are passed from parents to offspring _____

○ **I need extra help with** _____

Go to **MY SCIENCE** ⑤ **COACH** online for help with this subject.

What Happens During Meiosis?

How do sex cells end up with half the number of chromosomes as body cells? The answer to this question is a form of cell division called meiosis. **Meiosis** (my OH sis) is the process by which the number of chromosomes is reduced by half as sex cells form. You can trace the events of meiosis in **Figure 3.** Here, the parent cell has four chromosomes arranged in two pairs. 🔑 **During meiosis, the chromosome pairs separate into two different cells. The sex cells that form later have only half as many chromosomes as the other cells in the organism.**

FIGURE 3 ···

> ART IN MOTION **Meiosis**

During meiosis, a cell produces sex cells with half the number of chromosomes.

✎ **Interpret Diagrams** Fill in the missing terms in the spaces provided, and complete the diagram.

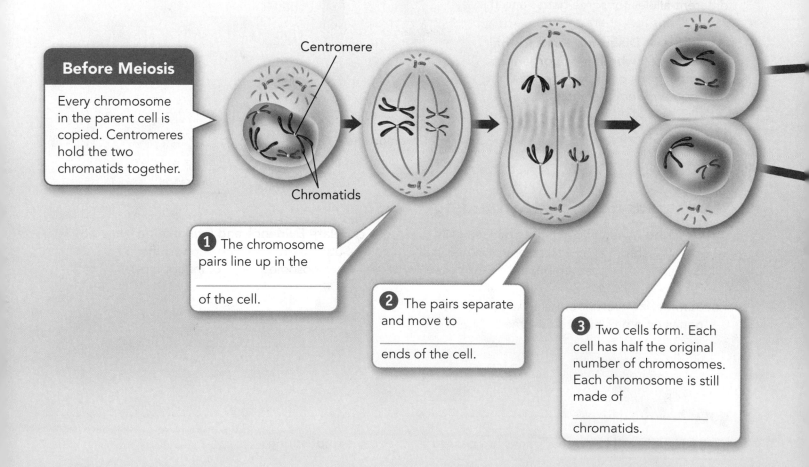

Before Meiosis

Every chromosome in the parent cell is copied. Centromeres hold the two chromatids together.

Centromere

Chromatids

1 The chromosome pairs line up in the

_____

of the cell.

2 The pairs separate and move to

_____

ends of the cell.

3 Two cells form. Each cell has half the original number of chromosomes. Each chromosome is still made of

_____

chromatids.

During meiosis, a cell divides into two cells. Then each of these cells divides again, forming a total of four cells. The chromosomes duplicate only before the first cell division.

Each of the four sex cells shown below receives two chromosomes—one chromosome from each pair in the original cell. When two sex cells join at fertilization, the new cell that forms has the full number of chromosomes. In this case, the number is four. The organism that grows from this cell got two of its chromosomes from one parent and two from the other parent.

did you know?...................

Researchers at Florida State University have found evidence that a single protein may control how chromosomes separate during meiosis. They are trying to figure out whether taking action during meiosis can prevent the development of some genetic disorders.

4 In each cell, the _____ move to the center.

5 The centromeres split, and the _____ separate. They become single chromosomes and move to opposite ends of the cell.

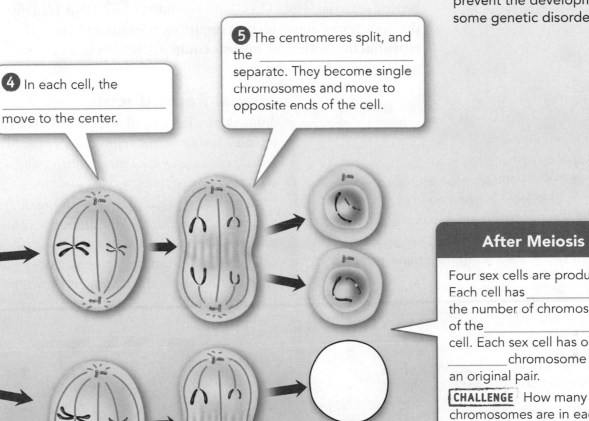

After Meiosis

Four sex cells are produced. Each cell has _____ the number of chromosomes of the_____ cell. Each sex cell has only _____ chromosome from an original pair.

[CHALLENGE] How many chromosomes are in each cell in Step 3?

_____

Lab zone   Do the Quick Lab *Modeling Meiosis.*

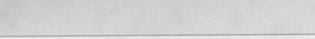

🔑 **Assess Your Understanding**

got it? ....

O **I get it!** Now I know that during meiosis, the number of chromosomes_____

_____

O **I need extra help with** _____

Go to MY SCIENCE 💬 COACH *online for help with this subject.*

How Do Sexual and Asexual Reproduction Compare?

You now know that sexual reproduction through meiosis starts with the joining of two sex cells. As a result, offspring receive chromosomes (and DNA, or genetic material) from both sexes. Recall that some organisms can reproduce asexually. In many of these organisms, asexual reproduction takes place through mitosis. During mitosis, a parent cell divides into two new cells. No new genetic material is introduced during mitosis. **DNA transfer through sexual reproduction requiring meiosis and asexual reproduction requiring mitosis equip organisms in different ways for survival.**

Sexual Reproduction Like many animals, you developed after two sex cells joined. During sexual reproduction, the female egg cell and the male sperm cell of two parent organisms join together to produce a new organism. The joining of two cells with different DNA produces an offspring with a combination of physical characteristics from both parents. Most animals, including the mammals shown in **Figure 4**, reproduce sexually.

FIGURE 4 ·······················

Sexual Reproduction

These wolf cubs and guinea pig pups are products of sexual reproduction.

✎ **Use the photos to answer the questions.**

1. **Interpret Photos** How do the offspring in each photo differ from their parent?

_____

_____

_____

2. **Explain** Why do the parent and the offspring look different?

_____

_____

_____

Asexual Reproduction

Asexual Reproduction During asexual reproduction, one parent produces a new organism identical to itself. This new organism receives an exact copy of the parent's DNA. Some animals, including sponges, jellyfish, and worms, reproduce asexually. The hydra, shown in **Figure 5**, reproduces asexually through budding. In budding, a new animal grows out of the parent and breaks off. Some animals reproduce asexually by dividing in two.

Comparing Asexual and Sexual Reproduction

Both sexual and asexual reproduction offer survival advantages and disadvantages. An advantage of asexual reproduction is that one parent can quickly produce many identical offspring. But a major disadvantage is that offspring have the same DNA as the parent. The offspring have no variation from the parent and may not survive changes in the environment. In contrast, sexual reproduction has the advantage of producing offspring with new combinations of DNA. These offspring may have characteristics that help them survive under unfavorable conditions. However, a disadvantage of sexual reproduction is that it requires finding a mate, and the development of offspring takes a longer time. Use **Figure 6** to compare asexual and sexual reproduction. Then look at **Figure 7** on the next page.

FIGURE 5 ·······················

A Chip off the Old Block

Budding is the most common form of asexual reproduction for this hydra, a type of cnidarian.

✏ **Relate Text to Visuals** How does this photo show asexual reproduction?

_____

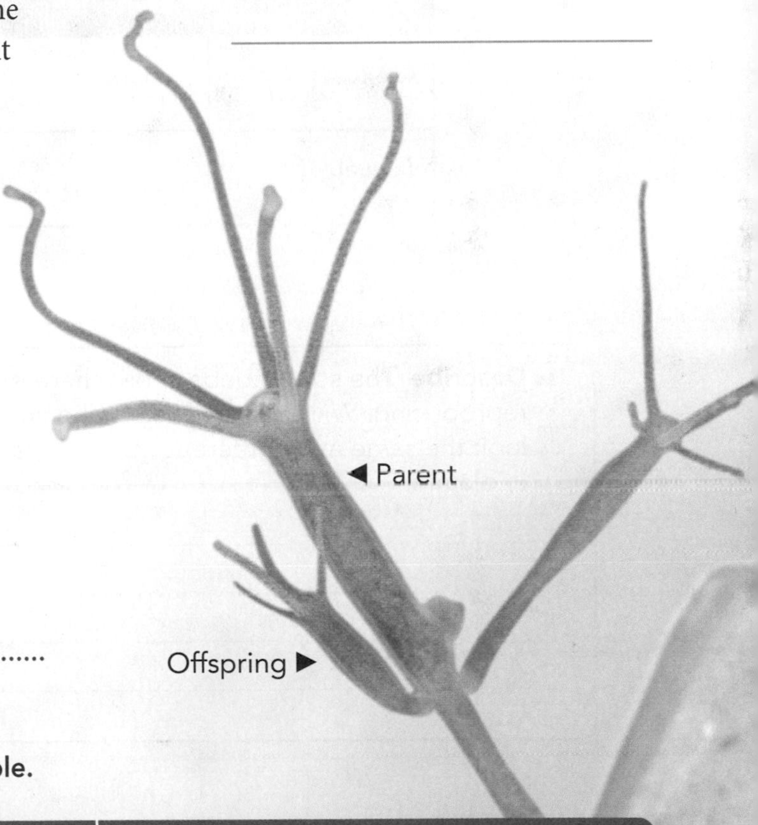

_____

_____

_____

◀ Parent

Offspring ▶

FIGURE 6 ·······················

Asexual and Sexual Reproduction

Compare and Contrast Write an advantage and a disadvantage of each type of reproduction in the table.

	Asexual Reproduction	Sexual Reproduction
Advantage		
Disadvantage		

FIGURE 7 ···

Same or Different?

Offspring don't always look like their parents. The type of
reproduction and genes determine why this is so.

✏ **Review** Fill in the table to review the two types of
reproduction. Then complete the tasks that go with each photo.

Type of Reproduction	Number of Parents	Mitosis or Meiosis	Offspring DNA Compared to Parent(s)	How Offspring Looks Compared to Parent(s)
Asexual				
Sexual				

1. **Describe** The soil amoeba shown here is
reproducing. Will the offspring of the amoeba
look the same as or different from the parent?
Explain.

_____

_____

_____

_____

Soil amoeba
reproducing

2. **Predict** In rabbits, the allele for black fur (*B*) is dominant over the allele for white fur (*b*). Is it possible for the two rabbits shown below to produce a white offspring? Draw a Punnett square to justify your answer.

_____

_____

3. **Interpret Tables** Suppose both of the rabbits have the genotype *Bb*. What is the probability that an offspring will have white fur? What is the probability that it will have black fur?

_____

_____

_____

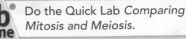

Do the Quick Lab *Comparing Mitosis and Meiosis.*

Assess Your Understanding

2a. **Define** (Sexual/Asexual) reproduction involves the joining of sperm and egg.

b. **Compare and Contrast** The offspring of (sexual/asexual) reproduction have a better chance of surviving changes in the environment than the offspring of (sexual/asexual) reproduction.

c. **Summarize** How does mitosis cause an offspring to have the same DNA as its parent?

_____

_____

_____

_____

_____

d. **CHALLENGE** In rare cases, female sharks born in captivity that have never been exposed to male sharks have become pregant. Is this an example of asexual or sexual reproduction?

_____

_____

_____

_____

_____

got it?..

O **I get it!** Now I know that organisms are equipped for survival in different ways as a result of_____

_____

_____

O **I need extra help with** _____

Go to **MY SCIENCE** **COACH** *online for help with this subject.*

325

5 Mutations

🔑 **How Can Mutations Affect an Organism?**

🔑 **How Is Cancer Related to Mutations and the Cell Cycle?**

my planet Diary

Dairy DNA

Every mammal, from mice to monkeys to whales, drinks milk as a baby. But humans are the only mammals that can digest milk and other dairy products throughout their lifetime. Humans have a mutation (a change in DNA) that allows their bodies to break down lactose, a sugar in dairy products. However, not all people can digest dairy products. Many people are lactose intolerant, meaning their bodies cannot break down lactose. Lactose-intolerant people have the original DNA without the mutation. While many other mutations are considered harmful, this mutation is helpful to humans. And just think—ice cream might never have been invented if humans couldn't break down lactose!

MISCONCEPTION

Communicate Discuss these questions with a group of classmates. Write your answers below.

1. Do you think lactose intolerance is a serious condition? Explain.

   _____

   _____

2. Do you think people with this condition can *never* have milk?

   _____

   _____

   _____

> **PLANET DIARY** Go to **Planet Diary** to learn more about mutations.

Lab zone® Do the Inquiry Warm-Up *Oops!*

Vocabulary
- mutation • cancer • tumor
- chemotherapy

Skills
- Reading: Summarize
- Inquiry: Calculate

How Can Mutations Affect an Organism?

Some traits are not inherited from parent organisms. Traits can also be a result of a change in DNA. A **mutation** is any change in the DNA of a gene or chromosome. For example, instead of the base sequence AAG, the DNA might have the sequence ACG. **Mutations can cause a cell to produce an incorrect protein during protein synthesis. As a result, the organism's trait may be different from what it normally would be.**

If a mutation occurs in a body cell, such as a skin cell, the mutation will not be passed on to the organism's offspring. But if a mutation occurs in a sex cell (egg or sperm), the mutation can be passed on to an offspring and affect the offspring's traits.

Types of Mutations Some mutations are the result of small changes in an organism's DNA. For example, a base pair may be added, a base pair may be substituted for another, or one or more bases may be deleted from a section of DNA. These types of mutations can occur during the DNA replication process. Other mutations may occur when chromosomes don't separate correctly during the formation of sex cells. When this type of mutation occurs, a cell can end up with too many or too few chromosomes. The cell can also end up with extra segments of chromosomes.

Summarize How can mutations change an organism's traits?

_____
_____
_____
_____

FIGURE 1 ....
Mutations
The types of mutations of DNA include deletion, addition, and substitution.
Interpret Diagrams Circle the added base pair on the third piece of DNA. Fill in the nitrogen bases on the fourth piece of DNA to illustrate a substitution.

Original DNA sequence

One base pair is removed (deletion).

One base pair is added (addition).

One base pair is switched for another (substitution).

Effects of Mutations Mutations introduce changes in an organism. Mutations can be harmful, helpful, or neither harmful nor helpful. A mutation is harmful if it reduces the organism's chances for survival and reproduction.

Whether a mutation is harmful or not depends partly on the organism's environment. The mutation that led to this alligator's white color would probably be harmful to it in the wild. A white alligator is more visible to its prey. This alligator may find it difficult to catch prey and may not get enough food to survive. A white alligator in a zoo has the same chance for survival as a green alligator because it does not hunt. In a zoo, the mutation neither helps nor harms the alligator.

Helpful mutations increase an organism's ability to survive and reproduce. Mutations have allowed some bacteria that are harmful to humans to become resistant to drugs. The drugs do not kill the bacteria with the mutations, so they continue to survive and reproduce.

FIGURE 2 ....

✏️ Review Check the phrase that best completes the sentence.

▶ VIRTUAL LAB **Alligator Mutation**

A white alligator does not blend into its natural habitat, but this color change may be a beneficial mutation for an organism if it

○ reduces its chances for survival.

○ increases its chances for survival.

○ decreases its chances for reproduction.

🔑 **Assess Your Understanding**

1a. Explain Mutations that occur in body cells (can/cannot) be passed on to offspring. Mutations that occur in sex cells (can/cannot) be passed on to offspring.

b. Apply Concepts Drug resistance in bacteria is a beneficial mutation for the bacteria, but how can it be harmful for humans?

_____

_____

_____

Lab ® Do the Quick Lab
zone *Effects of Mutations.*

got it?

○ **I get it!** Now I know that mutations affect an organism's traits by_____

_____

○ **I need extra help with** _____

_____

Go to **MY SCIENCE** ⓢ **COACH** online for help with this subject.

How Is Cancer Related to Mutations and the Cell Cycle?

Did you know cancer is not just one disease? There are more than 100 types of cancer, and they can occur in almost any part of the body. Cancer affects many people around the world, regardless of age, race, or gender. Cancers are often named for the place in the body where they begin. For example, lung cancer begins in lung tissues, as shown in **Figure 3.**

What Is Cancer? **Cancer** is a disease in which cells grow and divide uncontrollably, damaging the parts of the body around them. Cancer cells are like weeds in a garden. Weeds can overrun a garden by robbing plants of the space, sunlight, and water they need. Similarly, cancer cells can overrun normal cells.

Different factors work together in determining if a person gets cancer. Because of their inherited traits, some people are more likely than others to develop certain cancers. A woman with a mother or grandmother who had breast cancer has an increased chance of developing breast cancer herself. Some substances in the environment may also lead to cancer, like the tar in cigarettes or ultraviolet light from the sun or tanning beds. People who have a high-fat diet may also be more likely to develop cancer.

FIGURE 3 ·······
Lung Tumor X-Ray
Tumors can be visible in X-rays.
✎ **Interpret Photos** Circle the tumor in the X-ray above.

do the math!

You may have noticed labels like SPF 15 on your sunscreen. *SPF* stands for "sun protection factor," and the number lets you know how long the sunscreen works. For example, a person who burns in the sun after 10 minutes could use sunscreen with an SPF of 15 and stay in the sun for as long as 150 minutes ($10 \times 15 = 150$). This time can vary greatly and sunscreen should be reapplied often to prevent damaging sunburns.

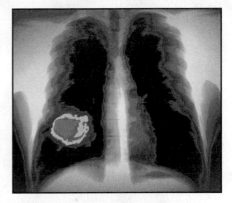

Sunscreen Strength Over Time

SPF	Time in the Sun	
20	a. ___ h	_____ min
30	b. ___ h	_____ min
55	c. ___ h	_____ min

❶ Fill in the table with the length of time for sun protection each SPF rating offers for someone who burns in 10 minutes without sunscreen.

❷ ▲**Calculate** At the beach, you put on SPF 25 at 8:00 A.M. and your friend puts on SPF 15 at 9:00 A.M. You both would burn in 10 minutes without sunscreen. Who should reapply their sunscreen first? When?

329

Cancer cell

Relate Cause and Effect
Underline a cause and circle the effect in each paragraph.

1 How Cancer Begins

Scientists think that cancer begins when something damages a portion of the DNA in a chromosome. The damage causes a mutation and the cells function abnormally. Normally, the cells in one part of the body live in harmony with the cells around them. Cells that go through the cell cycle divide in a controlled way. **Cancer begins when mutations disrupt the normal cell cycle, causing cells to divide in an uncontrolled way.** Without the normal controls on the cell cycle, the cells may grow too large and divide too often.

Tumor

2 How a Tumor Forms

At first, one cell develops in an abnormal way. As the cell divides over and over, more and more abnormal cells are produced. In time, these cells form a tumor. A **tumor** is a mass of abnormal cells that develops when cells divide and grow uncontrollably.

3 How Cancer Spreads

Tumors often take years to grow to a noticeable size. During that time, the cells become more and more abnormal as they continue to divide. Some of the cancerous cells may break off from the tumor and enter the bloodstream. In this way, the cancer can spread to other areas of the body.

Bloodstream

How Cancer Is Treated People with cancer can undergo a variety of treatments. Treatments include surgery, radiation, and drugs that destroy the cancer cells.

When cancer is detected before it has spread to other parts of the body, surgery is usually the best treatment. If doctors can completely remove a cancerous tumor, the person may be cured. If the cancer cells have spread or the tumor cannot be removed, doctors may use radiation. Radiation treatment uses beams of high-energy waves. The beams are more likely to destroy the fast-growing cancer cells than normal cells.

Chemotherapy is another treatment option. **Chemotherapy** is the use of drugs to treat a disease. Cancer-fighting drugs are carried throughout the body by the bloodstream. The drugs can kill cancer cells or slow their growth. Many of these drugs, however, destroy some normal cells as well, producing nausea and other side effects patients often experience with chemotherapy treatments.

Scientists are continuing to look for new ways to treat cancer. If scientists can better understand how the cell cycle is controlled, they may find ways to stop cancer cells from multiplying.

apply it!

Drugs are one cancer treatment option.

❶ If you were a cancer researcher working on a cure, would you want to design a chemotherapy drug that would speed up the cell cycle or slow it down? Why?

_____

_____

_____

_____

❷ CHALLENGE Based on what you have learned about cancer and chemotherapy, explain why you think cancer patients who are treated with chemotherapy drugs can lose their hair.

_____

_____

_____

_____

 Do the Quick Lab *What Happens When There Are Too Many Cells?*

🔑 Assess Your Understanding

2a. List What are the options for treating cancer?

_____

_____

b. Draw Conclusions Based on the fact that people can get cancer regardless of their genetics, what are some things you can do to lower your risk of getting cancer?

_____

_____

_____

_____

got it?

○ **I get it!** Now I know that cancer is related to mutations and the cell cycle because _____

_____

_____

_____

_____

○ **I need extra help with** _____

_____

Go to MY SCIENCE ⑤ COACH *online for help with this subject.*

Offspring inherit different forms of genes called _____ from each parent. Traits are affected by patterns of inheritance and interactions with the _____.

LESSON 1 What Is Heredity?

🔑 In all of his crosses, Mendel found that only one form of the trait appeared in the F_1 generation. However, in the F_2 generation, the "lost" form of the trait always reappeared in about one fourth of the plants.

🔑 An organism's traits are controlled by the alleles it inherits from its parents. Some alleles are dominant, while other alleles are recessive.

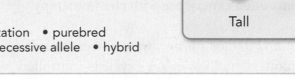

Tall   ×   Short

Vocabulary
• heredity • trait • genetics • fertilization • purebred
• gene • allele • dominant allele • recessive allele • hybrid

---

LESSON 2 Probability and Heredity

🔑 In a genetic cross, the combination of alleles that parents can pass to an offspring is based on probability.

🔑 An organism's phenotype is its physical appearance, or visible traits. An organism's genotype is its genetic makeup, or alleles.

Vocabulary
• probability • Punnett square • phenotype
• genotype • homozygous • heterozygous

LESSON 3 Patterns of Inheritance

🔑 Most traits are the result of complex patterns of inheritance.

🔑 Environmental factors can influence the way genes are expressed.

Vocabulary
• incomplete dominance
• codominance
• multiple alleles
• polygenic inheritance

LESSON 4 Chromosomes and Inheritance

🔑 Genes pass from parents to their offspring on chromosomes. Meiosis produces sex cells that have half as many chromosomes as body cells.

🔑 DNA transfer through sexual reproduction requiring meiosis and asexual reproduction requiring mitosis equip organisms in different ways for survival.

Vocabulary
• meiosis

LESSON 5 Mutations

🔑 Mutations can cause a cell to produce an incorrect protein during protein synthesis. As a result, the organism's trait may be different from what it normally would be.

🔑 Cancer begins when mutations disrupt the normal cell cycle, causing cells to divide in an uncontrolled way.

Vocabulary
• mutation • cancer • tumor • chemotherapy

Review and Assessment

LESSON 1 **What Is Heredity?**

1. Different forms of a gene are called

   a. alleles.   b. hybrids.

   c. genotypes.   d. chromosomes.

2. _____ is the scientific study of heredity.

3. **Explain** Mendel crossed two pea plants: one with green pods and one with yellow pods. The F_1 generation all had green pods. What color pods did the F_2 generation have? Explain your answer.

   _____

   _____

   _____

   _____

4. **Predict** The plant below is purebred for height (tall). Write the alleles of this plant. In any cross for height, what kind of offspring will this plant produce? Why?

   _____

   _____

   _____

   _____

5. **Compare and Contrast** How do dominant alleles and recessive alleles differ?

   _____

   _____

   _____

6. **Write About It** Write a diary entry as if you are Gregor Mendel. You may describe any part of his experiences, experiments, or observations.

LESSON 2 **Probability and Heredity**

7. Which of the following represents a heterozygous genotype?

   a. YY b. yy

   c. Yy d. $Y^H Y^H$

8. An organism's _____ is the way its genotype is expressed.

9. **Make Models** Fill in the Punnett square below to show a cross between two guinea pigs that are heterozygous for coat color. B is for black coat color, and b is for white coat color.

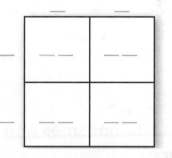

10. **Interpret Tables** What is the probability that an offspring from the cross above has each of the following genotypes?

    BB _____

    Bb _____

    bb _____

11. **Apply Concepts** What kind of cross might tell you if a black guinea pig is BB or Bb? Why?

    _____

    _____

    _____

12. **math!** A garden has 80 pea plants. Of this total, 20 plants have short stems and 60 plants have tall stems. What percentage of the plants have short stems? What percentage have tall stems?

LESSON 3
Patterns of Inheritance

13. A pattern of inheritance in which one allele is only partially dominant is

  a. codominance.   **b.** acquired traits.

  c. multiple alleles.   **d.** incomplete dominance.

14. Traits that have three or more phenotypes may be the result of _____ alleles.

15. Identify Faulty Reasoning Neither of Josie's parents plays an instrument. Josie thinks that she won't be able to play an instrument because her parents can't. Is she right? Why?

_____

_____

_____

_____

LESSON 4
Chromosomes and Inheritance

16. Genes are carried from parents to offspring on

  a. alleles.   **b.** chromosomes.

  c. phenotypes.   **d.** genotypes.

17. The process of _____ results in the formation of sex cells.

18. Summarize Why do chromosomes in body cells exist in pairs?

_____

_____

19. **Write About It** Consider the following statement: *Organisms that reproduce asexually are at a higher risk of extinction than organisms that reproduce sexually.* Do you agree or disagree? Explain your answer.

LESSON 5
Mutations

20. A mass of cancer cells is called a

  a. tumor.   **b.** chromosome.

  c. mutation.   **d.** phenotype.

21. A mutation is a change in _____.

22. Interpret Diagrams Circle the mutation shown in the illustration below.

Original DNA   After mutation

APPLY THE BIG Q

Why don't offspring always look like their parents?

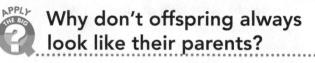

23. A species of butterfly has three alleles for wing color: blue, orange, and pale yellow. A blue butterfly mates with an orange butterfly. The following offspring result: about 25% are blue and 25% are orange. However, another 25% are speckled blue and orange, and 25% are yellow. Explain how these results could occur.

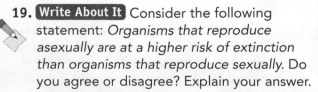

Offspring of blue butterfly and orange butterfly

_____

_____

_____

_____

Ohio Benchmark Practice

Multiple Choice

Mark only one answer for each question.

1. The Punnett square below shows a cross between two pea plants, each with round seeds. What is the missing genotype in the empty square?

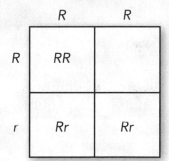

	R	R
R	RR	
r	Rr	Rr

  A. *rr*
  B. *rR*
  C. *Rr*
  D. *RR*

2. Suppose a new medication slows the cell cycle. How would this medication likely affect cancer?

  A. It might slow the rate of mutations.
  B. It might slow blood flow to the tumor.
  C. It might slow the division of cancerous cells.
  D. It might slow the effectiveness of chemotherapy.

3. For a particular plant, leaf texture is either fuzzy or smooth. A purebred fuzzy plant is crossed with a purebred smooth plant. All offspring are smooth. Which sentence best describes the alleles for this trait?

  A. Fuzzy is dominant over smooth.
  B. Smooth is dominant over fuzzy.
  C. The alleles are codominant.
  D. The alleles have incomplete dominance.

4. During _____, a cell divides to form two cells that have sets of chromosomes that are complete and identical to each other and to the parent cell.

  A. meiosis
  B. mitosis
  C. mutation
  D. fertilization

Short Answer

Write your answers to questions 5 and 6 on another sheet of paper.

5. In dogs, the allele for short hair (*A*) is dominant over the allele for long hair (*a*). Two short-haired dogs are the parents of eight puppies. Six puppies have short hair. Two have long hair. Draw two possible Punnett squares for a cross between two short-haired dogs. Explain which Punnett square shows the correct cross for this litter.

Use the diagram below to answer question 6.

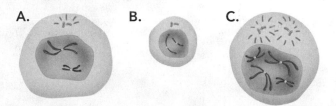

6. One of the cells shown is a parent cell about to undergo meiosis. Another cell is in the process of meiosis. A third cell is a sex cell that results from meiosis. Identify which cell is which, and explain your reasoning.

Everyday Science

Nature vs. Nurture

▼ This photograph shows a pair of otters, one of the species wildlife rehabilitators try to reintroduce into the wild.

In 1990, the Monterey Bay Aquarium in Monterey, California, released a young otter into the wild. Wildlife rehabilitators at the aquarium raised the otter and taught her how to find food. But, because she was used to receiving food and affection from people at the aquarium, she did not know to avoid other humans. After the otter pestered some local divers, she had to be returned to live at the aquarium.

So, which behaviors do animals learn, and which behaviors "just come naturally"? Actually, the line between inherited behaviors and learned behaviors is rarely clear. Although wild otters are naturally shy around humans, the otter at the Monterey Bay Aquarium had learned to expect food and affection from humans. As a result, wildlife rehabilitators commonly use puppets or animal costumes to keep the animals they care for from becoming too familiar with humans.

Design It Choose a species, such as deer, otter, or panda, that is raised in captivity and returned to the wild. Design a rehabilitation activity to help orphaned animals learn a skill that they will need to survive in the wild. Explain the features of your rehabilitation activity to your class.

Seeing
Spots

You would probably recognize a Dalmatian if you saw one—Dalmatians typically have white coats with distinctive black or brown spots. Spots are a defining characteristic of the Dalmatian breed. These spots can be large or small, but all Dalmatians have them.

In Dalmatians, spots are a dominant trait. When two Dalmatians breed, each parent contributes a gene for spots. The trait for spots is controlled by one set of genes with only two possible alleles. No matter how many puppies are in a litter, they will all develop spots.

But what if a Dalmatian breeds with another dog that isn't a Dalmatian? While the puppies won't develop the distinctive Dalmatian pattern, they will have spots, because the allele for spots is dominant. Some puppies will have many tiny spots and some will have large patches! Dalmatians, like leopards, cannot change their spots.

Newborn Dalmatian puppies are white—their spots develop when the puppies are about a week old. ▼

Predict It! Dalmatians' spots may be black or liver (brown), but never both on the same dog. Liver is a recessive allele. Use a Punnett square to predict the color of the spots on the offspring of a liver Dalmatian and a black Dalmatian with a recessive liver allele. Display your prediction on a poster.

337

HOW CAN SCIENTISTS IDENTIFY HUMAN REMAINS?

How can genetic information be used?

These forensic scientists are putting together the skeletons of war victims. They can determine the age, sex, height, and ancestry of each body by examining bones. But that does not identify who the person was. Other scientists work to determine the identities of the victims.

△Develop Hypotheses How do you think a scientist might figure out a person's identity from bones?

_____

_____

_____

_____

_____

▶UNTAMED SCIENCE Watch the **Untamed Science** video to learn more about genetic technology.

Human Genetics and Genetic Technology

10 Getting Started

Check Your Understanding

1. Background Read the paragraph below and then answer the question.

Abdul has a white mouse named Pug. Both of Pug's parents had black fur, but they each had one **allele** for white fur and one allele for black fur. Because the **dominant allele** is for black fur, there was only a 25 percent **probability** that Pug would have white fur.

> An **allele** is a different form of a gene.
>
> The trait determined by a **dominant allele** always shows up in an organism if the allele is present.
>
> **Probability** is a number that describes how likely it is that an event will occur.

- What is the probability that Pug's parents would have an offspring with black fur? _____

▶ MY READING WEB If you had trouble completing the question above, visit **My Reading Web** and type in *Human Genetics and Genetic Technology.*

Vocabulary Skill

High-Use Academic Words High-use academic words are words that are used frequently in classrooms. Look for the words below as you read this chapter.

Word	Definition	Example
normal	*adj.* usual; typical, expected	It is *normal* to feel nervous about going to a new school.
resistant	*adj.* capable of preventing something from happening	The fabric stays clean easily because it is *resistant* to stains.

2. Quick Check Choose the word that best completes each sentence.

- Some bacteria are _____ to common antibiotic medicines, so they are not killed by them.

- A _____ body temperature in a human is about 37°C.

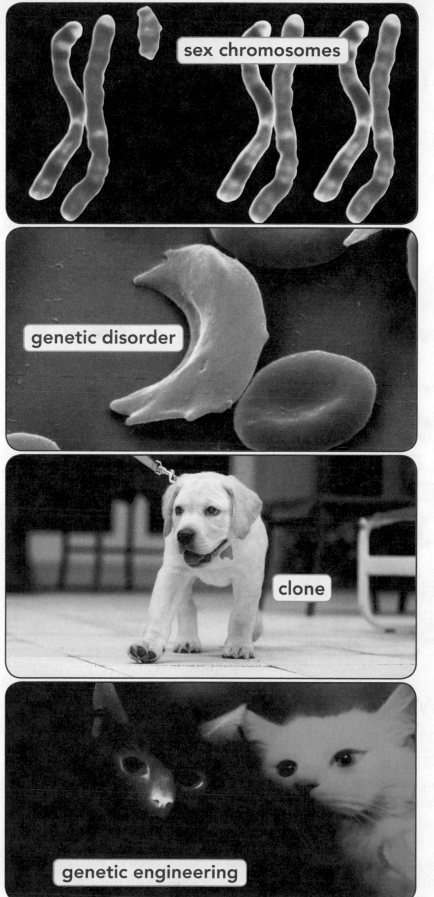

sex chromosomes

genetic disorder

clone

genetic engineering

Chapter Preview

LESSON 1
- sex chromosomes
- sex-linked gene
- carrier
- ↻ Relate Cause and Effect
- △ Infer

LESSON 2
- genetic disorder
- pedigree
- karyotype
- ↻ Outline
- △ Make Models

LESSON 3
- selective breeding
- inbreeding
- hybridization
- clone
- genetic engineering
- gene therapy
- ↻ Ask Questions
- △ Draw Conclusions

LESSON 4
- genome
- ethics
- ↻ Summarize
- △ Communicate

⟩ VOCAB FLASH CARDS For extra help with vocabulary, visit **Vocab Flash Cards** and type in *Human Genetics and Genetic Technology.*

Human Inheritance

 What Are Some Patterns of Human Inheritance?

 What Are the Functions of the Sex Chromosomes?

my planeт DiaRY

BLOG

Posted by: Hannah

Location: Old Tappan, New Jersey

I have many traits and characteristics that my parents have passed down to me. I have brown hair, like my mom's, but it's curly, like my dad's. I also have my dad's dark brown eyes, while my mom has blue. Both my parents have fair skin tone, but I have an olive complexion like my grandfather. I'm an interesting mix of all my relatives.

Write your answer below.

What characteristics do you have that resemble those of your relatives?

_____

_____

_____

_____

_____

> PLANET DIARY Go to **Planet Diary** to learn more about human inheritance.

Lab zone® Do the Inquiry Warm-Up *How Tall Is Tall?*

What Are Some Patterns of Human Inheritance?

Look at the other students in your classroom. Some people have curly hair; others have straight hair. Some people are tall, some are short, and many others are in between. You'll probably see eyes of many different colors, ranging from pale blue to dark brown. The different traits you see are determined by a variety of inheritance patterns. **Some human traits are controlled by single genes with two alleles, and others by single genes with multiple alleles. Still other traits are controlled by many genes that act together.**

Vocabulary
- sex chromosomes
- sex-linked gene
- carrier

Skills
- ▶ Reading: Relate Cause and Effect
- △ Inquiry: Infer

Single Genes With Two Alleles
A number of human traits, such as a dimpled chin or a widow's peak, are controlled by a single gene with either a dominant or a recessive allele. These traits have two distinctly different physical appearances, or phenotypes.

Single Genes With Multiple Alleles
Some human traits are controlled by a single gene that has more than two alleles. Such a gene is said to have multiple alleles—three or more forms of a gene that code for a single trait. Even though a gene may have multiple alleles, a person can carry only two of those alleles. This is because chromosomes exist in pairs. Each chromosome in a pair carries only one allele for each gene. Recall that an organism's genetic makeup is its genotype. The physical characteristics that result are called the organism's phenotype.

Human blood type is controlled by a gene with multiple alleles. There are four main blood types—A, B, AB, and O. Three alleles control the inheritance of blood types. The allele for blood type A is written as I^A. The allele for blood type B is written as I^B. The allele for blood type A and the allele for blood type B are codominant. This means that both alleles for the gene are expressed equally. A person who inherits an I^A allele from one parent and an I^B allele from the other parent will have type AB blood. The allele for blood type O—written as i—is recessive. **Figure 1** shows the different allele combinations that result in each blood type.

FIGURE 1 ....

Inheritance of Blood Type
The table below shows which combinations of alleles result in each human blood type.

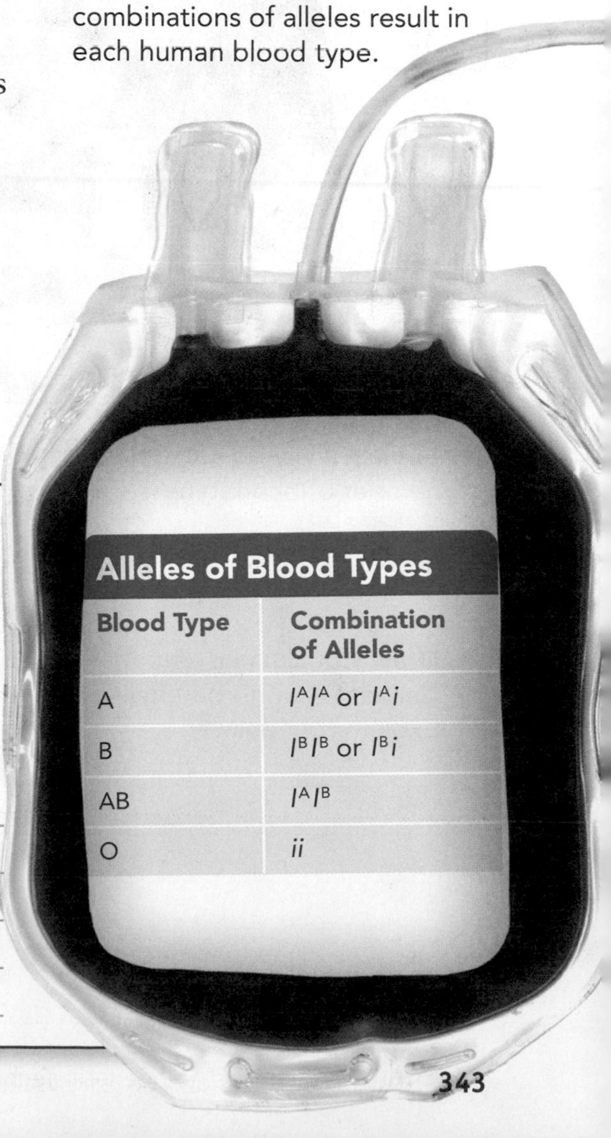

Alleles of Blood Types

Blood Type	Combination of Alleles
A	$I^A I^A$ or $I^A i$
B	$I^B I^B$ or $I^B i$
AB	$I^A I^B$
O	ii

apply it!

Use what you have learned about blood types and **Figure 1** to answer the following questions.

❶ **Interpret Tables** Genotypes are listed in the (left/right) column of the table, while phenotypes are on the (left/right).

❷ △ **Infer** Why are there more genotypes than phenotypes for blood types?

_____

_____

_____

_____

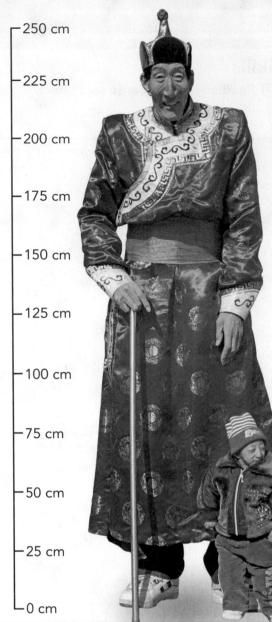

250 cm
225 cm
200 cm
175 cm
150 cm
125 cm
100 cm
75 cm
50 cm
25 cm
0 cm

Traits Controlled by Many Genes

Traits Controlled by Many Genes If you look around your classroom, you'll see that height in humans has more than two distinct phenotypes. In fact, there is an enormous variety of phenotypes for height. Some human traits show a large number of phenotypes because the traits are controlled by many genes. The alleles of the different genes act together as a group to produce a single trait. At least four genes control height in humans. You can see the extreme range of heights in **Figure 2.** Skin color is another human trait that is controlled by many genes.

FIGURE 2 ···

Extreme Heights

Human heights are known to range from the tall Bao Xishun, at 236 cm, to the short He Pingping, at 76 cm.

✎ **On the scale, mark your height and the heights of Bao Xishun and He Pingping.**

1. **Calculate** How many times taller are you than He Pingping?

_____

2. **Predict** Do you think Bao Xishun's parents are also tall? Why?

_____

_____

 Do the Quick Lab *The Eyes Have It.*

🔑 Assess Your Understanding

1a. Explain Why do some traits exhibit a large number of phenotypes?

_____

_____

b. Draw Conclusions Aaron has blood type O. Can either of his parents have blood type AB? Explain your answer.

_____

_____

_____

_____

got it?

○ **I get it!** Now I know that some human traits are controlled by _____

_____

_____

_____

○ **I need extra help with** _____

_____

Go to **MY SCIENCE COACH** *online for help with this subject.*

What Are the Functions of the Sex Chromosomes?

The body cells of humans contain 23 chromosome pairs, or 46 chromosomes. The **sex chromosomes** are one of the 23 pairs of chromosomes in each body cell. 🔑 **The sex chromosomes carry genes that determine a person's gender as being either male or female. They also carry genes that determine other traits.**

Girl or Boy?
The sex chromosomes are the only chromosome pair that do not always match. Girls have two sex chromosomes that match. The two chromosomes are called X chromosomes. Boys have two sex chromosomes that do not match. They have an X chromosome and a Y chromosome. The Y chromosome is much smaller than the X chromosome. To show the size difference, the sex chromosomes in **Figure 3** have been stained and magnified.

Sex Chromosomes and Fertilization
When egg cells and sperm cells form, what happens to the sex chromosomes? Since both of a female's sex chromosomes are X chromosomes, all eggs carry one X chromosome. Males, however, have two different sex chromosomes. Therefore, half of a male's sperm cells carry an X chromosome, while half carry a Y chromosome.

When a sperm cell with an X chromosome fertilizes an egg, the egg has two X chromosomes. The fertilized egg will develop into a girl. When a sperm with a Y chromosome fertilizes an egg, the egg has one X chromosome and one Y chromosome. The fertilized egg will develop into a boy.

X Chromosome

Y Chromosome

X   Y

FIGURE 3 ·······························

X Chromosomes

Male or Female?
The father's chromosome determines the sex of his child.

✏️ **Using the genotypes given for the mother and father, complete the Punnett square to show their child's genotype and phenotype.**

1. **Calculate** What is the probability that the child will be a girl? A boy?

_____

_____

X

X

2. **Interpret Diagrams** What sex will the child be if a sperm with a Y chromosome fertilizes an egg? _____

345

● Relate Cause and Effect
Underline the cause of
sex-linked traits in males and
circle the effect of the traits.

Sex-Linked Genes

The genes for some human traits are carried on the sex chromosomes. Genes found on the X and Y chromosomes are often called **sex-linked genes** because their alleles are passed from parent to child on a sex chromosome. Traits controlled by sex-linked genes are called sex-linked traits. One sex-linked trait is red-green colorblindness. A person with this trait cannot see the difference between red and green. Normal vision is dominant, while colorblindness is recessive.

FIGURE 4

▶ VIRTUAL LAB **X and Y Chromosomes**

The human X chromosome is larger and carries more genes than the human Y chromosome.

Y Chromosome

X Chromosome

Recall that a Y chromosome is smaller than an X chromosome. Females have two X chromosomes, but males have one X chromosome and one Y chromosome. These chromosomes have different genes.

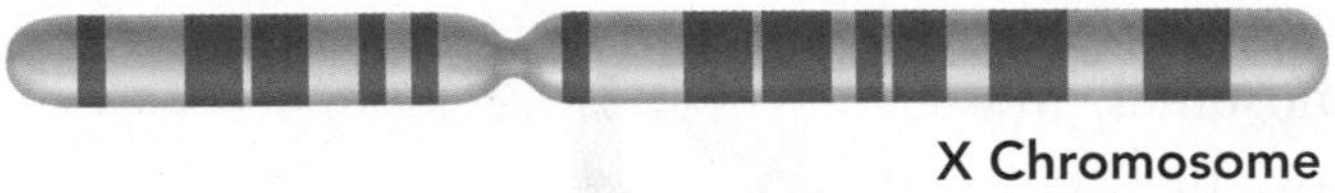

Most of the genes on the X chromosome are not on the Y chromosome. So an allele on an X chromosome may have no corresponding allele on a Y chromosome.

Like other genes, sex-linked genes can have dominant and recessive alleles. In females, a dominant allele on an X chromosome will mask a recessive allele on the other X chromosome. But in males, there is usually no matching allele on the Y chromosome to mask the allele on the X chromosome. As a result, any allele on the X chromosome—even a recessive allele—will produce the trait in a male who inherits it. This means that males are more likely than females to express a sex-linked trait that is controlled by a recessive allele. Individuals with colorblindness may have difficulty seeing the numbers in **Figure 5.** Test your vision below.

FIGURE 5

Colorblindness

Most colorblind individuals have difficulty seeing red and green.

✎ **Communicate** Working with a partner, look at the circles. Write the number you see in the space below each circle.

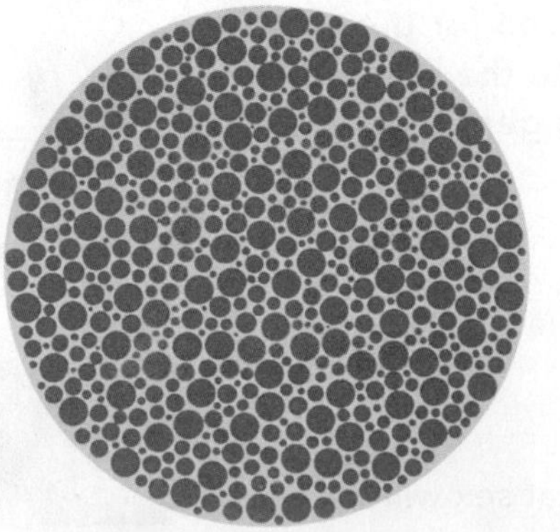

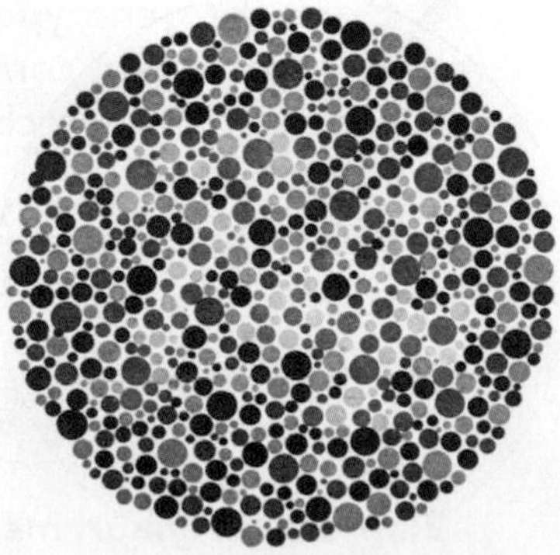

Inheritance of Colorblindness

Colorblindness is a trait controlled by a recessive allele on the X chromosome. Many more males than females have red-green colorblindness. You can understand why this is the case by examining the Punnett square in **Figure 6.** Both parents have normal color vision. Notice that the mother carries the dominant allele for normal vision (X^C) and the recessive allele for colorblindness (X^c). A **carrier** is a person who has one recessive allele for a trait and one dominant allele. A carrier of a trait controlled by a recessive allele does not express the trait. However, the carrier can pass the recessive allele on to his or her offspring. In the case of sex-linked traits, only females can be carriers because they are the only ones who can carry two alleles for the trait.

FIGURE 6 ··

Colorblindness Punnett Square

Red-green colorblindess is a sex-linked trait.

✏️ **Using the parents' information and the key, complete the Punnett square.**

1. **Identify** Complete the Punnett square by filling in the child's genotype, sex, and phenotype. For each child, draw the correct shape, and color it in to match the key.

2. **Calculate** What is the probability that this couple will have a colorblind child?

   _____

3. **Apply Concepts** What allele combination would a daughter need to inherit to be colorblind?

   _____

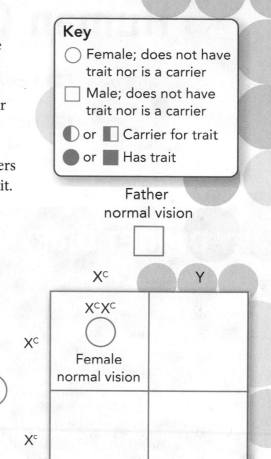

Key

○ Female; does not have trait nor is a carrier

□ Male; does not have trait nor is a carrier

◐ or ◨ Carrier for trait

● or ■ Has trait

Father
normal vision

Mother
carrier ◐

  Do the Lab Investigation
How Are Genes on the Sex Chromosomes Inherited?

🔑 Assess Your Understanding

2a. **Review** What is the sex of a person who is a carrier for colorblindness? _____

b. **CHALLENGE** Mary and her mother are both colorblind. Is Mary's father colorblind, too? How do you know?

_____

_____

_____

_____

got it?

○ I get it! Now I know that the functions of the sex chromosomes are _____

_____

_____

○ I need extra help with _____

_____

Go to **MY SCIENCE** ⑤ **COACH** online for help with this subject.

Human Genetic Disorders

UNLOCK THE BIG Q?

🔑 How Are Genetic Disorders Inherited in Humans?

🔑 How Are Genetic Disorders Traced, Diagnosed, and Treated?

my pLaneT DiaRY

Doggie Diagnosis

Maybe you have a dog or know someone who does. Did you know that dogs and humans can have some of the same health problems? It is not uncommon for dogs to have cancer, diabetes, allergies, epilepsy, and eye diseases. Scientists are studying the genes and genetic mutations that cause diseases in dogs in the hopes of better understanding human diseases. Most diseases in dogs are caused by a mutation on one gene. In humans, the mutations can be on multiple genes. The genes that cause diseases in dogs are much easier to find than those in humans. So far, scientists are looking into the genes that cause blindness, cancer, and spinal cord disorders in dogs.

German shepherds can have a form of cancer similar to breast cancer in humans.

Dachshunds and humans can both suffer from blindness.

DISCOVERY

Communicate Discuss the questions with a classmate. Then write your answers.

1. Why are scientists studying dog genes to understand human diseases?

_____

_____

_____

_____

2. In what other ways could studying dog diseases be beneficial?

_____

_____

_____

_____

_____

> **PLANET DIARY** Go to **Planet Diary** to learn more about human genetic disorders.

Golden retrievers can have cancer that affects the blood vessels.

Lab zone® Do the Inquiry Warm-Up *How Many Chromosomes?*

Vocabulary
- genetic disorder
- pedigree
- karyotype

Skills
- Reading: Outline
- Inquiry: Make Models

How Are Genetic Disorders Inherited in Humans?

Many of the athletes who compete in the Special Olympics have disabilities that result from genetic disorders. A **genetic disorder** is an abnormal condition that a person inherits through genes or chromosomes. **Some genetic disorders are caused by mutations in the DNA of genes. Other disorders are caused by changes in the overall structure or number of chromosomes.** In this lesson, you will learn about some common genetic disorders.

Cystic Fibrosis Cystic fibrosis is a genetic disorder in which the body produces abnormally thick mucus in the lungs and intestines. The thick mucus fills the lungs, making it hard for the affected person to breathe. Cystic fibrosis occurs when two mutated alleles are inherited, one from each parent. The mutation causes three bases to be removed from a DNA molecule.

Sickle-Cell Disease Sickle-cell disease is caused by a mutation that affects hemoglobin. Hemoglobin is a protein in red blood cells that carries oxygen. The red blood cells of people with the disease have a sickle, or crescent, shape. Sickle-shaped red blood cells cannot carry as much oxygen as normal cells and also clog blood vessels. The allele for the sickle-cell trait (S) is codominant with the normal allele (A). A person with one normal allele and one sickle-cell allele (AS) will produce both normal hemoglobin and abnormal hemoglobin. This person usually does not have symptoms of the disease. He or she has enough normal hemoglobin to carry oxygen to cells. A person with two sickle-cell alleles (SS) will have the disease.

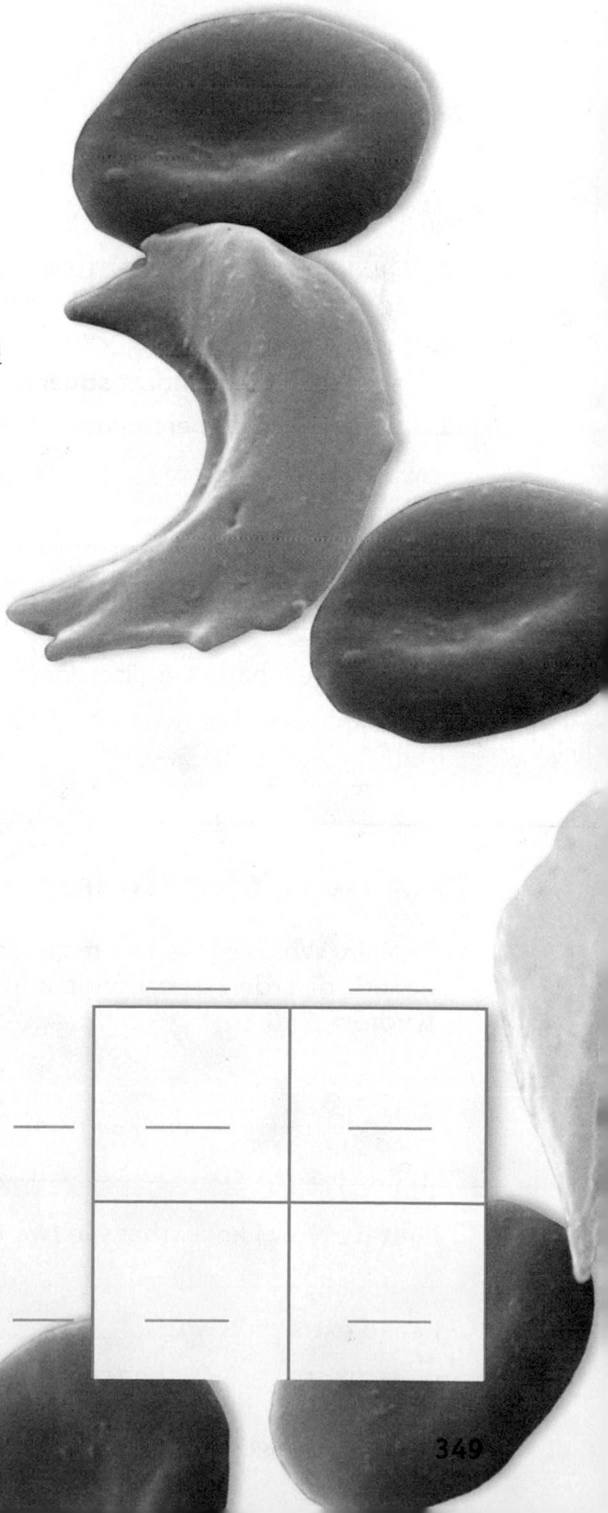

FIGURE 1 ···
Sickle-Cell Disease
In a person with sickle-cell disease, red blood cells can become sickle-shaped instead of round.

✎ **Predict** A man has sickle-cell disease. His wife does not have the disease, but is heterozygous for the sickle-cell trait. Use the parents' information to fill in the Punnett square. What is the probability that their child will have sickle-cell disease?

349

Outline After you read this section, make an outline on a separate sheet of paper that includes the different types of genetic disorders. Use the red headings to help you organize your outline.

Hemophilia Hemophilia is a genetic disorder in which a person's blood clots very slowly or not at all. People with the disorder do not produce enough of one of the proteins needed for normal blood clotting. The danger of internal bleeding from small bumps and bruises is very high. Hemophilia is caused by a recessive allele on the X chromosome. Because hemophilia is a sex-linked disorder, it occurs more frequently in males than in females.

Down Syndrome In Down syndrome, a person's cells have an extra copy of chromosome 21. Instead of a pair of chromosomes, a person with Down syndrome has three copies of chromosome 21. Down syndrome most often occurs when chromosomes fail to separate properly during meiosis, when sex cells (egg and sperm) form. People with Down syndrome have some degree of mental retardation. Heart defects are also common, but can be treated.

FIGURE 2

INTERACTIVE ART **Hemophilia**

Hemophilia occurs more often in males than in females.

Cross a carrier female, X^HX^h, with a healthy male, X^HY, and fill in the Punnett square.

1. **Calculate** What percentage of the offspring
   would be normal? ____________
   would be carriers? ____________
   would have hemophilia? ____________
2. CHALLENGE To have a daughter with hemophilia, the father must have the disorder (X^hY) and the mother must have one of two genotypes. What are they?
   ____

	____	____
____	____	____
____	____	____

Lab zone® Do the Quick Lab *What Went Wrong?*

Assess Your Understanding

1a. Explain Which of the two major causes of genetic disorders is responsible for Down syndrome?

____

____

b. Infer Why is hemophilia more common in males?

____

____

____

got it?

O **I get it!** Now I know that the two major causes of genetic disorders are ______________________________

____

O I need extra help with ______________________________

Go to MY SCIENCE COACH *online for help with this subject.*

How Are Genetic Disorders Traced, Diagnosed, and Treated?

Years ago, only Punnett squares were used to predict whether a child might have a genetic disorder. 🔑 **Today, doctors use tools such as pedigrees, karyotypes, and genetic testing to trace and diagnose genetic disorders. People with genetic disorders are helped through medical care, education, and job training.**

Pedigrees Suppose that you are interested in tracing the occurrence of a trait through several generations of a family. What would you do? A **pedigree** is a chart or "family tree" that tracks which members of a family have a particular trait. The trait in a pedigree can be an ordinary trait, such as eye color, or a genetic disorder. The pedigree shown below is for albinism, a condition in which a person's skin, hair, and eyes lack normal coloring.

apply it!

This pedigree shows the inheritance of the allele for albinism in three generations of a family.

1 **Interpret Diagrams** Circle the place in the pedigree that shows an albino male.

Key
- ◯ Female; does not have trait nor is a carrier
- ☐ Male; does not have trait nor is a carrier
- ◖ or ◧ Carrier for trait
- ● or ■ Has trait

A horizontal line connecting a male and a female represents a marriage.

A vertical line and a bracket connect the parents to their children.

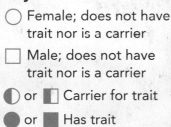

2 ⚠ **Make Models** Using what you have learned about pedigrees and pedigree symbols, construct a two-generation pedigree for sickle-cell disease, starting with parents who are both carriers, *AS × AS*. (*Hint:* Construct Punnett squares on a separate sheet of paper to determine the possible genotypes of the offspring.)

Karyotypes To detect a chromosomal disorder such as Down syndrome, doctors examine karyotypes. A **karyotype** (KA ree uh typ) is a picture of all the chromosomes in a person's cell. Look at **Figure 3.** As you can see, the chromosomes in a karyotype are arranged in pairs. A karyotype can reveal whether a person has the correct number of chromosomes in his or her cells.

FIGURE 3 ···

Karyotypes

Look at the karyotypes below. One is a normal karyotype and the other is an abnormal karyotype.

✎ **Working with a classmate, compare the two karyotypes.**

1. **Interpret Photos** What numbered set of chromosomes are the most different between the karyotypes? _____

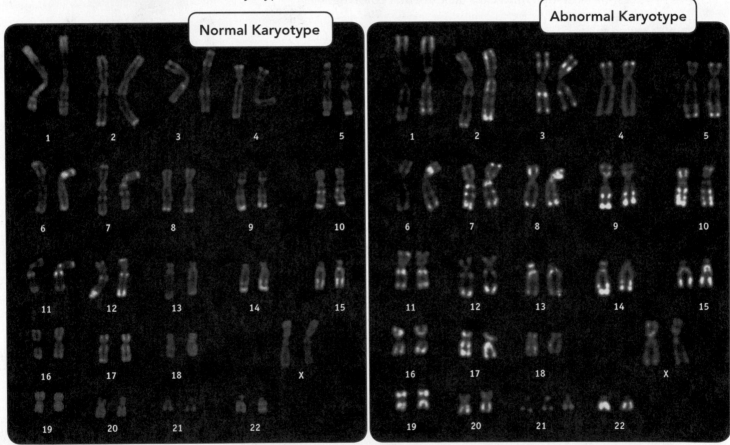

2. **Draw Conclusions** What can you conclude about the individual with the abnormal karyotype? Use evidence to support your answer.

_____

_____

_____

_____

Genetic Counseling

A couple that has a family history of a genetic disorder may turn to a genetic counselor for advice. Genetic counselors help couples understand their chances of having a child with a particular genetic disorder. Genetic counselors also help couples prepare for having children with a disorder. Karyotypes, pedigree charts, and Punnett squares assist genetic counselors in their work.

With advances in technology, new tests have been developed to screen for genetic disorders. Genetic tests examine genes, DNA, enzymes, and proteins to see if an individual has a genetic disorder or carries a gene for a genetic disorder. Whether or not the person develops the disease also depends on many other genetic factors, environmental conditions, and lifestyle.

Dealing With Genetic Disorders

People with genetic disorders face serious challenges, but they can be helped. Medical treatments help people with the symptoms of some disorders. For example, physical therapy helps remove mucus from the lungs of people with cystic fibrosis. People with sickle-cell disease take folic acid, a vitamin, to help their bodies manufacture red blood cells. Because of education and job training programs, adults with Down syndrome can find work in banks, restaurants, and other places. Most genetic disorders do not prevent people from living active, productive lives.

did you know?

Malaria is an infectious disease that kills more than a million people a year. This disease is transmitted to people when they are bitten by an infected mosquito. However, people who have the gene that causes sickle-cell disease are less likely to develop malaria.

FIGURE 4 ·····························

Genetic Disorders

These athletes have Down syndrome, a genetic disorder.

✎ **List** Name two types of programs that benefit individuals with Down syndrome.

_____

_____

_____

 Lab zone   Do the Quick Lab *Family Puzzle.*

🔑 Assess Your Understanding

got it? ··

○ **I get it!** Now I know that genetic disorders are traced, diagnosed, and treated by _____

_____

○ **I need extra help with** _____

Go to **MY SCIENCE** 🔵 **COACH** online for help with this subject.

Advances in Genetics

UNLOCK THE BIG ?

How Can Organisms Be Produced With Desired Traits?

my PLANET DiARY

Zorses, Zonies, and Zedonks

Most people can tell the difference between a zebra and a horse. But would you be able to tell the difference among a zorse, a zony, and a zedonk? All three types of animals are zebroids, or zebra hybrids. These animals result when a zebra mates with a horse, a pony, or a donkey. Zebroids do not usually occur in nature. They generally result when people cross them on purpose. People may have first crossed zebras and horses in an effort to develop disease-resistant transportation animals for use in Africa. Zebras are resistant to African sleeping sickness. It was hoped that zorses, the offspring of zebras and horses, would have this resistance.

FUN FACT

Communicate Discuss these questions with a classmate. Write your answers below.

1. Why may zebras and horses have been first crossed by people?

_____

_____

2. If zebras and horses do not usually mate in nature, should people intentionally cross them? Why or why not?

_____

_____

_____

_____

_____

> PLANET DIARY Go to **Planet Diary** to learn more about advances in genetics.

Lab zone® Do the Inquiry Warm-Up *What Do Fingerprints Reveal?*

Vocabulary
- selective breeding
- inbreeding
- hybridization
- clone
- genetic engineering
- gene therapy

Skills
- Reading: Ask Questions
- Inquiry: Draw Conclusions

How Can Organisms Be Produced With Desired Traits?

Unless you are an identical twin, your DNA is different from everyone else's. Because of advances in genetics, DNA evidence can show many things, such as family relationships or the ability to produce organisms with desirable traits. **Selective breeding, cloning, and genetic engineering are three different methods for developing organisms with desired traits.**

Selective Breeding The process of selecting organisms with desired traits to be parents of the next generation is called **selective breeding.** Thousands of years ago, in what is now Mexico, the food that we call corn was developed in this way. Every year, farmers saved seeds from the healthiest plants that produced the best food. In the spring, they planted only those seeds. This process was repeated over and over. In time, farmers developed plants that produced better corn. People have used selective breeding with many types of plants and animals. Two techniques for selective breeding are inbreeding and hybridization.

Ask Questions Before you read this lesson, preview the red headings. In the graphic organizer below, ask a question for each heading. As you read, write answers to your questions.

Question	Answer
What is selective breeding?	Selective breeding is

Vocabulary High-Use Academic **Words** Use the word *resistant* to explain how hybridization can be useful.

_____

_____

_____

_____

_____

_____

Inbreeding The technique of **inbreeding** involves crossing two individuals that have similar desirable characteristics. Suppose a male and a female golden retriever are both friendly and have the same coloring. Their offspring will probably also have those qualities. Inbreeding produces organisms that are genetically very similar. When inbred organisms are mated, the chance of their offspring inheriting two recessive alleles increases. This can lead to genetic disorders. For example, inherited hip problems are common in golden retrievers and other types of inbred dogs.

Hybridization In **hybridization** (hy brid ih ZAY shun), breeders cross two genetically different individuals. Recall that a hybrid organism has two different alleles for a trait. The hybrid organism that results is bred to have the best traits from both parents. For example, a farmer might cross corn that produces many kernels with corn that is resistant to disease. The farmer is hoping to produce a hybrid corn plant with both of the desired traits. Roses and other types of flowers are also commonly crossed.

apply it!

Since the late eighteenth century, gardeners and plant breeders have used hybridization to develop roses with certain characteristics.

❶ **Observe** Look at each rose below. One characteristic for each flower is given to you. List any other observable characteristics you see.

❷ **Draw Conclusions** Based on the characteristics of the two roses, draw with colored pencils or describe what you think the hybrid offspring will look like. Name the flower and list its characteristics.

Parent A

fragrant

_____

_____

_____

Parent B

survives cold temperatures

_____

_____

_____

Hybrid name:_____

_____

_____

_____

do the math!

Changing Rice Production

This data table shows how worldwide rice production changed between 1965 and 2005. New hybrid varieties of rice plants are one factor that has affected the amount of rice produced.

Year	Yield
1965	2.04
1970	2.38
1975	2.52
1980	2.75
1985	3.26
1990	3.53
1995	3.66
2000	3.89
2005	4.09

Worldwide Rice Production

Rice Production (metric tons per hectare) — 0, 1, 2, 3, 4, 5

Year — 1965, 1975, 1985, 1995, 2005

1 Graph Plot the data from the table and draw a line graph.

2 Interpret Data What is the approximate difference between rice production in 1965 and 2005? _____

3 CHALLENGE What other factors might help account for the difference in rice production between 1965 and 2005?

_____

_____

_____

Cloning For some organisms, such as the dog shown in **Figure 1,** a technique called cloning can be used to produce offspring with desired traits. A **clone** is an organism that has exactly the same genes as the organism from which it was produced. It isn't hard to clone some kinds of plants such as African violets. Just cut a stem from one plant and put the stem in soil. Water it, and soon you will have a whole new plant. The new plant is genetically identical to the plant from which the stem was cut.

Genetic Engineering Geneticists have developed another powerful technique for producing organisms with desired traits. In this process, called **genetic engineering,** genes from one organism are transferred into the DNA of another organism. Genetic engineering can produce medicines and improve food crops.

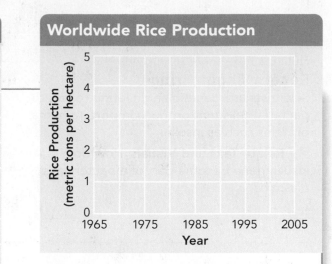

FIGURE 1 ···

Cloning

This puppy, Lancelot Encore, is thought to be the first commercially cloned puppy in the United States. His owners paid $150,000 to have him cloned in South Korea.

✎ **Make Judgments** Would you pay $150,000 to clone a pet? Why or why not?

_____

_____

357

FIGURE 2

Genetic Engineering

Scientists use genetic engineering to create bacterial cells that produce important human proteins such as insulin.

✏️ **Relate Text and Visuals** How does a human insulin gene become part of a bacterium's plasmid?

_____

_____

_____

_____

_____

_____

_____

Genetic Engineering in Bacteria One type of bacterium is genetically engineered to produce a human protein called insulin. Many people with diabetes need insulin injections. Bacteria have a single DNA molecule in the cytoplasm. Some bacterial cells also contain small circular pieces of DNA called plasmids. You can see how scientists insert the DNA for the human insulin gene into the plasmid of a bacterium in **Figure 2**. Once the gene is inserted into the plasmid, the bacterial cell and all of its offspring will contain this human gene. As a result, the bacteria produce the protein that the human gene codes for—in this case, insulin. Because bacteria can reproduce quickly, large amounts of insulin can be produced in a short time.

❶ Small rings of DNA, or plasmids, can be found in some bacterial cells.

❷ Scientists remove the plasmid. An enzyme cuts open the plasmid and removes the human insulin gene from its chromosome.

❸ The human insulin gene attaches to the open ends of the plasmid to form a closed ring.

❹ Some bacterial cells take up the plasmids that have the insulin gene.

❺ When the cells reproduce, the new cells will contain copies of the "engineered" plasmid. The foreign gene directs the cells to produce human insulin.

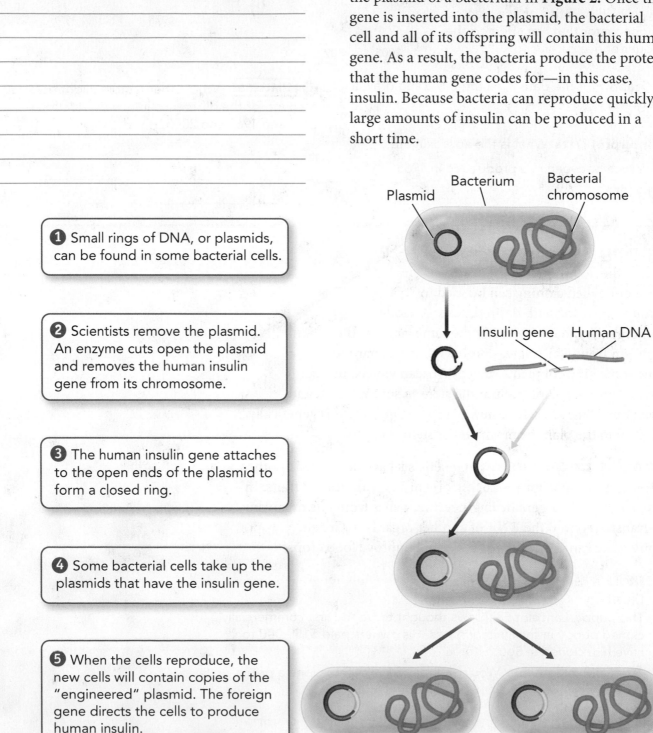

Genetic Engineering in Other Organisms

Scientists can also use genetic engineering techniques to insert genes into animals. For example, human genes can be inserted into the cells of cows. The cows then produce milk containing the human protein coded by the gene. Scientists have used this technique to produce the blood-clotting protein needed by people with hemophilia.

Genes have also been inserted into the cells of plants, such as tomatoes and rice. Some of the genes enable the plants to survive in cold temperatures or in poor soil. Other genetically engineered crops can resist insect pests or contain more nutrients.

Gene Therapy Someday it may be possible to use genetic engineering to correct some genetic disorders in humans. This process, called gene therapy, will involve inserting copies of a gene directly into a person's cells. For example, doctors may be able to treat hemophilia by replacing the defective allele on the X chromosome. The inserted gene would provide the body the correct instructions to clot blood normally.

Concerns About Genetic Engineering

Some people are concerned about the long-term effects of genetic engineering. For example, some people think that genetically engineered crops may not be entirely safe. People fear that these crops may harm the environment or cause health problems in humans. To address such concerns, scientists are studying the effects of genetic engineering.

FIGURE 3 ·····················

▶ ART IN MOTION **Glow Cats**

A fluorescent protein was added to the cells of the cat below. This protein allows the cat to glow red when exposed to ultraviolet light. The cat above lacks this protein.

Lab zone® Do the Quick Lab *Selective Breeding.*

🔑 Assess Your Understanding

1a. Identify The technique of crossing two individuals with similar characteristics is (inbreeding/hybridization).

b. Explain Why are identical twins not clones according to the text definition?

_____

_____

c. Apply Concepts Lupita has a houseplant. Which method would be the best way of producing a similar plant for a friend? Explain your answer.

_____

_____

_____

_____

got it? ·····································

○ **I get it!** Now I know that the three ways of producing organisms with desired traits are

_____

_____

○ **I need extra help with** _____

_____

Go to MY SCIENCE ⬤ COACH *online for help with this subject.*

359

Ohio

LESSON

4 Using Genetic Information

UNLOCK
THE BIG

🔑 **What Are Some Uses of Genetic Information?**

my planet Diary

TECHNOLOGY

Freedom Fighters

DNA technology saves lives, and not just through medicine. Since 1992, hundreds of innocent people have been freed from prison—some from death row—thanks to DNA testing. The Innocence Project is an organization that uses DNA testing to free prisoners who were wrongfully convicted. First, a sample of DNA is obtained from evidence saved from the crime scene. Then, a sample is taken from the prisoner. Laboratory procedures allow scientists to compare the two samples. If the prisoner's DNA is different from the DNA at the crime scene, the evidence may help free the prisoner.

Infer If the DNA from the crime scene matches the DNA from the prisoner, what might that suggest?

_____

_____

_____

_____

_____

_____

> PLANET DIARY Go to **Planet Diary** to learn more about using genetic information.

Lab zone® Do the Inquiry Warm-Up *Using Genetic Information.*

What Are Some Uses of Genetic Information?

Each person's genes contain unique information about that particular person's growth and development. If we could "read" those genes, think of all we could learn! 🔑 **Genetic information can be used positively to identify individuals and to learn about health and disease, or negatively to discriminate against people.**

Vocabulary
- genome
- ethics

Skills
- ⟳ Reading: Summarize
- △ Inquiry: Communicate

Human Genome Project

Imagine trying to crack a code that is six billion letters long. That's exactly what scientists working on the Human Genome Project did. An organism's full set of DNA is called its **genome.** The main goal of the Human Genome Project was to identify the DNA sequence of the entire human genome. In 2003, the project was completed. Scientists continue to research the functions of the tens of thousands of human genes.

DNA Fingerprinting

DNA technology used in the Human Genome Project can also identify people and show whether people are related. DNA from a person's cells is broken down into small pieces, or fragments. Selected fragments are used to produce a pattern called a DNA fingerprint. Except for identical twins, no two people have exactly the same DNA fingerprint.

Genetic "fingerprints" can tie a person to the scene of a crime or prevent the wrong person from going to jail. They also can be used to identify skeletal remains. Today, soldiers and sailors give blood and saliva samples so their DNA fingerprints can be saved. DNA records can be used to identify the bodies of unknown soldiers or civilians.

apply it!

DNA fingerprints are stored in national DNA databases such as the Combined DNA Index System (CODIS). Databases contain the genetic information from crime scenes, convicted offenders, and missing persons. Law enforcement uses these databases to see if the DNA they have collected matches a known sample.

△ **Communicate** Discuss the following statement with a partner. Identify the pros and cons related to the statement.
Each citizen of the United States should have his or her DNA fingerprint added to the national databases.

Pros: _____

_____

Cons: _____

_____

Summarize What is the main purpose of the Genetic Information Nondiscrimination Act?

_____

_____

_____

_____

Genetic Discrimination As it becomes easier to obtain genetic information, there are concerns about who can access that information. There are concerns about how it can be used, too. For example, soldiers provide the government with a DNA sample for identification. It could be possible for the government to use their DNA in other ways such as in criminal cases or paternity suits. **Ethics** is the study of principles about what is right and wrong, fair and unfair. Using genetic information in an ethical way means using it in a way that is fair and just.

The Genetic Information Nondiscrimination Act (GINA) was signed into law in 2008. This act makes it illegal for health insurance companies and employers to discriminate against individuals based on genetic information. It also makes it illegal for insurance companies and employers to ask or tell individuals that they must have a genetic test done.

EXPLORE THE BIG **?**

We Are Family!

How can genetic information be used?

FIGURE 1

INTERACTIVE ART You have been assigned to develop a family pedigree. Several members of this family have a hairline that comes to a point on their forehead. This characteristic, called a widow's peak, is a dominant trait.

Complete these tasks.

1. **Make Models** Draw and label this family's pedigree that shows how children may have inherited a widow's peak from their parents.

Genetic Privacy Doctors are expected to protect patients' privacy by not revealing their medical information. Patients' medical records may include information such as their medical history and their family's medical history. This information could indicate if a patient is at risk for developing a disease or mental illness. Details about a person's lifestyle may also be included in medical records. Doctors may record if a person drinks alcohol, smokes, or participates in sports that are dangerous.

If a patient has a genetic condition, the patient's relatives are likely at risk, too. Should other family members have the right to know? Or should a patient's medical records be kept private?

2. ⊙ **Summarize** What tools and techniques would you use if you wanted to know what your chances were of inheriting a genetic disease from a family member?

_____

_____

_____

_____

_____

3. **Evaluate the Impact on Society** If you learn that you have inherited a particular trait or genetic disease, who would you want to know? For each group of people listed, mark whether or not you think they should have the right to access your personal genetic information. Then explain why in the space below.

Immediate family members   Yes / No

_____

_____

Your principal and teachers   Yes / No

_____

_____

_____

Do the Quick Lab
Extraction in Action.

🔑 Assess Your Understanding

1a. Define What is a genome?

_____

_____

b. **CHALLENGE** Do you think it is ethical for doctors to share a patient's medical records? Explain.

_____

_____

_____

_____

_____

_____

c. ANSWER THE BIG **?** How can genetic information be used?

_____

_____

_____

_____

_____

got it? ....

○ **I get it!** Now I know that there are positive and negative ways of using genetic information such as _____

_____

_____

○ **I need extra help with** _____

Go to **MY SCIENCE COACH** *online for help with this subject.*

10 Study Guide

Genetic information can be used to _____,
_____, and _____.

LESSON 1 Human Inheritance

🔑 Some human traits are controlled by single genes with two alleles, and others by single genes with multiple alleles. Still other traits are controlled by many genes that act together.

🔑 The sex chromosomes carry genes that determine whether a person is male or female. They also carry genes that determine other traits.

Vocabulary
• sex chromosomes • sex-linked gene • carrier

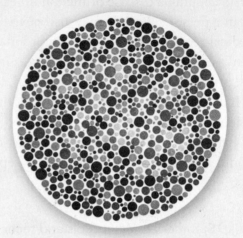

LESSON 2 Human Genetic Disorders

🔑 Some genetic disorders are caused by mutations in the DNA of genes. Other disorders are caused by changes in the overall structure or number of chromosomes.

🔑 Today, doctors use tools such as pedigrees, karyotypes, and genetic testing to help trace and diagnose genetic disorders. People with genetic disorders are helped through medical care, education, and job training.

Vocabulary
• genetic disorder • pedigree • karyotype

LESSON 3 Advances in Genetics

🔑 Selective breeding, cloning, and genetic engineering are three methods for developing organisms with desired traits.

Vocabulary
• selective breeding
• inbreeding
• hybridization
• clone
• genetic engineering
• gene therapy

LESSON 4 Using Genetic Information

🔑 Genetic information can be used positively to identify individuals and to learn about health and disease, or negatively to discriminate against people.

Vocabulary
• genome • ethics

Review and Assessment

LESSON 1 Human Inheritance

1. Which human trait is controlled by a single gene with multiple alleles?

   a. height   b. dimples

   c. skin color   d. blood type

2. Colorblindness is carried on the X chromosome and is more common in males than in females because it is a _____ _____

3. **Compare and Contrast** Describe the main differences between the inheritance patterns for a dimpled chin and for height.

   _____

   _____

   _____

   _____

   _____

   _____

4. **Interpret Data** Complete the Punnett square below to show the possible genotypes for the offspring of a colorblind mother and a father with normal vision. Circle the genotypes that would produce colorblind offspring.

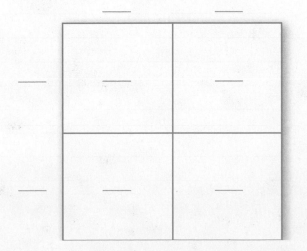

LESSON 2 Human Genetic Disorders

5. Which of the following would most likely be used to diagnose Down syndrome?

   a. a pedigree   b. a karyotype

   c. a Punnett square   d. a blood-clotting test

6. Cystic fibrosis and hemophilia are two examples of _____

7. **Make Generalizations** What information is shown by a karyotype?

   _____

   _____

8. **Relate Cause and Effect** How does the cause of cystic fibrosis differ from the cause of Down syndrome?

   _____

   _____

   _____

   _____

   _____

9. **Interpret Diagrams** The pedigree chart below shows the inheritance of sickle-cell disease. Circle all the individuals on the chart who have the disease. Draw a square around individuals who are carriers.

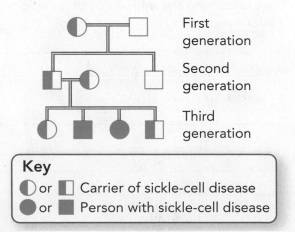

First generation

Second generation

Third generation

Key
- ◐ or ◨ Carrier of sickle-cell disease
- ● or ■ Person with sickle-cell disease

10 Review and Assessment

LESSON 3 Advances in Genetics

10. An organism that has the same genes as the organism that produced it is called a

   a. clone.   **b.** hybrid.

   c. genome.   **d.** pedigree.

11. Inbreeding and hybridization are two different

types of _____

12. **Write About It** Suppose that you are giving a presentation about genetic engineering to a group of people who are not familiar with the topic. Write a short speech that includes a definition of genetic engineering, a description of how it is used, and an explanation of some of the concerns about its use.

LESSON 4 Using Genetic Information

13. Genetic fingerprinting is a tool that is used in

   a. gene therapy.   **b.** selective breeding.

   c. cloning.   **d.** identification.

14. An organism's _____ is its full

set of DNA.

15. **Apply Concepts** Around the globe, people are discussing the ethical use of genetic information. Why is this a concern?

_____

_____

_____

_____

_____

_____

_____

 How can genetic information be used?

16. Genetic information can be applied in healthcare, agriculture, forensics, and many other fields. Using at least three vocabulary terms from this chapter, describe a situation in which genetic information such as this karyotype could have either a positive or negative impact on your daily life. Explain your reasoning.

_____

_____

_____

_____

_____

_____

_____

_____

_____

_____

_____

_____

Ohio Benchmark Practice

Multiple Choice

Circle the letter of the best answer.

1. This Punnett square shows the possible genotypes for the offspring of a colorblind father and a mother who is a carrier. If this couple has a daughter, what is the probability that she will be colorblind?

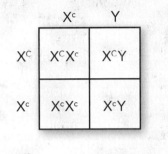

	X^c	Y
X^c	$X^c X^c$	$X^c Y$
X^c	$X^c X^c$	$X^c Y$

   A 0 percent   **B** 25 percent
   C 50 percent   **D** 100 percent

2. Inserting a human gene into a bacterial plasmid is an example of

   A inbreeding.
   B selective breeding.
   C DNA fingerprinting.
   D genetic engineering.

3. What was the main goal of the Human Genome Project?

   A to clone a human
   B to identify the sequence of the human genome
   C to protect the genetic privacy of individuals
   D to collect the genetic fingerprints of all humans

4. Which of the following is a selective breeding technique?

   A cloning   **B** forensics
   C inbreeding   **D** gene therapy

5. How is human blood type inherited?

   A through a sex-linked gene
   B through a single gene with multiple alleles
   C through many genes, which produce many possible combinations of genes and alleles
   D through a single gene with two alleles, one that is dominant and one that is recessive

Short Answer

Use the key below and your knowledge of science to help you answer Question 6. Write your answer on a separate piece of paper.

6. Sasha's mother has sickle-cell disease. Her father does not have the disease and is not a carrier. Sasha has one brother and one sister. Using the key below, draw a pedigree chart that shows the genotypes of each person in Sasha's family.

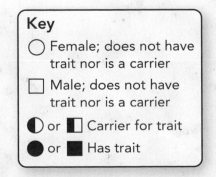

Key

○ Female; does not have trait nor is a carrier

□ Male; does not have trait nor is a carrier

◑ or ◨ Carrier for trait

● or ■ Has trait

MINI BUT MIGHTY

On TV crime shows, cases are solved in one hour. In real life, lab results may take weeks or months. Who knows how many more criminals could be caught if the lab techniques could be improved?

Scientists have recently developed technology that can run the same genetic tests that a lab can. "Lab-on-a-chip" devices are small and portable. They can usually produce results within an hour, right where the sample is taken. Scientists hope that one day, the units will be as small as a USB flash drive and affordable for everyone. Doctors could then diagnose and treat patients more quickly. Scientists at a crime scene could also get the answers they need almost immediately!

Analyze It Can you imagine any risks of a lab-on-a-chip? Do research about this new technology with its costs and benefits in mind. Make a presentation to your class on the impacts this device may have.

Museum of Science.

CODIS:
THE DNA DATABASE

Genetic evidence is one of the most powerful tools that investigators can use to solve a crime. A genetic fingerprint is the unique information stored in a piece of each person's DNA. Forensic investigators use a computer program called the Combined DNA Index System (CODIS) to identify suspects by using their DNA fingerprint. CODIS compares DNA fingerprints that are stored in databases across the country. These DNA fingerprints can be used to link different crime scenes or to identify a suspect. CODIS has also been used to prove that convicted criminals are innocent.

CODIS has been used in more than 79,000 criminal investigations. However, the system is limited by the amount of information in the databases. Many law enforcement agencies do not have enough people to analyze all of the genetic samples gathered from crime scenes. As a result, the CODIS system is incomplete. As more information is added to the system, the technology will become more and more useful.

Write About It Find out more about how genetic evidence is used to investigate crimes. Then, write a short detective story to explain how a forensic investigator uses genetic technologies to solve a burglary.

DNA samples can be collected at a crime scene and analyzed at a lab. Then, the analysis can be entered into a database to make the information available to CODIS.

The DNA from a human hair, like the one shown in this photomicrograph, can be used as evidence in criminal cases. ▶

369

DOES THIS FISH HAVE LEGS?

THE BIG ?

How do life forms change over time?

This is not your average fish. Besides having bright red lips, the rosy-lipped batfish is a poor swimmer. Instead of using its pectoral fins for swimming, the batfish uses them to crawl along the seafloor.

△Develop Hypotheses How do you think the batfish's leglike fins help it survive?

_____

_____

_____

_____

_____

_____

_____

▷ UNTAMED SCIENCE Watch the **Untamed Science** video to learn more about adaptations.

11 Getting Started

Check Your Understanding

1. Background Read the paragraph below and then answer the question.

Last fall, Jerome collected more than 100 seeds from a single sunflower in his garden. In the spring, he planted all the seeds. He was not surprised that the new plants all varied in many **traits.** Jerome knows that, because of **sexual reproduction,** each plant's **DNA** is different.

> A **trait** is a characteristic that an organism passes to offspring through its genes.
>
> **Sexual reproduction** results in offspring that are genetically different from each parent.
>
> **DNA** is genetic material that carries information about an organism and is passed from parent to offspring.

• How are the plants' different traits related to sexual reproduction?

_____

_____

> MY READING WEB If you had trouble completing the question above, visit **My Reading Web** and type in *Change Over Time.*

Vocabulary Skill

Identify Multiple Meanings Familiar words may mean something else in science. Look at the different meanings of the words below.

Word	Everyday Meaning	Scientific Meaning
theory	*n.* a guess **Example:** Sue has a theory that soccer is harder to play than basketball.	*n.* a well-tested concept that explains a wide range of observations **Example:** The cell theory says that all organisms are made of cells.
adaptation	*n.* a change in an individual's behavior **Example:** Talia's adaptation to her new school was hard, but she did it.	*n.* a trait that helps an individual survive and reproduce **Example:** Fur is an adaptation to cold.

2. Quick Check Circle the sentence that uses the scientific meaning of the word *theory.*

• Evolutionary *theory* describes change over time.

• Do you have a *theory* about why Sarah is a vegetarian?

variation

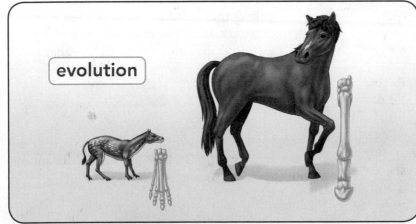

homologous structures

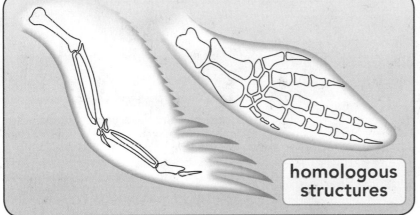

evolution

adaptation

Chapter Preview

LESSON 1
- species
- fossil
- adaptation
- evolution
- scientific theory
- natural selection
- variation

⟳ **Relate Cause and Effect**
△ **Develop Hypotheses**

LESSON 2
- homologous structures

⟳ **Identify the Main Idea**
△ **Communicate**

LESSON 3
- gradualism
- punctuated equilibrium

⟳ **Compare and Contrast**
△ **Make Models**

LESSON 4
- biodiversity • keystone species
- gene • extinction
- endangered species
- threatened species
- habitat destruction
- habitat fragmentation
- poaching • captive breeding

⟳ **Compare and Contrast**
△ **Infer**

> **VOCAB FLASH CARDS** For extra help with vocabulary, visit **Vocab Flash Cards** and type in *Change Over Time.*

Darwin's Theory

UNLOCK THE BIG ?

🔑 **What Was Darwin's Hypothesis?**

🔑 **What Is Natural Selection?**

my planet DiaRY

Charles Darwin

In 1839, Charles Darwin published his book *The Voyage of the Beagle*. Read the following excerpt about an animal Darwin encountered while in the Galápagos Islands.

The inhabitants believe that these animals are absolutely deaf; certainly they do not overhear a person walking close behind them. I was always amused when overtaking one of these great monsters, as it was quietly pacing along, to see how suddenly, the instant I passed, it would draw in its head and legs, and uttering a deep hiss fall to the ground with a heavy sound, as if struck dead. I frequently got on their backs, and then giving a few raps on the hinder part of their shells, they would rise up and walk away; — but I found it very difficult to keep my balance.

VOICES FROM HISTORY

Communicate Discuss these questions with a classmate. Write your answers below.

1. What kind of animal do you think Darwin was describing?

_____

_____

2. Describe your reaction to an unusual animal that you may have seen at a zoo, at an aquarium, or in a pet store. What was your first impression of the animal?

_____

_____

_____

▶ **PLANET DIARY** Go to **Planet Diary** for more information about Charles Darwin.

Lab zone® Do the Inquiry Warm-Up *How Do Living Things Vary?*

Vocabulary

- species • fossil • adaptation
- evolution • scientific theory
- natural selection • variation

Skills

⟳ Reading: Relate Cause and Effect

△ Inquiry: Develop Hypotheses

What Was Darwin's Hypothesis?

In 1831, the British ship HMS *Beagle* set sail from England on a five-year trip around the world. Charles Darwin was on board. Darwin was a naturalist—a person who observes and studies the natural world.

Diversity Darwin was amazed by the diversity of living things that he saw during the voyage. He wondered why they were so different from those in England. Darwin saw insects that looked like flowers. He also observed sloths, slow-moving animals that spent much of their time hanging in trees. Today, scientists know that organisms are even more diverse than Darwin thought. In fact, scientists have identified more than 1.6 million species of organisms on Earth. A **species** is a group of similar organisms that can mate with each other and produce fertile offspring. The exact number of species is unknown because many areas of Earth have not yet been studied.

Fossils Darwin saw fossils of animals that had died long ago. A **fossil** is the preserved remains or traces of an organism that lived in the past. Darwin was puzzled by some of the fossils he observed. For example, he saw fossils that resembled the bones of living sloths but were much larger in size. He wondered what had happened to the ancient, giant ground sloths. See **Figure 1.**

FIGURE 1 ······

Sloth Similarities

Darwin thought that the fossil bones of the giant ground sloths (left) resembled the bones of modern-day sloths (above).

✎ **Observe** List two similarities that you notice between the two sloths.

Similarities

The Galápagos penguin is the northernmost penguin in the world! It lives on the equator and is kept cool by ocean currents. The Galápagos penguin is the rarest penguin species and is endangered.

Galápagos Organisms

The *Beagle* made many stops along the Atlantic and Pacific coasts of South America. From the Pacific coast, the ship traveled west to the Galápagos Islands. Darwin observed many unusual life forms there. He compared organisms from the Galápagos Islands to organisms that lived elsewhere. He also compared organisms living on the different islands.

Comparisons to South American Organisms

Darwin discovered many similarities between Galápagos organisms and those found in South America. Many of the birds and plants on the islands resembled those on the mainland. However, he also noted important differences between the organisms. For instance, you can see differences between island and mainland iguanas in **Figure 2**.

Darwin became convinced that species do not always stay the same. Instead, he thought species could change and even produce new species over time. Darwin began to think that maybe the island species were somehow related to South American species. Perhaps, he thought, the island species had become different from their mainland relatives over time.

FIGURE 2 ··

Comparing Iguanas

The iguanas on the Galápagos Islands have large claws that allow them to grip slippery rocks so they can feed on seaweed.

The iguanas on the mainland have smaller claws that allow them to climb trees so they can eat leaves.

✎ **Infer** The color of each iguana is an adaptation to its

○ food. ○ habitat.

○ predators. ○ climate.

Explain your answer.

_____

_____

_____

FIGURE 3 ···

▶ INTERACTIVE ART Galápagos Finches
The structure of each bird's beak is an adaptation
to the type of food the bird eats. Birds with long,
pointed, sharp beaks pick at cacti. Those with
short, thick beaks crush seeds.

Birds with narrow, pointed beaks grasp insects.
Those with short, hooked beaks tear open fruit.

✎ **Interpret Diagrams** Look at the different
beak structures. Draw a line from each finch to
the type of food you think it eats.

Comparisons Among the Islands Darwin also discovered
many differences among organisms on the different Galápagos
Islands. For example, the tortoises on one island had dome-shaped
shells. Those on another island had saddle-shaped shells. A government official in the islands told Darwin that he could tell which
island a tortoise came from just by looking at its shell.

Adaptations Birds were also different from one island to the
next. Look at **Figure 3.** When Darwin returned to England, he
learned that the different birds were all finches. Darwin
concluded that the finch species were all related to a single ancestor
species that came from the mainland. Over time, different finches
developed different beak shapes and sizes that were well suited to
the food that they ate. Beak shape is an example of an **adaptation**,
a trait that increases an organism's ability to survive and reproduce.

·················· ✎ ··················
Vocabulary Identify Multiple
Meanings Write a sentence
using the everyday meaning of
the word *adapt*.

_____

_____

_____

_____

_____

Darwin's Hypothesis Darwin thought about what he had seen during his voyage on the *Beagle*. By this time, Darwin was convinced that organisms change over time. The process of change over time is called **evolution.** Darwin, however, wanted to know *how* organisms change. Over the next 20 years, he consulted with other scientists and gathered more information. Based on his observations, Darwin reasoned that plants or animals that arrived on the Galápagos Islands faced conditions that were different from those on the nearby mainland. **Darwin hypothesized that species change over many generations and become better adapted to new conditions**.

Darwin's ideas are often referred to as a theory of evolution. A **scientific theory** is a well-tested concept that explains a wide range of observations. From the evidence he collected, Darwin concluded that organisms on the Galápagos Islands had changed over time.

apply it!

The first labradoodle dog was bred in 1989. A labradoodle is a cross between a standard poodle and a Labrador retriever. The poodle is very smart and has fur that sheds very little. The poodle may be less irritating for people allergic to dogs. Labradors are gentle, easily trained, and shed seasonally.

Standard poodle   Labrador retriever   Labradoodle

1 Make Generalizations Why do you think people breed these two dogs together?

_____

_____

2 Develop Hypotheses Would you expect the first labradoodle puppies to be the same as puppies produced several generations later? Explain.

_____

_____

Artificial Selection Darwin studied the offspring of domesticated animals that were produced by artificial selection in an effort to understand how evolution might occur. In artificial selection, only the organisms with a desired characteristic, such as color, are bred. Darwin himself had bred pigeons with large, fan-shaped tails. By repeatedly allowing only those pigeons with many tail feathers to mate, Darwin produced pigeons with two or three times the usual number of tail feathers. Darwin thought that a process similar to artificial selection might happen in nature. But he wondered what natural process selected certain traits.

FIGURE 4 ....
Artificial Selection
The pigeons that Darwin bred were all descended from the rock dove (left). Pigeons can be bred for characteristics such as color, beak shape, wingspan, and feather patterns.

✎ **Describe** If you were to breed an animal, what would it be and what traits would you want it to have?

_____

_____

_____

 Do the Quick Lab
Bird Beak Adaptations.

🔑 Assess Your Understanding

1a. List Make a list of three observations that Darwin made during the *Beagle's* voyage.

_____

_____

_____

b. Describe An adaptation is a trait that

increases an organism's ability to _____

and _____

c. △ **Develop Hypotheses** How does artificial selection support Darwin's hypothesis?

_____

_____

_____

_____

got it? ....

○ **I get it!** Now I know that Darwin's hypothesis was _____

_____

○ **I need extra help with** _____

Go to **MY SCIENCE COACH** *online for help with this subject.*

What Is Natural Selection?

In 1858, Darwin and Alfred Russel Wallace, another British biologist, both proposed the same explanation for how evolution occurs. The next year, Darwin described his explanation in his book *The Origin of Species*. In this book, Darwin proposed that evolution occurs by means of natural selection. **Natural selection** is the process by which individuals that are better adapted to their environment are more likely to survive and reproduce more than other members of the same species. Darwin identified factors that affect the process of natural selection: overproduction, variation, and competition. **Figure 5** shows how natural selection might happen in a group of sea turtles.

Overproduction Darwin knew that most species produce far more offspring than can possibly survive. In many species, so many offspring are produced that there are not enough resources—food, water, and living space—for all of them.

Factors That Affect Natural Selection
How do life forms change over time?

FIGURE 5 ⋯⋯⋯⋯⋯⋯⋯⋯⋯⋯⋯⋯⋯⋯⋯⋯⋯⋯⋯⋯⋯⋯⋯⋯⋯⋯⋯⋯⋯⋯⋯⋯⋯⋯⋯⋯⋯

▶ **REAL-WORLD INQUIRY** Overproduction, variation, and competition are factors that affect the process of natural selection.

✎ **Summarize** Examine the sequence below that shows how natural selection could affect a group of sea turtles over time. Label each factor in the illustration and write a brief caption explaining what is occurring.

Variation Members of a species differ from one another in many of their traits. Any difference between individuals of the same species is called a **variation.** For example, sea turtles may differ in color, size, the ability to swim quickly, and shell hardness.

Competition Since food, space, and other resources are limited, the members of a species must compete with one another to survive. Competition does not always involve physical fights between members of a species. Instead, competition is usually indirect. For example, some turtles may not find enough to eat. A slower turtle may be caught by a predator, while a faster turtle may escape. Only a few turtles will survive to reproduce.

Selection Darwin observed that some variations make individuals better adapted to their environment. Those individuals are more likely to survive and reproduce. Their offspring may inherit the helpful characteristic. The offspring, in turn, will be more likely to survive and reproduce, and pass the characteristic to their offspring. After many generations, more members of the species will have the helpful characteristic.

In effect, the environment selects organisms with helpful traits to become parents of the next generation. 🔑 **Darwin proposed that, over a long time, natural selection can lead to change. Helpful variations may accumulate in a species, while unfavorable ones may disappear.**

✏️

⟳ **Relate Cause and Effect**
Fill in the graphic organizer to identify the factors that cause natural selection.

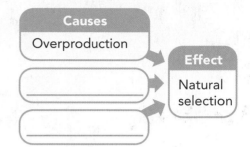

Causes
Overproduction
_____
_____

Effect
Natural selection

_____
_____
_____
_____

Environmental Change

Environmental Change A change in the environment can affect an organism's ability to survive and therefore lead to natural selection. For example, monkey flowers are plants that do not normally grow in soil that has a high concentration of copper. However, because of genetic variation, some varieties of monkey flower now grow near copper mines. In **Figure 6** you can see how natural selection might have resulted in monkey flowers that can grow in copper-contaminated soil.

Genes and Natural Selection Without variations, all the members of a species would have the same traits and the same chance of surviving and reproducing. But where do variations come from? How are they passed on from parents to offspring?

Darwin could not explain what caused variations or how they were passed on. As scientists later learned, variations can result from changes in genes and the shuffling of different forms of genes when egg and sperm join. Genes, such as those for hair color and height, are passed from parents to their offspring. Only traits that are inherited, or controlled by genes that are passed on to offspring, can be acted upon by natural selection.

do the math!

The typical clutch size, or number of eggs, a loggerhead sea turtle can lay at once is around 113. Even with producing so many offspring, the loggerhead sea turtle is endangered in many areas. Suppose that scientists counted the number of eggs laid at seven different nesting sites along the southeast coast of the United States. The following year, scientists check the nesting sites to see how many offspring survived and returned.

Loggerhead Sea Turtle Data

Site	A	B	C	D	E	F	G
Clutch Size	114	103	121	118	107	103	104
Returning Turtles	45	35	55	53	40	66	38

1 Calculate Determine the mean for the clutch sizes of the seven nesting sites in the table. _____ How does the mean compare to the typical clutch size for loggerheads? _____

_____

_____

2 Interpret Data Do you think clutch size influences the survival rates of the offspring? Use the data to support your answer.

_____

_____

_____

3 CHALLENGE Hypothesize why Site F had the largest number of returning turtles.

_____

_____

_____

_____

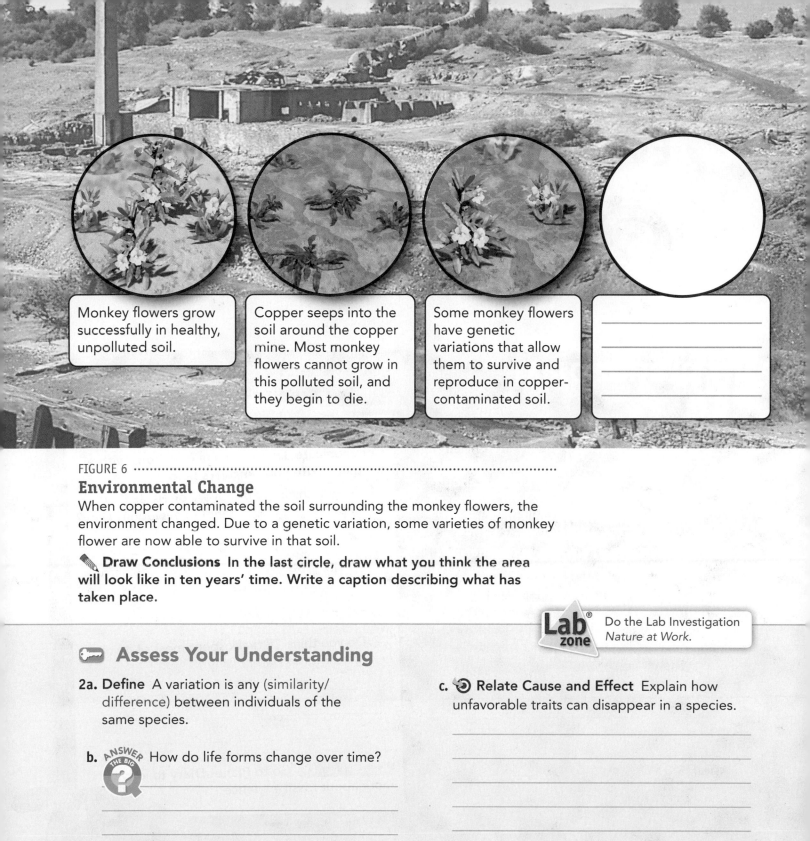

Monkey flowers grow successfully in healthy, unpolluted soil.

Copper seeps into the soil around the copper mine. Most monkey flowers cannot grow in this polluted soil, and they begin to die.

Some monkey flowers have genetic variations that allow them to survive and reproduce in copper-contaminated soil.

FIGURE 6 ....

Environmental Change

When copper contaminated the soil surrounding the monkey flowers, the environment changed. Due to a genetic variation, some varieties of monkey flower are now able to survive in that soil.

✎ **Draw Conclusions** In the last circle, draw what you think the area will look like in ten years' time. Write a caption describing what has taken place.

Lab zone® Do the Lab Investigation *Nature at Work.*

🔑 Assess Your Understanding

2a. Define A variation is any (similarity/difference) between individuals of the same species.

b. ANSWER THE BIG ? How do life forms change over time?

c. 🎯 Relate Cause and Effect Explain how unfavorable traits can disappear in a species.

got it? ....

○ **I get it!** Now I know that natural selection occurs _____

○ **I need extra help with** _____

Go to **MY SCIENCE COACH** *online for help with this subject.*

Evidence of Evolution

🔑 **What Evidence Supports Evolution?**

MY PLANET DiARY

DISCOVERY

Moving On Up

In 2004, researchers on Ellesmere Island, Nunavut, in the Canadian Arctic, found a fossil that provides information about when fish first came onto land. The fossil, called *Tiktaalik*, is 375 million years old. *Tiktaalik* has characteristics of both fish and four-legged animals. Like other fish, it has fins. However, the fins have interior bones that helped push the animal up in the shallow waters close to shore to find food. The discovery of *Tiktaalik* has provided new fossil evidence to help scientists understand the relationship between marine vertebrates and land vertebrates.

Researcher from Ellesmere Island

Communicate Discuss these questions with a partner. Write your answers below.

1. Do you think the discovery of *Tiktaalik* is important to understanding evolution? Why?

_____

_____

_____

_____

2. Do you think *Tiktaalik* spent most of its time on land or in water? Why?

_____

_____

_____

▸ **PLANET DIARY** Go to **Planet Diary** to learn more about fossil evidence.

This model of *Tiktaalik* shows what it may have looked like 375 million years ago.

Lab zone ® Do the Inquiry Warm-Up *How Can You Classify a Species?*

Vocabulary
• homologous structures

Skills
⊃ Reading: Identify the Main Idea
△ Inquiry: Communicate

What Evidence Supports Evolution?

Since Darwin's time, scientists have found a great deal of evidence that supports the theory of evolution. 🔑 **Fossils, patterns of early development, similar body structures, and similarities in DNA and protein structures all provide evidence that organisms have changed over time.**

Fossils By examining fossils, scientists can infer the structures of ancient organisms. Fossils show that, in many cases, organisms that lived in the past were very different from organisms alive today. The millions of fossils that scientists have collected are called the fossil record. The fossil record provides clues about how and when new species evolved and how organisms are related.

Similarities in Early Development Scientists also infer evolutionary relationships by comparing the early development of different organisms. For example, the organisms in **Figure 1** look similar during the early stages of development. All four organisms have a tail. They also have a row of tiny slits along their throats. The similarities suggest that these vertebrate species are related and share a common ancestor.

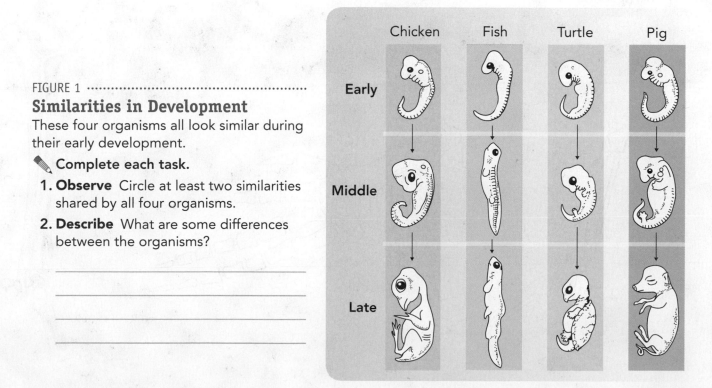

FIGURE 1 ···
Similarities in Development
These four organisms all look similar during their early development.

✎ **Complete each task.**

1. **Observe** Circle at least two similarities shared by all four organisms.

2. **Describe** What are some differences between the organisms?

_____
_____
_____
_____

Chicken   Fish   Turtle   Pig

Early

Middle

Late

Similarities in Body Structure

An organism's body structure is its basic body plan, which in vertebrates includes how its bones are arranged. Fishes, amphibians, reptiles, birds, and mammals all have an internal skeleton with a backbone. This similarity provides evidence that these animal groups all evolved from a common ancestor.

Similar structures that related species have inherited from a common ancestor are known as **homologous structures** (hoh MAHL uh gus). In **Figure 2,** you can see some examples of homologous structures. These include a bird's wing, a dolphin's flipper, and a dog's leg.

Sometimes fossils show structures that are homologous with structures in living species. For example, scientists have recently found fossils of ancient whalelike creatures. The fossils show that the ancestors of today's whales had legs and walked on land. This evidence supports other evidence that whales and other vertebrates share a common ancestor that had a skeleton with a backbone.

FIGURE 2 ....

▶ INTERACTIVE ART ◀ **Homologous Structures**
The bones in a bird's wing, a dolphin's flipper, and a dog's leg have similar structures.

✏️ **Interpret Diagrams** Use the drawing of the dog's leg as a guide. Color in the matching bones in the bird's wing and the dolphin's flipper with the appropriate colors.

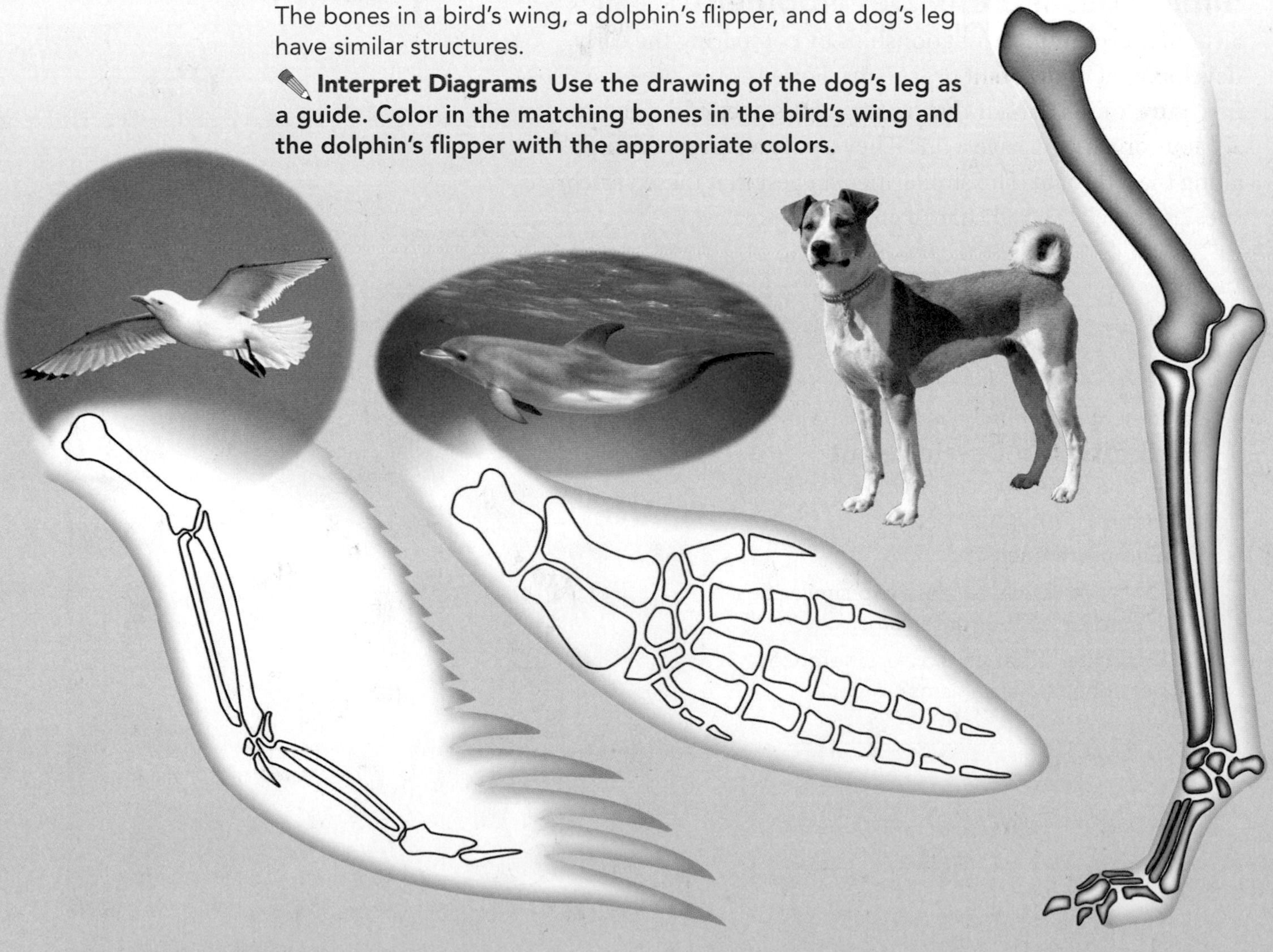

Similarities in DNA and Protein Structure

Why do some species have similar body structures and development patterns? Scientists infer that the species inherited many of the same genes from a common ancestor.

Recall that genes are segments of DNA. Scientists compare the sequence of nitrogen bases in the DNA of different species to infer how closely related the two species are. The more similar the DNA sequences, the more closely related the species are. The DNA bases along a gene specify what type of protein will be produced. Therefore, scientists can also compare the order of amino acids in a protein to see how closely related two species are.

In most cases, evidence from DNA and protein structure has confirmed conclusions based on fossils, embryos, and body structure. For example, DNA comparisons show that dogs are more similar to wolves than to coyotes. Scientists had already reached this conclusion based on similarities in the structure and development of these three species.

apply it!

The table shows the sequence of amino acids in one region of a protein, cytochrome c, for five different animals. Each letter corresponds to a different amino acid in the protein.

Section of Cytochrome *c* Protein in Animals												
Animal	**Amino Acid Position in the Sequence**											
	39	40	41	42	43	44	45	46	47	48	49	50
Horse	N	L	H	G	L	F	G	R	K	T	G	Q
Donkey	N	L	H	G	L	F	G	R	K	T	G	Q
Rabbit	N	L	H	G	L	F	G	R	K	T	G	Q
Snake	N	L	H	G	L	F	G	R	K	T	G	Q
Turtle	N	L	N	G	L	I	G	R	K	T	G	Q

❶ **Interpret Tables** Which species is most distantly related to the horse? _____

❷ **Communicate** Explain how amino acid sequences provide information about evolutionary relationships among organisms.

_____
_____
_____
_____
_____
_____

Lab zone Do the Quick Lab *Finding Proof.*

Assess Your Understanding

1a. Define _____ structures are structurally similar body parts in related species.

b. [CHALLENGE] Insects and birds both have wings. What kinds of evidence might show whether or not insects and birds are closely related? Explain.

_____
_____
_____
_____

got it?

○ **I get it!** Now I know that the theory of evolution is supported by evidence that includes _____

_____
_____
_____

○ **I need extra help with** _____

Go to **MY SCIENCE COACH** online for help with this subject.

Rate of Change

UNLOCK
THE BIG
?

🔑 **How Do New Species Form?**

🔑 **What Patterns Describe the Rate of Evolution?**

MY PLANET DIARY

Crickets, Maggots, and Flies, Oh My!

A male cricket chirps to attract a mate. Unfortunately, chirping also attracts a parasitic fly. Parasitic flies listen for chirping crickets. When a cricket is located, a female fly deposits larvae onto the cricket's back. The larvae, or maggots, burrow into the cricket. The maggots come out seven days later, killing the cricket in the process. Parasitic flies reduced the cricket population on the Hawaiian island of Kauai between 1991 and 2001. By 2003, the cricket population on Kauai had increased. The male crickets were silent! In about 20 cricket generations, the crickets had evolved into an almost silent population.

Lab zone Do the Inquiry Warm-Up *Making a Timeline.*

FUN FACT

Communicate Discuss these questions with a classmate. Write your answers below.

1. Why do you think the crickets on Kauai evolved so quickly?

_____

_____

_____

2. If most of the male crickets can no longer chirp, how do you think it might affect the size of the cricket population?

_____

_____

_____

_____

> **PLANET DIARY** Go to **Planet Diary** to learn more about evolution.

How Do New Species Form?

Natural selection explains how variations can lead to changes in a species. But how could an entirely new species form? 🔑 **A new species can form when a group of individuals remains isolated from the rest of its species long enough to evolve different traits that prevent reproduction.** Isolation, or complete separation, occurs when some members of a species become cut off from the rest of the species. One way this can happen is when a natural barrier, such as a river, separates group members.

Vocabulary
- gradualism
- punctuated equilibrium

Skills
- Reading: Compare and Contrast
- Inquiry: Make Models

FIGURE 1 ....

Kaibab and Abert's Squirrels
The Kaibab squirrel (left) and the Abert's squirrel (right) have been isolated from each other for a long time. Eventually, this isolation may result in two different species.

Identify What conditions might differ from one side of the Grand Canyon to the other that would cause the squirrels to be different colors?

_____

_____

_____

Key

Range of Kaibab squirrel	Range of Abert's squirrel

As you can see in **Figure 1,** the populations of Kaibab and Abert's squirrels are separated by the Grand Canyon. The two kinds of squirrels are the same species, but they have slightly different characteristics. For example, the Kaibab squirrel has a black belly, while Abert's squirrel has a white belly. It is possible that one day these squirrels will become so different that they will no longer be able to mate with each other and will become separate species.

 Do the Quick Lab
Large-Scale Isolation.

🔑 Assess Your Understanding

got it? ....

○ **I get it!** Now I know that new species form when _____

_____

○ **I need extra help with** _____

Go to **my science coach** *online for help with this subject.*

What Patterns Describe the Rate of Evolution?

The fossil record has provided scientists with a lot of important information about past life on Earth. For example, scientists have found many examples of the appearance of new species as older species vanish. Sometimes the new species appear rapidly, and at other times they are the result of more gradual change.

🔑 **Scientists have developed two patterns to describe the pace of evolution: gradualism and punctuated equilibrium.**

Gradual Change Some species in the fossil record seem to change gradually over time. **Gradualism** involves small changes that add up to major changes over a long period of time. Since the time scale of the fossil record involves hundreds, thousands, or even millions of years, there is plenty of time for gradual changes to produce new species. The fossil record contains many examples of species that are intermediate between two others. One example is the horse relative, *Merychippus*, shown in **Figure 2**. Many such intermediate forms seem to be the result of gradual change.

···············

✏️

⟳ Compare and Contrast
Identify the similarity and the key differences between gradualism and punctuated equilibrium.

• Both describe the

_____

• Gradualism states that evolution occurs (quickly/slowly) and (steadily/in short bursts).

• Punctuated equilibrium states that evolution occurs (quickly/slowly) over_____ periods of time.

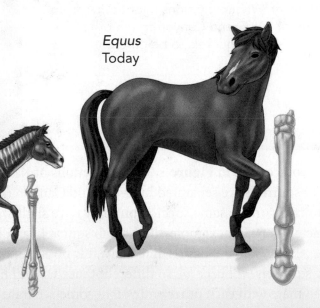

Equus
Today

Merychippus
35 million
years ago

Hyracotherium
53 million
years ago

FIGURE 2 ····················
⊳ART IN MOTION Horse Evolution
Horses left a rich and detailed fossil record of their evolution. Many intermediate forms have been found between modern horses and their four-toed ancestors. *Merychippus* is shown here.

✏️ **Answer these questions.**

1. List Name two differences between the horses.

_____
_____

2. CHALLENGE How could the evolution of the shape of the leg and the number of toes have benefited *Equus*?

_____
_____
_____
_____

Rapid Change Scientists have also found that many species remain almost unchanged during their existence. Then, shortly after they become extinct, related species often appear in the fossil record. This pattern, in which species evolve during short periods of rapid change and then don't change much, is called **punctuated equilibrium.** Today most scientists think that evolution can occur rapidly at some times, and more gradually at others.

apply it!

Two patterns that describe the rate of evolution are modeled at the right.

⚠ **Make Models** Look at the shells in the key. For each pattern, decide if—and at what point—each shell belongs on the timelines. Using colored pencils, draw and color in the shells at their correct locations to show how they have evolved over time.

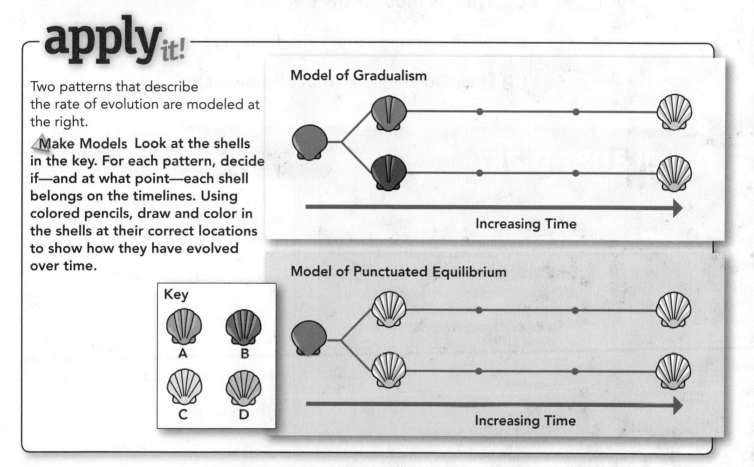

Model of Gradualism

Increasing Time

Key

A B
C D

Model of Punctuated Equilibrium

Increasing Time

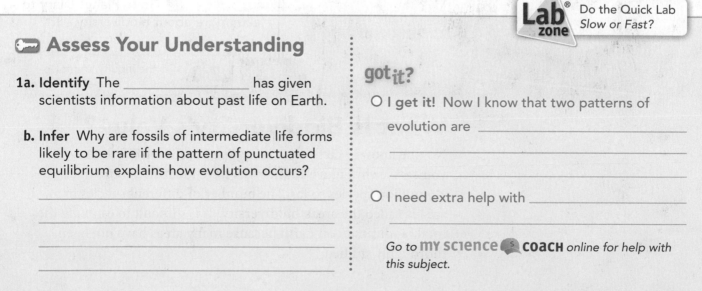

Lab zone® Do the Quick Lab
Slow or Fast?

🔑 Assess Your Understanding

1a. Identify The _____ has given scientists information about past life on Earth.

b. Infer Why are fossils of intermediate life forms likely to be rare if the pattern of punctuated equilibrium explains how evolution occurs?

_____

_____

_____

got it?

○ **I get it!** Now I know that two patterns of evolution are _____

_____

_____

○ **I need extra help with** _____

_____

Go to **my science coach** *online for help with this subject.*

Biodiversity

UNLOCK THE BIG ?

🔑 **What Is Biodiversity's Value?**

🔑 **What Factors Affect Biodiversity?**

🔑 **How Do Humans Affect Biodiversity?**

MY PLANET DIARY

BLOG

Posted by: Max

Location: Hagerstown, Maryland

I went to summer camp to learn about wildlife and how to protect it. One of the activities that I liked the most was making "bat boxes." These are wooden homes for brown bats, which often need places to nest. Making these houses is important, because without brown bats, there would be too many mosquitoes. I hope the bats like their new homes as much as I loved making them.

Communicate Discuss the question with a group of classmates. Then write your answers below.

How do you think helping the bats in an area helps other species nearby?

_____

_____

_____

_____

_____

_____

_____

▶ **PLANET DIARY** Go to **Planet Diary** to learn more about biodiversity.

Lab zone® Do the Inquiry Warm-Up
How Much Variety Is There?

What Is Biodiversity's Value?

No one knows exactly how many species live on Earth. As you can see in **Figure 1,** scientists have identified more than 1.6 million species so far. The number of different species in an area is called the area's **biodiversity.** It is difficult to estimate the total biodiversity on Earth because many areas have not been thoroughly studied.

Vocabulary

- biodiversity • keystone species • gene • extinction
- endangered species • threatened species
- habitat destruction • habitat fragmentation
- poaching • captive breeding

Skills

⊙ **Reading:** Compare and Contrast

△ **Inquiry:** Infer

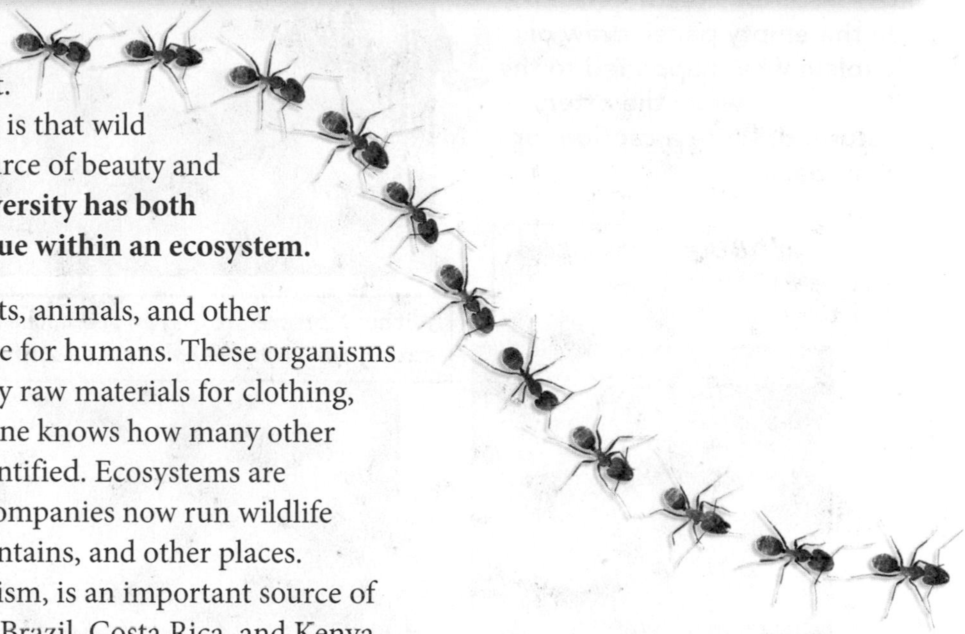

There are many reasons why preserving biodiversity is important. One reason to preserve biodiversity is that wild organisms and ecosystems are a source of beauty and recreation. ⚷ **In addition, biodiversity has both economic value and ecological value within an ecosystem.**

Economic Value Many plants, animals, and other organisms are economically valuable for humans. These organisms provide people with food and supply raw materials for clothing, medicine, and other products. No one knows how many other useful species have not yet been identified. Ecosystems are economically valuable, too. Many companies now run wildlife tours to rain forests, savannas, mountains, and other places. This ecosystem tourism, or ecotourism, is an important source of jobs and money for such nations as Brazil, Costa Rica, and Kenya.

Ecological Value All the species in an ecosystem are connected to one another. Species may depend on each other for food and shelter. A change that affects one species can affect all the others.

Some species play a particularly important role in their ecosystems. A **keystone species** is a species that influences the survival of many other species in an ecosystem. Sea otters, as shown in **Figure 2,** are one example of a keystone species.

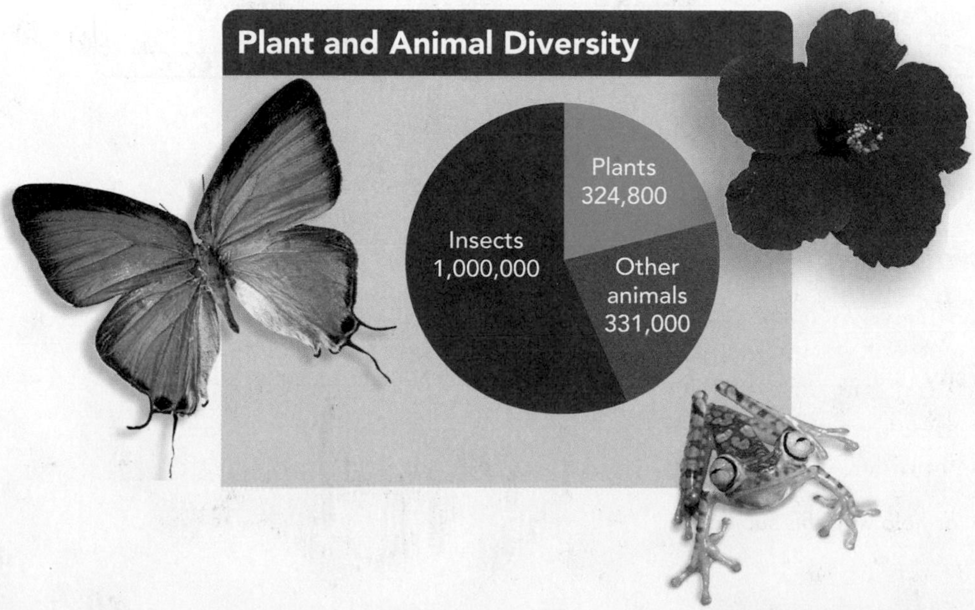

FIGURE 1 ·······································

Species Diversity

There are many more species of insects than plant or other animal species on Earth!

✎ **Calculate** What percentage of species shown on the pie graph do insects represent? Round your answer to the nearest tenth.

_____

Plant and Animal Diversity

Plants 324,800

Insects 1,000,000

Other animals 331,000

FIGURE 2 ....

Keystone Otters

Sea otters are a keystone species in the kelp forest ecosystem.

✎ **Describe** Read the comic. In the empty panel, draw or explain what happened to the kelp forest when the otters returned. Write a caption for your panel.

The sea otter is a keystone species in a kelp forest ecosystem.

In the 1800s, many otters were killed for their fur.

Without otters preying on them, the population of kelp-eating sea urchins exploded, destroying kelp forests.

Under new laws that banned the hunting of sea otters, the sea otter population grew again.

Lab zone Do the Quick Lab *Modeling Keystone Species.*

🗝 Assess Your Understanding

got it? ....

○ **I get it!** Now I know that biodiversity has _____

_____

○ **I need extra help with** _____

Go to **MY SCIENCE ⊙ COACH** *online for help with this subject.*

What Factors Affect Biodiversity?

Biodiversity varies from place to place on Earth. 🔑 **Factors that affect biodiversity in an ecosystem include climate, area, niche diversity, genetic diversity, and extinction.**

Climate The tropical rain forests of Latin America, southeast Asia, and central Africa are the most diverse ecosystems in the world. The reason for the great biodiversity in the tropics is not fully understood. Many scientists hypothesize that it has to do with climate. For example, tropical rain forests have fairly constant temperatures and large amounts of rainfall throughout the year. Many plants grow year-round. This continuous growing season means that food is always available for other organisms.

Area See **Figure 3**. Within an ecosystem, a large area will usually contain more species than a small area. For example, you would usually find more species in a 100-square-meter area than in a 10-square-meter area.

FIGURE 3 ·······················

Park Size

A park manager has received three park plans. The dark green area represents the park.

✏️ **Complete each task.**

1. **Identify** Circle the plan the manager should choose to support the most biodiversity.

2. **Calculate** Suppose that 15 square meters of the park could support seven species of large mammals. About how many species could the park you circled support?

10 m
10 m

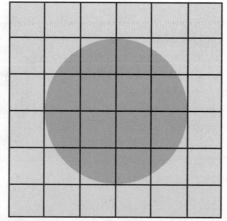

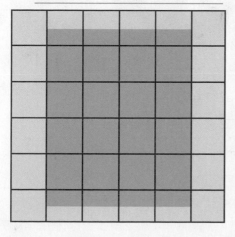

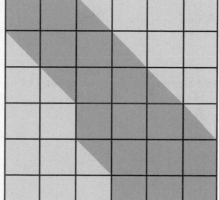

395

Niche Diversity
Coral reefs are the second most diverse ecosystems in the world. Found only in shallow, warm waters, coral reefs are often called the rain forests of the sea. A coral reef supports many different niches. Recall that a niche is the role of an organism in its habitat, or how it makes its living. A coral reef enables a greater number of species to live in it than a more uniform habitat, such as a flat sandbar, does.

Genetic Diversity
Diversity is very important within a species. The greatest genetic diversity exists among species of unicellular organisms. Organisms in a healthy population have diverse traits such as color and size. **Genes** are located within cells and carry the hereditary information that determines an organism's traits. Organisms inherit genes from their parents.

The organisms in one species share many genes. But each organism also has some genes that differ from those of other individuals. Both the shared genes and the genes that differ among individuals make up the total gene pool of that species. Species that lack a diverse gene pool are less able to adapt to and survive changes in the environment.

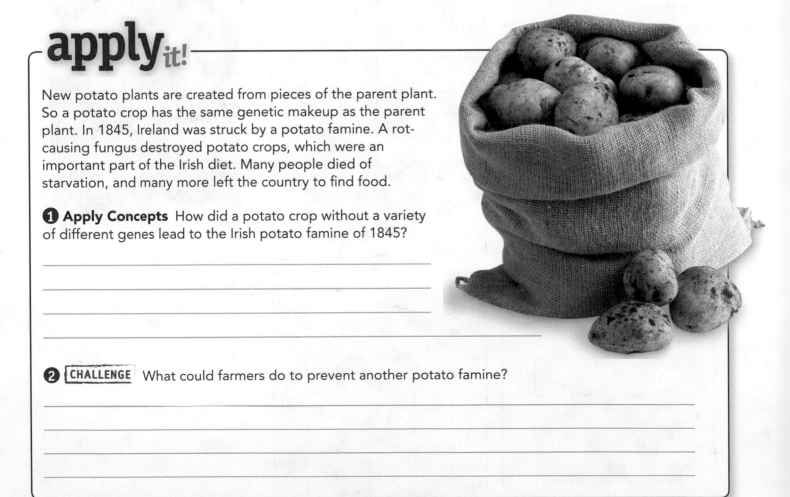

apply it!

New potato plants are created from pieces of the parent plant. So a potato crop has the same genetic makeup as the parent plant. In 1845, Ireland was struck by a potato famine. A rot-causing fungus destroyed potato crops, which were an important part of the Irish diet. Many people died of starvation, and many more left the country to find food.

❶ Apply Concepts How did a potato crop without a variety of different genes lead to the Irish potato famine of 1845?

_____

_____

_____

_____

❷ CHALLENGE What could farmers do to prevent another potato famine?

_____

_____

_____

_____

Extinction of Species The disappearance of all members of a species from Earth is called **extinction.** Extinction is a natural process that occurs when organisms do not adapt to changes in their environment. About 99 percent of the species that have ever lived on Earth are now extinct. In the last few centuries, the number of species becoming extinct has increased dramatically. Once a population drops below a certain level, the species may not recover. People have directly caused the extinction of many species through habitat destruction, hunting, or other actions.

Species in danger of becoming extinct in the near future are called **endangered species.** Species that could become endangered in the near future are called **threatened species.** Endangered and threatened species are found on every continent and in every ocean.

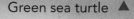

Green sea turtle ▲

FIGURE 4 ···
Endangered Species
Large animals, like the green sea turtle, are the most publicized endangered species. Did you know insects and plants can also be endangered? ✏️ ⚠️ **Infer Why do you think some endangered species get more attention than others?**

_____
_____
_____
_____
_____

Blackburn's ▲
sphinx moth

Lab® Do the Quick Lab
zone *Grocery Gene Pool.*

🔑 Assess Your Understanding

1a. Review A (smaller/larger) area will contain more species than a (smaller/larger) area.

b. Explain How is biodiversity related to niches?

_____
_____
_____

c. 🔄 **Compare and Contrast** What is the difference between an endangered species and a threatened species?

_____
_____
_____

got**it?** ···

○ **I get it!** Now I know that the factors that affect biodiversity include _____

_____

○ **I need extra help with** _____

Go to **MY SCIENCE** ⓢ **COACH** *online for help with this subject.*

How Do Humans Affect Biodiversity?

Humans interact with their surroundings every day. The many choices people make impact the environment and affect species. 🔑 **Biodiversity can be negatively or positively affected by the actions of humans.**

Damaging Biodiversity A natural event, such as a hurricane, can damage an ecosystem, wiping out populations or even entire species. Human activities can also threaten biodiversity and cause extinction. These activities include habitat destruction, poaching, pollution, and the introduction of exotic species.

Habitat Destruction The major cause of extinction is **habitat destruction,** the loss of a natural habitat. Clearing forests or filling in wetlands changes those ecosystems. Breaking larger habitats into smaller, isolated pieces, or fragments, is called **habitat fragmentation.** See **Figure 5.** Some species may not survive such changes to their habitats.

Poaching The illegal killing or removal of wildlife from their habitats is called **poaching.** Some endangered species are valuable to poachers. Animals can be sold as pets or used to make jewelry, coats, belts, or shoes. Plants can be sold as houseplants or used to make medicines.

Pollution Some species are endangered because of pollution. Pollution may reach animals through the water they drink, the air they breathe, or the food they eat. Pollutants may kill or weaken organisms or cause birth defects.

Exotic Species Introducing exotic species into an ecosystem can threaten biodiversity. Exotic species can outcompete and damage native species. The gypsy moth was introduced into the United States in 1869 to increase silk production. Gypsy moth larvae have eaten the leaves off of millions of acres of trees in the northeastern United States.

FIGURE 5 ·····

Habitat Fragmentation

Breaking habitats into pieces can have negative effects on the species that live there.

✏️ **Interpret Diagrams** In the first diagram below, a road divides a habitat in two. On the second diagram, redraw the road so it divides the habitat's resources equally.

Protecting Biodiversity

Some people who preserve biodiversity focus on protecting individual endangered species. Others try to protect entire ecosystems. Three methods of protecting biodiversity are captive breeding, laws and treaties, and habitat preservation.

Captive Breeding **Captive breeding** is the mating of animals in zoos or on wildlife preserves. Scientists care for the young, and then release them into the wild. Much of the sandhill crane habitat in the United States has been destroyed. To help the population, some cranes have been taken into captivity. The young are raised and trained by volunteers to learn the correct behaviors, such as knowing how and where to migrate. They are then released into the wild.

⊙ Compare and Contrast
The photos on top show young sandhill cranes being raised by their parents. The photos on the bottom show humans copying this process to increase the crane population. What is a possible disadvantage of the human approach?

_____

_____

_____

_____

399

Same Land, Different Use

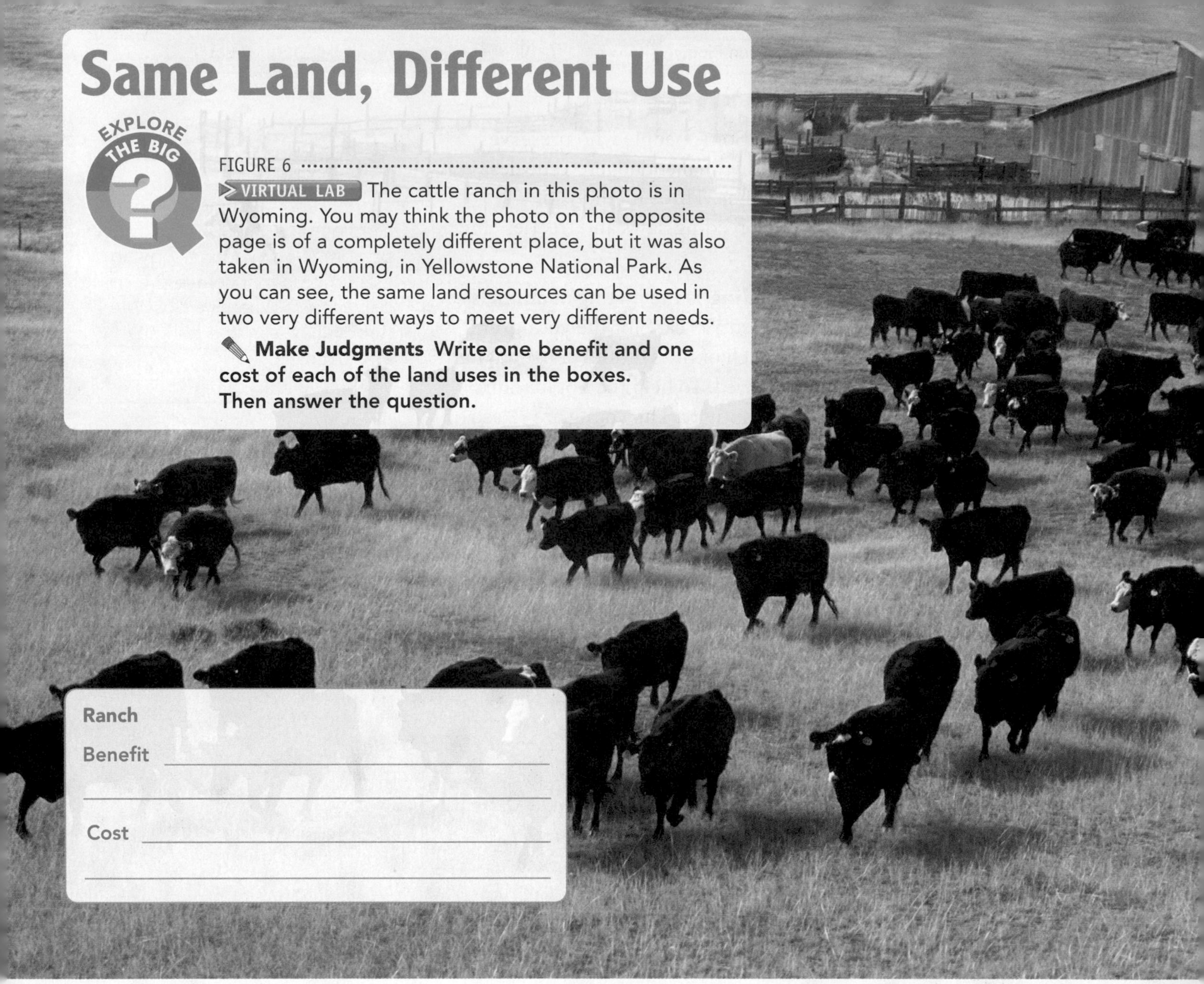

FIGURE 6 ....

> **VIRTUAL LAB** The cattle ranch in this photo is in Wyoming. You may think the photo on the opposite page is of a completely different place, but it was also taken in Wyoming, in Yellowstone National Park. As you can see, the same land resources can be used in two very different ways to meet very different needs.

✎ **Make Judgments** Write one benefit and one cost of each of the land uses in the boxes. Then answer the question.

Ranch

Benefit _____

_____

Cost _____

_____

Laws and Treaties In the United States, the Endangered Species Act prohibits trade of products made from threatened or endangered species. This law also requires the development of plans to save endangered species. The Convention on International Trade in Endangered Species is an international treaty that lists more than 800 threatened and endangered species that cannot be traded for profit or other reasons anywhere in the world.

Habitat Preservation The most effective way to preserve biodiversity is to protect whole ecosystems. Protecting whole ecosystems saves endangered species, the species they depend upon, and those that depend upon them. Many countries have set aside wildlife habitats as parks and refuges. Today, there are about 7,000 nature parks, preserves, and refuges in the world.

National Park

Benefit _____

_____

Cost _____

_____

Do you think we should preserve our resources, use them, or have a balance of both? Explain your answer.

_____

_____

_____

_____

_____

_____

Lab ® Do the Quick Lab
zone *Humans and Biodiversity.*

🔑 Assess Your Understanding

2a. Define What is poaching?

_____

_____

_____

_____

b. **ANSWER THE BIG ?** How do life forms change over time?

_____

_____

_____

_____

got it? ....

○ **I get it!** Now I know that humans affect biodiversity_____

_____

○ **I need extra help with** _____

Go to MY SCIENCE ⬤ₛ COACH *online for help with this subject.*

11 Study Guide

Living things change over time, or _____, through a process called _____

LESSON 1 Darwin's Theory

🔑 Darwin hypothesized that species change over many generations and become better adapted to new conditions.

🔑 Darwin proposed that, over a long time, natural selection can lead to change. Helpful variations may accumulate in a species, while unfavorable ones may disappear.

Vocabulary
- species • fossil • adaptation • evolution
- scientific theory • natural selection • variation

LESSON 2 Evidence of Evolution

🔑 Fossils, patterns of early development, similar body structures, and similarities in DNA and protein structures all provide evidence that organisms have changed over time.

Vocabulary
- homologous structures

LESSON 3 Rate of Change

🔑 A new species can form when a group of individuals remains isolated from the rest of its species long enough to evolve different traits that prevent reproduction.

🔑 Scientists have developed two patterns to describe the pace of evolution: gradualism and punctuated equilibrium.

Vocabulary
• gradualism
• punctuated equilibrium

LESSON 4 Biodiversity

🔑 Biodiversity has both economic value and ecological value within an ecosystem.

🔑 Factors that affect biodiversity include climate, area, and niche diversity, genetic diversity, and extinction.

🔑 Biodiversity can be negatively or positively affected by the actions of humans.

Vocabulary
• biodiversity   • keystone species   • gene   • extinction
• endangered species   • threatened species   • habitat destruction
• habitat fragmentation   • poaching   • captive breeding

1. A trait that helps an organism to survive and reproduce is called a(n)

   a. variation.   b. adaptation.

   c. species.   d. selection.

2. Two organisms that can mate and produce fertile offspring are members of the same

   _____

3. **Infer** Why are Darwin's ideas classified as a scientific theory?

   _____
   _____
   _____
   _____

4. **Apply Concepts** What is one factor that affects natural selection? Give an example.

   _____
   _____
   _____
   _____
   _____

5. **Compare and Contrast** Identify one similarity and one difference between natural selection and artificial selection.

   _____
   _____
   _____
   _____
   _____
   _____

6. **Write About It** You are a reporter in the 1800s interviewing Charles Darwin about his theory of evolution. Write three questions you would ask him. Then write answers that Darwin might have given.

7. Similar structures that related species have inherited from a common ancestor are called

   a. adaptations.

   b. fossils.

   c. ancestral structures.

   d. homologous structures.

8. The more _____ the DNA sequences between two organisms are, the more closely related the two species are.

9. **Draw Conclusions** Look at the drawing, at the right, of the bones in a crocodile's leg. Do you think that crocodiles share a common ancestor with birds, dolphins, and dogs? Support your answer with evidence.

   Crocodile

   _____
   _____
   _____
   _____

10. **Make Judgments** What type of evidence is the best indicator of how closely two species are related? Explain your answer.

    _____
    _____
    _____
    _____
    _____
    _____
    _____
    _____
    _____

Review and Assessment

LESSON 3 Rate of Change

11. The pattern of evolution that involves short periods of rapid change is called

    a. adaptation.

    b. gradualism.

    c. isolation.

    d. punctuated equilibrium.

12. _____ involves tiny changes in a species that slowly add up to major changes over time.

13. Apply Concepts A population of deer lives in a forest. Draw a picture that illustrates how a geographic feature could isolate this deer population into two separate groups. Label the geographic feature.

14. Develop Hypotheses Describe the conditions that could cause these two groups of deer to become separate species over time.

_____

_____

_____

_____

_____

_____

LESSON 4 Biodiversity

15. The most effective way to preserve biodiversity is through

    a. captive breeding.

    b. habitat destruction.

    c. habitat preservation.

    d. habitat fragmentation.

16. _____ occurs when all members of a species disappear from Earth.

17. Predict How could the extinction of a species today affect your life in 20 years?

_____

_____

_____

_____

_____

_____

_____

_____

_____

_____

_____

How do life forms change over time?

18. Suppose that over several years, the climate in an area becomes much drier than it was before. How would plants, like the ones shown below, be affected? Using the terms *variation* and *natural selection*, predict what changes you might observe in the plants as a result of this environmental change.

_____
_____
_____
_____
_____
_____
_____
_____
_____
_____
_____
_____
_____
_____
_____
_____

Ohio Benchmark Practice

Multiple Choice

Circle the letter of the best answer.

1. The illustration below has no title. Which of the following titles would best describe the concept shown in this drawing?

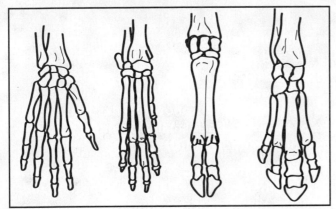

   A. Wrist Bone Adaptations
   B. Similarities in Wrist Bone Development
   C. Evolutionary Change Through Gradualism
   D. Homologous Structures in Four Animals

2. The process by which individuals that are better adapted to their environment are more likely to survive and reproduce than other members of the same species is called

   A. natural selection.
   B. evolution.
   C. competition.
   D. overproduction.

3. Which of the following is the best example of an adaptation that helps organisms survive in their environment?

   A. green coloring in lizards living on gray rocks
   B. a thick coat of fur on animals that live in the desert
   C. an extensive root system in desert plants
   D. thin, delicate leaves on plants in a cold climate

4. Which of the following sets of factors did Darwin identify as affecting natural selection?

   A. adaptations, gradualism, and evolution
   B. overproduction, variation, and competition
   C. adaptations, traits, and variations
   D. predation, competition, and mutualism

5. Evolution that occurs slowly is described by the pattern of _____, while rapid changes are described by

   _____.

   A. gradualism; natural selection
   B. homologous structures; fossils
   C. gradualism; punctuated equilibrium
   D. natural selection; punctuated equilibrium

6. Which of the following terms describes a species that is in danger of becoming extinct in the near future?

   A. captive species
   B. keystone species
   C. threatened species
   D. endangered species

Extended Response

Use the diagram below and your knowledge of science to help you answer Question 6. Write your answer on a separate piece of paper.

7. This drawing shows variations in wing size within a species of fly. Describe a situation in which natural selection might favor flies with the smallest wings.

Science and Society

THE INCREDIBLE SHRINKING FISH

For years, fishers have followed a simple rule: keep the big fish and release the small fish. This practice aims to keep fish populations stable by allowing young fish to reach reproductive age. However, a scientist named David Conover thinks that this practice of throwing back small fish might be affecting the evolution of fish species.

Not all small fish are young. Like humans, adult fish come in different sizes. Conover hypothesized that removing the largest fish from fish populations might result in populations of smaller fish because smaller adult fish would survive to reproduce more often than larger adult fish. To test this hypothesis, Conover's team divided a population of 6,000 fish into different groups. Over four generations, the scientists selectively removed 90 percent of the fish in each group before they could reproduce.

The results showed that over just a few generations, selection pressures can influence not only the size of fish, but also the health of fish populations. Currently, Conover is researching ways to change fishing regulations so fish populations can recover.

▲ The practice of commercial fishing may be leading to populations of smaller and smaller fish.

This diagram shows how Dr. Conover and his team set up and performed their experiment. It also shows the results. ▶

Design It If current policies are causing the average size of fish to decrease, what is the best way to help fish populations recover? Design an experiment that would test your method for helping fish populations recover.

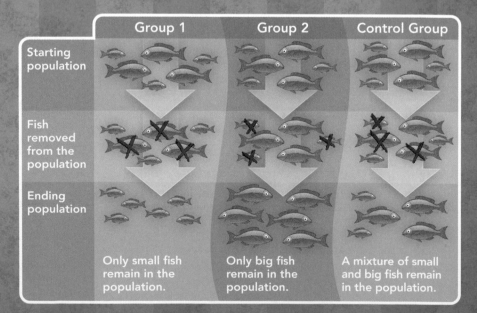

	Group 1	Group 2	Control Group
Starting population			
Fish removed from the population			
Ending population			
	Only small fish remain in the population.	Only big fish remain in the population.	A mixture of small and big fish remain in the population.

WALKING WHALES?

Over 50 million years, whales evolved from a species of doglike land mammals to the aquatic giants we know today.

Mesonychids

Ambulocetus

Dalanistes

Takracetus

Dorudon

Blue Whale

If you could visit Earth 50 million years ago, you would see many amazing sights. One of the strangest things you might see is the ancestor of modern whales— walking on land!

For years, scientists have thought that whales evolved from land-dwelling mammals. About 50 million years ago, the ancestors of modern whales had four legs and were similar to large dogs. Over 50 million years, whales evolved to become the giant marine mammals we recognize today. However, scientists have had difficulty finding fossils of whales that show how this dramatic change occurred. These missing links could reveal how whales lost their legs.

Now, several new discoveries are helping scientists fill in the blanks in the evolutionary history of whales. A fossil whale skeleton discovered in Washington State has a pelvis with large cuplike sockets. These sockets likely held short legs that enabled the whale to move on land. Other whale fossils, found in Alabama, include large hind limbs that probably helped the animals swim. Researchers have also discovered the gene mutation that could have been responsible for whales losing their legs about 35 million years ago.

Design It Find out more about the evolutionary history of whales. How is a whale flipper similar to a bat wing and a human hand? Design a poster that shows the evolutionary history of whales.

WHY WON'T THIS ACROBAT LAND ON HER HEAD?

How do objects react to forces?

This teen is part of a traveling youth circus that performs in New England. As a circus trouper, she may do stunts such as tumbling and swinging on a trapeze. These stunts often appear to be gravity-defying and dangerous, but the troupers know how to perform in a way that lets them land safely.

△ **Develop Hypotheses** How does this athlete land on her feet?

_____

_____

_____

_____

_____

_____

> **UNTAMED SCIENCE** Watch the **Untamed Science** video to learn more about forces.

Forces and Motion

12 Getting Started

Check Your Understanding

1. **Background** Read the paragraph below and then answer the question.

The dashboard of a car displays your speed so that you know how fast you're going. Since this reading doesn't change when you turn, you don't know the car's velocity. If the car did show you your change in velocity, you could calculate the car's acceleration.

> **Speed** is the distance an object travels per unit of time.
>
> **Velocity** is speed in a given direction.
>
> **Acceleration** is the rate at which velocity changes with time.

• What are three ways to accelerate (change velocity)?

_____

_____

> **MY READING WEB** If you had trouble completing the question above, visit **My Reading Web** and type in *Forces and Motion*.

Vocabulary Skill

Latin Word Origins Many science words in English come from Latin. For example, the word *solar*, which means "of the sun," comes from the Latin *sol*, which means "sun."

Latin Word	Meaning of Latin Word	Example
fortis	strong	force, *n.* a push or pull exerted on an object
iners	inactivity	inertia, *n.* the tendency of an object to resist any change in its motion
centrum	center	centripetal force, *n.* a force that causes an object to move in a circle

2. **Quick Check** Choose the word that best completes the sentence.

• A _____ always points toward the center of a circle.

force

ZOO

friction

gravity

inertia

Chapter Preview

LESSON 1
- acceleration
- ⟳ Identify the Main Idea
- △ Graph

LESSON 2
- force
- newton
- net force
- ⟳ Relate Text and Visuals
- △ Make Models

LESSON 3
- friction
- sliding friction
- static friction
- fluid friction
- rolling friction
- gravity
- mass
- weight
- ⟳ Identify Supporting Evidence
- △ Design Experiments

LESSON 4
- inertia
- ⟳ Ask Questions
- △ Infer

LESSON 5
- momentum
- law of conservation of momentum
- ⟳ Identify the Main Idea
- △ Calculate

LESSON 6
- free fall
- satellite
- centripetal force
- ⟳ Relate Cause and Effect
- △ Create Data Tables

> VOCAB FLASH CARDS For extra help with vocabulary, visit **Vocab Flash Cards** and type in *Forces and Motion.*

413

Acceleration

🔑 **What Is Acceleration?**

🔑 **How Do You Graph Acceleration?**

MY PLANET DIARY

Jumping Spider

A small spider, less than 2 centimeters in length, spots an insect. The spider crouches and crawls slowly forward. Then it lifts its front legs and leaps, landing right on its victim!

Amazingly, a jumping spider has the ability to jump 10 to 40 times its body length. To capture prey from that far away, it must accurately estimate its initial velocity. Once the spider jumps, the force of gravity controls its motion, causing it to follow a curved path. Its velocity changes at every point along the path until it lands on its prey.

FUN FACT

Write your answer to the question below.

Think of a sport or activity in which the goal is to hit a target from far away. What are some of the challenges?

_____

_____

_____

_____

_____

> PLANET DIARY Go to **Planet Diary** to learn more about acceleration.

Lab zone Do the Inquiry Warm-Up *Will You Hurry Up?*

What Is Acceleration?

Suppose you are a passenger in a car stopped at a red light. When the light changes to green, the driver steps on the accelerator. As a result, the car speeds up, or accelerates. In everyday language, acceleration means "the process of speeding up."

Acceleration has a more precise definition in science. Scientists define **acceleration** as the rate at which velocity changes. Recall that velocity describes both the speed and direction of an object. A change in velocity can involve a change in either speed or direction—or both. 🔑 **In science, acceleration refers to increasing speed, decreasing speed, or changing direction.**

Vocabulary
• acceleration

Skills
↪ Reading: Identify the Main Idea
△ Inquiry: Graph

Changing Speed Whenever an object's speed changes, the object accelerates. You can tell an object is accelerating by comparing its motion to another object, called a reference point. A car that speeds up to pass another car is accelerating. In this case, the car being passed is the reference point. People can accelerate too. For example, you accelerate when you coast down a hill on your bike.

Just as objects can speed up, they can also slow down. This change in speed is sometimes called deceleration, or negative acceleration. A car decelerates as it comes to a stop at a red light. A water skier decelerates as the boat slows down.

Changing Direction Even an object that is traveling at a constant speed can be accelerating. Recall that acceleration can be a change in direction as well as a change in speed. Therefore, a car accelerates as it follows a gentle curve in the road or changes lanes. A softball accelerates when it changes direction as it is hit.

Many objects continuously change direction without changing speed. The simplest example of this type of motion is circular motion, or motion along a circular path. For example, the seats on a Ferris wheel accelerate because they move in a circle.

↪ **Identify the Main Idea**
Underline the main idea in the section called Changing Speed.

FIGURE 1 ....

Acceleration
In a soccer game, a ball shows three types of acceleration—increasing speed, decreasing speed, and changing direction.

✎ **Interpret Photos** Label the type of acceleration occurring in each photo.

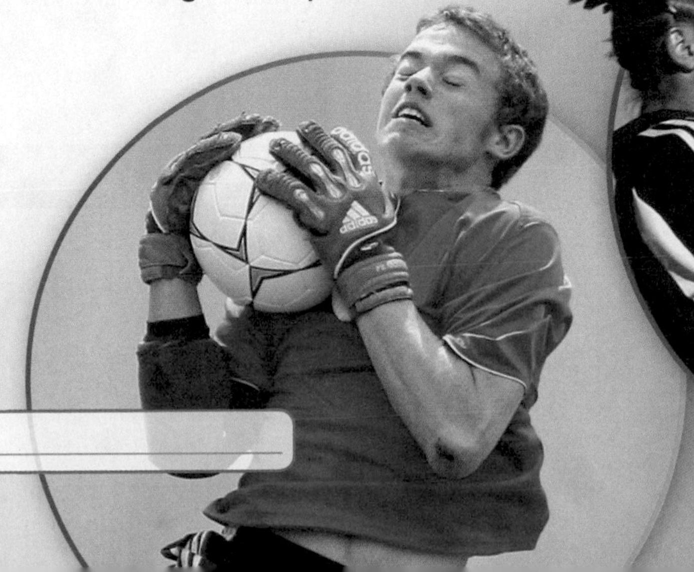

0.0s   1.0s   2.0s   3.0s

0 m/s   8 m/s   16 m/s   24 m/s

FIGURE 2 ·······················

Acceleration

The airplane is accelerating at a rate of 8 m/s^2.

✎ **Predict** Determine the speed of the airplane at 4.0 s and 5.0 s. Write your answers in the boxes next to each airplane.

Calculating Acceleration

Acceleration describes the rate at which velocity changes. If an object is not changing direction, you can describe its acceleration as the rate at which its speed changes. To determine the acceleration of an object moving in a straight line, you calculate the change in speed per unit of time. This is summarized by the following equation.

$$\text{Acceleration} = \frac{\text{Final Speed} - \text{Initial Speed}}{\text{Time}}$$

If speed is measured in meters per second (m/s) and time is measured in seconds, the SI unit of acceleration is meters per second per second, or m/s^2. Suppose speed is measured in kilometers per hour and time is measured in hours. Then the unit for acceleration is kilometers per hour per hour, or km/h^2.

To understand acceleration, imagine a small airplane moving down a runway. **Figure 2** shows the airplane's speed after each second of the first three seconds of its acceleration. To calculate the acceleration of the airplane, you must first subtract the initial speed of 0 m/s from its final speed of 24 m/s. Then divide the change in speed by the time, 3 seconds.

$$\text{Acceleration} = \frac{24 \text{ m/s} - 0 \text{ m/s}}{3 \text{ s}}$$

$$\text{Acceleration} = 8 \text{ m/s}^2$$

The airplane accelerates at a rate of 8 m/s^2. This means that the airplane's speed increases by 8 m/s every second. Notice in **Figure 2** that after each second of travel, the airplane's speed is 8 m/s greater than its speed in the previous second.

FIGURE 3 ·······················

Deceleration

An airplane touches down on the runway with a speed of 70 m/s. It decelerates at a rate of −5 m/s^2.

✎ **Predict** Determine the speed of the airplane after each second of its deceleration. Write your answers in the table to the right.

Time (s)	1	2	3	4
Speed (m/s)				

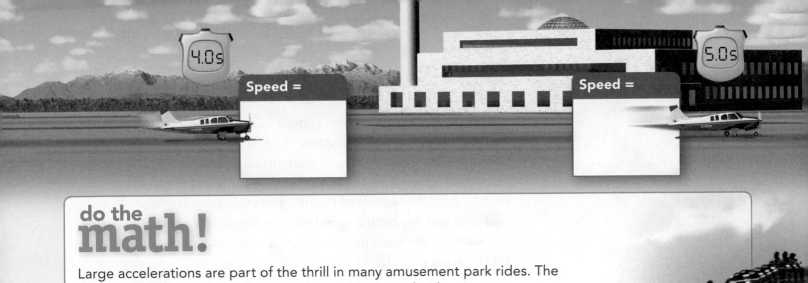

Speed =

Speed =

do the
math!

Large accelerations are part of the thrill in many amusement park rides. The problems below are based on actual amusement park rides.

1 Calculate One type of ride falls straight down for 3 seconds. During this time, the ride accelerates from a speed of 0 m/s to a speed of 30 m/s. What is the average acceleration of the ride?

Initial speed = _____ Final speed = _____ Time = _____
Average acceleration =

2 Calculate A roller coaster accelerates from a speed of 4 m/s to 22 m/s in 3 seconds. What is the average acceleration of the ride?

Initial speed = _____ Final speed = _____ Time = _____
Average acceleration =

Lab zone Do the Quick Lab
Describing Acceleration.

🗝 Assess Your Understanding

1a. Define The rate at which velocity changes is
called _____

b. Infer A softball has a (positive/negative) acceleration when it is thrown. A softball has a (positive/negative) acceleration when it is caught.

c. Explain A girl skates around the perimeter of a circular ice rink at a constant speed of 2 m/s. Is the girl accelerating? Explain.

_____
_____

got it?

○ **I get it!** Now I know that in science
acceleration refers to _____
_____
_____
_____

○ **I need extra help with** _____

Go to **MY SCIENCE ⬥ COACH** *online for help with this subject.*

How Do You Graph Acceleration?

Suppose you bike down a long, steep hill. At the top of the hill, your speed is 0 m/s. As you start down the hill, your speed increases. Each second, you move at a greater speed and travel a greater distance than the second before. During the five seconds it takes you to reach the bottom of the hill, you are an accelerating object. 🔑 **You can use both a speed-versus-time graph and a distance-versus-time graph to analyze the motion of an accelerating object.**

FIGURE 4 ·······································

▷ VIRTUAL LAB **Speed-Versus-Time Graph**

The data in the table show how your speed changes during each second of your bike ride.

✎ **Use the data to answer the questions.**

Time (s)	Speed (m/s)
0	0
1	2
2	4
3	6
4	8
5	10

1. ◢**Graph** Use this data to plot a line graph. Plot time on the horizontal axis. Plot speed on the vertical axis. Give the graph a title.

2. **Calculate** What is the slope of the graph?

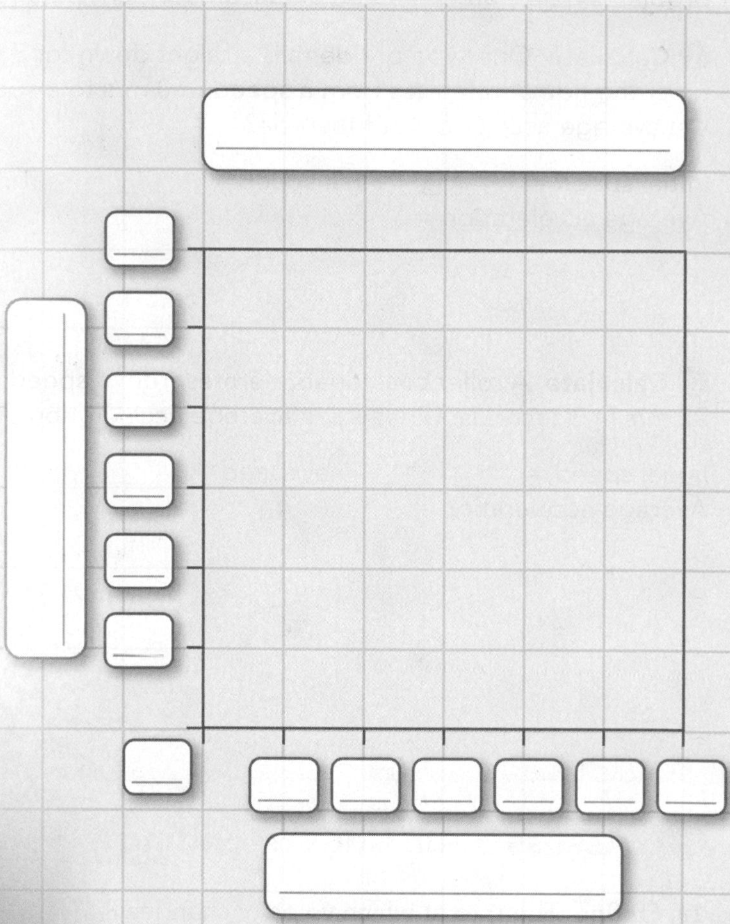

Analyzing a Speed-Versus-Time Graph

Look at the speed-versus-time graph that you made in **Figure 4.** What can you learn about your motion by analyzing this graph? First, since the line slants upward, the graph shows that your speed was increasing. Next, since the line is straight, you can tell that your acceleration was constant. A slanted, straight line on a speed-versus-time graph means that the object is accelerating at a constant rate. Your acceleration is the slope of the line.

FIGURE 5 ···

> INTERACTIVE ART Distance-Versus-Time Graph

The data in the table show how your distance changes during each second of your bike ride.

✎ **Use the data to answer the questions.**

Time (s)	Distance (m)
0	0
1	1
2	4
3	9
4	16
5	25

1. **Graph** Use this data to create a line graph. Plot time on the horizontal axis. Plot distance on the vertical axis. Give the graph a title.

2. **CHALLENGE** How does the distance change with time?

_____

_____

_____

_____

Analyzing a Distance-Versus-Time Graph

Look at the distance-versus-time graph that you made in **Figure 5**. The curved line tells you that during each second, you traveled a greater distance than the second before. For example, you traveled a greater distance during the third second than you did during the first second.

The curved line in **Figure 5** also tells you that during each second your speed was greater than the second before. Recall that the slope of a distance-versus-time graph is the speed of an object. From second to second, the slope of the line in **Figure 5** gets steeper. Since the slope is increasing, you can conclude that your speed was also increasing. You were accelerating.

Lab zone Do the Quick Lab *Graphing Acceleration.*

🔑 Assess Your Understanding

got it? ···

○ **I get it!** Now I know that the two types of graphs that you can use to analyze the motion of an

accelerating object are _____

_____

○ **I need extra help with** _____

Go to **my science** 💬 **coach** *online for help with this subject.*

The Nature of Force

UNLOCK THE BIG ?

🔑 How Are Forces Described?

🔑 How Do Forces Affect Motion?

my planet Diary

MISCONCEPTIONS

Forced to Change

Misconception: Any object that is set in motion will slow down on its own.

Fact: A force is needed to change an object's state of motion.

A soccer ball sits at rest. You come along and kick it, sending it flying across the field. It eventually slows to a stop. You applied a force to start it moving, and then it stopped all on its own, right?

No! Forces cause *all* changes in motion. Just as you applied a force to the ball to speed it up from rest, the ground applied a force to slow it down to a stop. If the ground didn't apply a force to the ball, it would keep rolling forever without slowing down or stopping.

Answer the questions below.

1. Give an example of a force you apply to slow something down.

_____

_____

2. Where might it be possible to kick a soccer ball and have it never slow down?

_____

_____

_____

▶ PLANET DIARY Go to **Planet Diary** to learn more about forces.

Lab® zone

Do the Inquiry Warm-Up *Is the Force With You?*

Vocabulary
- force
- newton
- net force

Skills
- ↪ Reading: Relate Text and Visuals
- △ Inquiry: Make Models

How Are Forces Described?

In science, the word *force* has a simple and specific meaning. A **force** is a push or a pull. When one object pushes or pulls another object, the first object exerts a force on the second object. You exert a force on a computer key when you push it. You exert a force on a chair when you pull it away from a table.

🔑 **Like velocity and acceleration, a force is described by its strength and by the direction in which it acts.** Pushing to the left is a different force from pushing to the right. The direction and strength of a force can be represented by an arrow. The arrow points in the direction of the force, as shown in **Figure 1.** The length of the arrow tells you the strength of the force—the longer the arrow, the greater the force. The strength of a force is measured in the SI unit called the **newton** (N), after scientist Sir Isaac Newton.

FIGURE 1 ···

Describing Forces

Forces act on you whenever your motion changes. In the photos at the right, two men are celebrating an Olympic victory. Forces cause them to pull each other in for a hug, lean over, and fall into the pool.

✏️ **Identify** In the box within each photo, draw an arrow that represents the force acting on the person on the right. The first one is done as an example.

Lab zone   Do the Quick Lab *What Is Force?*

🔑 **Assess Your Understanding**

got it? ··

○ I get it! Now I know that forces are described by _____

_____

○ I need extra help with _____

Go to **my science** ◌ **COACH** online for help with this subject.

FIGURE 2

▶ INTERACTIVE ART Net Force

The change in motion of an object is determined by
the net force acting on the object.

✎ **Make Models** Calculate and draw an arrow for the
net force for each situation in the boxes below.

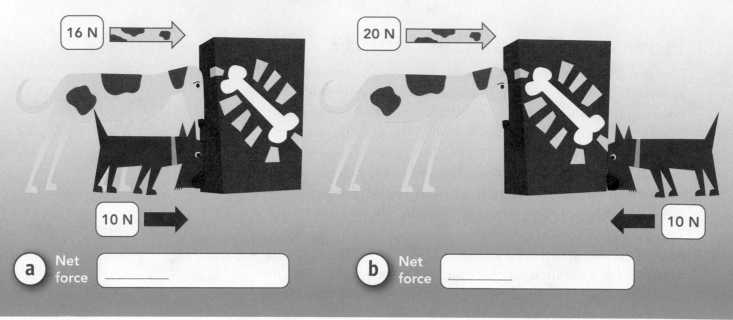

ⓐ Net force _____

ⓑ Net force _____

How Do Forces Affect Motion?

Often more than one force acts on an object at the same time. The combination of all the forces on an object is called the **net force.** The net force determines if and how an object will accelerate.

You can find the net force on an object by adding together the strengths of all the individual forces acting on the object. Look at **Figure 2a.** The big dog pushes on the box with a force of 16 N to the right. The small dog pushes on the box with a force of 10 N to the right. The net force on the box is the sum of these forces. The box will accelerate to the right. In this situation, there is a nonzero net force. 🔑 **A nonzero net force causes a change in the object's motion.**

What if the forces on an object aren't acting in the same direction? In **Figure 2b,** the big dog pushes with a force of 20 N. The small dog still pushes with a force of 10 N, but now they're pushing against each other. When forces on an object act in opposite directions, the strength of the net force is found by subtracting the strength of the smaller force from the strength of the larger force. You can still think of this as *adding* the forces together if you think of all forces that act to the right as positive forces and all forces that act to the left as negative forces. The box will accelerate to the right. When forces act in opposite directions, the net force is in the same direction as the larger force.

🔄 **Relate Text and Visuals** Use the information in the text to determine the net force of these two force arrows.

Circle the net force below.

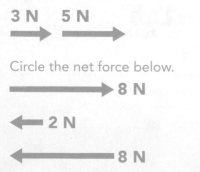

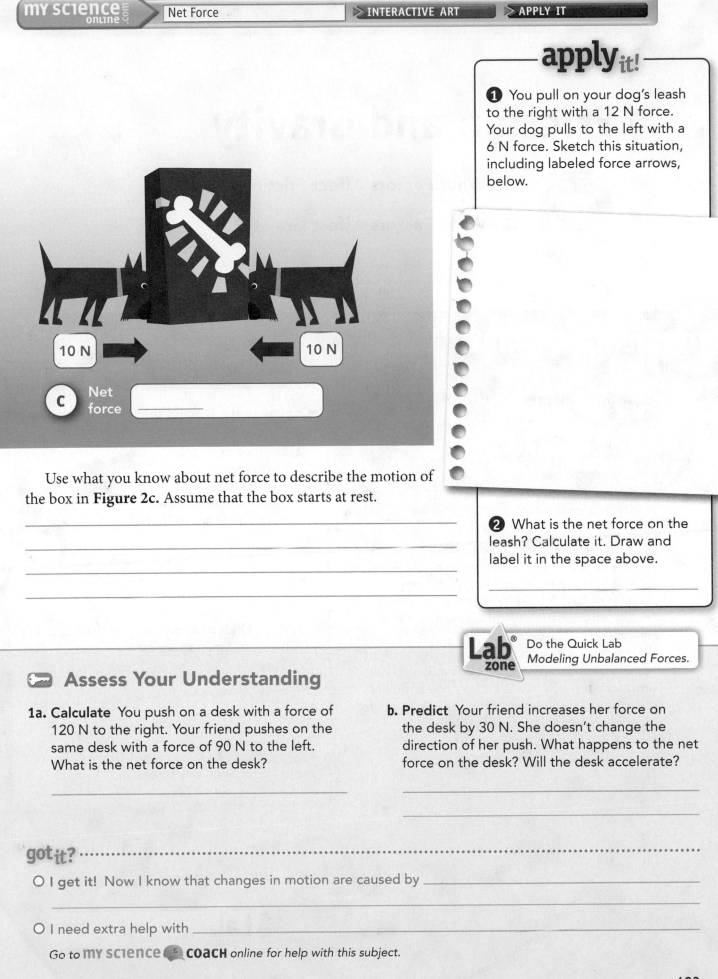

c Net force _____

Use what you know about net force to describe the motion of the box in **Figure 2c.** Assume that the box starts at rest.

_____

_____

_____

_____

apply it!

❶ You pull on your dog's leash to the right with a 12 N force. Your dog pulls to the left with a 6 N force. Sketch this situation, including labeled force arrows, below.

❷ What is the net force on the leash? Calculate it. Draw and label it in the space above.

_____

Lab zone Do the Quick Lab
Modeling Unbalanced Forces.

🔑 Assess Your Understanding

1a. Calculate You push on a desk with a force of 120 N to the right. Your friend pushes on the same desk with a force of 90 N to the left. What is the net force on the desk?

_____

_____

b. Predict Your friend increases her force on the desk by 30 N. She doesn't change the direction of her push. What happens to the net force on the desk? Will the desk accelerate?

_____

_____

got it? ....

○ I get it! Now I know that changes in motion are caused by _____

_____

○ I need extra help with _____

Go to my science COACH *online for help with this subject.*

Friction and Gravity

🔑 **What Factors Affect Friction?**

🔑 **What Factors Affect Gravity?**

MY PLANET DIARY

Space Athletes

Have you ever seen pictures of astronauts playing golf on the moon or playing catch in a space station? Golf balls and baseballs can float or fly farther in space, where gravitational forces are weaker than they are on Earth. Imagine what professional sports would be like in reduced gravity!

You may not have to imagine much longer. At least one company specializes in airplane flights that simulate a reduced gravity environment. Similar to NASA training flights that astronauts use when preparing to go into space, these flights allow passengers to fly around the cabin. In environments with reduced gravity, athletes can perform jumps and stunts that would be impossible on Earth. As technology improves, permanent stadiums could be built in space for a whole new generation of athletes.

CAREERS

Communicate Discuss these questions with a partner and then answer them below.

1. Sports can be more fun in reduced gravity. What jobs could be harder or less fun to do in space? Why?

_____

_____

_____

2. What kinds of sports do you think could be more fun in space? Why?

_____

_____

_____

▶ PLANET DIARY Go to **Planet Diary** to learn more about everyday forces.

Lab zone® Do the Inquiry Warm-Up *Observing Friction.*

Vocabulary
- friction • sliding friction • static friction
- fluid friction • rolling friction • gravity
- mass • weight

Skills
- Reading: Identify Supporting Evidence
- Inquiry: Design Experiments

What Factors Affect Friction?

If you slide a book across a table, the surface of the book rubs against the surface of the table. The force that two surfaces exert on each other when they rub against each other is called **friction.**

Two factors that affect the force of friction are the types of surfaces involved and how hard the surfaces are pushed together. The football player in **Figure 1** is pushing on a blocking sled. If his coach wanted to make it harder to move the sled, the coach could change the surface of the sled. Covering the bottom of the sled with rubber would increase friction and make the sled harder to move. In general, smooth surfaces produce less friction than rough surfaces.

What would happen if the football player switched to a much heavier sled? He would find the heavier sled harder to push because it pushes down harder against the ground. Similarly, if you rubbed your hands together forcefully, there would be more friction than if you rubbed your hands together lightly. Friction increases when surfaces push harder against each other.

Friction acts in a direction opposite to the direction of the object's motion. Without friction, a moving object will not stop until it strikes another object.

Vocabulary Latin Word Origins
Friction comes from the Latin word *fricare*. Based on the definition of friction, what do you think *fricare* means?
- ○ to burn
- ○ to rub
- ○ to melt

FIGURE 1 ....

> ART IN MOTION **Friction and Different Surfaces**
The strength of friction depends on the types of surfaces involved. **Sequence** Rank the surfaces above by how hard it would be to push a sled over them, from easiest (1) to hardest (3). (Each surface is flat.) What does this ranking tell you about the amount of friction over these surfaces?

_____

_____

Sliding Friction

Sliding friction occurs when two solid surfaces slide over each other. Sliding friction is what makes moving objects slow down and stop. Without sliding friction, a penguin that slid down a hill wouldn't stop until he hit a wall!

✏️ **Classify** Label five examples of sliding friction and compare with a classmate.

Friction acts opposite the direction of motion.

Direction of motion →

← Friction

Static Friction

Static friction acts between objects that aren't moving. Think about trying to push a couch across the room. If you don't push hard enough, it won't move. The force that's keeping you from moving it is static friction. Once you push hard enough to overcome static friction, the couch starts moving and there is no more static friction. However, there is sliding friction.

✏️ **Classify** Label five examples of static friction and compare with a classmate.

Draw an arrow representing the frictional force at work.

Fluid Friction

Fluids, such as water and air, are materials that flow easily. **Fluid friction** occurs when a solid object moves through a fluid. Fluid friction is easier to overcome than sliding friction. This is why sidewalks become slippery when they get wet.

✏️ **Classify** Label five examples of fluid friction and compare with a classmate.

Draw an arrow representing the frictional force at work.

Rolling Friction

When an object rolls across a surface, **rolling friction** occurs. Rolling friction is much easier to overcome than sliding friction for similar materials. That's why it's easy to push a bike along the sidewalk when the wheels can turn, but much harder to push the bike if you're applying the brakes and the tires slide, not roll.

✏️ **Classify** Label five examples of rolling friction and compare with a classmate.

Draw an arrow representing the frictional force at work.

Your family is moving and isn't sure how to best overcome friction while moving furniture. You have a spring scale, wood blocks to represent your furniture, and sandpaper, aluminum foil, marbles, and olive oil as possible surfaces to slide your furniture over.

⚠ **Design Experiments** **Design an experiment that will help you determine which material will reduce friction the most.**

You know that friction occurs between surfaces when they slide against each other. If you measure the applied force required to push something across a surface, you know that your applied force would (increase/decrease) as friction increased.

STEP ① **Measure** How would you determine your applied force in this experiment?

_____

_____

_____

STEP ② **Control Variables** What variables would you have to control to keep your results accurate?

_____

_____

_____

STEP ③ **Create Data Tables** Draw the data table you would use when performing this experiment.

🔑 **Assess Your Understanding**

1a. List Name four types of friction and give an example of each.

_____

_____

_____

_____

_____

b. Classify What types of friction occur between your bike tires and the ground when you ride over cement, ride through a puddle, and apply your brakes?

_____

Lab ® Do the Lab Investigation
zone *Sticky Sneakers.*

got it?

○ **I get it!** Now I know that friction is affected by

_____

_____

_____

○ **I need extra help with** _____

_____

Go to **my science** **coach** *online for help with this subject.*

What Factors Affect Gravity?

A skydiver would be surprised if she jumped out of a plane and did not fall. We are so used to objects falling that we may not have thought about why they fall. One person who thought about it was Sir Isaac Newton. He concluded that a force acts to pull objects straight down toward the center of Earth. **Gravity** is a force that pulls objects toward each other.

Universal Gravitation Newton realized that gravity acts everywhere in the universe, not just on Earth. It is the force that makes the skydivers in **Figure 2** fall to the ground. It is the force that keeps the moon orbiting around Earth. It is the force that keeps all the planets in our solar system orbiting around the sun.

What Newton realized is now called the law of universal gravitation. The law of universal gravitation states that the force of gravity acts between all objects in the universe that have mass. This means that any two objects in the universe that have mass attract each other. You are attracted not only to Earth but also to the moon, the other planets in the solar system, and all the objects around you. Earth and the objects around you are attracted to you as well. However, you do not notice the attraction among small objects because these forces are extremely small compared to the force of Earth's attraction.

FIGURE 2 ....

Observing Gravity
Newton published his work on gravity in 1687.

✏ **Observe** What observations might you make today that would lead you to the same conclusions about gravity? Write down your ideas below.

_____

_____

_____

_____

_____

_____

Factors Affecting Gravity

A gravitational force exists between any two objects in the universe. However, you don't see your pencil fly toward the wall the way you see it fall toward Earth. That's because the gravitational force between some objects is stronger than the force between others. You observe only the effects of the strongest gravitational forces. ⟶ **Two factors affect the gravitational attraction between objects: mass and distance.** **Mass** is a measure of the amount of matter in an object. The SI unit of mass is the kilogram.

The more mass an object has, the greater the gravitational force between it and other objects. Earth's gravitational force on nearby objects is strong because the mass of Earth is so large. The more massive planets in **Figure 3** interact with a greater gravitational force than the less massive planets. Gravitational force also depends on the distance between the objects' centers. As distance increases, gravitational force decreases. That's why Earth can exert a visible gravitational force on a pencil in your room and not on a pencil on the moon.

⟲ **Identify Supporting Evidence** Underline the factors that determine how strong the gravitational force is between two objects.

FIGURE 3 ···

Gravitational Attraction

Gravitational attraction depends on two factors: mass and distance. Suppose there was a solar system that looked like this.

✎ **Interpret Diagrams** Use the diagram below to compare the gravitational force between different planets and their sun. Assume all planets are made of the same material, so bigger planets have more mass.

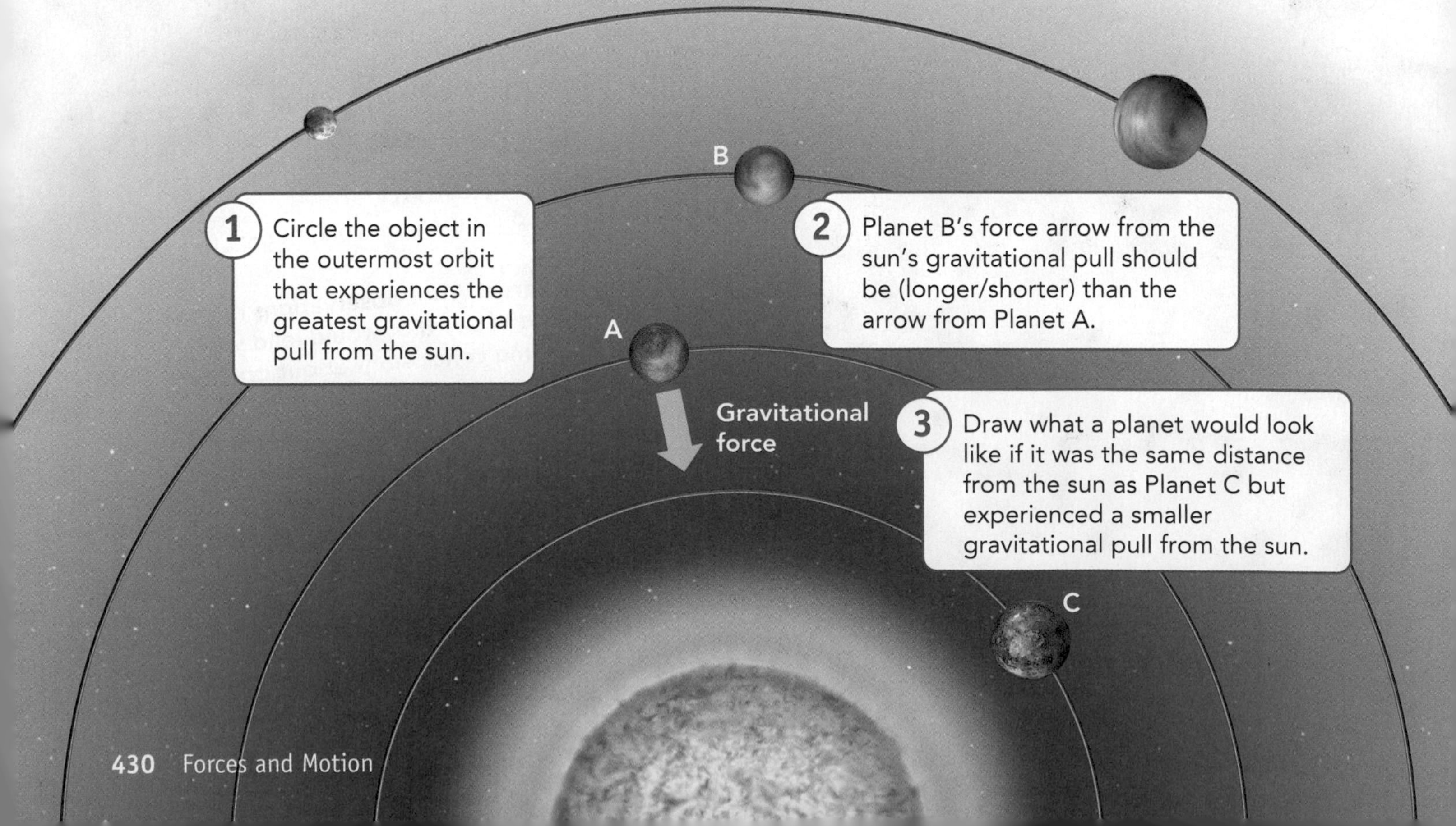

B

① Circle the object in the outermost orbit that experiences the greatest gravitational pull from the sun.

② Planet B's force arrow from the sun's gravitational pull should be (longer/shorter) than the arrow from Planet A.

A

Gravitational force

③ Draw what a planet would look like if it was the same distance from the sun as Planet C but experienced a smaller gravitational pull from the sun.

C

Earth
60 N

Moon
_____ N

Mars
_____ N

Weight and Mass Mass is sometimes confused with weight. Mass is a measure of the amount of matter in an object. Weight is a measure of the force of gravity on an object. When you stand on a bathroom scale, it displays the gravitational force Earth is exerting on you.

At any given time, your mass is the same on Earth as it would be on any other planet. But weight varies with the strength of the gravitational force. The dog in **Figure 4** has a different weight at different places in the solar system. On the moon, he would weigh about one sixth of what he does on Earth. On Mars, he would weigh just over a third of what he does on Earth.

FIGURE 4 ··

Weight and Mass

The Mars Phoenix Lander weighs about 3,400 N on Earth. It weighs about 1,300 N on Mars. ✎ Predict **The first scale shows the dog's weight on Earth. Predict its weight on the moon and on Mars. Enter those weights in the boxes on the other two scales.**

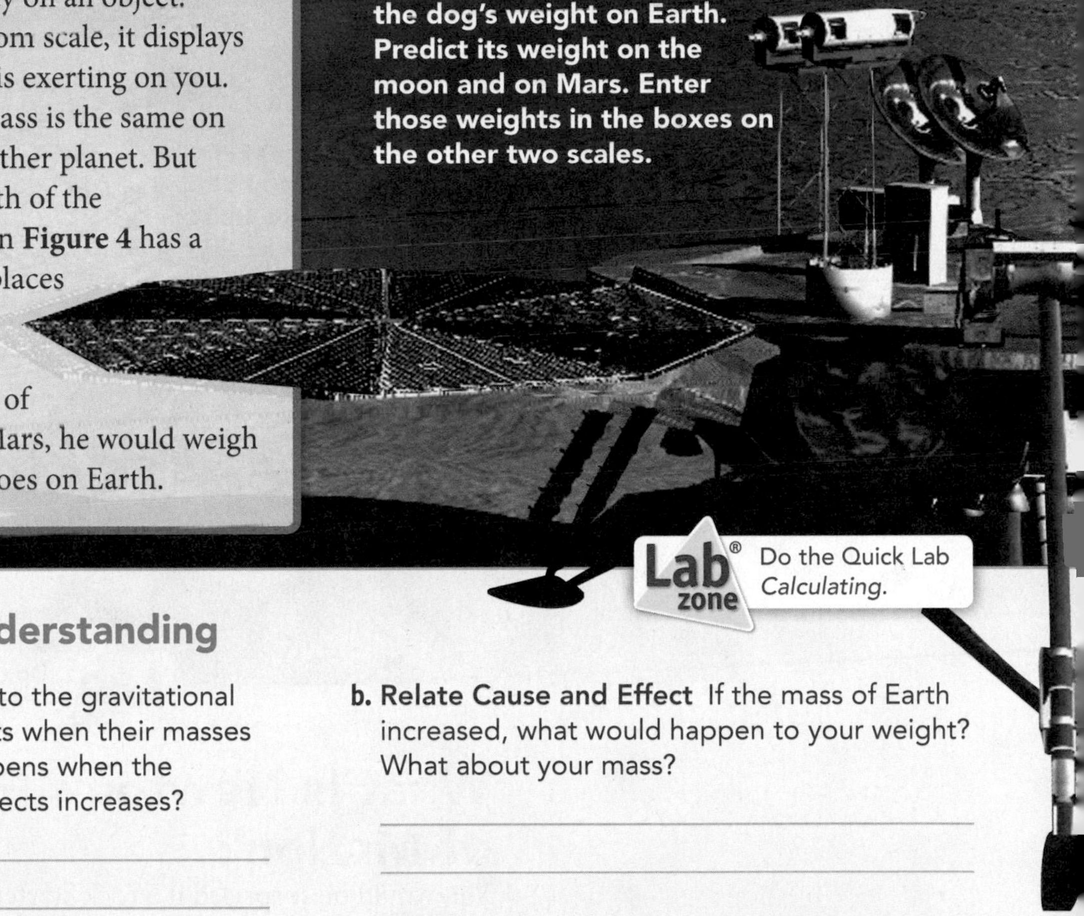

Lab zone® Do the Quick Lab *Calculating.*

🔑 Assess Your Understanding

2a. Describe What happens to the gravitational force between two objects when their masses are increased? What happens when the distance between the objects increases?

_____

_____

_____

b. Relate Cause and Effect If the mass of Earth increased, what would happen to your weight? What about your mass?

_____

_____

_____

got it? ···

○ **I get it!** Now I know that the factors that affect the gravitational force between objects are _____

_____

○ **I need extra help with** _____

Go to MY SCIENCE ⓢ COACH online for help with this subject.

431

Newton's Laws of Motion

UNLOCK THE BIG

🔑 **What Is Newton's First Law of Motion?**

🔑 **What Is Newton's Second Law of Motion?**

🔑 **What Is Newton's Third Law of Motion?**

my planet Diary

VOICES FROM HISTORY

Horse Force

"If a horse draws a stone tied to a rope, the horse (if I may so say) will be equally drawn back towards the stone...."

—Sir Isaac Newton

Scientists have used everyday examples to explain their ideas for hundreds of years. The quotation is from Newton's *Mathematical Principles of Natural Philosophy*, which was first published in the 1680s. Newton used this book to set down his laws of motion. These three simple laws describe much of the motion around you, and they continue to be studied today.

Answer the question below.
What current scientific discoveries might be taught in schools hundreds of years from now?

_____

_____

_____

_____

▶ **PLANET DIARY** Go to **Planet Diary** to learn more about Newton.

Lab zone ® Do the Inquiry Warm-Up *What Changes Motion?*

What Is Newton's First Law of Motion?

You would be surprised if a rock started rolling on its own or a raindrop paused in midair. If an object is not moving, it will not start moving until a force acts on it. If an object is moving, it will continue at a constant velocity until a force acts to change its speed or its direction. 🔑 **Newton's first law of motion states that an object at rest will remain at rest unless acted upon by a nonzero net force. An object moving at a constant velocity will continue moving at a constant velocity unless acted upon by a nonzero net force.**

Vocabulary
• inertia

Skills
⊙ Reading: Ask Questions
△ Inquiry: Infer

Inertia All objects, moving or not, resist changes in motion. Resistance to change in motion is called inertia (in UR shuh). Newton's first law of motion is also called the law of inertia. Inertia explains many common events, including why you move forward in your seat when the car you are in stops suddenly. You keep moving forward because of inertia. A force, such as the pull of a seat belt, is needed to pull you back. Roller coasters like the one in **Figure 1** have safety bars for the same reason.

Inertia Depends on Mass Some objects have more inertia than others. Suppose you need to move an empty backpack and a full backpack. The greater the mass of an object, the greater its inertia, and the greater the force required to change its motion. The full backpack is harder to move than the empty one because it has more mass and therefore more inertia.

FIGURE 1 ······

Inertia
A roller coaster is hard to stop because it has a lot of inertia. ✏ △Infer Use Newton's first law of motion to explain why you feel tossed around whenever a roller coaster goes over a hill or through a loop.

_____

_____

_____

_____

Lab zone® Do the Quick Lab
Around and Around.

⊶ Assess Your Understanding

got it? ···

○ **I get it!** Now I know that Newton's first law of motion states that _____

_____

○ **I need extra help with** _____

Go to MY SCIENCE ⑤ COACH online for help with this subject.

What Is Newton's Second Law of Motion?

Which is harder to push, a full shopping cart or an empty one? Who can cause a greater acceleration on a shopping cart, a small child or a grown adult?

Changes in Force and Mass

Suppose you increase the force on a cart without changing its mass. The acceleration of the cart will also increase. Your cart will also accelerate faster if something falls out. This reduces the mass of the cart, and you keep pushing just as hard. The acceleration of the sled in **Figure 2** will change depending on the mass of the people on it and the force the sled dogs apply. Newton realized these relationships and found a way to represent them mathematically.

Determining Acceleration

🔑 **Newton's second law of motion states that an object's acceleration depends on its mass and on the net force acting on it.** This relationship can be written as follows.

$$\text{Acceleration} = \frac{\text{Net force}}{\text{Mass}}$$

This formula can be rearranged to show how much force must be applied to an object to get it to accelerate at a certain rate.

$$\text{Net force} = \text{Mass} \times \text{Acceleration}$$

FIGURE 2 ·······························

Newton's Second Law
Suppose that four dogs pull a sled carrying two people.

✏️ **Explain** Use words and fill in the pictures to show how you can change the dog/person arrangement to change the sled's acceleration.

How could you increase the sled's acceleration?
_____
_____
_____
_____

How could you decrease the sled's acceleration?
_____
_____
_____
_____

Acceleration is measured in meters per second per second (m/s^2). Mass is measured in kilograms (kg). Newton's second law shows that force is measured in kilograms times meters per second per second ($kg \cdot m/s^2$). This unit is also called the newton (N), which is the SI unit of force. One newton is the force required to give a 1-kg mass an acceleration of 1 m/s^2.

do the math!

Every year in cities around the world, teams create cars, push them across platforms, and hope they will fly. Unfortunately, the cars always end up accelerating down into the water.

1 **Calculate** If a 100-N net force acts on a 50-kg car, what will the acceleration of the car be?

_____

2 After that same car leaves the platform, gravity causes it to accelerate downward at a rate of 9.8 m/s^2. What is the gravitational force on the car?

_____

 Do the Quick Lab Newton's Second Law.

⚷ Assess Your Understanding

1a. Review What equation allows you to calculate the force acting on an object?

_____

b. Calculate What is the net force on a 2-kg skateboard accelerating at a rate of 2 m/s^2?

_____

c. Predict If the mass of the skateboard doubled but the net force on it remained constant, what would happen to the acceleration of the skateboard?

_____

_____

_____

got it? ....

○ I get it! Now I know that Newton's second law of motion describes the relationship _____

_____

○ I need extra help with _____

Go to **my science** **coach** online for help with this subject.

FIGURE 3 ·············
Action-Reaction Pairs
A swimmer moves because the water pushes her forward when she pushes back on it.

✎ **Interpret Diagrams** Draw arrows to show the action and reaction forces between the gymnast and the balance beam. Draw your own example in the space provided.

In the swimmer image: Reaction force | Action force

⟳ **Ask Questions** Action and reaction force pairs are all around you, but they aren't always obvious. Write down a question about a situation in which you can't identify what force pairs are at work.

_____

_____

_____

_____

_____

_____

What Is Newton's Third Law of Motion?

If you leaned against a wall and it didn't push back on you, you'd fall through. The force exerted by the wall is equal in strength and opposite in direction to the force you exert on the wall. 🔑 **Newton's third law of motion states that if one object exerts a force on another object, then the second object exerts a force of equal strength in the opposite direction on the first object.** Another way to state Newton's third law is that for every action there is an equal but opposite reaction.

Action-Reaction Pairs Pairs of action and reaction forces are all around you. When you walk, you push backward on the ground with your feet. Think of this as an action force. (It doesn't matter which force is called the "action" force and which is called the "reaction" force.) The ground pushes forward on your feet with an equal and opposite force. This is the reaction force. You can only walk because the ground pushes you forward! In a similar way, the swimmer in **Figure 3** moves forward by exerting an action force on the water with her hands. The water pushes on her hands with an equal reaction force that propels her body forward.

Detecting Motion If you drop your pen, gravity pulls the pen downward. According to Newton's third law, the pen pulls Earth upward with an equal and opposite reaction force. You see the pen fall. You *don't* see Earth accelerate toward the pen. Remember Newton's second law. If mass increases and force stays the same, acceleration decreases. The same force acts on both Earth and your pen. Since Earth has such a large mass, its acceleration is so small that you don't notice it.

Do Action-Reaction Forces Cancel?

You have learned that two equal forces acting in opposite directions on an object cancel each other out and produce no change in motion. So why don't the action and reaction forces in Newton's third law of motion cancel out as well?

Action and reaction forces do not cancel out because they act on different objects. The swimmer in **Figure 3** exerts a backward action force on the water. The water exerts an equal but opposite forward reaction force on her hands. The action and reaction forces act on different objects—the action force acts on the water and the reaction force acts on her hands.

Unlike the swimmer and the water, the volleyball players in **Figure 4** both exert a force on the *same* object—the volleyball. Each player exerts a force on the ball equal in strength but opposite in direction. The forces on the volleyball are balanced. The ball does not move toward one player or the other.

did you **know?**

Newton's third law of motion explains why rockets accelerate in space, even though there is no water or air to push off of. Inside rockets, gas is produced. When the rockets push that gas backward out of the rocket, a reaction force occurs that pushes the rocket forward.

Forces on hands

Force on ball

Force on ball

FIGURE 4 ....

Action-Reaction Forces
All the horizontal forces on the volleyball cancel out.

✏ **Apply Concepts** In the dog illustration above, use Newton's third law of motion to draw and label any missing force arrows for all the objects.

What Makes a Bug Go *Splat*?

How do objects react to forces?

FIGURE 5

>**VIRTUAL LAB** Splat! A bug has just flown into the windshield of an oncoming car. The car must have hit the bug much harder than the bug hit the car, right? ✎ **Apply Concepts** Use Newton's laws of motion to make sense of the situation and answer the questions.

A

Buzz!

In order for the bug to fly through the air, a force has to push the bug forward. Identify this force. How does the bug produce it? (*Hint:* Think back to how a swimmer moves through the water.)

_____

_____

_____

_____

_____

The bug was at rest on a tree when it saw the car and decided to fly toward it. If the bug has a mass of 0.05 kg and accelerates at 2 m/s², what's the net force on the bug?

_____

B Vroom!

The driver hates killing bugs. When she saw one coming toward the windshield, she braked suddenly and hoped it would get out of the way. (Sadly, it did not.) When she hit the brakes, she felt that she was thrown forward. Use one of Newton's laws to explain why.

_____

_____

_____

_____

_____

C Splat!

The unfortunate bug hits the windshield with a force of 1 N. If you call this the action force, what is the reaction force? Does the car hit the bug any harder than the bug hits the car? Use one of Newton's laws to explain why or why not.

_____

_____

_____

_____

_____

Compare the forces on the bug and the car again. Use another one of Newton's laws to explain why the bug goes *splat* and the car keeps going, without noticeably slowing down.

_____

_____

_____

_____

Lab zone Do the Quick Lab *Interpreting Illustrations.*

Assess Your Understanding

2a. Identify A dog pulls on his leash with a 10-N force to the left, but doesn't move. Identify the reaction force.

_____

_____

_____

b. ANSWER THE BIG **?** Using all three of Newton's laws, explain how objects react to forces.

_____

_____

_____

_____

_____

_____

_____

_____

_____

_____

_____

_____

_____

_____

got it? ....

O **I get it!** Now I know that Newton's third law of motion states that _____

_____

_____

_____

O **I need extra help with** _____

_____

_____

Go to **MY SCIENCE COACH** *online for help with this subject.*

439

Momentum

🔑 **What Is an Object's Momentum?**

MY PLANET DIARY

Air Hockey Science

Whoosh—you've just scored a goal! The puck is about to go back into play. How can you keep the puck out of your goal and get it back into your opponent's? One of the factors you have to consider is momentum. Momentum is a physical quantity that all moving objects have. If you know about momentum, you can predict how an object will act when it collides with other objects. With some quick scientific thinking, you can get the puck to bounce all over the table and back into your opponent's goal!

Answer the questions below.

1. Why might it be better to try to bounce a puck off the wall rather than shoot it straight into your opponent's goal?

_____

_____

_____

_____

2. Where else could it be helpful to know how objects act after colliding?

_____

_____

_____

_____

▶ **PLANET DIARY** Go to **Planet Diary** to learn more about momentum.

Lab zone® Do the Inquiry Warm-Up *How Pushy Is a Straw?*

Vocabulary
• momentum
• law of conservation of momentum

Skills
⤵ Reading: Identify the Main Idea
△ Inquiry: Calculate

What Is an Object's Momentum?

Is it harder to stop a rolling bowling ball or a rolling marble? Does your answer depend on the velocities of the objects? All moving objects have what Newton called a "quantity of motion." Today it's called momentum. **Momentum** (moh MEN tum) is a characteristic of a moving object that is related to the mass and the velocity of the object. 🔑 **The momentum of a moving object can be determined by multiplying the object's mass by its velocity.**

Momentum = Mass × Velocity

Since mass is measured in kilograms and velocity is measured in meters per second, the unit for momentum is kilograms times meters per second (kg·m/s). Like velocity, acceleration, and force, momentum is described by both a direction and a strength. The momentum of an object is in the same direction as its velocity.

The more momentum a moving object has, the harder it is to stop. For example, a 0.1-kg baseball moving at 40 m/s has a momentum of 4 kg·m/s in the direction it's moving.

Momentum = 0.1 kg × 40 m/s

Momentum = 4 kg·m/s

But a 1,200-kg car moving at the same speed as the baseball has a much greater momentum: 48,000 kg·m/s. The velocity of an object also affects the amount of momentum it has. For example, a tennis ball served by a professional tennis player has a large momentum. Although the ball has a small mass, it travels at a high velocity.

Word Origins *Momentum* comes from the Latin word *movere*. Based on the definition of momentum, which of these is the definition of *movere*?

○ to spin
○ to move
○ to sit

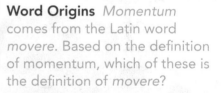

apply it!

△ **Calculate** In each question below, calculate the desired quantity.

❶ The lioness has a mass of 180 kg and a velocity of 16 m/s to the right. What is her momentum?

_____

_____

_____

❷ The warthog has a mass of 100 kg. What does the warthog's speed have to be for it to have the same momentum as the lioness?

_____

441

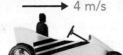

Identify the Main Idea
Circle a sentence that relates the main idea of this section to two colliding cars. Then underline two supporting examples.

FIGURE 1 ....
▶ INTERACTIVE ART Conservation of Momentum

Calculate Complete the equations describing the momentum of each collision. Identify the direction in each case.

Conservation of Momentum
Imagine you're driving a go-cart. If you ran into another go-cart that was at rest and got stuck to it, what do you think would happen to your momentum? Before you hit the other go-cart, your momentum was just your mass times your velocity. How has the additional mass changed that momentum? It actually hasn't changed it at all!

A quantity that is conserved is the same after an event as it was before. The **law of conservation of momentum** states that, in the absence of outside forces like friction, the total momentum of objects that interact does not change. The amount of momentum two cars have is the same before and after they interact.

🔑 **The total momentum of any group of objects remains the same, or is conserved, unless outside forces act on the objects.**

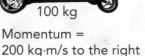

Before → 4 m/s

100 kg

Momentum = 400 kg·m/s to the right

Total momentum = _____ kg·m/s _____

→ 2 m/s

100 kg

Momentum = 200 kg·m/s to the right

"Non-Sticky" Collisions

Look at this example of a collision. When two objects of the same mass don't stick together and outside forces (such as friction) are negligible, the objects just trade velocities. The car that is going faster before the collision will end up slowing down, and the car that is going slower before the collision will end up speeding up.

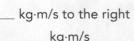

After → 2 m/s

→ 4 m/s

Momentum = _____ kg·m/s to the right   Momentum = _____ kg·m/s to the right

Total momentum = _____ kg·m/s _____

"Sticky" Collisions

Sometimes objects end up sticking together during a collision. These two cars, which have the same mass, got tangled together after they collided. Since the green car was at rest and had a momentum of zero, only the blue car had any momentum before the collision. After they collided and stuck together, the cars shared that momentum. The total momentum of the two cars stayed the same.

Before

→ 4 m/s   0 m/s

100 kg   100 kg

Momentum = _____ kg·m/s to the right   Momentum = _____ kg·m/s

Total momentum = _____ kg·m/s _____

After

→ ?

Total mass = _____

Total momentum = _____ kg·m/s _____

What must the velocity be? _____

Lab zone ® Do the Quick Lab *Colliding Cars.*

Assess Your Understanding

1a. Explain How can a heavy moving van have the same momentum as a small motorcycle?

_____
_____
_____
_____
_____

b. Calculate What is the momentum of a 750-kg car traveling at a velocity of 25 m/s?

_____

c. Infer The total momentum of two marbles before a collision is 0.06 kg·m/s. No outside forces act on the marbles. What is the total momentum of the marbles after the collision?

_____

got it? ....

○ **I get it!** Now I know that momentum is conserved unless _____

_____

○ **I need extra help with** _____

Go to MY SCIENCE COACH *online for help with this subject.*

Free Fall and Circular Motion

 UNLOCK THE BIG ?

🔑 What Is Free Fall?

🔑 What Keeps a Satellite in Orbit?

my planeт Diary

Finding Yourself

The GPS (Global Positioning System) is a "constellation" of satellites that orbit 10,600 miles above Earth. The GPS makes it possible for people with ground receivers to pinpoint their geographic location. The first GPS satellites were placed in orbit in 1978. These early satellites were expected to operate for approximately five years. Newer satellites have an expected lifespan of seven to eight years.

GPS Satellites in Orbit		
Years	Number of GPS Satellites Launched	Number of Operating GPS Satellites
1978–1982	6	6
1983–1987	4	8
1988–1992	17	21
1993–1997	12	27
1998–2002	5	28
2003–2007	11	31

SCIENCE STATS

Interpret Data Use the data in the table to answer the questions below.

1. What is the total number of satellites launched from 1978 to 2007? How many were still operating as of 2007?

_____

_____

_____

2. How many satellites stopped operating between 2003 and 2007?

_____

_____

_____

▶ PLANET DIARY Go to **Planet Diary** to learn more about the GPS.

Lab® zone Do the Inquiry Warm-Up *What Makes an Object Move in a Circle?*

Vocabulary
- free fall • satellite
- centripetal force

Skills
- Reading: Relate Cause and Effect
- Inquiry: Create Data Tables

What Is Free Fall?

When the only force acting on an object is gravity, the object is said to be in **free fall.** The force of gravity causes the object to accelerate. **Free fall is motion where the acceleration is caused by gravity.** When something falls on Earth, there is fluid friction from the air around it. This friction acts against gravity, reducing the acceleration of falling objects. Air friction increases as an object falls. If an object falls for long enough, increased air friction will reduce its acceleration to zero. The object will continue to fall, but it will fall at a constant velocity.

Near the surface of Earth, the acceleration due to gravity is 9.8 m/s². If there were no air friction, a falling object would have a velocity of 9.8 m/s after one second and 19.6 m/s after two seconds. Since air friction reduces acceleration, an object falling on Earth for one second will actually have a velocity that is less than 9.8 m/s.

FIGURE 1 ···

Free Fall

The photo shows a tennis ball and a crumpled piece of paper of different masses as they fall during a fraction of a second. If the only force acting on them were gravity, they would fall at exactly the same rate and line up perfectly. However, air friction is also present. Air friction has a greater effect on the paper's acceleration than on the tennis ball's acceleration. This causes the tennis ball to fall faster.

do the math!

Create Data Tables Suppose you had a chamber with no air, eliminating the force of air friction. Complete the table below for an object that is dropped from rest. Remember the formula Velocity = Acceleration × Time. The acceleration due to gravity is 9.8 m/s².

Time (s)	Velocity (m/s)
0	_____
1	_____
2	_____
3	_____
4	_____

 Lab zone ® Do the Quick Lab *Which Lands First?*

Assess Your Understanding

got it? ··

○ **I get it!** Now I know that free fall is _____

_____

○ **I need extra help with** _____

Go to **my science** s **COACH** *online for help with this subject.*

What Keeps a Satellite in Orbit?

Objects don't always fall down in straight lines. If you throw a ball horizontally, the ball will move away from you while gravity pulls the ball to the ground. The horizontal and vertical motions act independently, and the ball follows a curved path toward the ground. If you throw the ball faster, it will land even farther in front of you. The faster you throw an object, the farther it travels before it lands.

Satellite Motion This explains how **satellites,** which are objects that orbit around other objects in space, follow a curved path around Earth. What would happen if you were on a high mountain and could throw a ball as fast as you wanted? The faster you threw it, the farther away it would land. But, at a certain speed, the curved path of the ball would match the curved surface of Earth. Although the ball would keep falling due to gravity, Earth's surface would curve away from the ball at the same rate. The ball would fall around Earth in a circle, as shown in **Figure 2.**

↻ **Relate Cause and Effect**
On the next page, underline the effect a centripetal force has on an object's motion. Circle the effect of turning off a centripetal force.

FIGURE 2

Satellite Motion

A satellite launched from Earth enters orbit because the curve of its path matches the curved surface of Earth.

✎ **Make Models** On the picture at the right, draw arrows representing the gravitational force on the ball at each point.

[CHALLENGE] Explain why Earth's atmosphere would prevent this baseball from ever actually being thrown into orbit. Why is this not a problem for satellites?

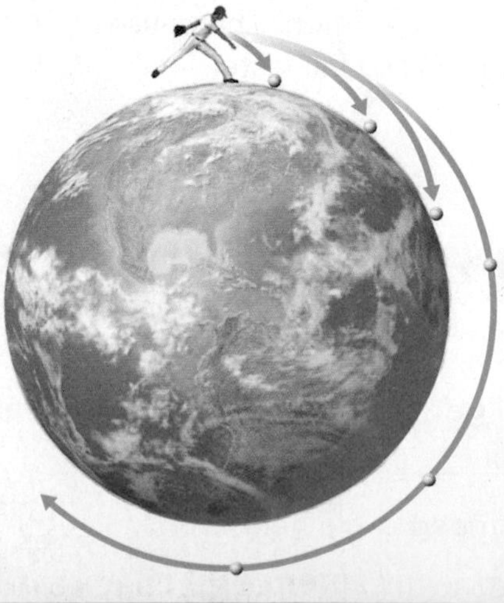

_____

_____

_____

🔑 **Satellites in orbit around Earth continuously fall toward Earth, but because Earth is curved they travel around it.** In other words, a satellite is a falling object that keeps missing the ground! It falls around Earth rather than onto it. Once it has entered a stable orbit, a satellite does not need fuel. It continues to move ahead due to its inertia. At the same time, gravity continuously changes the satellite's direction. Most satellites are launched at a speed of about 7,900 m/s. That's more than 17,000 miles per hour!

Centripetal Force Many manufactured satellites orbit Earth in an almost circular path. Recall that an object traveling in a circle is accelerating because it constantly changes direction. If an object is accelerating, a force must be acting on it. A force that causes an object to move in a circular path is a **centripetal force** (sen TRIP ih tul). The word *centripetal* means "center-seeking." Centripetal forces always point toward the center of the circle an object is moving in. If you could turn off a centripetal force, inertia would cause the object to fly off in a straight line. For example, the string of a yo-yo being swung in a circle provides a centripetal force. Cutting the string would cut off the centripetal force, and the yo-yo would fly off in a straight line.

apply it!

Identify What is creating the centripetal force in each situation below?

❶ A tetherball swinging around a pole

_____

❷ Mars orbiting around the sun

_____

❸ A child standing on a merry-go-round

_____

Lab zone Do the Quick Lab *Orbiting Earth.*

🔑 Assess Your Understanding

1a. Identify What is the force that causes objects to move in circles?

_____

b. Predict If Earth's gravity could be turned off, what would happen to satellites that are currently in orbit? Explain your reasoning.

_____
_____
_____
_____

got it?

○ **I get it!** Now I know that satellites stay in orbit because _____
_____
_____

○ **I need extra help with** _____

Go to **my science COACH** *online for help with this subject.*

447

Changes in motion are caused by _____. _____ laws describe these changes in motion.

LESSON 1 Acceleration

🔑 In science, acceleration refers to increasing speed, decreasing speed, or changing direction.

🔑 You can use both a speed-versus-time graph and a distance-versus-time graph to analyze the motion of an accelerating object.

Vocabulary
• acceleration

LESSON 2 The Nature of Force

🔑 Like velocity and acceleration, a force is described by its strength and by the direction in which it acts.

🔑 A nonzero net force causes a change in the object's motion.

Vocabulary
• force • newton
• net force

LESSON 3 Friction and Gravity

🔑 Two factors that affect the force of friction are the types of surfaces involved and how hard the surfaces are pushed together.

🔑 Two factors affect the gravitational attraction between objects: their masses and distance.

Vocabulary
• friction • sliding friction
• static friction • fluid friction
• rolling friction • gravity
• mass • weight

LESSON 4 Newton's Laws of Motion

🔑 Objects at rest will remain at rest and objects moving at a constant velocity will continue moving at a constant velocity unless they are acted upon by nonzero net forces.

🔑 The acceleration of an object depends on its mass and on the net force acting on it.

🔑 If one object exerts a force on another object, then the second object exerts a force of equal strength in the opposite direction on the first object.

Vocabulary
• inertia

Study Guide Continued

LESSON 5 Momentum

🔑 The momentum of a moving object can be determined by multiplying the object's mass by its velocity.

🔑 The total momentum of any group of objects remains the same, or is conserved, unless outside forces act on the objects.

Vocabulary
• momentum
• law of conservation of momentum

LESSON 6 Free Fall and Circular Motion

🔑 Free fall is motion where the acceleration is caused by gravity.

🔑 Satellites in orbit around Earth continuously fall toward Earth, but because Earth is curved they travel around it.

Vocabulary
• free fall • satellite • centripetal force

12 Review and Assessment

LESSON 1 Acceleration

1. The rate at which velocity changes is

   a. acceleration.   **b.** direction.

   c. speed.   **d.** velocity.

2. You can calculate the acceleration of an object moving in a straight line by dividing the

_____ by the time.

The graph below shows the speed of a downhill skier during a period of several seconds. Use the graph to answer Question 3.

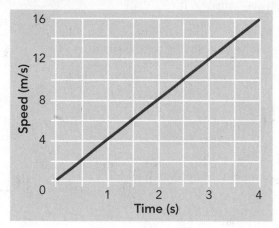

3. Read Graphs What is the skier's acceleration?

_____

_____

_____

4. math! A ball is dropped from a window and takes 2 seconds to reach the ground. It starts from rest and reaches a final speed of 20 m/s. What is the ball's acceleration?

_____

_____

_____

5. **Write About It** Describe how a baseball player accelerates as he runs around the bases after hitting a home run.

LESSON 2 The Nature of Force

6. When a nonzero net force acts on an object, the force

   a. changes the motion of the object.

   b. must be greater than the reaction force.

   c. does not change the motion of the object.

   d. is equal to the weight of the object.

7. The SI unit of force is the _____

8. Calculate What is the net force on the box? Be sure to specify direction.

LESSON 3 Friction and Gravity

9. Friction always acts

   a. in the same direction as motion.

   b. opposite the direction of motion.

   c. perpendicular to the direction of motion.

   d. at a 30° angle to the direction of motion.

10. The factors that affect the gravitational force

between two objects are _____

_____

11. List What are two ways you can increase the frictional force between two objects?

_____

_____

12. **Write About It** Design a ride for an amusement park. Describe the ride and explain how friction and gravity will affect the ride's design.

Review and Assessment

Newton's Laws of Motion

13. Which of Newton's laws of motion is also called the law of inertia?

    a. First   **b.** Second

    c. Third   **d.** Fourth

14. Newton's second law states that force is equal

to _____

15. Interpret Diagrams Look at the diagram below of two students pulling a bag of volley-ball equipment. The friction force between the bag and the floor is 4 N. What is the net force acting on the bag? What is the acceleration of the bag?

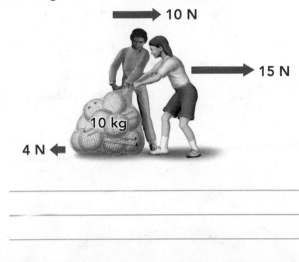

10 N

15 N

10 kg

4 N

_____

_____

_____

_____

16. Apply Concepts Suppose you are an astronaut making a space walk outside your space station and your jet pack runs out of fuel. How can you use your empty jet pack to get you back to the station?

_____

_____

_____

_____

_____

Momentum

17. Momentum is calculated by multiplying

    a. mass times velocity.   **b.** weight times mass.

    c. force times speed.   **d.** inertia times force.

18. The SI unit of momentum is _____

19. Explain How can two objects of different masses have the same momentum?

_____

_____

_____

_____

_____

20. Design Experiments Design an experiment in which you could show that momentum is not conserved in a collision between two marbles when friction is present.

_____

_____

_____

_____

_____

_____

_____

_____

_____

_____

_____

21. **Write About It** Pick two sports. Explain how knowing about momentum could help you predict what will happen in the game when you watch these sports on TV.

12 Review and Assessment

Free Fall and Circular Motion

22. Satellites remain in orbit around Earth because

    a. the moon's gravitational pull on them is equal to Earth's pull.

    b. no forces act on them.

    c. their motors keep them moving in circles.

    d. the curve of their paths as they fall matches the curve of Earth.

23. Centripetal forces always point _____

_____

24. Calculate Determine the velocity of an object that started from rest and has been in free fall for 10 seconds. Assume there is no air resistance.

_____

APPLY THE BIG ? **How do objects react to forces?**

25. Forces are all around you. Describe an example of each of Newton's laws of motion that you experience before you get to school in the morning.

_____

_____

_____

_____

_____

_____

_____

_____

_____

_____

Ohio Benchmark Practice

Multiple Choice

Circle the letter of the best answer.

Force Force   Motion

1. In the balloon diagram above, why don't the two forces cancel each other out?

   A They are not equal.

   B They both act on the air.

   C They both act on the balloon.

   D They act on different objects.

2. What force makes it less likely for a person to slip on a dry sidewalk than on an icy sidewalk?

   A gravity

   B friction

   C inertia

   D momentum

3. A 5-kg cat accelerates at a rate of 2 m/s². What is the net force acting on the cat?

   A 10 N

   B 7 N

   C 3 N

   D 2.5 N

4. According to Newton's first law, what will plates at rest on a tablecloth do when the tablecloth is pulled out from under them? (Ignore outside forces such as friction.)

   A fly off the table and hit the ground

   B accelerate with the tablecloth

   C resist the change in motion and stay at rest

   D accelerate in the opposite direction from the tablecloth

5. In a game of tug-of-war, you pull on the rope with a force of 100 N to the right and your friend pulls on the rope with a force of 100 N to the left. What is the net force on the rope?

   A 200 N to the right

   B 200 N to the left

   C 0 N

   D 100 N to the right

Extended Response

Use your knowledge of science to help you answer Question 6. Write your answer on a separate sheet of paper.

6. Use all three of Newton's laws of motion to describe what happens when a car starts off at rest, is pushed across a platform, and then accelerates downward.

safety restraints

Did you wear your seat belt the last time you rode in a car? Seat belts are safety restraints designed to protect you from injury while you travel in a moving vehicle, whether you stop suddenly to avoid a crash or are stopped suddenly by a crash.

Without a seat belt, inertia would cause the driver and passengers in a car that suddenly stopped to continue traveling forward. Without a restraint, a 75-kilogram driver driving at 50 km/h would experience 12,000 newtons of force in a crash! A safety restraint prevents that forward motion and keeps the driver and passengers safe.

Safety harnesses and seat belts are available in many different designs. Most seat belts are three-point harnesses. Five- and seven-point harnesses are used in vehicles like race cars and fighter jets.

Debate It Most states have laws that require drivers and passengers to wear seat belts. Research the seat belt laws in your state, and participate in a class debate about whether the seat belts are strong enough.

Race car drivers travel at higher speeds than most drivers experience. A five-point harness provides extra security at these high speeds. ▼

POTENTIAL ENERGY

An object does not have to be moving to have energy. Some objects have energy as a result of their shapes or positions. When you lift a book up to your desk from the floor or compress a spring by winding a toy, you transfer energy to it. The energy you transfer is stored, or held in readiness. It might be used later if the book falls or the spring unwinds. Energy that results from the position or shape of an object is called **potential energy.** This type of energy has the potential to do work.

Gravitational Potential Energy Potential energy related to an object's height is called **gravitational potential energy.** The gravitational potential energy of an object is equal to the work done to lift it to that height. Remember that work is equal to force multiplied by distance. The force you use to lift the object is equal to its weight. The weight of an object is related to its mass, so gravitational potential energy is also related to an object's mass. The distance you move the object is its height above the ground. You can calculate an object's gravitational potential energy using this equation.

$$\text{Gravitational potential energy} = \text{Weight} \times \text{Height}$$

For example, suppose a book has a weight of 10 newtons (N). If the book is lifted 2 meters off the ground, the book has 10 newtons times 2 meters, or 20 joules, of gravitational potential energy.

Elastic Potential Energy An object has a different type of potential energy due to its shape. **Elastic potential energy** is the energy associated with objects that can be compressed or stretched. For example, when the girl in the image below presses down on the trampoline, the trampoline changes shape. The trampoline now has potential energy. When the girl pushes off of the trampoline, the stored energy sends the girl upward.

Elastic Potential Energy

The energy stored in a stretched object, such as the trampoline, is elastic potential energy.

✎ **Interpret Diagrams** Rank the amount of elastic potential energy of the trampoline from greatest to least. A ranking of one is the greatest. Write your answers in the circles. Then explain your answers in the space to the right.

HOW CAN THIS TRAIN MOVE WITHOUT TOUCHING THE TRACK?

How are electricity and magnetism related?

This type of train is called a maglev, or magnetic levitation train, and operates at speeds of 430 km/h (about twice as fast as a conventional train). It does not have a traditional engine, which means it does not give off any pollutants. Instead, the maglev train uses electricity in the track to power magnets that propel the train forward and levitation magnets to keep the train floating about 10 mm above the track.

> UNTAMED SCIENCE Watch the **Untamed Science** video to learn more about electromagnetism.

Draw Conclusions How can this train move without touching the track?

_____

_____

_____

_____

Electromagnetism

Getting Started

Check Your Understanding

1. **Background** Read the paragraph below and then answer the question.

While Chung works, his computer shuts down. Both the street and his house are dark, so he knows there is no **electricity.** A fallen tree has snapped an electric wire. The wire was the **conductor** that brought him power. Chung reaches for the light switch, but then remembers that no **electric current** will flow when he turns it on.

• How can electricity be restored to Chung's house?

_____

_____

> MY READING WEB If you had trouble completing the question above, visit **My Reading Web** and type in *Electromagnetism.*

Electricity is a form of energy sometimes created by the movement of charged particles.

A material through which charges can easily flow is a **conductor.**

Electric current is the continuous flow of electric charges through a material.

Vocabulary Skill

Use Context to Determine Meaning Science books often use unfamiliar words. Look for context clues in surrounding words and phrases to figure out the meaning of a new word. In the paragraph below, look for clues to the meaning of *magnetic force.*

The attraction or repulsion between magnetic poles is **magnetic force.** A force is a push or pull that can cause an object to change its motion. A magnetic force is produced when magnetic poles interact.

Example	Magnetic force
Definition	*n.* attraction or repulsion between magnetic poles
Explanation	Force is a push or pull.
Other Information	Magnetic force is produced when magnetic poles interact.

2. **Quick Check** In the paragraph above, circle the explanation of the word *force.*

magnetic pole

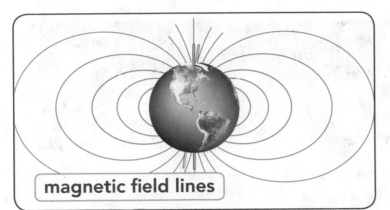

magnetic field lines

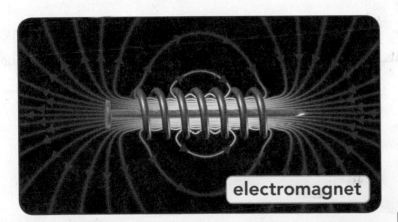

electromagnet

generator

Chapter Preview

LESSON 1
- magnet
- magnetism
- magnetic pole
- magnetic force
- ↻ Summarize
- △ Infer

LESSON 2
- magnetic field
- magnetic field lines
- compass
- magnetic declination
- ↻ Identify the Main Idea
- △ Observe

LESSON 3
- electric force
- electric field
- static electricity
- conservation of charge
- friction
- conduction
- induction
- polarization
- static discharge
- ↻ Relate Cause and Effect
- △ Draw Conclusions

LESSON 4
- electric current
- electric circuit
- conductor
- insulator
- voltage
- resistance
- ↻ Ask Questions
- △ Classify

LESSON 5
- electromagnetism
- solenoid
- electromagnet
- ↻ Relate Cause and Effect
- △ Predict

LESSON 6
- galvanometer
- electric motor
- ↻ Sequence
- △ Graph

LESSON 7
- electromagnetic induction
- direct current
- alternating current
- generator
- transformer
- ↻ Ask Questions
- △ Make Models

> VOCAB FLASH CARDS
For extra help with vocabulary, visit **Vocab Flash Cards** and type in *Electromagnetism*.

459

What Is Magnetism?

UNLOCK THE BIG ?

🗝 **What Are the Properties of Magnets?**

🗝 **How Do Magnetic Poles Interact?**

MY PLANET DIARY

FUN FACTS

Crocodile Sense

Crocodiles are threatened animals. So, if they are not protected, they may become endangered and then disappear altogether. However, in Florida, many crocodiles live where people do, so they threaten people's safety.

To keep both people and crocodiles safe, biologists tried to move crocodiles away from people. But there was a problem. Crocodiles use Earth's magnetic field to help them navigate. Whenever they relocated a crocodile, it eventually returned, if it was not killed on the way back. But then the biologists heard that scientists in Mexico had taped a magnet to each side of a crocodile's head before relocating it. They thought that the magnets would interfere with the crocodile's ability to use Earth's magnetic field to find its way back. Biologists here did the same thing. So far, it has been successful.

Communicate Discuss the following questions with a partner. Write your answers below.

Why do you think it is important to relocate crocodiles?

_____

_____

_____

_____

_____

_____

▶ PLANET DIARY Go to **Planet Diary** to learn more about magnetism.

Lab zone Do the Inquiry Warm-Up *Natural Magnets.*

What Are the Properties of Magnets?

Imagine that you're in Shanghai, China, zooming along in a maglev train propelled by magnets. Your 30-kilometer trip from the airport to the city station takes less than eight minutes. The same trip in a taxi would take about an hour.

Vocabulary

- magnet
- magnetism
- magnetic pole
- magnetic force

Skills

- Reading: Summarize
- Inquiry: Infer

Magnets When you think of magnets, you might think about the objects that hold notes to your refrigerator. But magnets can be large, like the one in **Figure 1.** They can be small like those on your refrigerator, in your wallet, on your kitchen cabinets, or on security tags at a store. A magnet is any material that attracts iron and materials that contain iron.

Discovering Magnets Magnets have many modern uses, but they are not new. The ancient Greeks discovered that a rock called magnetite attracted materials containing iron. The rocks also attracted or repelled other magnetic rocks. The attraction or repulsion of magnetic materials is called **magnetism.**

Magnets have the same properties as magnetite rocks. Magnets attract iron and materials that contain iron. Magnets attract or repel other magnets. In addition, one end of a magnet will always point north when allowed to swing freely.

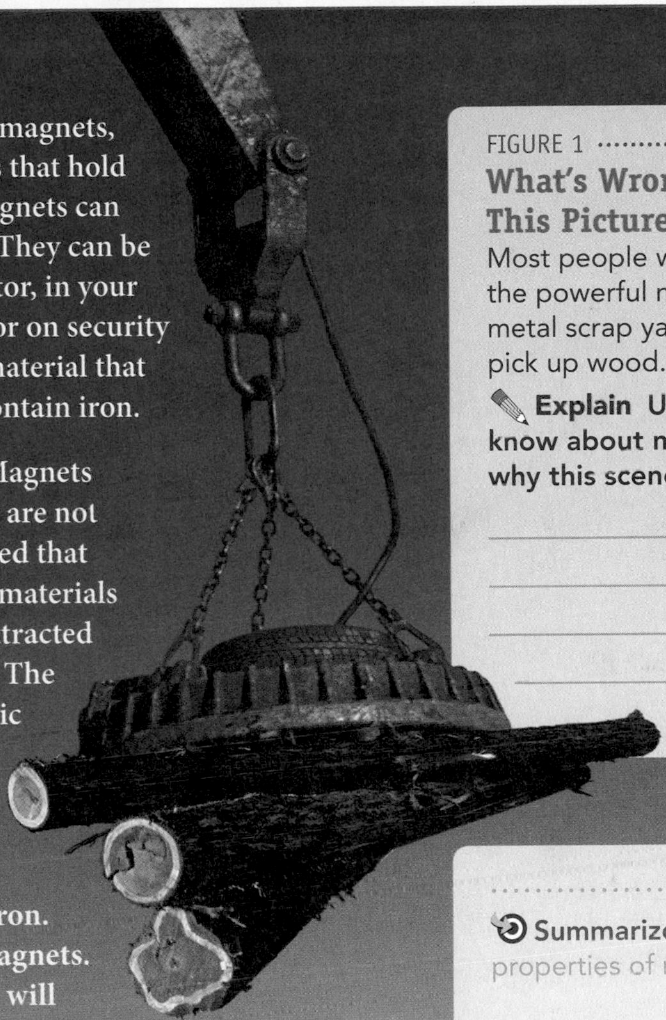

FIGURE 1

What's Wrong With This Picture?

Most people would not expect the powerful magnet used at a metal scrap yard to be able to pick up wood.

✏ **Explain** Use what you know about magnets to explain why this scene is impossible.

_____
_____
_____
_____
_____

✏ **Summarize** Summarize the properties of magnetite.

_____
_____
_____
_____

Lab zone Do the Lab Investigation *Detecting Fake Coins.*

⚷ Assess Your Understanding

got it? ....

O **I get it!** Now I know that three properties of magnets are that magnets _____
_____

O **I need extra help with** _____

Go to **MY SCIENCE COACH** online for help with this subject.

South pole

How Do Magnetic Poles Interact?

Any magnet, no matter what its size or shape, has two ends. Each one is called a **magnetic pole.** The magnetic effect of a magnet is strongest at the poles. The pole of a magnet that points north is labeled the *north pole*. The other pole is labeled the *south pole*. A magnet always has both a north pole and a south pole.

Magnetic Interactions What happens if you bring two magnets together? The answer depends on how you hold the poles of the magnets. If you bring the north pole of one magnet near the south pole of another, the two unlike poles attract one another. However, if you bring two north poles together, the like poles move away from each other.  **Magnetic poles that are unlike attract each other, and magnetic poles that are alike repel each other.** You can see how bar magnets interact in **Figure 2.**

FIGURE 2 ·······························

▶ ART IN MOTION **Attraction and Repulsion**
These pairs of magnets show how magnetic poles interact.

✎ **Relate Text and Visuals** Draw and label what happens when two south poles are near each other. Then draw arrows representing the direction of the force on each magnet.

North pole

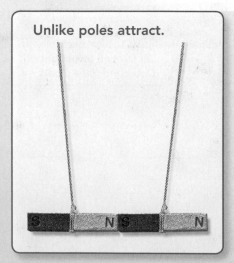

Unlike poles attract.

Like poles repel.

Magnetic Force The attraction or repulsion between magnetic poles is **magnetic force.** A force is a push or a pull that can cause an object to move. A magnetic force is produced when magnetic poles come near each other and interact. Any material that exerts a magnetic force is a magnet.

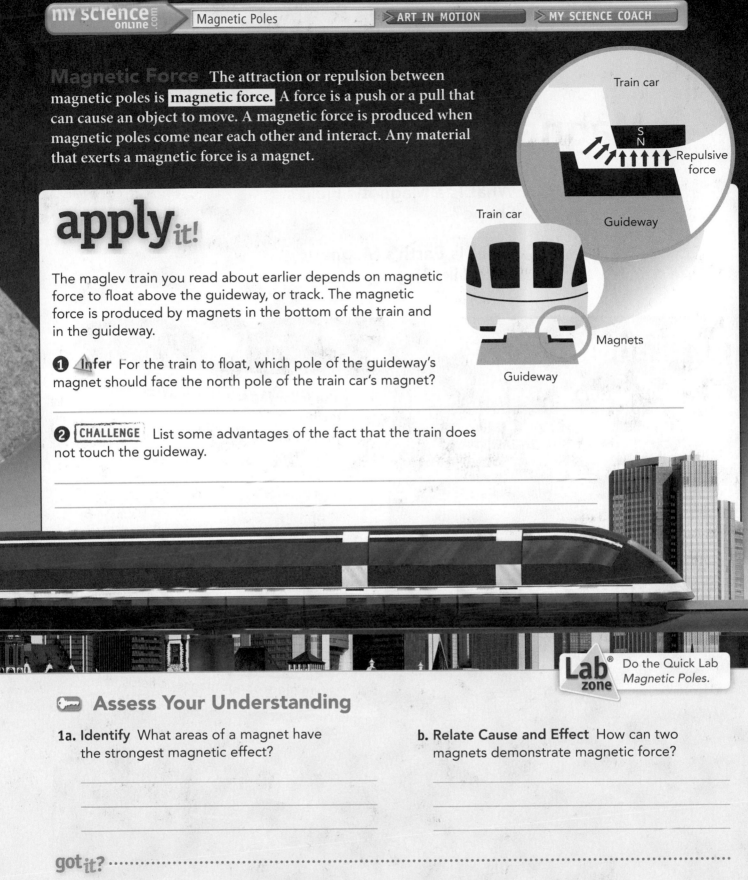

Train car

S
N

Repulsive force

Train car

Guideway

apply it!

The maglev train you read about earlier depends on magnetic force to float above the guideway, or track. The magnetic force is produced by magnets in the bottom of the train and in the guideway.

Magnets

Guideway

❶ **Infer** For the train to float, which pole of the guideway's magnet should face the north pole of the train car's magnet?

_____

❷ **CHALLENGE** List some advantages of the fact that the train does not touch the guideway.

_____

_____

Lab zone ® Do the Quick Lab *Magnetic Poles.*

⚷ Assess Your Understanding

1a. Identify What areas of a magnet have the strongest magnetic effect?

_____

_____

b. Relate Cause and Effect How can two magnets demonstrate magnetic force?

_____

_____

got it? ....

○ **I get it!** Now I know that magnetic poles that are unlike _____

and magnetic poles that are alike _____

○ **I need extra help with** _____

Go to MY SCIENCE ⓢ COACH online for help with this subject.

Ohio

LESSON

2

Magnetic Fields

UNLOCK THE BIG ?

🔑 **What Is a Magnetic Field's Shape?**

🔑 **What Is Earth's Magnetic Field Like?**

my planet Diary

Cow Magnets

You probably know that cows eat grass. Did you know that they also eat metal? When cows graze, they may ingest metal objects that contain iron such as nails, wires, and old cans. If the metal is sharp, it could pierce the cow's stomach, causing infection, illness, or even death.

To ensure that their cows are safe, farmers have their cows swallow a magnet. Once inside the cow's stomach, the magnet attracts the iron in the metal that the cow eats. This keeps the metal from moving around and possibly puncturing other organs. One magnet can protect a cow for life.

FUN FACTS

Read the following questions. Write your answers below.

1. Why is it dangerous for a cow to eat metal?

_____

_____

_____

_____

2. As a farmer, what else could you do to keep metal objects from harming the cows?

_____

_____

▶ **PLANET DIARY** Go to **Planet Diary** to learn more about magnetic fields.

Lab zone

Do the Inquiry Warm-Up
Predict the Field.

Vocabulary
- magnetic field
- magnetic field lines
- compass
- magnetic declination

Skills
- **Reading:** Identify the Main Idea
- **Inquiry:** Observe

What Is a Magnetic Field's Shape?

You know that a magnetic force is strongest at the poles of a magnet. But magnetic force is not limited to the poles. It is exerted all around a magnet. The area of magnetic force around a magnet is known as its **magnetic field.** Because of magnetic fields, magnets can interact without even touching.

Representing Magnetic Field Lines Figure 1 shows the magnetic field of a bar magnet. The **magnetic field lines** are shown in purple. Magnetic field lines are lines that map out the invisible magnetic field around a magnet. **Magnetic field lines spread out from one pole, curve around the magnet, and return to the other pole.** The lines form complete loops from pole to pole and never cross. Arrowheads indicate the direction of the magnetic field lines. They always leave the north pole and enter the south pole. The closer together the lines are, the stronger the field. Magnetic field lines are closest together at the poles.

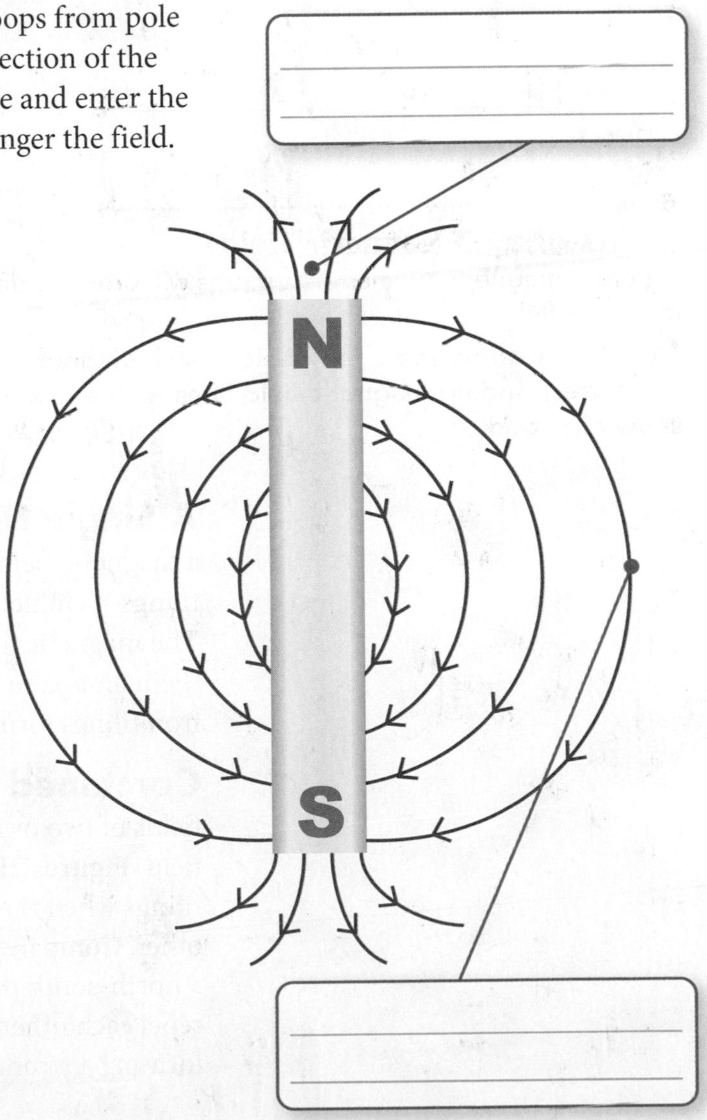

FIGURE 1 ....

Magnetic Field Lines
Magnetic fields are invisible, but you can represent a field using magnetic field lines.

✎ **Complete the tasks below.**

1. **Relate Text and Visuals** In the boxes, identify where the magnetic field is strong and where it is weak.

2. [CHALLENGE] Forces that affect objects without touching them are called *field* forces. Is gravity a field force? Explain.

_____

_____

_____

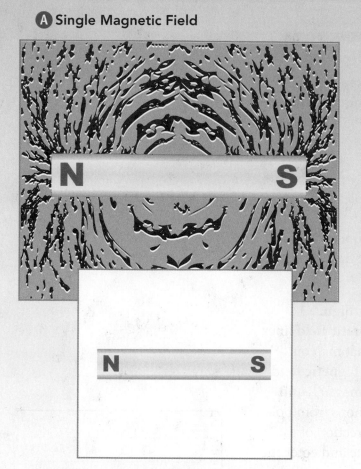

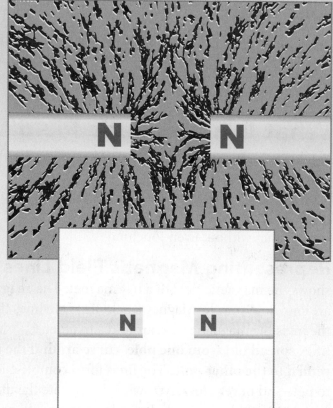

FIGURE 2 ....

> INTERACTIVE ART Magnetic Fields
Different magnetic pole arrangements will produce different
magnetic fields.

✎ **Make Models** In the box below each diagram, draw
the corresponding magnetic field lines with arrowheads to
show direction.

A Single Magnetic Field Although you cannot see
a magnetic field, you can see its effects. **Figure 2A** shows iron
filings sprinkled on a sheet of clear plastic that covers one magnet.
The magnetic forces of the magnet act on the iron filings and align
them along the invisible magnetic field lines. The result is that the
iron filings form a pattern similar to magnetic field lines.

Combined Magnetic Fields When the magnetic
fields of two or more magnets overlap, the result is a combined
field. **Figures 2B** and **2C** show the effects of magnetic force on iron
filings when the poles of two bar magnets are brought near each
other. Compare the pattern of a north-north pole arrangement and
a north-south pole arrangement. The fields from two like poles
repel each other. But the fields from unlike poles attract each other,
forming a strong field between the magnets.

C Combined Magnetic Field, North-South

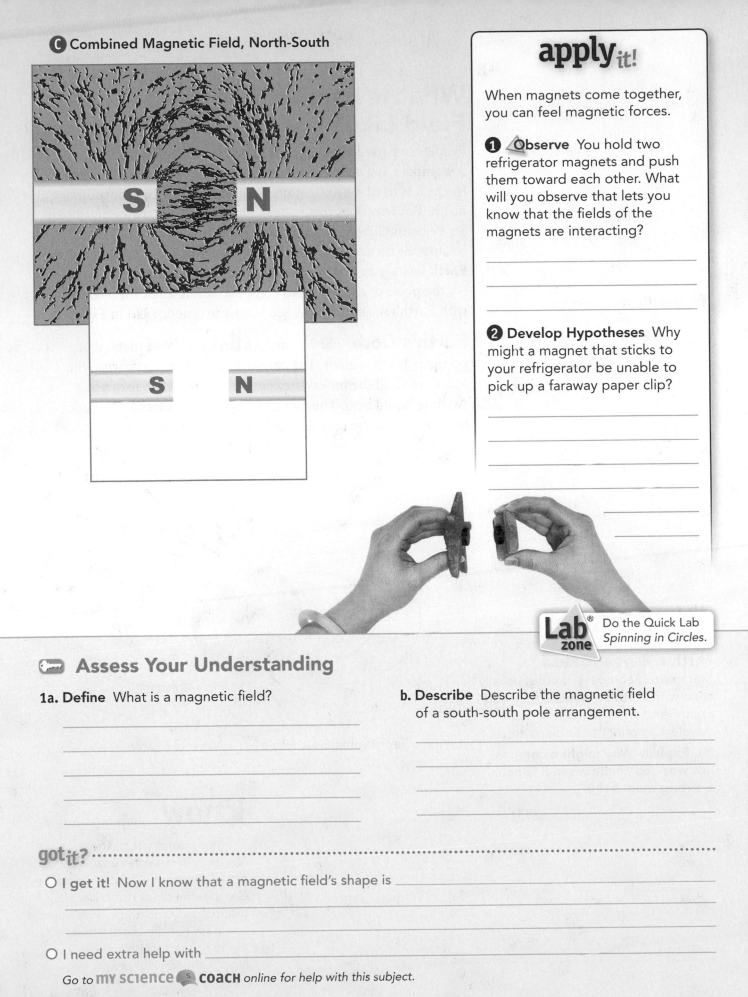

Lab zone® Do the Quick Lab *Spinning in Circles.*

apply it!

When magnets come together, you can feel magnetic forces.

1 ⚠ **Observe** You hold two refrigerator magnets and push them toward each other. What will you observe that lets you know that the fields of the magnets are interacting?

_____

_____

_____

2 **Develop Hypotheses** Why might a magnet that sticks to your refrigerator be unable to pick up a faraway paper clip?

_____

_____

_____

_____

_____

🔑 **Assess Your Understanding**

1a. Define What is a magnetic field?

_____

_____

_____

_____

b. Describe Describe the magnetic field of a south-south pole arrangement.

_____

_____

_____

_____

got**it?** ....

○ **I get it!** Now I know that a magnetic field's shape is _____

_____

○ **I need extra help with** _____

Go to **MY SCIENCE ⓢ COACH** *online for help with this subject.*

467

What Is Earth's Magnetic Field Like?

People have used compasses as tools for navigation for centuries. A **compass** is a device that has a magnet on a needle that spins freely. It is used for navigation because its needle usually points north. But why does that happen? In the late 1500s an Englishman, Sir William Gilbert, proved that a compass behaves as it does because Earth acts as a giant magnet. 🔑 **Just like a bar magnet, Earth has a magnetic field around it and two magnetic poles.** So, the poles of a magnetized compass needle align themselves with Earth's magnetic field. See Earth's magnetic field in **Figure 3**.

Earth's Core Earth's core is a large sphere of metal that occupies Earth's center. The core is divided into two parts—the outer core and the inner core. The outer core is made of hot swirling liquid iron. The motion of this iron creates a magnetic field similar to the magnetic field of a bar magnet.

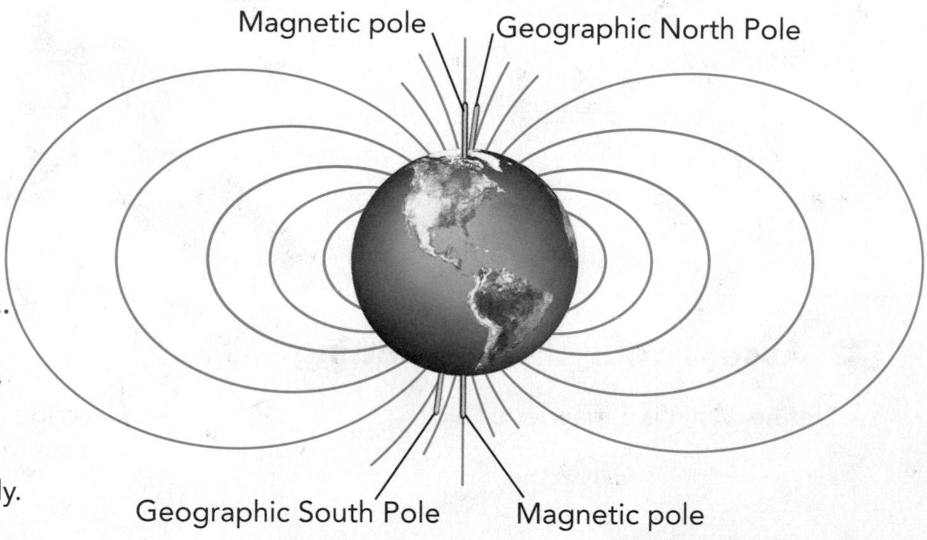

✏️ **Identify the Main Idea**
What is the main idea in the Earth's Core section?

_____

_____

_____

_____

Magnetic pole   Geographic North Pole

Geographic South Pole   Magnetic pole

FIGURE 3
Earth's Magnetic Field
Magnetized compass needles usually align with Earth's magnetic field and point north. This allows hikers and travelers to orient their maps correctly.

✏️ **Explain** Why might a compass not work correctly when it is near a strong magnet?

_____

_____

_____

_____

_____

_____

Earth's Magnetic Poles

Earth's Magnetic Poles You know that Earth has geographic poles. But Earth also has magnetic poles that are located on Earth's surface where the magnetic force is strongest. As you just saw in **Figure 3,** the magnetic poles are not in the same place as the geographic poles. Suppose you could draw a line between you and the geographic North Pole. Then imagine a second line drawn between you and the magnetic pole in the Northern Hemisphere. The angle between these two lines is the angle between geographic north and the north to which a compass needle points. This angle is known as **magnetic declination.**

The magnetic declination of a location changes. Earth's magnetic poles do not stay in one place as the geographic poles do.

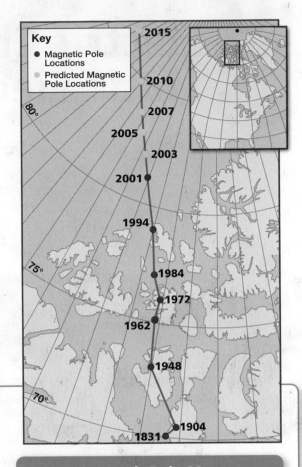

Key
- Magnetic Pole Locations
- Predicted Magnetic Pole Locations

do the math!

The last expedition to directly observe the pole's location was in May 2001. The map shows estimated positions after 2001.

1 Calculate What is the total distance the pole traveled from 1948 to 2001?

_____

_____

_____

2 Interpret Data What was the average speed of the pole's movement from 1948 to 2001?

_____

_____

Magnetic North Pole Movement

Year of Reading	Distance Moved Since Previous Reading (km)
1948	420
1962	150
1972	120
1984	120
1994	180
2001	287

Do the Quick Lab
Earth's Magnetic Field.

🔑 Assess Your Understanding

got it?..

○ I get it! Now I know that Earth has a magnetic field _____

_____

○ I need extra help with _____

Go to MY SCIENCE ⓢ COACH *online for help with this subject.*

Electric Charge and Static Electricity

UNLOCK THE BIG ?

🔑 **How Do Charges Interact?**

🔑 **How Does Charge Build Up?**

my planeT DiaRY

Force Fields

Misconception: Force fields exist only in science fiction stories.

Fact: Force fields are an important part of your everyday life.

You're actually sitting in a force field right now! A force field exists around any object that repels or attracts other objects. A giant gravitational force field surrounds Earth. This field keeps you from floating off into space. Earth's magnetic field makes compass needles point north. You make your own force field every time you get shocked when you reach for a doorknob!

MISCONCEPTIONS

Answer the questions below.

1. A gravitational field keeps you on Earth. What other uses might force fields have?

_____

_____

2. Describe how a different science fiction invention could be rooted in real science.

_____

_____

▶ **PLANET DIARY** Go to **Planet Diary** to learn more about force fields.

Lab zone® Do the Inquiry Warm-Up *Can You Move a Can Without Touching It?*

Vocabulary
- electric force • electric field • static electricity
- conservation of charge • friction • conduction
- induction • polarization • static discharge

Skills
- ⟳ Reading: Relate Cause and Effect
- △ Inquiry: Draw Conclusions

How Do Charges Interact?

You're already late for school and one of your socks is missing! You finally find it sticking to the back of your blanket. How did that happen? The explanation has to do with electric charges.

Types of Charge Atoms contain charged particles called electrons and protons. If two electrons come close together, they push each other apart. In other words, they repel each other. Two protons behave the same way. If a proton and an electron come close together, they attract one another. Protons attract electrons because the two have opposite electric charges. The charge on a proton is positive (+). The charge on an electron is negative (−).

The two types of electric charges interact in specific ways, as you see in **Figure 1**. 🔑 **Charges that are the same repel each other. Charges that are different attract each other.** The interaction between electric charges is called electricity. The force between charged objects is called **electric force.**

FIGURE 1 ···

Repel or Attract?

✎ △Draw Conclusions On each sphere, write if it has a positive (+) or a negative (−) charge. Compare your answers with a group. Can you tell for sure which spheres are positively charged and which are negatively charged? What conclusions can you draw?

_____

_____

_____

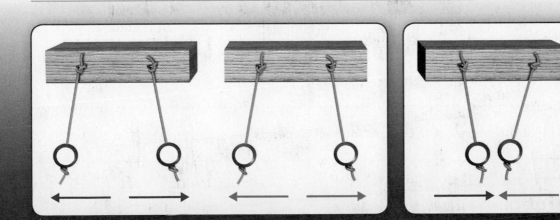

Electric Fields You may have heard of a gravitational field, which is the space around an object (such as a planet) where the object's gravitational force is exerted. Similarly, an electric field extends around a charged object. An **electric field** is a region around a charged object where the object's electric force is exerted on other charged objects. Electric fields and forces get weaker the farther away they are from the charge.

An electric field is invisible. You can use field lines to represent it, as shown in **Figure 2**. A field line shows the force that would be exerted on a positive charge at any point along that line. Positive charges are repelled by positive charges and attracted to negative charges, so field lines point away from positive charges and toward negative charges. Single charges have straight field lines, since a positive charge will be repelled away from or attracted to it in a straight line. When multiple charges are present, each charge exerts a force. These forces combine to make more complicated field lines.

FIGURE 2 ·····························

Electric Fields

Field lines show the direction of the force acting on a positive charge.

✎ **Answer the questions.**

1. **Identify** Identify which charge is positive and which charge is negative.

2. **Interpret Diagrams** The boxes on the electric field are the same size. How many field lines are inside the white box?

_____

3. **Interpret Diagrams** The blue box is closer to the charges. How many field lines are in this box?

_____

4. **Draw Conclusions** What is the relationship between the number of field lines in an area and the strength of the electric force?

_____

_____

_____

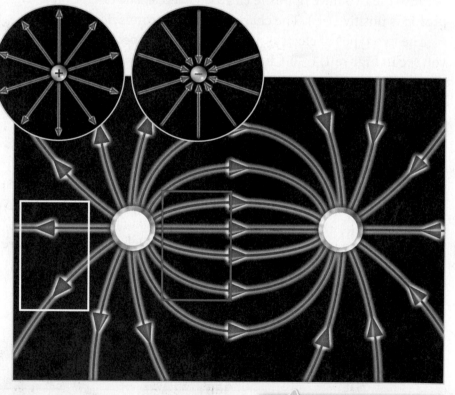

 Do the Quick Lab *Drawing Conclusions.*

🔑 **Assess Your Understanding**

got it? ···

○ **I get it!** Now I know that the way electric charges interact depends on _____

_____

○ **I need extra help with**_____

⟩ Go to MY SCIENCE ⓢ COACH *online for help with this subject.*

How Does Charge Build Up?

Most objects have no overall charge. An atom usually has as many electrons as it has protons, so each positive charge is balanced by a negative charge. This leaves the atom uncharged, or neutral.

An uncharged object can become charged by gaining or losing electrons. If an object loses electrons, it is left with more protons than electrons. It has an overall positive charge. If an object gains electrons, it will have an overall negative charge. The buildup of charges on an object is called **static electricity.** In static electricity, charges build up on an object, but they do not flow continuously.

FIGURE 3 ....

Charge Buildup

Rubbing two objects together can produce static electricity.

✎ **Interpret Photos** Circle the phrases that best complete the statements. Follow the directions to draw how the charges are arranged in each photo.

❶ The balloon is (positively/ negatively/not) charged. The balloon (attracts/repels/neither attracts nor repels) the girl's hair.

❷ Rubbing the balloon allows more electrons to move onto the balloon. The balloon is now (positively/negatively) charged. **Draw what the charges on the balloon look like now.**

❸ The (positive/negative) charges in the girl's hair are now attracted to the negative charges on the balloon. **Draw how the charges on the balloon are arranged now.**

Charging Objects

Charging Objects Charges are neither created nor destroyed. This is a rule known as the law of **conservation of charge.** An object can't become charged by destroying or creating its own electrons. If one object loses electrons, another object must pick them up. 🔑 **There are four methods by which charges can redistribute themselves to build up static electricity: by friction, by conduction, by induction, and by polarization.**

Charging by Friction

When two uncharged objects are rubbed together, some electrons from one object can move onto the other object. The object that gains electrons becomes negatively charged. The object that loses electrons becomes positively charged. Charging by **friction** is the transfer of electrons from one uncharged object to another by rubbing the objects together.

Charging by Conduction

When a charged object touches another object, electrons can be transferred. Charging by **conduction** is the transfer of electrons from one object to another by direct contact. Electrons transfer from the object that has more negative charge to the object that has more positive charge. A positively charged object, like the metal ball, gains electrons when an uncharged person touches it. The girl starts out neutral, but electrons move from her hair, through her arm, to the ball. This leaves her hair positively charged, and the strands repel each other.

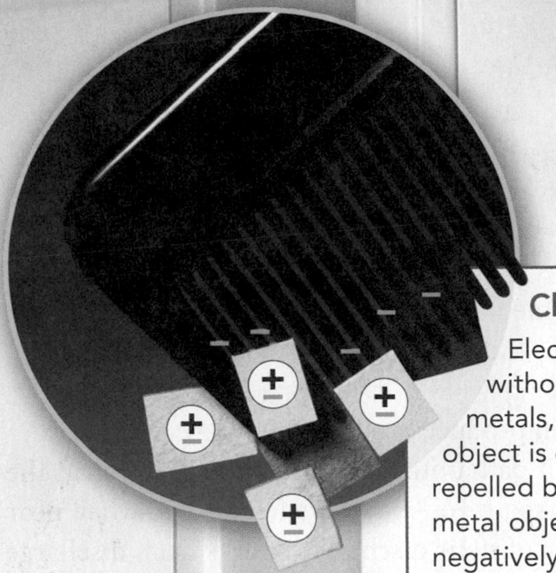

Charging by Induction and by Polarization

Electrons can react to the electric field of a charged object without touching the object itself. In some materials, like metals, electrons can easily leave their atoms. When a metal object is close to a negatively charged object, electrons are repelled by the field and move away from it. The close end of the metal object becomes positively charged, and the far end becomes negatively charged. The opposite happens if the other object is positively charged. This process is called **induction.**

In other materials, like the bits of paper in this photo, electrons move only within their own atoms. The electrons react to electric fields, resulting in individual atoms having charged ends that are attracted to charged objects. This is called **polarization.** Charges don't transfer between objects in polarization or induction, so neither method changes the *overall* charge of objects. *Parts* of objects end up charged in opposite ways.

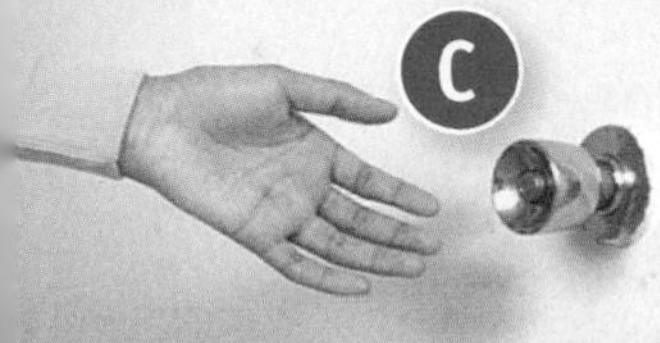

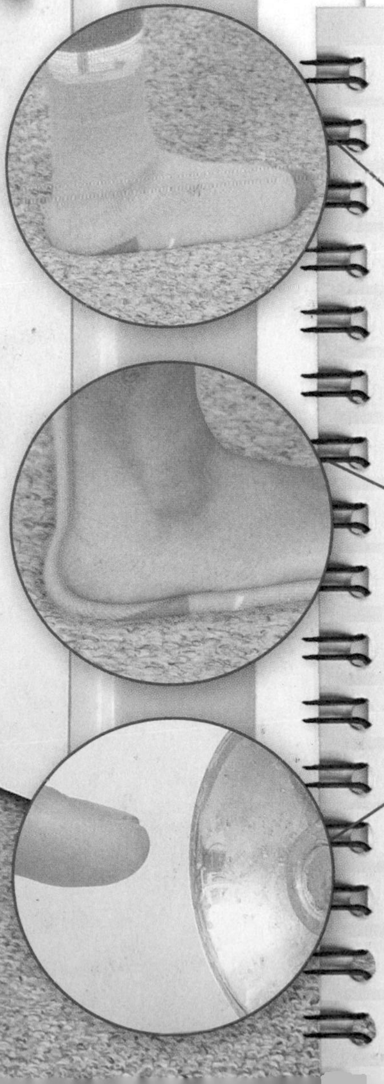

FIGURE 4 ···

> ART IN MOTION **Moving Electrons**

✎ **Explain** In each image at the left, draw how the charges are arranged in each step. Use arrows to show movement.

Ⓐ When the girl's sock rubs the carpet, electrons move from the carpet onto her sock. This causes an overall negative charge on the sock. **What method of charge redistribution is this? Explain.**

_____

_____

Ⓑ Charges move from the girl's foot to the rest of her body. **What method of charge redistribution is this? Explain.**

_____

_____

Ⓒ The electrons in the girl's fingertip produce an electric field that repels the electrons on the doorknob. The electrons on the doorknob move away from the finger. One end of the doorknob becomes positively charged. **What method of charge redistribution is this? Explain.**

_____

_____

did you know?

Machines called Van de Graaff generators can create lightning bolts indoors!

Static Discharge

If your hair becomes charged and sticks up after you remove a sweater, it doesn't stay that way forever. Positively charged objects gradually gain electrons from the air. Negatively charged objects gradually lose electrons to the air. The objects eventually become neutral again. The loss of static electricity as electric charges transfer from one object to another is called **static discharge.**

Static discharge often produces a spark. Moving electrons can heat the air around their path until it glows. The glowing air is the spark you see. The tiny spark you may have felt or seen when near a doorknob is an example of static discharge. Sparks from discharge happen more frequently during winter. This is because objects hold on to charge better in dry air. In humid weather, water collects on the surfaces of objects. The water picks up charge from the objects, so they don't stay charged as long as they would in dry weather.

apply it!

Draw Conclusions Anyone who works with computers has to be aware of static discharge. Even small discharges can damage electrical equipment.

1 What activities should you avoid to prevent static discharge while working on a computer?

_____

_____

_____

_____

2 What should the conditions of the room you are in be like?

_____

_____

_____

Lightning bolts are an example of static discharge. During thunderstorms, air swirls violently. Water droplets within the clouds become charged. Electrons move from areas of negative charge to areas of positive charge, producing an intense spark. That spark is lightning.

Some lightning reaches Earth. Negative charges at the bottoms of storm clouds create an electric field. This causes Earth's surface to become positively charged through induction. Electrons jump between the clouds and Earth's surface, producing a giant spark of lightning as they travel through the air.

✏️

◑ Relate Cause and Effect
Pick one example of cause and effect in this section. Underline the cause, and then circle the effect that results.

FIGURE 5 ·······························

Static Discharge

Lightning is just a much bigger version of the sparks you feel when you shock yourself on a doorknob.

✎ **Relate Text and Visuals** In the white circles, draw how positive and negative charges are arranged during a lightning strike.

Lab zone® Do the Quick Lab *Sparks Are Flying.*

🔑 Assess Your Understanding

1a. Describe What happens to an object's atoms when the object becomes positively charged?

_____

_____

b. CHALLENGE Explain how you could use a piece of silk and a glass rod to attract a stream of tap water.

_____

_____

_____

_____

got it? ··································

⭕ **I get it!** Now I know that the four methods of building up static electricity are _____

_____

_____

⭕ **I need extra help with** _____

Go to MY SCIENCE ⑤ COACH *online for help with this subject.*

477

Electric Current

UNLOCK THE BIG

🔑 **How Is Electric Current Made?**

🔑 **How Do Conductors Differ From Insulators?**

🔑 **What Affects Current Flow?**

my planeT DiaRY

CAREERS

Be a Superconductor—of Science!

John Vander Sande wants your city to run more efficiently. A company he cofounded is working to replace old power lines with materials that let electric current flow more efficiently. These materials are called superconductors. Superconductors are often found in lab equipment, as shown at the left, but companies like Vander Sande's are finding other uses for them. Vander Sande didn't start his career working with power lines. He began his work in materials science as a professor at the Massachusetts Institute of Technology (MIT). He got into superconducting by chance after hearing about discoveries at a lecture by one of his colleagues. He encourages everyone to stay open to opportunities in science, because they can pop up anywhere at any time.

Answer the question below.

Describe an instance in your life when hearing something by chance led to a new opportunity.

_____

_____

_____

_____

_____

▶ **PLANET DIARY** Go to **Planet Diary** to learn more about superconductors.

Lab zone® Do the Inquiry Warm-Up *How Can Current Be Measured?*

How Is Electric Current Made?

Dozens of sushi dishes ride along a conveyor belt in **Figure 1.** The conveyer belt carries full dishes past customers and carries empty plates back to the kitchen. You might be wondering what a conveyer belt of rice, vegetables, and fish could possibly have to do with electricity. Like the sushi plates, electric charges can be made to move in a confined path.

Vocabulary
- electric current
- electric circuit
- conductor
- insulator
- voltage
- resistance

Skills
- Reading: Ask Questions
- Inquiry: Classify

Flow of Electric Charges Lightning releases a large amount of electrical energy. However, the electric charge from lightning doesn't last long enough to power your radio or your TV. These devices need electric charges that flow continuously. They require electric current.

Recall that static electric charges do not flow continuously. **When electric charges are made to flow through a material, they produce an electric current.** **Electric current** is the continuous flow of electric charges through a material. The amount of charge that passes through a wire in a given period of time is the rate of electric current. The unit for the rate of current is the ampere, named for André Marie Ampère, an early investigator of electricity. The name of the unit is often shortened to amp or A. The number of amps describes the amount of charge flowing past a given point each second.

FIGURE 1 ·····························

Electric Current
The conveyor belt represents a current. If it represented a greater current, more plates would pass by you in the same amount of time. One way for this to occur would be for the belt to go faster.

✏️ **Make Models** Suppose the belt couldn't go faster. Draw a different way a greater current could be represented.

FIGURE 2 ······························

Circuits

Just like charges in a wire, people can move around in circuits. One possible jogging circuit is outlined in this photo.

✎ **Interpret Photos** Trace another possible circuit. What could break this circuit?

_____

_____

_____

_____

Current in a Circuit

The electric currents that power your computer and music player need very specific paths to work. In order to maintain an electric current, charges must be able to flow continuously in a loop. A complete, unbroken path that charges can flow through is called an **electric circuit.**

Someone jogging along the roads in **Figure 2** is moving like a charge in an electric circuit. If the road forms a complete loop, the jogger can move in a continuous path. However, the jogger cannot continue if any section of the road is closed. Similarly, if an electric circuit is complete, charges can flow continuously. If an electric circuit is broken, charges will not flow.

Electric circuits are all around you. All electrical devices, from toasters to televisions, contain electric circuits.

Lab® zone
Do the Quick Lab
Producing Electric Current.

🔑 Assess Your Understanding

1a. Review What is the unit of current?

_____

_____

b. Predict What could break the circuit between your home and an electric power plant?

_____

got_{it}?

○ **I get it!** Now I know that electric current is

made of _____

_____

○ I need extra help with _____

Go to **MY SCIENCE** 🅢 **COACH** *online for help with this subject.*

How Do Conductors Differ From Insulators?

You can safely touch the rubber coating on an appliance cord. If you touched the wire inside, you'd get shocked. That's because charges can flow more easily through some materials than others.

A **conductor** is a material through which charge can flow easily. Electrons can move freely, allowing conductors to be charged by induction. Metals, such as copper, are good conductors. This is why current-carrying wires are usually made out of metal.

Wires are surrounded by insulators. **Insulators** are materials, such as rubber, that do not allow charges to flow. However, electrons can move around within their own atoms, allowing for polarization. They can also be stripped off when charging by friction.

The difference between conductors and insulators comes from how strongly electrons are attached to atoms. 🔑 **The atoms in conductors have loosely bound electrons that can move freely. Electrons in insulators cannot move freely among atoms.**

⊙ **Ask Questions** Current, conductors, and insulators all show up in your daily life. Write down a question about one of these topics that you would like answered.

_____

_____

_____

apply it!

All objects are made up of conductors or insulators, not just the ones you usually see in electronic devices.

❶ **Identify** The gloves that electricians wear when working on power lines should be made out of (insulating/conducting) materials.

❷ **Classify** Circle the conductors in these photos. Be careful—only parts of some items are conductors!

Lab zone® Do the Quick Lab *Conductors and Insulators.*

🔑 **Assess Your Understanding**

got it? ....

○ **I get it!** Now I know that conductors and insulators are different because of _____

_____

○ **I need extra help with** _____

Go to **MY SCIENCE** ⑤ **COACH** *online for help with this subject.*

What Affects Current Flow?

Suppose you are on a water slide at an amusement park. You climb the steps, sit down, and whoosh! The water current carries you down the slide. Electric charges flow in much the same way water moves down the slide. 🔑 **Current flow is affected by the energy of the charges and the properties of the objects that the charges flow through.**

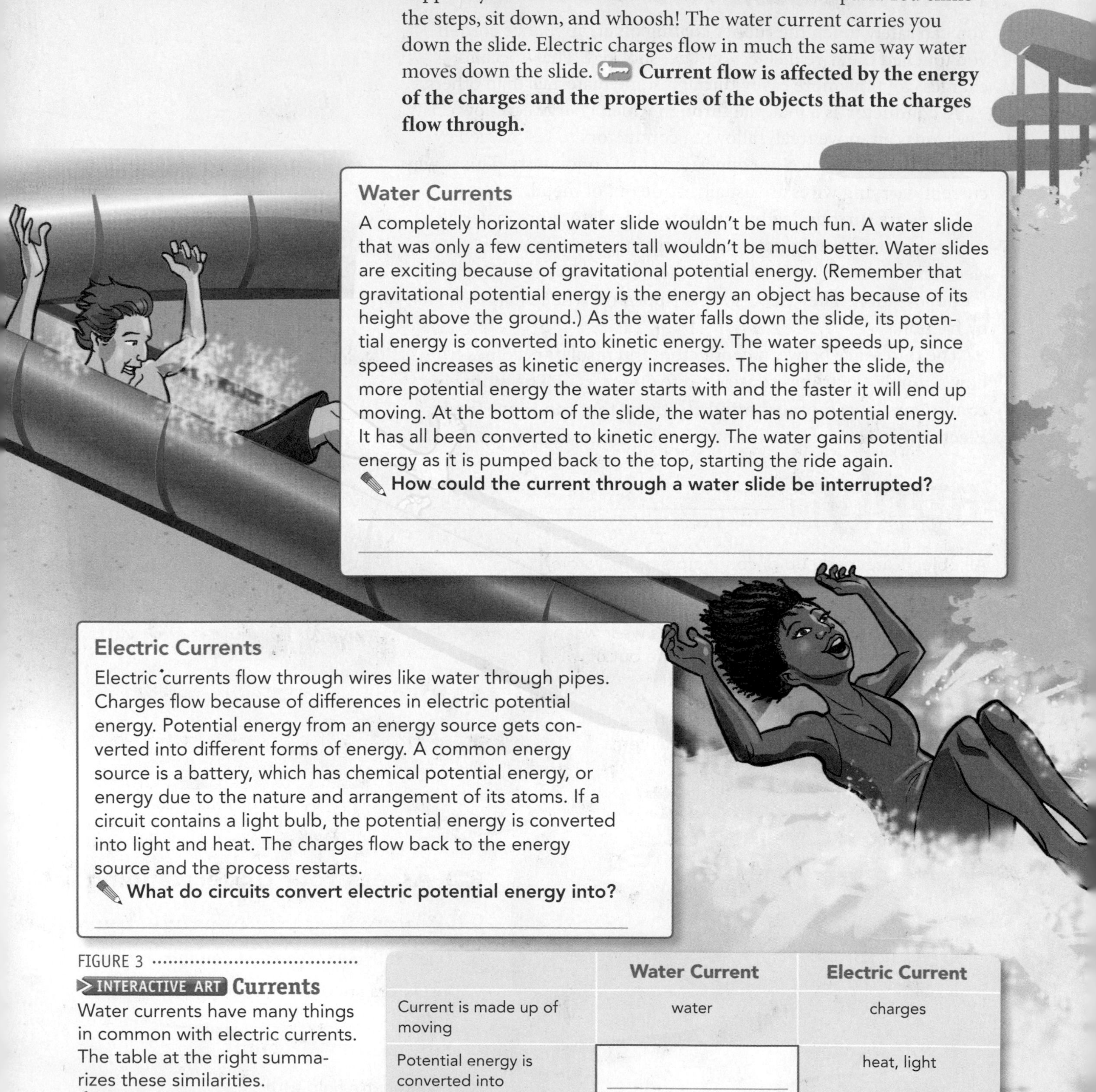

Water Currents

A completely horizontal water slide wouldn't be much fun. A water slide that was only a few centimeters tall wouldn't be much better. Water slides are exciting because of gravitational potential energy. (Remember that gravitational potential energy is the energy an object has because of its height above the ground.) As the water falls down the slide, its potential energy is converted into kinetic energy. The water speeds up, since speed increases as kinetic energy increases. The higher the slide, the more potential energy the water starts with and the faster it will end up moving. At the bottom of the slide, the water has no potential energy. It has all been converted to kinetic energy. The water gains potential energy as it is pumped back to the top, starting the ride again.

✏️ **How could the current through a water slide be interrupted?**

_____

_____

Electric Currents

Electric currents flow through wires like water through pipes. Charges flow because of differences in electric potential energy. Potential energy from an energy source gets converted into different forms of energy. A common energy source is a battery, which has chemical potential energy, or energy due to the nature and arrangement of its atoms. If a circuit contains a light bulb, the potential energy is converted into light and heat. The charges flow back to the energy source and the process restarts.

✏️ **What do circuits convert electric potential energy into?**

_____

FIGURE 3 ·························

▶ INTERACTIVE ART **Currents**

Water currents have many things in common with electric currents. The table at the right summarizes these similarities.

✏️ **Make Models** Complete the table.

	Water Current	Electric Current
Current is made up of moving	water	charges
Potential energy is converted into	_____	heat, light
The energy source for the circuit is a	_____	battery

Voltage

The *V* on a battery stands for volts, which is the unit of voltage. **Voltage** is the difference in electric potential energy *per charge* between two points in a circuit. (Electric potential energy per charge is also called electric potential.) This energy difference causes charges to flow. Because the voltage of a battery is related to energy per charge, it doesn't tell you how much total energy the battery supplies. A car battery and eight watch batteries both supply 12 volts, but eight watch batteries can't run a car. Each charge has the same amount of energy, but the car battery can provide that energy to many more charges. This results in a higher *total* energy. You can compare voltage to gravitational potential energy *per kilogram*. **Figure 4** shows the difference between total energy and energy per kilogram.

1
Mass: 50 kg
Height: 20 m
Energy/kg: 200 J/kg
Total Energy:
_____

FIGURE 4 ••••••••••••••••••••••••••

Voltage

The total electric potential energy a charge has depends on voltage, just as the gravitational potential energy a person has depends on his or her height above the ground. Total gravitational potential energy is the energy per kilogram times the number of kilograms, and total electric potential energy is the energy per charge times the number of charges.

✎ **Interpret Diagrams** Answer the questions.

1. In the boxes, calculate the amount of gravitational potential energy each person has.

2. Which two people represent batteries with the same voltage?

_____

3. Draw boxes around the two people who represent batteries that supply the same total amount of energy.

4. Gravitational potential energy per kilogram decreases as you go down the slide. This is like decreasing (voltage/total potential energy).

2
Mass: 100 kg
Height: 10 m
Energy/kg: 100 J/kg
Total Energy:
_____

3
Mass: 50 kg
Height: 10 m
Energy/kg: 100 J/kg
Total Energy:
_____

483

FIGURE 5 ·····························

Dimensions and Resistance

The length and diameter of a straw determine how difficult it is to drink through it. Similarly, the length and diameter of a wire determine how difficult it is for charge to flow through it.

✎ **Interpret Photos** Which of the straws in the photo would be the hardest to drink with? Explain. Is this straw like a wire with high or low resistance?

_____

_____

_____

_____

_____

_____

Resistance The amount of current in a circuit depends on more than voltage. Current also depends on the resistance of the circuit. **Resistance** is the measure of how difficult it is for charges to flow through an object. The greater the resistance, the less current there is for a given voltage. The unit of measure of resistance is the ohm (Ω).

The four factors that determine the resistance of an object are diameter, length, material, and temperature. Objects with different characteristics have different resistances. If more than one path is available, more current will flow through the path that has the lower resistance.

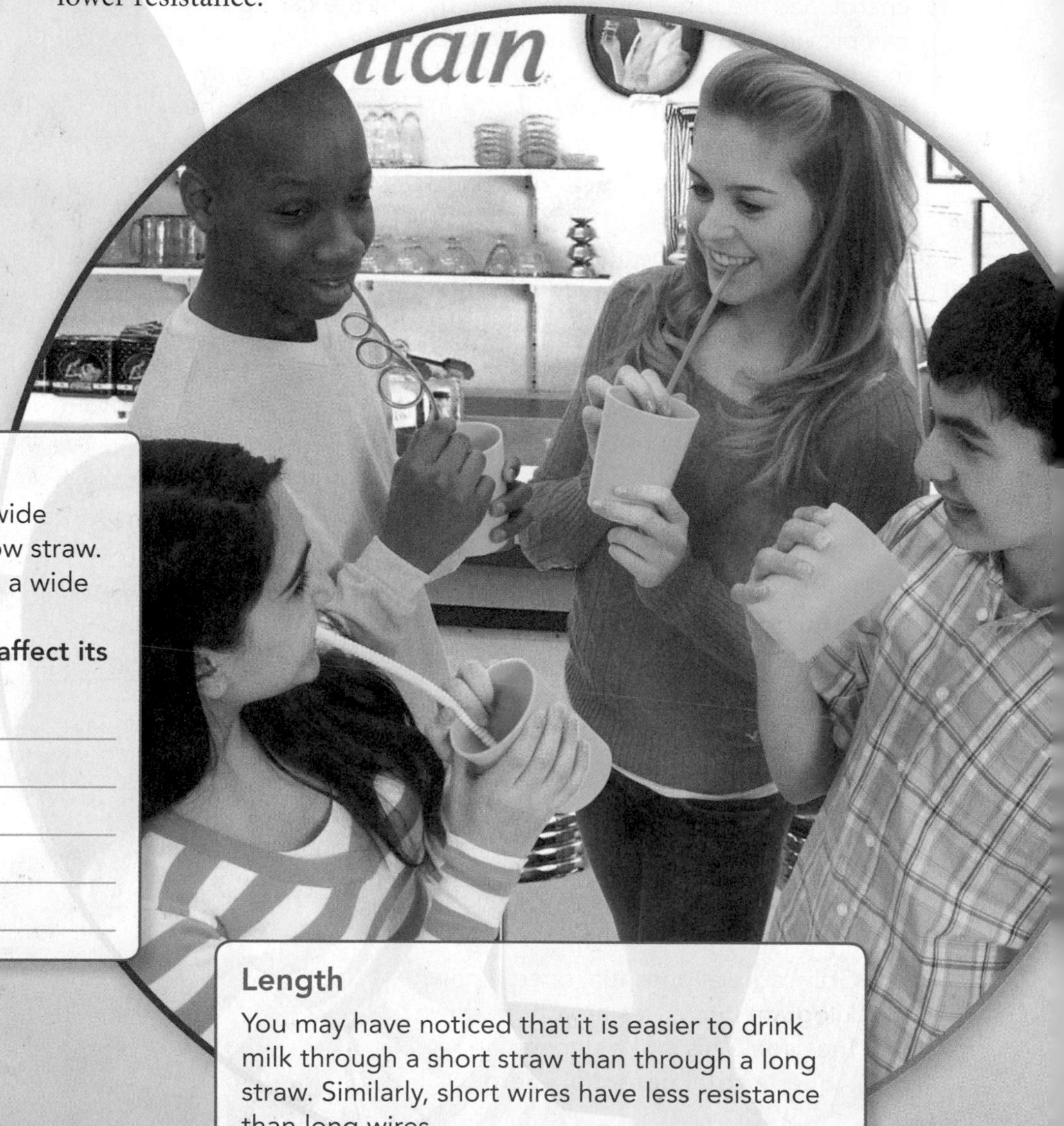

Diameter

Milk flows more easily through a wide straw than it does through a narrow straw. Current flows more easily through a wide wire than through a narrow wire.

✎ How does a wire's diameter affect its electrical resistance? Explain.

_____

_____

_____

_____

_____

Length

You may have noticed that it is easier to drink milk through a short straw than through a long straw. Similarly, short wires have less resistance than long wires.

✎ How does an object's length affect its electrical resistance?

_____

_____

_____

_____

FIGURE 6 ....
Materials and Resistance

When power lines fall down during storms, the workers repairing them must be careful to avoid electric shocks.

✏ **Solve Problems** What should workers wear while doing the job? What should they avoid wearing?

_____

_____

_____

Material

Some materials have electrons that are tightly held to their atoms. They have a high resistance because it is difficult for charges to move. Other materials have electrons that are loosely held to their atoms. They have a low resistance because charges can move through them easily.

✏ **Do conductors or insulators have a lower resistance? Explain.**

_____

_____

_____

_____

.... ✐ ....
Word Origins *Resistance* comes from the word *resist*, which comes from the Latin word *resistere*. What do you think *resistere* means?

○ to be opposed to

○ to run

○ to speed up

Temperature

The electrical resistance of most materials increases as temperature increases. As the temperature of most materials decreases, resistance decreases as well.

✏ **Why would it be useful to keep power lines cool in the summer?**

_____

_____

_____

_____

Lab zone Do the Quick Lab *Modeling Potential Difference.*

⚷ Assess Your Understanding

2a. List List the four factors that determine the resistance of an object.

_____

_____

b. [CHALLENGE] Battery A supplies 500 charges. Each charge has 2 J of energy. Battery B supplies 50 charges, each of which has 4 J of energy. Which battery supplies more total energy? Which has a higher voltage?

_____

got it? ....

○ **I get it!** Now I know that current is affected

by _____

○ **I need extra help with** _____

Go to **my science 🔊 coach** *online for help with this subject.*

485

Electromagnetic Force

🔑 **How Are Electric Currents and Magnetic Fields Related?**

🔑 **What Is a Magnetic Field Produced by a Current Like?**

🔑 **What Are the Characteristics of Solenoids and Electromagnets?**

my planeT DiaRY

FUN FACTS

More Than Just Plastic

How do plastic cards with stripes, such as your library card, work? The black stripe on the back of the card is made up of tiny magnetic particles. Information can be recorded on the stripe. When a card is swiped through a card-reading machine, the cardholder's information is relayed from the card to a computer or sent to a place for verification.

If the card is placed near magnetic material, the arrangement of the magnetic particles on the stripe can get rearranged. Once this happens, the card becomes useless because it no longer holds the cardholder's information. If you are ever given a credit card to use, make sure you keep it away from magnets or else you may leave the store empty-handed!

Communicate Discuss the question with a partner. Then write your answer below.

List types of cards that have a magnetic stripe.

_____

_____

_____

_____

_____

▷ **PLANET DIARY** Go to **Planet Diary** to learn more about electromagnetic force.

Lab ® Do the Inquiry Warm-Up
zone *Electromagnetism.*

Vocabulary
- electromagnetism
- electromagnet
- solenoid

Skills
- Reading: Relate Cause and Effect
- Inquiry: Predict

How Are Electric Currents and Magnetic Fields Related?

You know that a magnet has a magnetic field. But did you know that an electric current produces a magnetic field? In 1820, the Danish scientist Hans Christian Oersted (UR STED) accidentally discovered this fact. He was teaching a class at the University of Copenhagen. During his lecture he produced a current in a wire just like the current in a battery-powered flashlight. When he brought a compass near the wire, he observed that the compass needle changed direction.

Oersted's Experiment Oersted could have assumed that something was wrong with his equipment, but instead he decided to investigate further. So he set up several compasses around a wire. With no current in the wire, all of the compass needles pointed north. When he produced a current in the wire, he observed that the compass needles pointed in different directions to form a circle. Oersted concluded that the current had produced a magnetic field around the wire. Oersted's results showed that magnetism and electricity are related.

Cause	Effect
There is no current in the wire.	_____ _____ _____ _____
_____ _____ _____ _____	The compass needles pointed in different directions to form a circle.

✏️ **Relate Cause and Effect**
Use the information about Oersted's experiment to complete the chart.

Electric Current and Magnetism

Oersted's experiment showed that wherever there is electricity, there is magnetism. 🔑 **An electric current produces a magnetic field.** This relationship between electricity and magnetism is called **electromagnetism.** Although you cannot see electromagnetism directly, you can see its effect. That is, a compass needle moves when it is in a magnetic field produced by an electric current, as you can see in **Figure 1**.

FIGURE 1 ·······················

Moving Compass Needles

These photographs show you how an electric current produces a magnetic field.

✏️ **Interpret Photos** In the boxes, explain what is happening to the compass needles when the current in the wire is turned on or off.

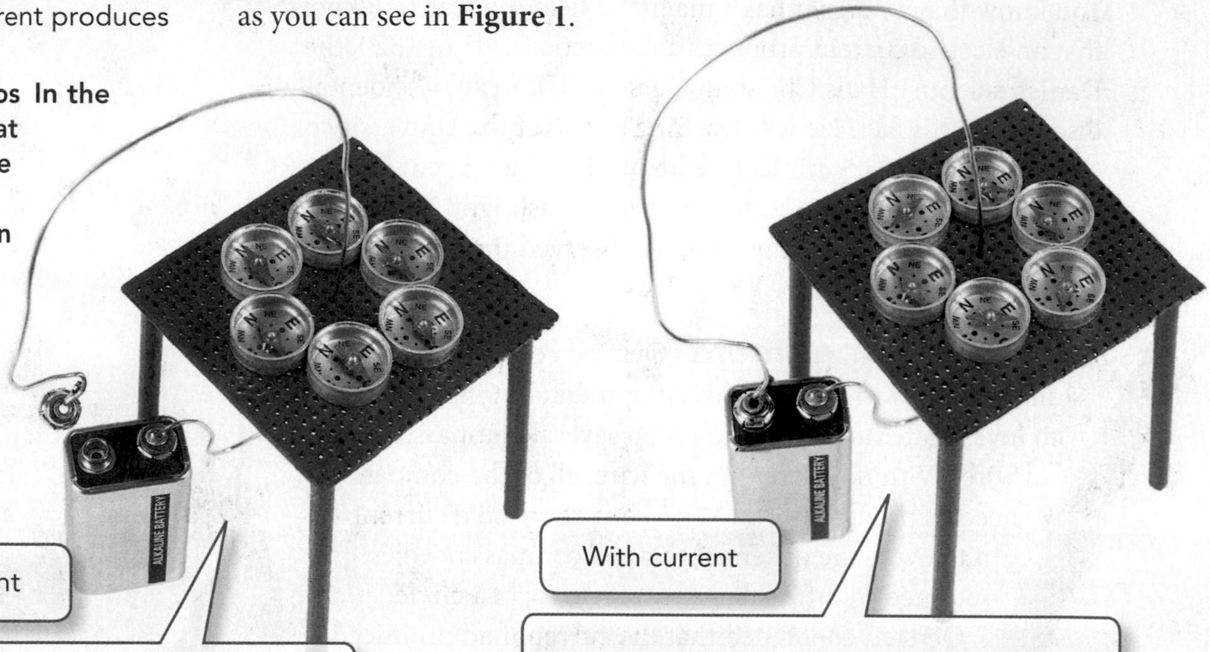

Without current

With current

🔑 **Assess Your Understanding**

1a. Explain What did Oersted conclude?

_____

_____

_____

b. 🔄 **Relate Cause and Effect** How does a current affect a compass?

_____

_____

Lab® zone Do the Quick Lab *Electric Current and Magnetism.*

got it? ···

○ **I get it!** Now I know that an electric current produces a _____

○ I need extra help with _____

Go to MY SCIENCE ⓢ COACH online for help with this subject.

What Is a Magnetic Field Produced by a Current Like?

🔑 **The magnetic field produced by a current has a strength and a direction. The field can be turned on or off, have its direction reversed, or have its strength changed.** To turn a magnetic field produced by a current on or off, you turn the current on or off. To change the direction of the magnetic field, you reverse the direction of the current.

There are two ways to change the strength of a magnetic field. First, you can increase the amount of current in the wire. Second, you can make a loop or coil in the wire. The magnetic field around the wire forms a circle. When you make a loop in a wire, the magnetic field lines bunch close together inside the loop. This strengthens the magnetic field. Every additional loop strengthens the magnetic field even more. **Figure 2** shows three different ways to change the characteristics of a magnetic field.

FIGURE 2 ···

Change Magnetic Field Characteristics

✏️ **Interpret Diagrams** Write the ways used to change the magnetic fields in diagrams A and B. In diagram C, draw a picture to show a third way to change magnetic fields and describe it.

C

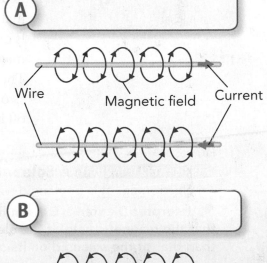

A

Wire Magnetic field Current

B

Bunched magnetic field

Do the Quick Lab *Magnetic Fields From Electric Current.*

🔑 Assess Your Understanding

got it? ···

○ **I get it!** Now I know that the magnetic field produced by a current can be changed by _____

_____

○ **I need extra help with** _____

    Go to **MY SCIENCE ⑤ COACH** online for help with this subject.

What Are the Characteristics of Solenoids and Electromagnets?

You know that you can strengthen the magnetic field around a wire with a current by coiling the wire. 🔑 **Both solenoids and electromagnets use electric current and coiled wires to produce strong magnetic fields.**

Solenoids By running current through a wire which is wound into many loops, you strengthen the magnetic field in the center of the coil as shown in **Figure 3**. A coil of wire with a current is called a **solenoid.** The two ends of a solenoid act like the poles of a magnet. However, the north and south poles change when the direction of the current changes.

Electromagnets If you place a material with strong magnetic properties inside a solenoid, the strength of the magnetic field increases. This is because the material, called a ferromagnetic material, becomes a magnet. A solenoid with a ferromagnetic core is called an **electromagnet.** Both the current in the wire and the magnetized core produce the magnetic field of an electromagnet. Therefore, the overall magnetic field of an electromagnet is much stronger than that of a solenoid. An electromagnet is turned on and off by turning the current on and off.

FIGURE 3 ···

> **REAL-WORLD INQUIRY** **A Solenoid and an Electromagnet**
An electromagnet is a solenoid with a ferromagnetic core.

✏️ **Interpret Diagrams** Explain how the diagram shows you that the magnetic field of the electromagnet is stronger than that of the solenoid on its own.

_____

_____

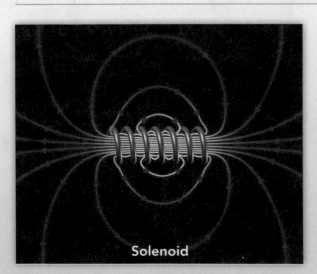

Solenoid

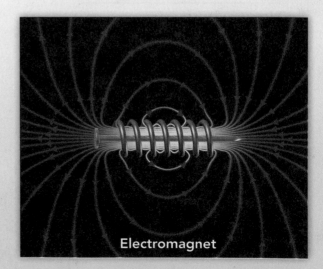

Electromagnet

Regulating Strength You can increase the strength of an electromagnet in four ways. First, you can increase the current in the solenoid. Second, you can add more loops of wire to the solenoid. Third, you can wind the coils of the solenoid closer together. Finally, you can use a material that is more magnetic than iron for the core. Alnico is such a material.

Using Electromagnets Electromagnets are very common. They are used in electric motors, earphones, and many other everyday objects. Electromagnets are even used in junkyards to lift old cars and other heavy steel objects.

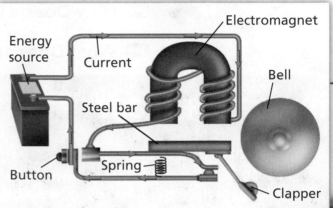

Energy source, Current, Electromagnet, Bell, Steel bar, Button, Spring, Clapper

Vocabulary Use Context to Determine Meaning Underline clues in the text that help you determine the meaning of *alnico*.

apply it!

An electromagnet makes a doorbell ring. A pushed button closes the circuit and turns on the electromagnet. Current flows through the electromagnet, producing a strong magnetic field.

1 Predict What effect will the magnetic field have on the steel bar? The clapper?

_____

_____

_____

2 CHALLENGE What turns off the electromagnet?

_____

Lab zone Do the Quick Lab *Electromagnet*.

Assess Your Understanding

2a. Define What is a solenoid?

_____

b. Apply Concepts What are four ways to make an electromagnet stronger?

_____

_____

_____

got it?

O **I get it!** Now I know that both solenoids and electromagnets _____

_____

_____

O **I need extra help with** _____

Go to MY SCIENCE COACH *online for help with this subject.*

Electricity, Magnetism, and Motion

UNLOCK
THE BIG
?

🔑 **How Is Electrical Energy Transformed Into Mechanical Energy?**

🔑 **How Does a Galvanometer Work?**

🔑 **What Does an Electric Motor Do?**

my planet Diary

DISCOVERY

Miniature Motor

In 1960, scientist and California Institute of Technology (Caltech) professor Richard Feynman publicly offered a prize of $1,000 to the first person to build an electric motor no larger than 0.3969 cubic millimeters. A Caltech graduate named William McLellan accepted the challenge. He used a toothpick, microscope slides, fine hairs from a paintbrush, and wires only 1/80th of a millimeter wide to build the world's smallest motor. McLellan showed his tiny motor to Feynman and collected the $1,000 prize. Scientists today have found many uses for tiny motors in products such as high-definition televisions, cars, and ink-jet printers.

A tiny motor capable of producing high-resolution, DVD-quality images.

Communicate Work with a partner to answer the question.
What might be some other uses of tiny motors?

_____

_____

_____

_____

_____

▶ **PLANET DIARY** Go to **Planet Diary** to learn more about electric motors.

 Lab zone Do the Inquiry Warm-Up *How Are Electricity, Magnets, and Motion Related?*

How Is Electrical Energy Transformed Into Mechanical Energy?

What do trains, fans, microwave ovens, and clocks have in common? The answer is that these objects, along with many other everyday objects, use electricity. In addition, all these objects move or have moving parts. How does electricity produce motion?

Vocabulary
- galvanometer • electric motor

Skills
- Reading: Sequence
- Inquiry: Graph

Energy and Motion As you know, magnetic force can produce motion. For example, magnets move together or apart when they are close. You also know that an electric current in a wire produces a magnetic field. So, a magnet can move a wire with a current, just as it would move another magnet. The direction of movement depends on the direction of the current. See **Figure 1.**

The ability to move an object over a distance is called energy. The energy associated with electric currents is called electrical energy. The energy an object has due to its movement or position is called mechanical energy.

Energy Transformation Energy can be transformed from one form into another. ⚷ **When a wire with a current is placed in a magnetic field, electrical energy is transformed into mechanical energy.** This transformation happens when the magnetic field produced by the current causes the wire to move.

FIGURE 1 ············
Producing Motion
A wire with a current can be moved by a magnet.

✏ **Complete the tasks.**

1. **Identify** What affects the direction of the wire's movement?

_____

_____

2. **Classify** In each box, write down the type of energy that is being pointed out.

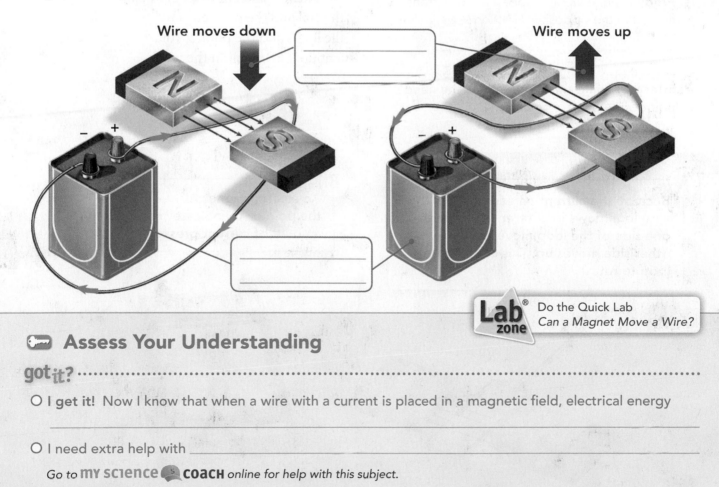

Wire moves down   Wire moves up

Do the Quick Lab
Can a Magnet Move a Wire?

⚷ Assess Your Understanding

got it? ·····································

○ **I get it!** Now I know that when a wire with a current is placed in a magnetic field, electrical energy

○ I need extra help with _____

Go to **my science ⑤ coach** online for help with this subject.

How Does a Galvanometer Work?

You have learned that a straight wire with a current moves when it is placed in a magnetic field. But what happens if you place a loop of wire with a current in a magnetic field? Look at **Figure 2.** The current in one side of the loop flows in the opposite direction than the current in the other side of the loop. The direction of the current determines the direction in which the wire moves. Therefore, the sides of the loop move in opposite directions. Once each side has moved as far up or down as it can go, it will stop moving. As a result, the loop can rotate only a half turn.

Inside a Galvanometer The rotation of a wire loop in a magnetic field is the basis of a galvanometer. A **galvanometer** is a device that measures small currents. 🗝 **An electric current turns the pointer of a galvanometer.** In a galvanometer, an electromagnet is suspended between opposite poles of two permanent magnets. The electromagnet's coil is attached to a pointer, as you can see in **Figure 2.** When a current is in the electromagnet's coil, it produces a magnetic field. This field interacts with the permanent magnet's field, causing the coil and the pointer to rotate. The distance the loops and the pointer rotate depends on the amount of current in the wire.

✎ ⊙ **Sequence** In the second paragraph on this page, underline and number the steps that explain how a galvanometer works.

FIGURE 2

How a Galvanometer Works

✎ Answer the questions about a galvanometer.

1. **Predict** What would happen if the current flowed in the opposite direction?

   _____

   _____

2. **Interpret Diagrams** Where does the needle point when there is no current?

   _____

A Because the current on each side of the wire loop flows in different directions, one side of the loop moves down as the other side moves up. This causes the loop to rotate.

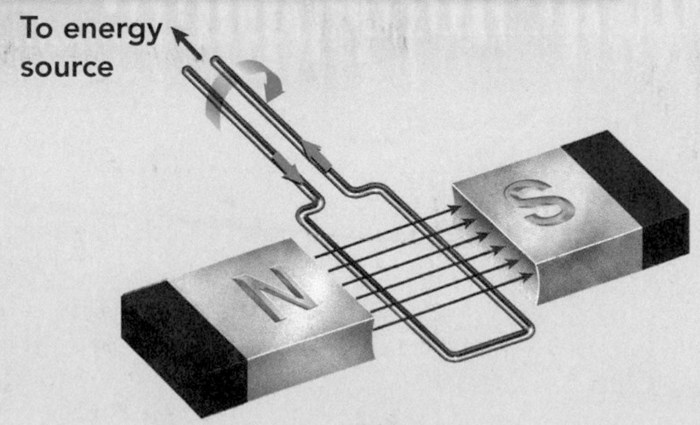

To energy source

B An electromagnet turns the pointer to indicate the amount of current present.

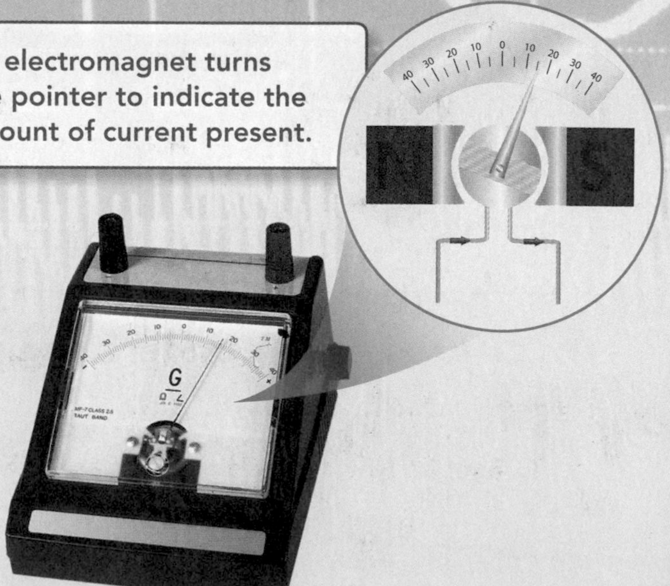

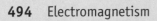

Uses of Galvanometers

Uses of Galvanometers A galvanometer has a scale that is marked to show how much the pointer turns for a known current. You can use the galvanometer to measure an unknown current. Galvanometers are useful in everyday life. For example, electricians use them in their work. Some cars use them as fuel gauges. Galvanometers are also used in lie detectors to measure how much current a person's skin conducts. People who are stressed sweat more. Water conducts electricity. Therefore, their moist skin conducts more electric current.

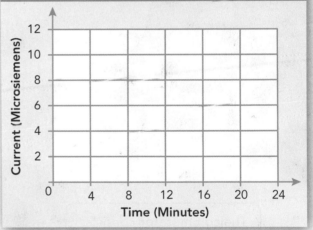

do the math!

This data from a galvanometer show the current conducted by a person's skin. The current is measured in microsiemens, a unit used to measure small amounts of electricity.

Minutes	0	4	8	12	16	20
Microsiemens	5	7	3	1	8	10

1. **Graph** Use the data in the table to plot points on the graph.

2. **CHALLENGE** What would a point at (24, 12) tell you about the person?

_____

_____

_____

_____

Skin Current

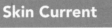

(Graph: Current (Microsiemens) on y-axis from 0 to 12; Time (Minutes) on x-axis from 0 to 24)

 Do the Quick Lab
How Galvanometers Work.

🔑 Assess Your Understanding

1a. Review What does a galvanometer measure?

_____

b. Relate Cause and Effect What causes the pointer to move in a galvanometer?

_____

got it?

○ **I get it!** Now I know that a galvanometer works by using _____

_____

○ **I need extra help with** _____

Go to **MY SCIENCE** ⓢ **COACH** *online for help with this subject.*

What Does an Electric Motor Do?

Have you ever wondered how a remote-controlled car moves? A remote-controlled car's wheels are turned by a rod, or axle, which is connected to an electric motor. An **electric motor** is a device that uses an electric current to turn an axle. 🔑 **An electric motor transforms electrical energy into mechanical energy.**

Look at **Figure 3** to read about the parts of a motor.

If current only flowed in one direction through the armature, the armature could only rotate a half a turn. However, the brushes and commutator enable the current in the armature to change direction. Current always flows from the positive to the negative terminal of a battery. The current in the armature is reversed each time the commutator moves to a different brush. This causes the side of the armature that just moved up to move down. The side that just moved down will move up. The armature rotates continuously. See **Figure 4**.

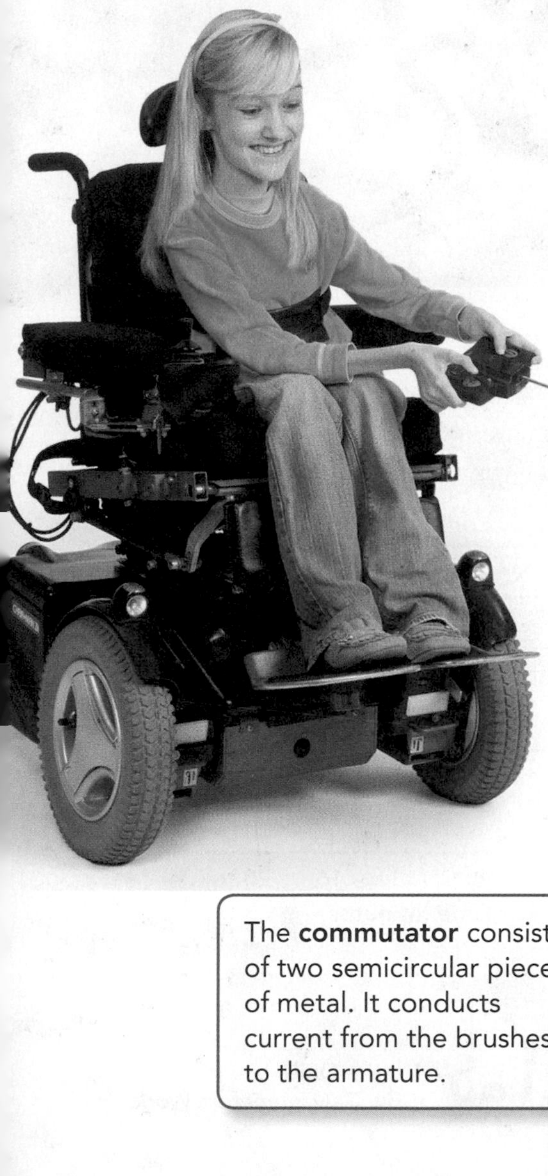

FIGURE 3 ·····················
Parts of a Motor
A simple electric motor contains four parts.

✏️ **Observe** Which part of an electric motor must be attached directly to the energy source?

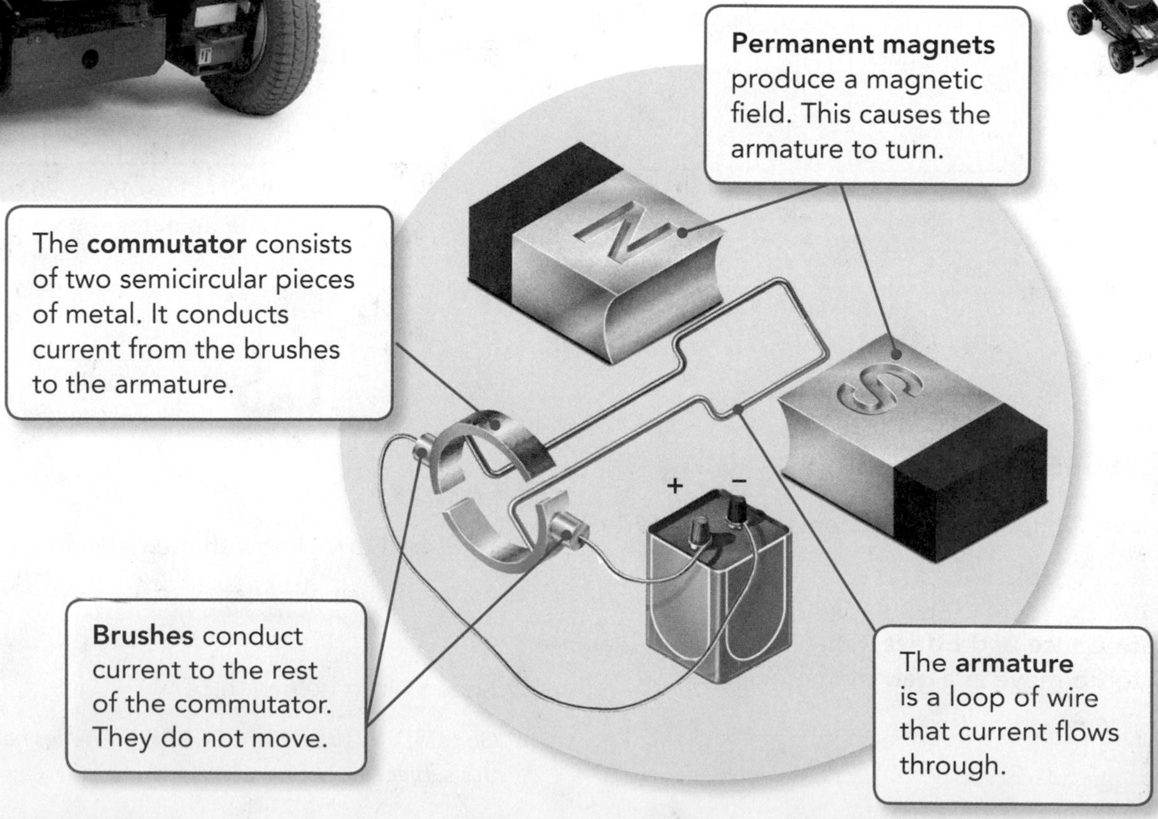

Permanent magnets produce a magnetic field. This causes the armature to turn.

The **commutator** consists of two semicircular pieces of metal. It conducts current from the brushes to the armature.

Brushes conduct current to the rest of the commutator. They do not move.

The **armature** is a loop of wire that current flows through.

FIGURE 4 ··········

> INTERACTIVE ART **How a Motor Works**
The magnetic field around the armature interacts with the field of the permanent magnet, allowing the armature to turn continuously. The direction of the current determines which way the armature turns.

✎ **Infer** Based on the direction the armature is turning in each diagram, draw arrows showing the direction of the current.

The current is in opposite directions on each side of the armature causing one side to move up while the other side moves down.

The commutator rotates with the armature. The direction of current reverses with each half turn so the armature spins continuously.

Lab zone Do the Quick Lab *Parts of an Electric Motor.*

Assess Your Understanding

2a. Define What is an electric motor?

_____

_____

_____

b. Summarize What makes the armature turn continuously?

_____

_____

got it?

○ **I get it!** Now I know that an electric motor transforms _____

_____

_____

○ **I need extra help with** _____

Go to **my science** COACH *online for help with this subject.*

497

Electricity From Magnetism

🔑 **How Can an Electric Current Be Produced in a Conductor?**

🔑 **How Does a Generator Work?**

🔑 **What Does a Transformer Do?**

my planet diary

CAREERS

MRI Technologist

Does working in the medical field interest you? Are you good at operating devices? Do you have a knack for soothing anxious people? If you answered yes, you should think about becoming an Magnetic Resonance Imaging (MRI) technologist.

When a patient is put into an MRI machine, radio waves and magnetic fields are used to create images of the patient's internal structures. The doctors use these detailed pictures to determine what is wrong with the patient. The MRI technologist's responsibilities include operating the MRI machine, comforting nervous patients, and maintaining patient confidentiality. You can become an MRI technologist by completing a bachelor's degree program, an associate's degree program, or a certificate program.

Read the following question. Write your answer below.

What do you think might happen to the MRI image if you wore metal jewelry while in the MRI machine? Why?

_____

_____

_____

▷ PLANET DIARY Go to **Planet Diary** to learn more about electricity from magnetism.

 Lab zone® Do the Inquiry Warm-Up *Electric Current Without a Battery.*

Vocabulary

- electromagnetic induction
- alternating current
- direct current
- generator
- transformer

Skills

- Reading: Ask Questions
- Inquiry: Make Models

How Can an Electric Current Be Produced in a Conductor?

An electric motor uses electrical energy to produce motion. Can motion produce electrical energy? In 1831, scientists discovered that moving a wire in a magnetic field can cause an electric current. This current allows electrical energy to be supplied to homes, schools, and businesses all over the world.

To understand how electrical energy is supplied by your electric company, you need to know how current is produced. A magnet can make, or induce, current in a conductor, such as a wire, as long as there is motion. 🔑 An electric current is induced in a conductor when the conductor moves through a magnetic field. Generating electric current from the motion of a conductor through a magnetic field is called **electromagnetic induction**. Current that is generated in this way is called induced current.

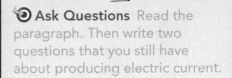

🖋 **Ask Questions** Read the paragraph. Then write two questions that you still have about producing electric current.

_____

_____

_____

_____

_____

_____

_____

_____

_____

_____

_____

_____

Induction of Electric Current

Michael Faraday and Joseph Henry each found that motion in a magnetic field will induce a current. Either the conductor can move through the magnetic field, or the magnet can move. In **Figure 1,** a conductor, the coil of wire, is connected to a galvanometer, forming a closed circuit. If the coil and the magnet do not move, the galvanometer's pointer does not move. However, when either the wire coil or the magnet moves, the galvanometer registers a current. Moving the coil or the magnet induces the current without any voltage source. The direction of an induced current depends on the direction that the coil or magnet moves. When the motion is reversed, the direction of the current also reverses.

FIGURE 1 ··

Motion Produces a Current

Electric current is induced in a wire whenever the magnetic field around it is changing. The field changes when either the magnet or the wire moves.

✎ Complete the tasks.

1. **Describe** Under each diagram, label the direction of the current using *clockwise* or *counterclockwise*.

2. CHALLENGE Make a general statement that relates the motion of the circuit (up or down) to the direction of the current (clockwise or counterclockwise).

_____

_____

_____

_____

_____

_____

_____

_____

Moving Coil

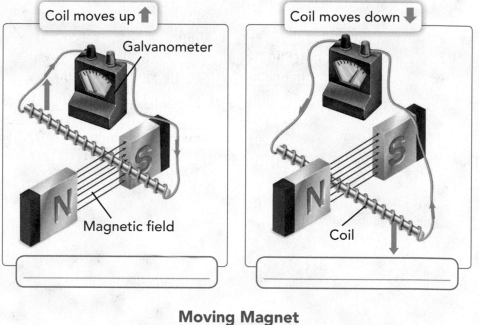

Moving Magnet

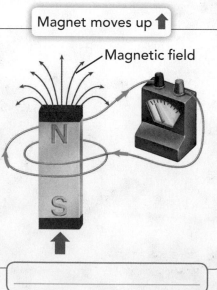
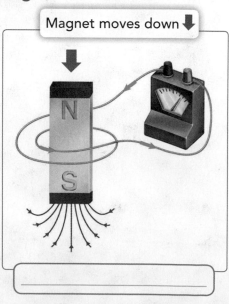

Alternating and Direct Current

A current with charges that flow in one direction is called **direct current,** or DC. A battery produces direct current when a battery is placed in a circuit and charges flow in one direction. They move from one end of the battery, around the circuit, and into the other end of the battery.

If a wire in a magnetic field changes direction repeatedly, the induced current also keeps changing direction. A constantly reversing current is called **alternating current,** or AC. You could induce alternating current by moving either the coil or the magnet up and down repeatedly in the **Figure 1** circuit.

Alternating current has a major advantage over direct current. An AC voltage can be easily raised or lowered. This means that a high voltage can be used to send electrical energy over great distances. Then the voltage can be reduced to a safer level for everyday use. The electric current in the circuits in homes, schools, and other buildings is alternating current. Look at **Figure 2** to learn about how electricity has changed over time.

1882
Direct Current

Thomas Edison opens a generating plant in New York City. It serves an area of about 2.6 square kilometers.

1888
Alternating Current

Nikola Tesla receives patents for a system of distributing alternating current.

Today
Direct and Alternating Current

An electric car runs on direct current from its battery. However, alternating current is needed to charge the battery.

1860

1880

Today

FIGURE 2 ....

The History of Electricity

The work of several scientists brought electricity from the laboratory into everyday use.

✏️ **Draw Conclusions** Why do you think we use alternating current today?

_____

_____

Lab ® Do the Quick Lab *Inducing*
zone *an Electric Current.*

🔑 **Assess Your Understanding**

1a. Describe What is one way to induce an electric current?

_____

_____

b. Classify Give an example of an electronic appliance that runs on AC and one that runs on DC.

_____

_____

got it? ....

○ **I get it!** Now I know that electric current is induced when _____

_____

○ **I need extra help with** _____

Go to **MY SCIENCE** 🔵 **COACH** *online for help with this subject.*

How Does a Generator Work?

An electric **generator** is a device that transforms mechanical energy into electrical energy. 🔑 **A generator uses motion in a magnetic field to produce current.**

In **Figure 3,** you can see how an AC generator works. Turn the crank, and the armature rotates in the magnetic field. As the armature rotates, one side of it moves up as the other moves down. This motion induces a current in the armature. Slip rings turn with the armature. The turning slip rings allow current to flow into the brushes. When the brushes are connected to a circuit, the generator can be used as an energy source.

The electric company uses giant generators to produce most of the electrical energy you use each day. Huge turbines turn the armatures of the generators. Turbines are circular devices with many blades. They spin when water, steam, or hot gas flows through them. This turns the armatures, which generates electric current.

FIGURE 3 ·······················

▷ INTERACTIVE ART **How a Generator Works**

In a generator, an armature rotates in a magnetic field to induce a current.

✎ **Describe** Write what each part of the generator does in the boxes.

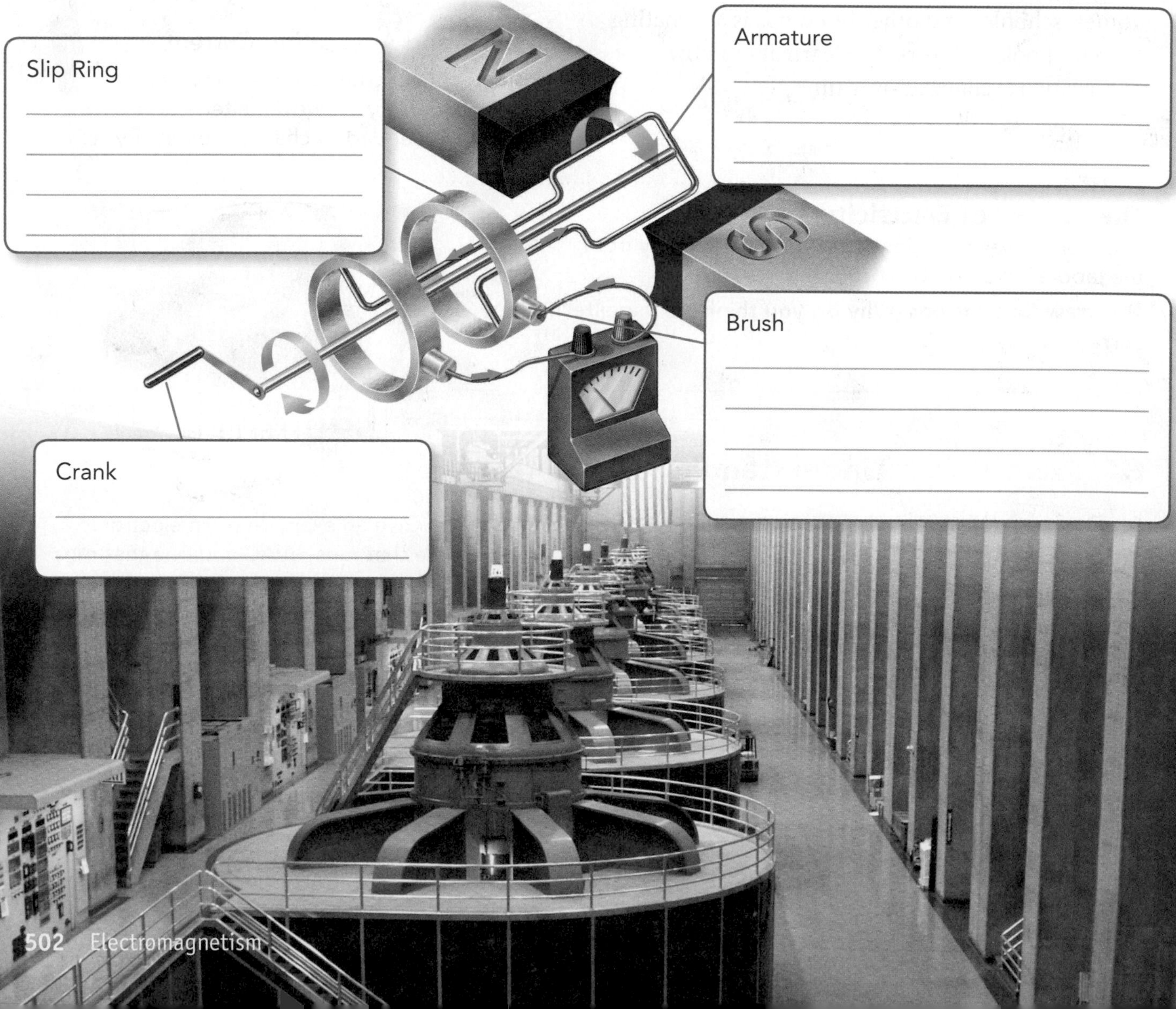

Slip Ring
_____
_____
_____

Crank
_____
_____

Armature
_____
_____
_____

Brush
_____
_____
_____

EXPLORE
THE BIG
?

ZAP!

How are electricity and magnetism related?

FIGURE 4 ·······························
Wind-up cell phone chargers are small generators that let you charge your cell phone anywhere.

✎ **Analyze Models and Systems** Complete the tasks below.

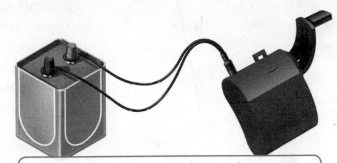

When I turn the crank of the wind-up cell phone charger, or generator, I turn an armature in a(n) _____.
This generates a(n) _____ in the wire, which powers the phone.

If you connect the output wires of the charger to a battery, _____ will flow through the armature, producing a _____. The permanent magnet in the charger will then cause the armature to _____. Draw what you will observe that lets you know this is happening.

 Lab zone® Do the Quick Lab
How Generators Work.

🔑 Assess Your Understanding

2a. Review What is one way to induce an electric current?

_____
_____
_____

b. ANSWER THE BIG ? How are electricity and magnetism related?

_____
_____
_____
_____

got it? ···

○ **I get it!** Now I know an electric current is induced when _____
_____

○ **I need extra help with** _____

Go to MY SCIENCE ⑤ COACH *online for help with this subject.*

What Does a Transformer Do?

The electrical energy generated by electric companies is transmitted over long distances at very high voltages. However, in your home, electrical energy is used at much lower voltages. Transformers change the voltage so you can use electricity.

🔑 **A transformer is a device that increases or decreases voltage.** A **transformer** consists of two separate coils of insulated wire wrapped around an iron core. The primary coil is connected to a circuit with a voltage source and alternating current. The secondary coil is connected to a separate circuit that does not contain a voltage source. The changing current in the primary coil produces a changing magnetic field. This changing magnetic field induces a current in the secondary coil.

The change in voltage from the primary coil to the secondary coil depends on the number of loops in each coil. In step-up transformers, as shown in **Figure 5,** the primary coil has fewer loops than the secondary coil. Step-up transformers increase voltage. In step-down transformers, the primary coil has more loops. Voltage is reduced. The greater the difference between the number of loops in the primary and secondary coils in a transformer, the more the voltage will change. The relationship is a ratio.

$$\frac{\text{voltage}_{\text{primary}}}{\text{voltage}_{\text{secondary}}} = \frac{\text{coils}_{\text{primary}}}{\text{coils}_{\text{secondary}}}$$

$$\frac{120\text{ v}}{6\text{ v}} = 20$$

In this transformer, the voltage in the primary coil is twenty times higher than the voltage in the secondary coil. This means there are twenty times as many loops in the primary coil as there are in the secondary coil. If the primary coil has forty loops, then the secondary coil has two.

FIGURE 5 ·····················

Transformers

A step-up transformer, like the one shown below, is used to help transmit electricity from generating plants. Step-down transformers are used in power cords for some small electronics.

✏️ ⚠️**Make Models Draw wire loops to show both the primary and secondary coils of this step-down transformer.**

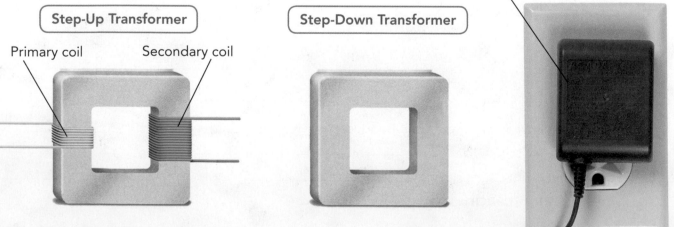

Step-Up Transformer

Primary coil · Secondary coil

Step-Down Transformer

This kind of plug contains a step-down transformer.

do the math!

Transforming Electricity

The illustration shows how transformers change voltage between the generating plant and your home. For each transformer in the illustration below, state whether it is a step-up or step-down transformer.

In the boxes, calculate the ratio of loops in the primary coil to loops in the secondary coil.

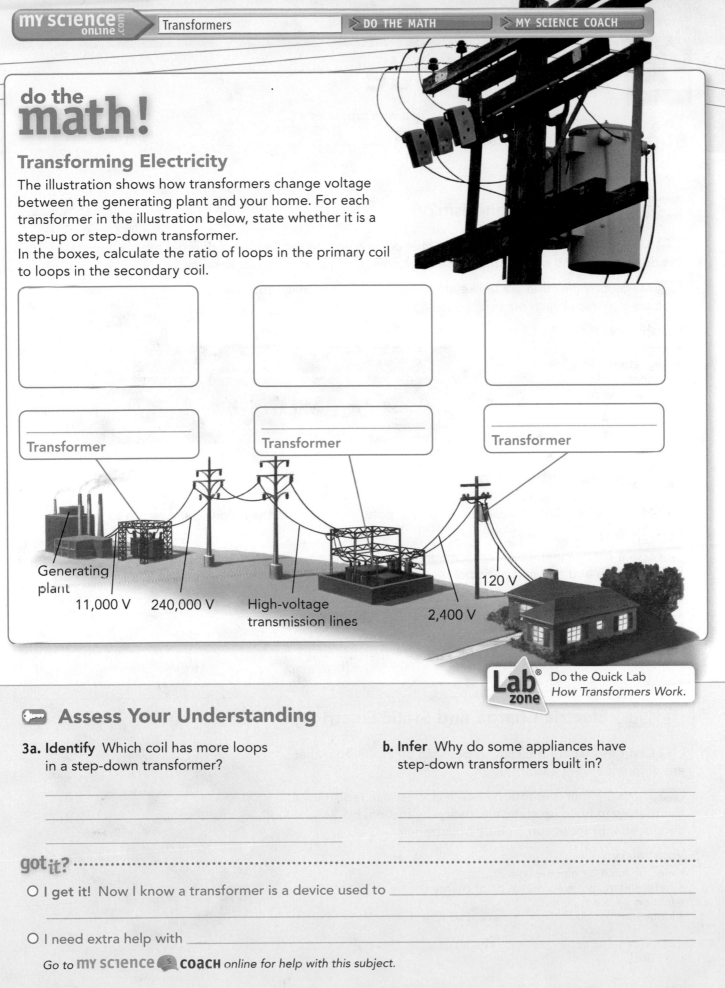

Transformer

Transformer

Transformer

Generating plant

11,000 V   240,000 V   High-voltage transmission lines   2,400 V   120 V

Lab zone   Do the Quick Lab
How Transformers Work.

🔑 Assess Your Understanding

3a. Identify Which coil has more loops in a step-down transformer?

_____

_____

b. Infer Why do some appliances have step-down transformers built in?

_____

_____

_____

got it? ....

○ **I get it!** Now I know a transformer is a device used to _____

_____

○ **I need extra help with** _____

Go to **my science** ⑤ **coach** *online for help with this subject.*

_____ in a wire produces a _____ and movement of a wire through a _____ produces _____.

LESSON 1 What Is Magnetism?

🔑 Magnets attract iron and materials that contain iron. Magnets attract or repel other magnets. In addition, one end of a magnet will always point north when allowed to swing freely.

🔑 Magnetic poles that are unlike attract each other, and magnetic poles that are alike repel each other.

Vocabulary
- magnet
- magnetism
- magnetic pole
- magnetic force

LESSON 2 Magnetic Fields

🔑 Magnetic field lines spread out from one pole, curve around the magnet, and return to the other pole.

🔑 Like a bar magnet, Earth has a magnetic field around it and two magnetic poles.

Vocabulary
- magnetic field
- magnetic field lines
- compass
- magnetic declination

LESSON 3 Electric Charge and Static Electricity

🔑 Charges that are the same repel each other. Charges that are different attract each other.

🔑 There are four methods by which charges can redistribute themselves to build up static electricity: by friction, by conduction, by induction, and by polarization.

Vocabulary
- electric force • electric field
- static electricity • conservation of charge
- friction • conduction
- induction • polarization • static discharge

Study Guide Continued

LESSON 4 Electric Current

🔑 When electric charges are made to flow through a material, they produce an electric current.

🔑 The atoms in conductors have loosely bound electrons that can move freely. Electrons in insulators cannot move freely among atoms.

🔑 Current flow is affected by the energy of the charges and the properties of the objects that the charges flow through.

Vocabulary
- electric current
- electric circuit
- conductor
- insulator
- voltage
- resistance

LESSON 5 Electromagnetic Force

🔑 An electric current produces a magnetic field.

🔑 The magnetic field produced by a current can be turned on or off, reverse direction, or change its strength.

🔑 Both solenoids and electromagnets use electric current and coiled wires to produce strong magnetic fields.

Vocabulary
- electromagnetism
- solenoid
- electromagnet

LESSON 6 Electricity, Magnetism, and Motion

🔑 By placing a wire with a current in a magnetic field, electrical energy can be transformed into mechanical energy.

🔑 An electric current turns the pointer of a galvanometer.

🔑 An electric motor transforms electrical energy into mechanical energy.

Vocabulary
- galvanometer
- electric motor

LESSON 7 Electricity From Magnetism

🔑 An electric current is induced in a conductor when the conductor moves through a magnetic field.

🔑 A generator uses motion in a magnetic field to produce current.

🔑 A transformer is a device that increases or decreases voltage.

Vocabulary
- electromagnetic induction
- direct current
- alternating current
- generator
- transformer

13 Review and Assessment

LESSON 1 **What Is Magnetism?**

1. A magnet is attracted to a soup can because the can has

   a. a south pole.　　**b.** a north pole.

   c. a magnetic field.　**d.** iron in it.

2. Any magnet, no matter its shape, has two ends, and each one is called a _____

3. **Predict** What will happen to a bar magnet suspended from a string when it swings freely?

   _____

   _____

   _____

4. **Interpret Diagrams** In the diagram, what do the arrows represent? Explain your answer.

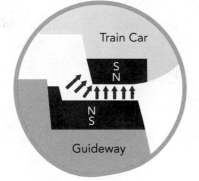

   _____

   _____

   _____

   _____

5. **Design Experiments** If two magnets' poles are not labeled, how can you tell which poles are the same and which are different?

   _____

   _____

   _____

   _____

LESSON 2 **Magnetic Fields**

6. A compass works because its magnetic needle

   a. points east.　　**b.** spins freely.

   c. points west.　　**d.** repels magnets.

7. _____map out the magnetic field around a magnet.

8. **Make Models** How is Earth like a magnet?

   _____

   _____

   _____

9. **Draw Conclusions** Look at the diagram below. Is the left magnetic pole a north or south pole? Explain your answer.

   _____

   _____

   _____

10. **Write About It** Imagine that you are the early inventor of the compass. Write an advertisement for your product that tells explorers how a compass works.

Review and Assessment

LESSON 3 Electric Charge and Static Electricity

11. What type of charge transfer occurs when two objects are rubbed together?

a. friction

b. induction

c. conduction

d. polarization

12. The transfer of electrons from a cloud to the ground during a lightning strike is an example of _____

13. Apply Concepts Draw the electric field for a single positive charge. Be sure to show which way the field lines point.

14. Relate Cause and Effect Explain what happens to the electrons in a metal object when it is held near a negatively charged object. What happens to the overall charge of the metal object?

_____

_____

_____

_____

_____

15. **Write About It** A park needs a sign to tell visitors what to do during a thunderstorm. Write a paragraph that explains why standing under a tall tree during a thunderstorm is dangerous.

LESSON 4 Electric Current

16. Which of these objects is an insulator?

a. gold ring

b. copper coin

c. glass rod

d. steel fork

17. An electric current is _____

_____

18. Classify The appliances in your home can be made of several different materials. What kinds of materials are the wires made of? What kinds of materials surround the wire for safety?

_____

19. Infer Copper wires carry electric current from power plants to users. How is the resistance of these power lines likely to vary during the year in an area that has very hot summers? Explain.

_____

_____

_____

_____

20. Make Models Water will not flow down a flat slide because there is no potential energy difference between the two ends. How could this situation be represented in an electric circuit? Explain your reasoning.

_____

_____

_____

_____

13 Review and Assessment

LESSON 5 Electromagnetic Force

21. The relationship between electricity and magnetism is called

  a. electrical energy.   **b.** induced current.

  c. electromagnetism. **d.** ferromagnetism.

22. A coil of wire with a current is called

  a _____

23. Relate Cause and Effect You have a magnetic field produced by a current. What would you do to change the direction and increase the strength of the field?

_____

_____

_____

_____

_____

_____

LESSON 6 Electricity, Magnetism, and Motion

24. Electrical energy is transformed into mechanical energy in a

  a. motor.   **b.** solenoid.

  c. transformer. **d.** electromagnet.

25. A galvanometer is a device that

measures _____

26. Compare and Contrast How is a motor similar to a galvanometer? How is it different?

_____

_____

_____

_____

_____

LESSON 7 Electricity From Magnetism

27. A device that changes the voltage of alternating current is a

  a. transformer.   **b.** motor.

  c. generator.   **d.** galvanometer.

28. Generating a current by moving a conductor in a magnetic field is _____

_____

29. Write About It You are a television news reporter covering the opening of a new dam that will help to generate electrical energy. Write a short news story describing how the dam transforms mechanical energy from the motion of the water into electrical energy.

APPLY THE BIG Q How are electricity and magnetism related?

30. A crane in a junkyard may have an electromagnet to lift heavy metal objects. Explain how electricity and magnetism work in an electromagnet so that a crane can lift heavy metal objects.

_____

_____

_____

_____

_____

_____

_____

_____

_____

_____

Ohio Benchmark Practice

Multiple Choice

Circle the letter of the best answer.

The graph below shows how a solenoid's loops affect its magnetic field strength. Use the graph to answer Question 1.

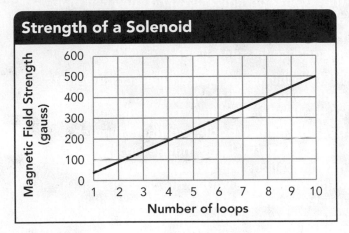

Strength of a Solenoid

1. Predict the strength of a 12-loop solenoid.

   A 300 gauss   **B** 600 gauss
   C 700 gauss   **D** 1200 gauss

2. You can increase a step-up transformer's voltage with

   A a power source connected to the primary coil.
   B a source connected to the secondary coil.
   C increasing the number of loops in the primary coil.
   D increasing the number of loops in the secondary coil.

3. To measure the current induced by moving a wire through a magnetic field, which piece of equipment would a scientist need?

   A a galvanometer
   B a transformer
   C an insulated wire
   D an LED

4. What happens when a magnet moves through a coil of wire?

   A The magnet loses magnetism.
   B A current is induced in the wire.
   C A current is induced in the magnet.
   D Electrical energy is transformed into mechanical energy.

5. How could you modify a solenoid to produce a stronger magnetic field?

   A Remove loops from the solenoid.
   B Convert the solenoid to an electromagnet by adding a ferromagnetic core.
   C Wind the loops farther apart.
   D Decrease the current in the solenoid.

Short Answer

Use the diagram below and your knowledge of science to help you answer Question 6. Write your answer on a separate sheet of paper.

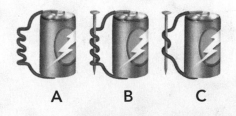

6. Three electromagnets are illustrated in the diagram above. Will the electromagnet labeled A or B produce a stronger magnetic field? Will the electromagnet B or C produce a stronger field? Explain your answers.

Technology and Society

MAGNETIC PICTURES

Now, instead of using X-rays, doctors use magnets to look in detail at systems inside the body. ▼

▲ This MRI of a healthy brain shows both hemispheres in bright pink and the cerebellum in green.

Doctors can look inside your body to detect infection, bleeding, or tumors in the brain—without surgery or high-energy radiation that can damage tissues. They can get very detailed views of ligaments, tendons, and muscles that reveal injuries. They can find breast cancers that mammograms miss, and they can map areas of low blood flow after a heart attack. How do they do this? They use Magnetic Resonance Imaging (MRI).

MRI machines use powerful electromagnets, radio waves, and computers to take pictures of the inside of bodies. This process works because human bodies contain so much water. First, the large magnet in the MRI machine aligns the hydrogen atoms in the water molecules within the field. Then, the machine emits a radio frequency pulse that spins all of the hydrogen atoms the same way. The hydrogen atoms release energy in the form of a radio signal as they return to their normal positions, and computers can turn that signal into pictures. Healthy tissues respond differently to the magnet than unhealthy or damaged tissues.

Research It MRI scanning rooms have strict rules about what is allowed inside because metal objects can become deadly. Research the safety concerns for MRI use on humans. Then write a safety brochure to share your findings.

A SHOCKING MESSAGE!

In the 1830s, before the telephone had been invented, people were experimenting with ways to communicate across long distances. Samuel Morse and Alfred Vail discovered that it was possible to use an electromagnet to send a signal through cheap wire.

The electromagnet is part of an electric circuit. On one end of the wire is a telegraph switch. Closing the switch completes the circuit, sending an electric current through the wire. Opening the switch stops the current. On the other end of the wire is a telegraph with an electromagnet, a metal key, and a metal plate. As the electric current flows through the electromagnet, a magnetic field forms.

Signal It Work with a partner to find resources that will help you construct your own electromagnetic telegraph machine! Predict which materials will best conduct a signal, and then verify your predictions by building a model.

The metal key is then attracted to the metal plate. The sender can close and open the switch quickly, making a short clicking sound called a "dot" on the other end. Or, the sender can hold the switch closed and create a longer sound, called a "dash." Leaving the switch open for a moment comes across as a "space," or a break in the sounds.

This pattern of dots, dashes, and spaces became a new tool for communicating without using voices—Morse code. Telegraph operators could spell out words and phrases. Three dots, followed by three dashes, followed by three dots, for example, is the Morse code signal for SOS, or help!

513

APPENDIX A

Safety Symbols

These symbols warn of possible dangers in the laboratory and remind you to work carefully.

 Safety Goggles Wear safety goggles to protect your eyes in any activity involving chemicals, flames or heating, or glassware.

 Lab Apron Wear a laboratory apron to protect your skin and clothing from damage.

 Breakage Handle breakable materials, such as glassware, with care. Do not touch broken glassware.

 Heat-Resistant Gloves Use an oven mitt or other hand protection when handling hot materials such as hot plates or hot glassware.

 Plastic Gloves Wear disposable plastic gloves when working with harmful chemicals and organisms. Keep your hands away from your face, and dispose of the gloves according to your teacher's instructions.

 Heating Use a clamp or tongs to pick up hot glassware. Do not touch hot objects with your bare hands.

 Flames Before you work with flames, tie back loose hair and clothing. Follow instructions from your teacher about lighting and extinguishing flames.

 No Flames When using flammable materials, make sure there are no flames, sparks, or other exposed heat sources present.

 Corrosive Chemical Avoid getting acid or other corrosive chemicals on your skin or clothing or in your eyes. Do not inhale the vapors. Wash your hands after the activity.

 Poison Do not let any poisonous chemical come into contact with your skin, and do not inhale its vapors. Wash your hands when you are finished with the activity.

 Fumes Work in a well-ventilated area when harmful vapors may be involved. Avoid inhaling vapors directly. Only test an odor when directed to do so by your teacher, and use a wafting motion to direct the vapor toward your nose.

 Sharp Object Scissors, scalpels, knives, needles, pins, and tacks can cut your skin. Always direct a sharp edge or point away from yourself and others.

 Animal Safety Treat live or preserved animals or animal parts with care to avoid harming the animals or yourself. Wash your hands when you are finished with the activity.

 Plant Safety Handle plants only as directed by your teacher. If you are allergic to certain plants, tell your teacher; do not do an activity involving those plants. Avoid touching harmful plants such as poison ivy. Wash your hands when you are finished with the activity.

 Electric Shock To avoid electric shock, never use electrical equipment around water, or when the equipment is wet or your hands are wet. Be sure cords are untangled and cannot trip anyone. Unplug equipment not in use.

 Physical Safety When an experiment involves physical activity, avoid injuring yourself or others. Alert your teacher if there is any reason you should not participate.

 Disposal Dispose of chemicals and other laboratory materials safely. Follow the instructions from your teacher.

 Hand Washing Wash your hands thoroughly when finished with an activity. Use soap and warm water. Rinse well.

 General Safety Awareness When this symbol appears, follow the instructions provided. When you are asked to develop your own procedure in a lab, have your teacher approve your plan before you go further.

APPENDIX B

Using a Laboratory Balance

The laboratory balance is an important tool in scientific investigations. You can use a balance to determine the masses of materials that you study or experiment with in the laboratory.

Different kinds of balances are used in the laboratory. One kind of balance is the triple-beam balance. The balance that you may use in your science class is probably similar to the balance illustrated in this Appendix. **To use the balance properly, you should learn the name, location, and function of each part of the balance you are using. What kind of balance do you have in your science class?**

The Triple-Beam Balance

The triple-beam balance is a single-pan balance with three beams calibrated in grams. The back, or 100-gram, beam is divided into ten units of 10 grams each. The middle, or 500-gram, beam is divided into five units of 100 grams each. The front, or 10-gram, beam is divided into ten units of 1 gram each. Each of the units on the front beam is further divided into units of 0.1 gram. What is the largest mass you could find with a triple-beam balance?

The following procedure can be used to find the mass of an object with a triple-beam balance:

1. Place the object on the pan.
2. Move the rider on the middle beam notch by notch until the horizontal pointer on the right drops below zero. Move the rider back one notch.
3. Move the rider on the back beam notch by notch until the pointer again drops below zero. Move the rider back one notch.
4. Slowly slide the rider along the front beam until the pointer stops at the zero point.
5. The mass of the object is equal to the sum of the readings on the three beams.

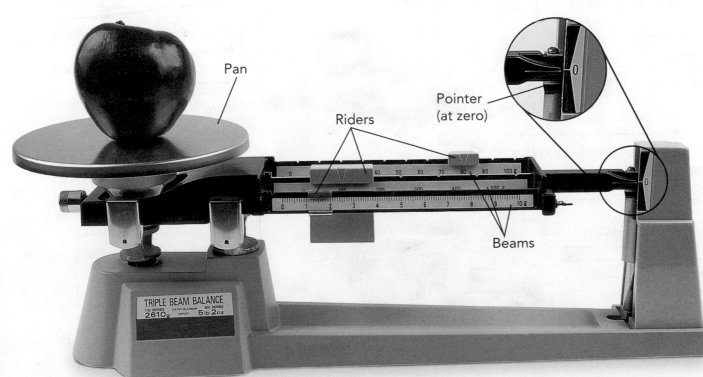

Pan

Riders

Pointer (at zero)

Beams

TRIPLE BEAM BALANCE
700 SERIES U.S. PAT. NO. 2,766,498 900 SERIES
2610g CAPACITY 5 lb 2 oz

APPENDIX C

Using a Microscope

The microscope is an essential tool in the study of life science. It allows you to see things that are too small to be seen with the unaided eye.

You will probably use a compound microscope like the one you see here. The compound microscope has more than one lens that magnifies the object you view.

Typically, a compound microscope has one lens in the eyepiece, the part you look through. The eyepiece lens usually magnifies 10×. Any object you view through this lens would appear 10 times larger than it is.

A compound microscope may contain one or two other lenses called objective lenses. If there are two, they are called the low-power and high-power objective lenses. The low-power objective lens usually magnifies 10×. The high-power objective lens usually magnifies 40×.

To calculate the total magnification with which you are viewing an object, multiply the magnification of the eyepiece lens by the magnification of the objective lens you are using. For example, the eyepiece's magnification of 10× multiplied by the low-power objective's magnification of 10× equals a total magnification of 100×.

Use the photo of the compound microscope to become familiar with the parts of the microscope and their functions.

The Parts of a Microscope

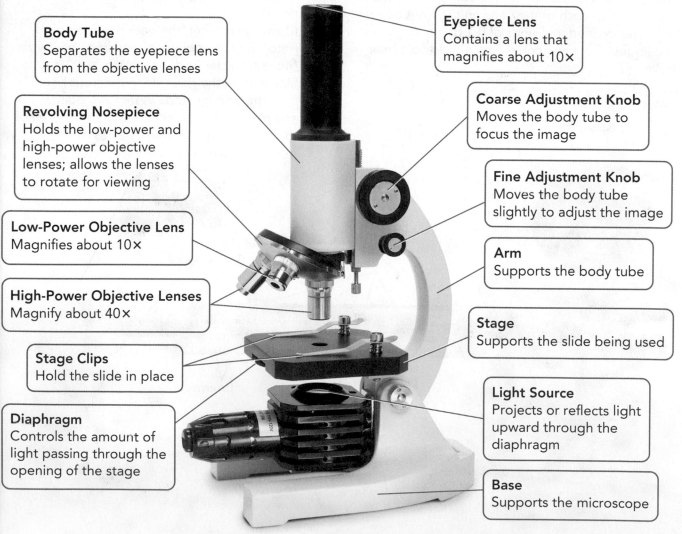

Body Tube
Separates the eyepiece lens from the objective lenses

Revolving Nosepiece
Holds the low-power and high-power objective lenses; allows the lenses to rotate for viewing

Low-Power Objective Lens
Magnifies about 10×

High-Power Objective Lenses
Magnify about 40×

Stage Clips
Hold the slide in place

Diaphragm
Controls the amount of light passing through the opening of the stage

Eyepiece Lens
Contains a lens that magnifies about 10×

Coarse Adjustment Knob
Moves the body tube to focus the image

Fine Adjustment Knob
Moves the body tube slightly to adjust the image

Arm
Supports the body tube

Stage
Supports the slide being used

Light Source
Projects or reflects light upward through the diaphragm

Base
Supports the microscope

Using the Microscope

Use the following procedures when you are working with a microscope.

1. To carry the microscope, grasp the microscope's arm with one hand. Place your other hand under the base.
2. Place the microscope on a table with the arm toward you.
3. Turn the coarse adjustment knob to raise the body tube.
4. Revolve the nosepiece until the low-power objective lens clicks into place.
5. Adjust the diaphragm. While looking through the eyepiece, also adjust the mirror until you see a bright white circle of light. **CAUTION:** *Never use direct sunlight as a light source.*
6. Place a slide on the stage. Center the specimen over the opening on the stage. Use the stage clips to hold the slide in place. **CAUTION:** *Glass slides are fragile.*
7. Look at the stage from the side. Carefully turn the coarse adjustment knob to lower the body tube until the low-power objective almost touches the slide.
8. Looking through the eyepiece, very slowly turn the coarse adjustment knob until the specimen comes into focus.
9. To switch to the high-power objective lens, look at the microscope from the side. Carefully revolve the nosepiece until the high-power objective lens clicks into place. Make sure the lens does not hit the slide.
10. Looking through the eyepiece, turn the fine adjustment knob until the specimen comes into focus.

Making a Wet-Mount Slide

Use the following procedures to make a wet-mount slide of a specimen.

1. Obtain a clean microscope slide and a coverslip. **CAUTION:** *Glass slides and coverslips are fragile.*
2. Place the specimen on the center of the slide. The specimen must be thin enough for light to pass through it.
3. Using a plastic dropper, place a drop of water on the specimen.
4. Gently place one edge of the coverslip against the slide so that it touches the edge of the water drop at a 45° angle. Slowly lower the coverslip over the specimen. If you see air bubbles trapped beneath the coverslip, tap the coverslip gently with the eraser end of a pencil.
5. Remove any excess water at the edge of the coverslip with a paper towel.

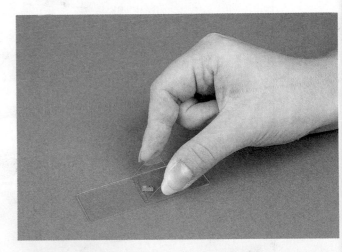

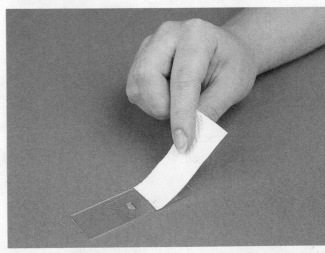

517

UNITED STATES
Physical

———— International boundary

———— State boundary

⊛ Washington, D.C. National capital

★ Atlanta State capital

● Detroit Major city

ELEVATION

Meters		Feet
Over 3,000		Over 10,000
1,500 to 3,000		5,000 to 10,000
6,00 to 1,500		2,000 to 5,000
300 to 600		1,000 to 2,000
150 to 300		500 to 1,000
0 to 150		0 to 500
Below sea level		Below sea level

WATER DEPTH

Less than 200		Less than 600
Greater than 200		Greater than 600

0   100   200   300 Miles

0 100 200 300 Kilometers

519

APPENDIX E

The Design Process

Engineers are people who use scientific and technological knowledge to solve practical problems. To design new products, engineers usually follow the process described here, even though they may not follow these steps in the same order each time.

Identify a Need

Before engineers begin designing a new product, they must first identify the need they are trying to meet or the problem they want to solve. For example, suppose you are a member of a design team in a company that makes model cars. Your team has identified a need: a model car that is inexpensive and easy to assemble.

Research the Problem

Engineers often begin by gathering information that will help them with their new design. This research may include finding articles in books, magazines, or on the Internet. It may also involve talking to other engineers who have solved similar problems. Engineers often perform experiments related to the product they want to design.

For your model car, you could look at cars that are similar to the one you want to design. You might do research on the Internet. You could also test some materials to see whether they will work well in a model car.

Design a Solution

Brainstorm Ideas When engineers design new products, they usually work in teams. Design teams often hold brainstorming meetings in which any team member can contribute ideas. **Brainstorming** is a creative process in which one team member's suggestions often spark ideas in other group members. Brainstorming can lead to new approaches to solving a design problem.

Document the Process As the design team works, its members document, or keep a record of, the process. Having access to documentation enables others to repeat, or replicate, the process in the future. Design teams document their research sources, ideas, lists of materials, and so on because any part of the process may be a helpful resource later.

Identify Constraints During brainstorming, a design team may come up with several possible designs. To better focus their ideas, team members consider constraints. A **constraint** is a factor that limits a product design. Physical characteristics, such as the properties of materials used to make your model car, are constraints. Money and time are also constraints. If the materials in a product cost a lot or if the product takes a long time to make, the design may be impractical.

Make Trade-offs Design teams usually need to make trade-offs. In a **trade-off,** engineers give up one benefit of a proposed design in order to obtain another. In designing your model car, you might have to make trade-offs. For example, you might decide to give up the benefit of sturdiness in order to obtain the benefit of lower cost.

Select a Solution After considering the constraints and trade-offs of the possible designs, engineers then select one idea to develop further. That idea represents the solution that the team thinks best meets the need or solves the problem that was identified at the beginning of the process. The decision includes selecting the materials that will be used in the first attempt to build a product.

Create, Test, and Evaluate a Prototype

Once the team has chosen a design plan, the engineers build a prototype. A **prototype** is a working model used to test a design. Engineers evaluate the prototype to see whether it meets the goal. They must determine whether it works well, is easy to operate, is safe to use, and holds up to repeated use.

Part of the evaluation includes collecting data in the form of measurements. For example, think of your model car. Once you decide how to build your prototype, what would you want to know about it? You might want to measure how much baggage it could carry or how its shape affects its speed.

Troubleshoot and Redesign

Few prototypes work perfectly, which is why they need to be tested. Once a design team has tested a prototype, the members analyze the results and identify any problems. The team then tries to **troubleshoot**, or fix the design problems. Troubleshooting allows the team to redesign the prototype to improve on how well the solution meets the need.

Communicate the Solution

A team needs to communicate the final design to the people who will manufacture and use the product. To do this, teams may use sketches, detailed drawings, computer simulations, and word descriptions. The team may also present the evidence that was collected when the prototype was tested. This evidence may include mathematical representations, such as graphs and data tables, that support the choice for the final design.

GLOSSARY

A

absolute age The age of a rock given as the number of years since the rock formed.
edad absoluta Edad de una roca basada en el número de años de su formación.

acceleration The rate at which velocity changes.
aceleración Ritmo al que cambia la velocidad.

accuracy How close a measurement is to the true or accepted value.
exactitud Cuán cerca está una medida del valor verdadero o aceptado.

adaptation An inherited behavior or physical characteristic that helps an organism survive and reproduce in its environment.
adaptación Comportamiento o característica física hereditaria que le permite a un organismo sobrevivir y reproducirse en un ambiente.

alleles The different forms of a gene.
alelos Diferentes formas de un gen.

alternating current Current consisting of charges that move back and forth in a circuit.
corriente alterna Corriente de cargas eléctricas que se mueven hacia delante y hacia atrás en un circuito.

amniotic egg An egg with a shell and internal membranes that keep the embryo moist; a major adaptation to life on land characteristic of reptiles, birds, and egg-laying mammals.
huevo amniótico Huevo con cáscara y membranas internas que mantiene al embrión húmedo; adaptación principal a la vida en la tierra, característica de los reptiles, las aves y los mamíferos que ponen huevos.

amphibian A vertebrate whose body temperature is determined by the temperature of its environment, and that lives its early life in water and its adult life on land.
anfibio Animal vertebrado cuya temperatura corporal depende de la temperatura de su entorno, y que vive la primera etapa de su vida en el agua y su vida adulta en la tierra.

analyzing Evaluating data to reach a conclusion about an experiment.
analizar Evaluar datos para llegar a una conclusion acerca de un experimento.

annual A flowering plant that completes its life cycle in one growing season.

anual Planta con flores que completa su ciclo de vida en una sola temporada de crecimiento.

anomalous data Data that do not fit with the rest of a data set.)
datos anómalos Información que no encaja con los otros datos de un conjunto de datos.

asthenosphere The soft layer of the mantle on which the lithosphere floats.
astenósfera Capa suave del manto en la que flota la litósfera.

atmosphere The relatively thin layer of gases that form Earth's outermost layer.
atmósfera Capa de gases relativamente delgada que forma la capa exterior de la Tierra.

B

basalt A dark, dense, igneous rock with a fine texture, found in oceanic crust.
basalto Roca ígnea, oscura y densa, de textura lisa, que se encuentra en la corteza oceánica.

batholith A mass of rock formed when a large body of magma cools inside the crust.
batolito Masa de roca formada cuando una gran masa de magma se enfría dentro de la corteza terrestre.

bias A subjective belief that affects a person's attitude toward something; an error in the design of an experiment that affects the results of the experiment.
predisposición Creencia subjetiva que afecta la actitud de una persona acerca de algo; un error en el diseño de un experimento que afecta los resultados del experimento.

biennial A flowering plant that completes its life cycle in two years.
bienal Planta con flores que completa su ciclo de vida en dos años.

biodiversity The total number of different species on Earth, including those on land, in the water, and in the air.
biodiversidad Número total de especies diferentes que habitan la Tierra, incluyendo especies terrestres, marinas y del aire.

biosphere The parts of Earth that contain living organisms.
biósfera Partes de la Tierra que contienen organismos vivos.

C

caldera The large hole at the top of a volcano formed when the roof of a volcano's magma chamber collapses.
caldera Gran agujero en la parte superior de un volcán que se forma cuando la tapa de la cámara magmática de un volcán se desploma.

cambium A layer of cells in a plant that produces new phloem and xylem cells.
cámbium Una capa de células de una planta que produce nuevas células de floema y xilema.

cancer A disease in which some body cells grow and divide uncontrollably, damaging the parts of the body around them.
cáncer Enfermedad en la que algunas células del cuerpo crecen y se dividen sin control, y causan daño a las partes del cuerpo que las rodean.

captive breeding The mating of animals in zoos or wildlife preserves.
reproducción en cautiverio Apareamiento de animales en zoológicos y reservas naturales.

carbon film A type of fossil consisting of an extremely thin coating of carbon on rock.
película de carbono Tipo de fósil que consiste en una capa de carbono extremadamente fina que recubre la roca.

carrier A person who has one recessive allele and one dominant allele for a trait.
portador Persona que tiene un alelo recesivo y un alelo dominante para un rasgo.

cast A fossil that is a solid copy of an organism's shape, formed when minerals seep into a mold.
vaciado Fósil que es una copia sólida de la forma de un organismo y que se forma cuando los minerales se filtran y crean un molde.

centripetal force A force that causes an object to move in a circle.
fuerza centrípeta Fuerza que hace que un objeto se mueva circularmente.

chemotherapy The use of drugs to treat diseases such as cancer.
quimioterapia Uso de medicamentos para tratar enfermedades como el cáncer.

cinder cone A steep, cone-shaped hill or small mountain made of volcanic ash, cinders, and bombs piled up around a volcano's opening.

cono de escoria Colina o pequeña montaña escarpada en forma de cono que se forma cuando ceniza volcánica, escoria y bombas se acumulan alrededor del cráter de un volcán.

classifying The process of grouping together items that are alike in some way.
clasificar Proceso de agrupar objetos con algún tipo de semejanza.

clone An organism that is genetically identical to the organism from which it was produced.
clon Organismo genéticamente idéntico al organismo del que proviene.

codominance A situation in which both alleles for a gene are expressed equally.
codominancia Situación en la que ambos alelos de un gen se manifiestan de igual manera.

comet A loose collection of ice and dust that orbits the sun, typically in a long, narrow orbit.
cometa Conjunto poco denso de hielo y partículas que orbitan alrededor del Sol. Generalmente su órbita es larga y estrecha.

compass A device with a magnetized needle that can spin freely; a compass needle always points north.
brújula Instrumento con una aguja imantada que puede girar libremente; la aguja siempre apunta hacia el norte.

complete metamorphosis A type of metamorphosis with four distinct stages: egg, larva, pupa, and adult.
metamorfosis completa Tipo de metamorfosis de cuatro etapas: huevo, larva, pupa y adulto.

composite volcano A tall, cone-shaped mountain in which layers of lava alternate with layers of ash and other volcanic materials.
volcán compuesto Montaña alta en forma de cono en la que las capas de lava se alternan con capas de ceniza y otros materiales volcánicos.

compression 1. Stress that squeezes rock until it folds or breaks. 2. The part of a longitudinal wave where the particles of the medium are close together.
compresión 1. Fuerza que oprime una roca hasta que se pliega o se rompe. 2. Parte de una onda longitudinal en la que las partículas del medio están más cerca.

conduction The transfer of heat from one particle of matter to another.
conducción Transferencia de energía térmica de una partícula de materia a otra.

GLOSSARY

cone The reproductive structure of a gymnosperm.
cono Estructura reproductora de una gimnosperma.

conservation of charge The law that states that charges are neither created nor destroyed.
conservación de carga eléctrica Ley que establece que las cargas no se crean ni se destruyen.

constructive force Any natural process that builds up Earth's surface.
fuerza constructiva Proceso natural que incrementa la superficie de la Tierra.

continental drift The hypothesis that the continents slowly move across Earth's surface.
deriva continental Hipótesis que establece que los continentes se desplazan lentamente en la superficie de la Tierra.

controlled experiment An experiment in which only one variable is manipulated at a time.
experimento controlado Experimento en el cual sólo se manipula una variable a la vez.

convection The transfer of heat by the movement of a fluid.
convección Transferencia de energía térmica por el movimiento de un líquido.

convection current The movement of a fluid, caused by differences in temperature, that transfers heat from one part of the fluid to another.
corriente de convección Movimiento de un líquido ocasionado por diferencias de temperatura, que transfiere calor de un punto del líquido a otro.

convergent boundary A plate boundary where two plates move toward each other.
borde convergente Borde de una placa donde dos placas se deslizan una hacia la otra.

crater 1. A large round pit caused by the impact of a meteoroid. 2. A bowl-shaped area that forms around a volcano's central opening.
cráter 1. Gran hoyo redondo que se forma por el impacto de un meteorito. 2. Área en forma de tazón que se forma en la abertura central de un volcán.

crust The layer of rock that forms Earth's outer surface.
corteza terrestre Capa de rocas que forma la superficie externa de la Tierra.

deep-ocean trench A deep valley along the ocean floor beneath which oceanic crust slowly sinks toward the mantle.
fosa oceánica profunda Valle profundo a lo largo del suelo oceánico debajo del cual la corteza oceánica se hunde lentamente hacia el manto.

density The measurement of how much mass of a substance is contained in a given volume.
densidad Medida de la masa de una sustancia que tiene un volumen dado.

dependent variable The factor that changes as a result of changes to the independent variable in an experiment; also called responding variable.
variable dependiente Factor que cambia a causa de los cambios de la variable independiente de un experimento; también se denomina variable de respuesta.

destructive force Any natural process that tears down or wears away Earth's surface.
fuerza destructiva Proceso natural que destruye o desgasta la superficie de la Tierra.

dike A slab of volcanic rock formed when magma forces itself across rock layers. (150)
dique discordante Placa de roca volcánica formada cuando el magma se abre paso a través de las capas de roca.

direct current Current consisting of charges that flow in only one direction in a circuit.
corriente directa Corriente de cargas eléctricas que fluyen en una sola dirección en un circuito.

divergent boundary A plate boundary where two plates move away from each other.
borde divergente Borde de una placa donde dos placas se separan.

dominant allele An allele whose trait always shows up in the organism when the allele is present.
alelo dominante Alelo cuyo rasgo siempre se manifiesta en el organismo, cuando el alelo está presente.

dormant Not currently active but able to become active in the future (as with a volcano).
inactivo Que no está activo en la actualidad pero puede ser activo en el futuro (como un volcán).

D

data Facts, figures, and other evidence gathered through observations.
dato Hechos, cifras u otra evidencia reunida por medio de observaciones.

E

earthquake The shaking that results from the movement of rock beneath Earth's surface.
terremoto Temblor que resulta del movimiento de la roca debajo de la superficie de la Tierra.

electric circuit A complete, unbroken path through which electric charges can flow.
circuito eléctrico Trayecto completo y continuo a través del cual pueden fluir las cargas eléctricas.

electric current The continuous flow of electric charges through a material.
corriente eléctrica Flujo continuo de cargas eléctricas a través de un material.

electric field The region around a charged object where the object's electric force is exerted on other charged objects.
campo eléctrico Región alrededor de un objeto cargado, donde su fuerza eléctrica interactúa con otros objetos cargados eléctricamente.

electric force The force between charged objects.
fuerza eléctrica Fuerza entre cuerpos cargados eléctricamente.

electric motor A device that transforms electrical energy to mechanical energy.
motor eléctrico Instrumento que convierte la energía eléctrica en energía mecánica.

electrical energy The energy of electric charges.
energía eléctrica Energía de las cargas eléctricas.

electromagnet A magnet created by wrapping a coil of wire with a current running through it around a core of material that is easily magnetised.
electroimán Imán creado al enrollar una espiral de alambre, por la cual fluye una corriente eléctrica, alrededor de un núcleo de material que se magnetiza fácilmente.

electromagnetic induction The process of generating an electric current from the motion of a conductor through a magnetic field.
inducción electromagnética Proceso por el cual se genera una corriente eléctrica a partir del movimiento de un conductor a través de un campo magnético.

electromagnetism The relationship between electricity and magnetism.
electromagnetismo Relación entre la electricidad y el magnetismo.

embryo 1. The young organism that develops from a zygote. **2.** A developing human during the first eight weeks after fertilization has occurred.
embrión 1. Organismo joven que se desarrolla a partir del cigoto. **2.** Un ser humano en desarrollo durante las primeras ocho semanas después de llevarse a cabo la fertilización.

empirical evidence Data and observations that are collected through scientific processes and that explain a particular observation.
evidencia empírica Datos y observaciones que se recopilan a través de procesos científicos y que explican una observación particular.

endangered species A species in danger of becoming extinct in the near future.
especie en peligro de extinción Especie que corre el riesgo de desaparecer en el futuro próximo.

energy The ability to do work or cause change
energía Capacidad para realizar un trabajo o producir cambios.

epicenter The point on Earth's surface directly above an earthquake's focus.
epicentro Punto de la superficie de la Tierra directamente sobre el foco de un terremoto.

era One of the three long units of geologic time between the Precambrian and the present.
era Cada una de las tres unidades largas del tiempo geológico entre el precámbrico y el presente.

estimate An approximation of a number based on reasonable assumptions.
estimación Aproximación de un número basada en conjeturas razonables.

ethics The study of principles about what is right and wrong, fair and unfair.
ética Estudio de los principios de qué es lo bueno y lo malo, lo justo y lo injusto.

evidence Observations and conclusions that have been repeated.
evidencia Observaciones y conclusiones que se han repetido.

evolution Change over time; the process by which modern organisms have descended from ancient organisms.
evolución Cambio con el tiempo; proceso por el cual los organismos modernos se originaron a partir de organismos antiguos.

extinct 1. Term used to refer to a group of related organisms that has died out and has no living members. **2.** Term used to describe a volcano that is no longer active and unlikely to erupt again.
extinto 1. Término que se refiere a un grupo de organismos que ha muerto y no tiene miembros vivos. **2.** Término que describe un volcán que ya no es activo y es poco probable que haga erupción otra vez.

GLOSSARY

extinction The disappearance of all members of a species from Earth.
extinción Desaparición de la Tierra de todos los miembros de una especie.

external fertilization When eggs are fertilized outside of a female's body.
fertilización externa Cuando los óvulos se fertilizan fuera del cuerpo de la hembra.

extrusion An igneous rock layer formed when lava flows onto Earth's surface and hardens.
extrusión Capa de roca ígnea formada cuando la lava fluye hacia la superficie de la Tierra y se endurece.

---------------- F ----------------

fault A break in Earth's crust along which rocks move.
falla Fisura en la corteza terrestre a lo largo de la cual se desplazan las rocas.

feedback Output that changes a system or allows the system to adjust itself.
retroalimentación Salida que cambia un sistema o permite que éste se ajuste.

fertilization The process in sexual reproduction in which an egg cell and a sperm cell join to form a new cell.
fertilización Proceso de la reproducción sexual en el que un óvulo y un espermatozoide se unen para formar una nueva célula.

field Any area outside of the laboratory.
campo Cualquier área fuera del laboratorio.

flower The reproductive structure of an angiosperm.
flor Estructura reproductora de una angiosperma.

fluid friction Friction that occurs as an object moves through a fluid.
fricción de fluido Fricción que ocurre cuando un cuerpo se mueve a través de un fluido.

focus The point beneath Earth's surface where rock first breaks under stress and causes an earthquake.
foco Punto debajo de la superficie de la Tierra en el que la roca empieza a romperse debido a una gran fuerza y causa un terremoto.

force A push or pull exerted on an object.
fuerza Empuje o atracción que se ejerce sobre un cuerpo.

fossil The preserved remains or traces of an organism that lived in the past.
fósil Restos o huellas preservados de un organismo que vivió en el pasado.

free fall The motion of a falling object when the only force acting on it is gravity.
caída libre Movimiento de un objeto que cae cuando la única fuerza que actúa sobre éste es la gravedad.

friction 1. The force that two surfaces exert on each other when they rub against each other.
fricción 1. Fuerza que dos superficies ejercen una sobre la otra al frotarse.

fruit The ripened ovary and other structures of an angiosperm that enclose one or more seeds.
fruto Ovario maduro y otras estructuras de una angiosperma que encierran una o más semillas.

---------------- G ----------------

galvanometer A device that uses an electromagnet to detect small amounts of current.
galvanómetro Instrumento que usa un electroimán para detectar la intensidad de una pequeña corriente.

gametophyte The stage in the life cycle of a plant in which the plant produces gametes, or sex cells.
gametofito Etapa del ciclo vital de una planta en la que produce gametos, es decir, células sexuales.

gene A sequence of DNA that determines a trait and is passed from parent to offspring.
gen Secuencia de ADN que determina un rasgo y que se pasa de los progenitores a los hijos.

gene therapy The process of changing a gene to treat a medical disease or disorder. An absent or faulty gene is replaced by a normal working gene.
terapia genética Proceso que consiste en cambiar un gen para tratar una enfermedad o un trastorno médico. El gen ausente o defectuoso se cambia por un gen con función normal.

generator A device that transforms mechanical energy into electrical energy.
generador eléctrico Instrumento que convierte la energía mecánica en energía eléctrica.

genetic disorder An abnormal condition that a person inherits through genes or chromosomes.
desorden genético Condición anormal que hereda una persona a través de los genes o cromosomas.

genetic engineering The transfer of a gene from the DNA of one organism into another organism, in order to produce an organism with desired traits.

ingeniería genética Transferencia de un gen desde el ADN de un organismo a otro, para producir un organismo con los rasgos deseados.

genetics The scientific study of heredity.
genética Ciencia que estudia la herencia.

genome A complete set of genetic information that an organism carries in its DNA.
genoma Toda la información genética que un organismo lleva en su ADN.

genotype An organism's genetic makeup, or allele combinations.
genotipo Composición genética de un organismo, es decir, las combinaciones de los alelos.

geologic time scale A record of the geologic events and life forms in Earth's history.
escala de tiempo geológico Registro de los sucesos geológicos y de las formas de vida en la historia de la Tierra.

geosphere The densest parts of Earth that include the crust, mantle, and core.
geósfera Partes más densos de la Tierra que incluye la corteza, el manto y el núcleo.

germination The sprouting of the embryo out of a seed; occurs when the embryo resumes its growth following dormancy.
germinación Brotamiento del embrión a partir de la semilla; ocurre cuando el embrión reanuda su crecimiento tras el estado latente.

gestation period The length of time between fertilization and birth of a mammal.
período de gestación Tiempo entre la fertilización y el nacimiento de un mamífero.

gradualism Pattern of evolution characterized by the slow and steady accumulation of small genetic changes over long periods of time.
gradualismo Evolución de una especie por medio de la acumulación lenta pero continua de cambios genéticos a través de largos períodos de tiempo.

granite A usually light-colored igneous rock that is found in continental crust.
granito Roca generalmente de color claro que se encuentra en la corteza continental.

graph A picture of information from a data table; shows the relationship between variables.
gráfica Representación visual de la información de una tabla de datos; muestra la relación entre las variables.

gravity The attractive force between objects; the force that moves objects downhill.
gravedad Fuerza que atrae a los cuerpos entre sí; fuerza que mueve un cuerpo cuesta abajo.

H

habitat destruction The loss of a natural habitat.
destrucción del habitat Pérdida de un hábitat natural.

habitat fragmentation The breaking of a habitat into smaller, isolated pieces.
fragmentación del hábitat Desintegración de un hábitat en porciones aisladas más pequeñas.

half-life The time it takes for half of the atoms of a radioactive element to decay.
vida media Tiempo que toma descomponer la mitad de los átomos de un elemento radiactivo.

heredity The passing of traits from parents to offspring.
herencia Transmisión de rasgos de padres a hijos.

heterozygous Having two different alleles for a particular gene.
heterocigoto Que tiene dos alelos distintos para un gen particular.

homeostasis The condition in which an organism's internal environment is kept stable in spite of changes in the external environment.
homeostasis Condición en la que el medio ambiente interno de un organismo se mantiene estable a pesar de cambios en el medio ambiente externo.

homologous structures Structures that are similar in different species and that have been inherited from a common ancestor.
estructuras homólogas Estructuras parecidas de especies distintas y que se han heredado de un antepasado común.

homozygous Having two identical alleles for a particular gene.
homocigoto Que tiene dos alelos idénticos para un gen particular.

hot spot An area where magma from deep within the mantle melts through the crust above it.

GLOSSARY

punto caliente Área en la que el magma de las profundidades del manto atraviesa la corteza.

hybrid An offspring of crosses that has two different alleles for a trait.
híbrido Descendiente de cruces que tiene dos alelos distintos para un rasgo.

hybridization A selective breeding method that involves crossing different individuals to bring together the best traits from both parents.
hibridación Técnica reproductiva en la que se cruzan individuos distintos para reunir los mejores rasgos de ambos progenitores.

hydroelectric power Electricity produced by the kinetic energy of water moving over a waterfall or dam. (189)
energía hidroeléctrica Electricidad producida a partir de la energía cinética del agua que baja por una catarata o presa.

hydrosphere The portion of Earth that consists of water in any of its forms, including oceans, glaciers, rivers, lakes, groundwater and water vapor.
hidrósfera Parte de la Tierra formada por agua en cualquiera de sus formas, ya sea océanos, glaciares, ríos, lagos, agua subterránea y vapor de agua.

hypothesis A possible explanation for a set of observations or answer to a scientific question; must be testable.
hipótesis Explicación posible de un conjunto de observaciones o respuesta a una pregunta científica; se debe poder poner a prueba.

I

inbreeding A selective breeding method in which two individuals with similar sets of alleles are crossed.
endogamia Técnica reproductiva en la que se cruzan dos individuos con conjuntos de alelos parecidos.

incomplete dominance A situation in which one allele is not completely dominant over another allele.
dominancia incompleta Situación en la que un alelo no es completamente dominante sobre el otro.

incomplete metamorphosis A type of metamorphosis with three stages: egg, nymph, and adult.
metamorfosis incompleta Tipo de metamorfosis de tres etapas: huevo, ninfa y adulto.

independent variable The one factor that a scientist changes during an experiment; also called manipulated variable.

variable independiente El único factor que un científico altera durante un experimento; también se denomina variable manipulada.

index fossil Fossils of widely distributed organisms that lived during a geologically short period.
fósil guía Fósiles de organismos altamente dispersos que vivieron durante un período geológico corto.

induction A method of redistributing the charge on an object by means of the electric field of another object; the objects have no direct contact.
inducción Método de redistribuir la carga de un cuerpo haciendo uso del campo eléctrico de otro; los cuerpos no están en contacto directo.

inertia The tendency of an object to resist a change in motion.
inercia Tendencia de un objeto a resistir un cambio en su movimiento.

inferring The process of making an inference, an interpretation based on observations and prior knowledge.
inferir Proceso de hacer una inferencia; interpretación basada en observaciones y conocimientos previos.

inner core A dense sphere of solid iron and nickel at the center of Earth. (15)
núcleo interno Esfera densa de hierro y níquel que se encuentra en el centro de la Tierra.

input Material, energy, or information that goes into a system.
entrada Material, energía o informacion que se agrega a un sistema.

insulator 1. A material that does not conduct heat well. 2. A material that does not easily allow electric charges to flow.
aislante 1. Material que no conduce bien el calor. 2. Material que no permite fácilmente que las cargas eléctricas fluyan.

internal fertilization When eggs are fertilized inside a female's body.
fertilización interna Cuando los óvulos se fertilizan dentro del cuerpo de la hembra.

International System of Units (SI) A system of units used by scientists to measure the properties of matter.
Sistema Internacional de Unidades (SI) Sistema de unidades que los científicos usan para medir las propiedades de la materia.

intertidal zone An area between the highest high-tide line on land and the point on the continental shelf exposed by the lowest low-tide line.

zona intermareal Área entre el punto más alto de la marea alta y el punto más bajo de la marea baja.

intrusion An igneous rock layer formed when magma hardens beneath Earth's surface.
intrusión Capa de roca ígnea formada cuando el magma se endurece bajo la superficie de la Tierra.

invertebrate An animal without a backbone.
invertebrado Animal sin columna vertebral.

island arc A string of volcanoes that form as the result of subduction of one oceanic plate beneath a second oceanic plate.
arco de islas Cadena de volcanes formados como resultado de la subducción de una placa océanica debajo de una segunda placa océanica.

K

karyotype A picture of all the human chromosomes in a cell grouped together in pairs and arranged in order of decreasing size.
cariotipo Fotografía de todos los cromosomas humanos en una célula agrupados en pares y ordenados de los más grandes a los más pequeños.

keystone species A species that influences the survival of many other species in an ecosystem.
especie clave Especie que tiene un impacto en la supervivencia de muchas otras especies de un ecosistema.

L

larva The immature form of an animal that looks very different from the adult.
larva Forma inmadura de un animal que luce muy distinta al adulto.

lava Liquid magma that reaches the surface.
lava Magma líquido que sale a la superficie.

lava flow The area covered by lava as it pours out of a volcano's vent.
colada de lava Área cubierta de lava a medida que ésta sale por el ventiladero del volcán.

law of conservation of momentum The rule that in the absence of outside forces the total momentum of objects that interact does not change.
principio de la conservación del momento Regla que establece que, en ausencia de fuerzas externas, la cantidad de movimiento total de los cuerpos que se relacionan no cambia.

law of superposition The geologic principle that states that in horizontal layers of sedimentary rock, each layer is older than the layer above it and younger than the layer below it.
ley de la superposición Principio geológico que enuncia que, en las capas horizontales de las rocas sedimentarias, cada capa es más vieja que la capa superior y más joven que la capa inferior.

linear graph A line graph in which the data points yield a straight line.
gráfica lineal Gráfica en la cual los puntos de los datos forman una línea recta.

lithosphere A rigid layer made up of the uppermost part of the mantle and the crust.
litósfera Capa rígida constituida por la parte superior del manto y la corteza.

M

magma The molten mixture of rock-forming substances, gases, and water from the mantle.
magma Mezcla fundida de las sustancias que forman las rocas, gases y agua, proveniente del manto.

magma chamber The pocket beneath a volcano where magma collects.
cámara magmática Bolsa debajo de un volcán en la que está acumulado el magma.

magnet Any material that attracts iron and materials that contain iron.
imán Material que atrae hierro o materiales que contienen el hierro.

magnetic declination The angle between geographic north and the north to which a compass needle points.
declinación magnética Ángulo (en una ubicación particular) entre el norte geográfico y el polo magnético ubicado en el hemisferio norte de la Tierra.

magnetic field The region around a magnet where the magnetic force is exerted.
campo magnético Área alrededor de un imán donde actúa la fuerza magnética.

magnetic field lines Lines that map out the magnetic field around a magnet.
líneas del campo magnético Líneas que representan el campo magnético alrededor de un imán.

magnetic force A force produced when magnetic poles interact.
fuerza magnética Fuerza que se produce cuando hay actividad entre los polos magnéticos.

GLOSSARY

magnetic pole The ends of a magnetic object, where the magnetic force is strongest.
polo magnético Extremo de un cuerpo magnético, donde la fuerza magnética es mayor.

magnetism The force of attraction or repulsion of magnetic materials.
magnetismo Poder de atracción o repulsión de los materiales magnéticos.

magnitude The measurement of an earthquake's strength based on seismic waves and movement along faults.
magnitud Medida de la fuerza de un sismo basada en las ondas sísmicas y en el movimiento que ocurre a lo largo de las fallas.

mammal A vertebrate whose body temperature is regulated by its internal heat, and that has skin covered with hair or fur and glands that produce milk to feed its young.
mamífero Animal vertebrado cuya temperatura corporal es regulada por su calor interno, que tiene pelaje o pelo y que tiene glándulas que producen leche para alimentar a sus crías.

mantle The layer of hot, solid material between Earth's crust and core.
manto Capa de material caliente y sólido entre la corteza terrestre y el núcleo.

mass The amount of matter in an object.
masa Cantidad de materia que hay en un cuerpo.

mass extinction When many types of living things become extinct at the same time.
extinción en masa Situación que ocurre cuando muchos tipos de seres vivos se extinguen al mismo tiempo.

mass number The sum of protons and neutrons in the nucleus of an atom.
número de masa Suma de los protones y neutrones en el núcleo de un átomo.

mean The numerical average of a set of data.
media Promedio numérico de un conjunto de datos.

mechanical energy Kinetic or potential energy associated with the motion or position of an object.
energía mecánica Energía cinética o potencial asociada con el movimiento o la posición de un cuerpo.

median The middle number in a set of data.
mediana Número del medio de un conjunto de datos.

medusa A cnidarian body form characterized by an open umbrella shape and adapted for a free-swimming life.
medusa Cnidario con cuerpo que tiene la forma de una sombrilla abierta y que está adaptado para nadar libremente.

meiosis The process that occurs in the formation of sex cells (sperm and egg) by which the number of chromosomes is reduced by half.
meiosis Proceso durante la formación de las células sexuales (espermatozoide y óvulo) por el cual el número de cromosomas se reduce a la mitad.

meniscus The curved upper surface of a liquid in a column of liquid.
menisco Superficie superior curva de un líquido en una columna de líquido.

metamorphosis A process in which an animal's body undergoes major changes in shape and form during its life cycle.
metamorfosis Proceso por el cual el cuerpo de un animal cambia de forma radicalmente durante su ciclo vital.

metric system A system of measurement based on the number 10.
sistema métrico Sistema de medidas basado en el número 10.

mid-ocean ridge An undersea mountain chain where new ocean floor is produced; a divergent plate boundary. (80)
cordillera oceánica central Cadena montañosa submarina donde se produce el nuevo suelo oceánico; borde de placa divergente.

mode The number that appears most often in a list of numbers.
moda Número que aparece con más frecuencia en una lista de números.

model A representation of a complex object or process, used to help people understand a concept that they cannot observe directly.
modelo Representación de un objeto o proceso complejo que se usa para explicar un concepto que no se puede observar directamente.

Modified Mercalli scale A scale that rates the amount of shaking from an earthquake.
escala modificada de Mercalli Escala que evalúa la intensidad del temblor de un terremoto.

mold A type of fossil that is a hollow area in sediment in the shape of an organism or part of an organism.
molde Tipo de fósil que consiste en una depresión del sedimento que tiene la forma de un organismo o de parte de un organismo.

moment magnitude scale A scale that rates earthquakes by estimating the total energy released by an earthquake.
escala de magnitud de momento Escala con la que se miden los sismos estimando la cantidad total de energía liberada por un terremoto.

momentum The product of an object's mass and velocity.
momento Producto de la masa de un cuerpo multiplicada por su velocidad.

multiple alleles Three or more possible alleles of a gene that determine a trait.
alelo múltiple Tres o más alelos posibles del gen que determina un rasgo.

mutation Any change in the DNA of a gene or a chromosome.
mutación Cualquier cambio del ADN de un gen o cromosoma.

N

natural selection The process by which organisms that are best adapted to their environment are most likely to survive and reproduce.
selección natural Proceso por el que los organismos que se adaptan mejor a su ambiente tienen mayor probabilidad de sobrevivir y reproducirse.

net force The overall force on an object when all the individual forces acting on it are added together.
fuerza neta Fuerza total que se ejerce sobre un cuerpo cuando se suman las fuerzas individuales que actúan sobre él.

neutron A small particle in the nucleus of the atom, with no electrical charge.
neutrón Partícula pequeña en el núcleo del átomo, que no tiene carga eléctrica.

newton A unit of measure that equals the force required to accelerate 1 kilogram of mass at 1 meter per second per second.
newton Unidad de medida equivalente a la fuerza necesaria para acelerar 1 kilogramo de masa a 1 metro por segundo cada segundo.

nonlinear graph A line graph in which the data points do not fall along a straight line.
gráfica no lineal Gráfica lineal en la que los puntos de datos no forman una línea recta.

normal fault A type of fault where the hanging wall slides downward; caused by tension in the crust.

falla normal Tipo de falla en la cual el labio elevado o subyacente se desliza hacia abajo como resultado de la tensión de la corteza.

nucleus 1. In cells, a large oval organelle that contains the cell's genetic material in the form of DNA and controls many of the cell's activities. **2.** The central core of an atom which contains protons and neutrons. 3. The solid core of a comet.
núcleo 1. En las células, orgánulo grande y ovalado que contiene el material genético de la célula en forma de ADN y que controla muchas de las funciones celulares. **2.** Parte central del átomo que contiene los protones y los neutrones. 3. Centro sólido de un cometa.

nymph A stage of incomplete metamorphosis that usually resembles the adult insect.
ninfa Estado de la metamorfosis incompleta que generalmente se asemeja al insecto adulto.

O

objective reasoning Reasoning that is based on evidence.
razonamiento objetivo Razonamiento basado en la evidencia.

observing The process of using one or more of your senses to gather information.
observar Proceso de usar uno o más de tus sentidos para reunir información.

opinion An idea about a situation that is not supported by evidence.
opinión Idea sobre una situación que la evidencia no sustenta.

organ A body structure that is composed of different kinds of tissues that work together.
órgano Estructura del cuerpo compuesta de distintos tipos de tejidos que trabajan conjuntamente.

organ system A group of organs that work together to perform a major function.
sistema de órganos Grupo de órganos que trabajan juntos para realizar una función importante.

organism A living thing.
organismo Un ser vivo.

outlier An abnormal or irregular data point; a point on a graph that is clearly not part of the trend.
valor atípico Punto de datos anormal o irregular; punto en una gráfica que se aleja demasiado de los valores esperados.

GLOSSARY

outer core A layer of molten iron and nickel that surrounds the inner core of Earth.
núcleo externo Capa de hierro y níquel fundidos que rodea el núcleo interno de la Tierra.

output Material, energy, result, or product that comes out of a system.
salida Material, energía, resultado o producto que un sistema produce.

ovary **1.** A flower structure that encloses and protects ovules and seeds as they develop. **2.** Organ of the female reproductive system in which eggs and estrogen are produced.
ovario **1.** Estructura de una flor que encierra y protege a los óvulos y las semillas durante su desarrollo. **2.** Órgano del sistema reproductivo femenino en el que se producen los óvulos y el estrógeno.

ovule A plant structure in seed plants that produces the female gametophyte; contains an egg cell.
óvulo Estructura vegetal de las plantas de semilla que produce el gametofito femenino; contiene una célula reproductora femenina.

P

P wave A type of seismic wave that compresses and expands the ground.
onda P Tipo de onda sísmica que comprime y expande el suelo.

paleontologist A scientist who studies fossils to learn about organisms that lived long ago.
paleontólogo Científico que estudia fósiles para aprender acerca de los organismos que vivieron hace mucho tiempo.

Pangaea The name of the single landmass that began to break apart 200 million years ago and gave rise to today's continents.
Pangea Nombre de la masa de tierra única que empezó a dividirse hace 200 millones de años y que le dio origen a los continentes actuales.

pedigree A chart that shows the presence or absence of a trait according to the relationships within a family across several generations.
genealogía Diagrama que muestra la presencia o ausencia de un rasgo según las relaciones familiares a través de varias generaciones.

percent error A calculation used to determine how accurate, or close to the true value, an experimental value really is.
error porcentual Cálculo usado para determinar cuán exacto, o cercano al valor verdadero, es realmente un valor experimental.

perennial A flowering plant that lives for more than two years.
perenne Planta con flores que vive más de dos años.
petal A colorful, leaflike structure of some flowers.

period One of the units of geologic time into which geologists divide eras.
período Una de las unidades del tiempo geológico en las que los geólogos dividen las eras.

petrified fossil A fossil in which minerals replace all or part of an organism.
fósil petrificado Fósil en el cual los minerales reemplazan todo el organismo o parte de él.

phenotype An organism's physical appearance, or visible traits.
fenotipo Apariencia física, o rasgos visibles, de un organismo.

pipe A long tube through which magma moves from the magma chamber to Earth's surface.
chimenea Largo tubo por el que el magma sube desde la cámara magmática hasta la superficie de la tierra.

pistil The female reproductive part of a flower.
pistilo Parte reproductora femenina de una flor.

placenta An organ in most pregnant mammals, including humans, that links the mother and the developing embryo and allows for the passage of materials between them.
placenta Órgano de la mayoría de los mamíferos preñados, incluyendo a los seres humanos, que conecta a la madre con el embrión en desarrollo y que permite el intercambio de materiales.

plate tectonics The theory that pieces of Earth's lithosphere are in constant motion, driven by convection currents in the mantle.
tectónica de placas Teoría según la cual las partes de la litósfera de la Tierra están en continuo movimiento, impulsadas por las corrientes de convección del manto.

plateau A large landform that has high elevation and a more or less level surface.
meseta Accidente geográfico que tiene una elevación alta y cuya superficie está más o menos nivelada.

poaching Illegal killing or removal of wildlife from their habitats.
caza ilegal Matanza o eliminación de la fauna silvestre de su hábitat.

polarization The process through which electrons are attracted to or repelled by an external electric field, causing the electrons to move within their own atoms.

polarización Proceso por el cual un campo eléctrico externo atrae o repele a los electrones y hace que éstos se muevan dentro de su átomo.

pollination The transfer of pollen from male reproductive structures to female reproductive structures in plants.
polinización Transferencia del polen de las estructuras reproductoras masculinas de una planta a las estructuras reproductoras femeninas.

polygenic inheritance The inheritance of traits that are controlled by two or more genes, such as height in humans.
herencia poligénica Herencia de los rasgos controlados por dos o más genes, como la altura en los seres humanos.

polyp A cnidarian body form characterized by an upright vase shape and usually adapted for a life attached to an underwater surface.
pólipo Cnidario con cuerpo de forma tubular y que está adaptado para vivir fijo en un fondo acuático.

precision How close a group of measurements are to each other.
precisión Cuán cerca se encuentran un grupo de medidas.

predicting The process of forecasting what will happen in the future based on past experience or evidence.
predecir Proceso de pronosticar lo que va a suceder en el futuro, basándose en evidencia o experiencias previas.

pressure The force pushing on a surface divided by the area of that surface.
presión Fuerza que actúa contra una superficie, dividida entre el área de esa superficie.

probability A number that describes how likely it is that a particular event will occur.
probabilidad Número que describe cuán probable es que ocurra un suceso.

process A sequence of actions in a system.
proceso Secuencia de acciones en un sistema.

pseudoscience A set of beliefs that may make use of science but whose conclusions and predictions are not based on observation, objective reasoning, or scientific evidence.
pseudociencia Conjunto de creencias que pueden basarse en la ciencia, pero cuyas conclusiones no se derivan de la observación, el razonamiento objetivo o evidencia científica.

punctuated equilibrium Pattern of evolution in which long stable periods are interrupted by brief periods of more rapid change.

equilibrio puntual Patrón de la evolución en el que los períodos largos estables son interrumpidos por breves períodos de cambio rápido.

Punnett square A chart that shows all the possible combinations of alleles that can result from a genetic cross.
cuadrado de Punnett Tabla que muestra todas las combinaciones posibles de los alelos que se pueden derivar de un cruce genético.

pupa The third stage of complete metamorphosis, in which a larva develops into an adult insect.
pupa Tercera etapa de la metamorfosis completa, en la que la larva se convierte en insecto adulto.

purebred An offspring of many generations that have the same form of a trait.
raza pura Descendiente de varias generaciones que tienen los mismos rasgos.

pyroclastic flow The flow of ash, cinders, bombs, and gases down the side of a volcano during an explosive eruption.
flujo piroclástico Flujo de ceniza, escoria, bombas y gases que corre por las laderas de un volcán durante una erupción explosiva.

Q

qualitative observation An observation that deals with characteristics that cannot be expressed in numbers.
observación cualitativa Observación que se centra en las características que no se pueden expresar con números.

quantitative observation An observation that deals with a number or amount.
observación cuantitativa Observación que se centra en un número o cantidad.

R

radiation The transfer of energy by electromagnetic waves.
radiación Transferencia de energía por medio de ondas magnéticas.

radioactive decay The process in which the nuclei of radioactive elements break down, releasing fast-moving particles and energy.

GLOSSARY

desintegración radiactiva Proceso de descomposición del núcleo de los elementos radiactivos que libera partículas en movimiento y energía.

range The difference between the greatest value and the least value in a set of data.
rango Diferencia entre el mayor y el menor valor de un conjunto de datos.

recessive allele An allele that is hidden whenever the dominant allele is present.
alelo recesivo Alelo que se no manifiesta cuando el alelo dominante está presente.

relative age The age of a rock compared to the ages of other rocks.
edad relativa Edad de una roca comparada con la edad de otras rocas.

repeated trial A repetition of an experiment to gather additional data and determine whether the experiment's results support the hypothesis.
prueba repetida Repetición de un experimento para recopilar datos adicionales y determinar si los resultados de un experimento sustentan la hipótesis.

replication The process by which a cell makes a copy of the DNA in its nucleus before cell division.
replicación Proceso en el que la célula copia el ADN de su núcleo antes de la división celular.

reptile A vertebrate whose temperature is determined by the temperature of its environment, that has lungs and scaly skin, and that lays eggs on land.
reptil Animal vertebrado cuya temperatura depende de la temperatura de su entorno, que tiene pulmones, piel con escamas y que pone huevos en la tierra.

resistance The measurement of how difficult it is for charges to flow through an object.
resistencia Medida de la dificultad de una carga eléctrica para fluir por un cuerpo.

response An action or change in behavior that occurs as a result of a stimulus.
respuesta Acción o cambio del comportamiento que ocurre como resultado de un estímulo.

reverse fault A type of fault where the hanging wall slides upward; caused by compression in the crust.
falla inversa Tipo de falla en la cual el labio superior se desliza hacia arriba como resultado de compresión de la corteza.

Richter scale A scale that rates an earthquake's magnitude based on the size of its seismic waves.

escala de Richter Escala con la que se mide la magnitud de un terremoto según el tamaño de sus ondas sísmicas.

Ring of Fire A major belt of volcanoes that rims the Pacific Ocean.
Cinturón de Fuego Gran cadena de volcanes que rodea el océano Pacífico.

rift valley A deep valley that forms where two plates move apart.
valle de fisura Valle profundo que se forma cuando dos placas se separan.

rolling friction Friction that occurs when an object rolls over a surface.
fricción de rodamiento Fricción que ocurre cuando un cuerpo rueda sobre una superficie.

root cap A structure that covers the tip of a root, protecting the root from injury as the root grows through soil.
cofia Estructura que cubre la punta de una raíz y la protege de cualquier daño mientras crece en la tierra.

---------------- S ----------------

S wave A type of seismic wave in which the shaking is perpendicular to the direction of the wave.
onda S Tipo de onda sísmica que hace que el suelo se mueva en una dirección perpendicular a la onda.

satellite Any object that orbits around another object in space.
satélite Cualquier cuerpo que orbita alrededor de otro cuerpo en el espacio.

science A way of learning about the natural world through observations and logical reasoning; leads to a body of knowledge.
ciencia Estudio del mundo natural a través de observaciones y del razonamiento lógico; conduce a un conjunto de conocimientos.

scientific explanation A generalization that makes sense of observations by using logical reasoning.
explicación científica Generalización que usa el razonamiento lógico para darle sentido a las observaciones.

scientific inquiry The ongoing process of discovery in science; the diverse ways in which scientists study the natural world and propose explanations based on evidence they gather.
indagación científica Proceso continuo de descubrimiento en la ciencia; diversidad de métodos

con los que los científicos estudian el mundo natural y proponen explicaciones del mismo basadas en la evidencia que reúnen.

scientific literacy The knowledge and understanding of scientific terms and principles required for evaluating information, making personal decisions, and taking part in public affairs.
conocimiento científico Conocimiento y comprensión de los términos y principios científicos necesarios para evaluar información, tomar decisiones personales y participar en actividades públicas.

scientific theory A well-tested explanation for a wide range of observations or experimental results.
teoría científica Explicación comprobada de una gran variedad de observaciones o resultados de experimentos.

sea-floor spreading The process by which molten material adds new oceanic crust to the ocean floor.
despliegue del suelo oceánico Proceso mediante el cual la materia fundida añade nueva corteza oceánica al suelo oceánico.

seismic wave Vibrations that travel through Earth carrying the energy released during an earthquake.
ondas sísmicas Vibraciones que se desplazan por la Tierra, y que llevan la energía liberada durante un terremoto.

seismogram The record of an earthquake's seismic waves produced by a seismograph.
sismograma Registro producido por un sismógrafo de las ondas sísmicas de un terremoto.

seismograph A device that records ground movements caused by seismic waves as they move through Earth.
sismógrafo Aparato con el que se registran los movimientos del suelo ocasionados por las ondas sísmicas a medida que éstas se desplazan por la Tierra.

selective breeding Method of breeding that allows only those organisms with desired traits to produce the next generation.
cruce selectivo Técnica reproductiva por medio de la cual sólo los organismos con rasgos deseados producen la próxima generación.

sepal A leaflike structure that encloses and protects the bud of a flower.
sépalo Estructura similar a una hoja que encierra y protege el capullo de una flor.

sex chromosomes A pair of chromosomes carrying genes that determine whether a person is male or female.
cromosomas sexuales Par de cromosomas portadores de genes que determinan el sexo (masculino o femenino) de una persona.

sex-linked gene A gene that is carried on a sex (X or Y) chromosome.
gen ligado al sexo Gen de un cromosoma sexual (X o Y).

shearing Stress that pushes masses of rock in opposite directions, in a sideways movement.
cizallamiento Fuerza que presiona masas de roca en sentidos opuestos, de lado a lado.

shield volcano A wide, gently sloping mountain made of layers of lava and formed by quiet eruptions.
volcán en escudo Montaña ancha de pendientes suaves, compuesta por capas de lava y formada durante erupciones que no son violentas.

significant figures All the digits in a measurement that have been measured exactly, plus one digit whose value has been estimated.
cifras significativas En una medida, todos los dígitos que se han medido con exactitud, más un dígito cuyo valor se ha estimado.

silica A material found in magma that is formed from the elements oxygen and silicon; it is the primary substance of Earth's crust and mantle.
sílice Material presente en el magma, compuesto por los elementos oxígeno y silicio; es el componente más común de la corteza y el manto de la Tierra.

sill A slab of volcanic rock formed when magma squeezes between layers of rock.
dique concordante Placa de roca volcánica formada cuando el magma a través de capas de roca.

sporophyte The stage in the life cycle of a plant in which the plant produces spores.
esporofito Etapa del ciclo vital de una planta en la que produce esporas.

stamen The male reproductive part of a flower.
estambre Parte reproductora masculina de una flor.

stimulus Any change or signal in the environment that can make an organism react in some way.
estímulo Cualquier cambio o señal del medio ambiente que puede causar una reacción en un organismo.

skepticism An attitude of doubt.
escepticismo Actitud de duda.

sliding friction Friction that occurs when one solid surface slides over another.
fricción de deslizamiento Fricción que ocurre cuando una superficie sólida se desliza sobre otra.

solenoid A coil of wire with a current.
solenoide Bobina de alambre con una corriente.

GLOSSARY

species A group of similar organisms that can mate with each other and produce offspring that can also mate and reproduce.
especie Grupo de organismos semejantes que pueden cruzarse y producir descendencia fértil.

stamen The male reproductive part of a flower.
estambre Parte reproductora masculina de una flor.

static discharge The loss of static electricity as electric charges transfer from one object to another.
descarga estática Pérdida de la electricidad estática cuando las cargas eléctricas se transfieren de un cuerpo a otro.

static electricity A buildup of charges on an object.
electricidad estática Acumulación de cargas eléctricas en un cuerpo.

static friction Friction that acts between objects that are not moving.
fricción estática Fricción que actúa sobre los cuerpos que no están en movimiento.

stoma Small opening on the underside of a leaf through which oxygen, water, and carbon dioxide can move (plural: stomata).
estoma Pequeña abertura en la superficie inferior de la hoja a través de cual ocurre el intercambio de oxígeno, agua y dióxido de carbono.

stress A force that acts on rock to change its shape or volume.
presión Fuerza que actúa sobre las rocas y que cambia su forma o volumen.

strike-slip fault A type of fault in which rocks on either side move past each other sideways with little up or down motion.
falla transcurrente Tipo de falla en la cual las rocas a ambos lados se deslizan horizontalmente en sentidos opuestos, con poco desplazamiento hacia arriba o abajo.

subduction The process by which oceanic crust sinks beneath a deep-ocean trench and back into the mantle at a convergent plate boundary.
subducción Proceso mediante el cual la corteza oceánica se hunde debajo de una fosa oceánica profunda y vuelve al manto por el borde de una placa convergente.

surface wave A type of seismic wave that forms when P waves and S waves reach Earth's surface.
onda superficial Tipo de onda sísmica que se forma cuando las ondas P y las ondas S llegan a la superficie de la Tierra.

system A group of related parts that work together to perform a function or produce a result.
sistema Grupo de partes relacionadas que trabajan conjuntamente para realizar una función o producir un resultado.

T

tadpole The larval form of a frog or toad.
renacuajo Estado de larva de una rana o un sapo.

tension Stress that stretches rock so that it becomes thinner in the middle.
tensión Fuerza que estira una roca, de modo que es más delgada en el centro.

threatened species A species that could become endangered in the near future.
especie amenazada Especie que puede llegar a estar en peligro de extinción en el futuro próximo.

tissue A group of similar cells that perform a specific function.
tejido Grupo de células semejantes que realizan una función específica.

trace fossil A type of fossil that provides evidence of the activities of ancient organisms.
vestigios fósiles Tipo de fósil que presenta evidencia de las actividades de los organismos antiguos.

trade-off An exchange in which one benefit is given up in order to obtain another.
sacrificar una cosa por otra Intercambio en el que se renuncia a un beneficio para obtener otro.

trait A specific characteristic that an organism can pass to its offspring through its genes.
rasgo Característica específica que un organismo puede transmitir a sus descendientes a través de los genes.

transform boundary A plate boundary where two plates move past each other in opposite directions.
borde de transformación Borde de una placa donde dos placas se deslizan, en sentidos opuestos, y se pasan la una a la otra.

transformer A device that increases or decreases voltage, which often consists of two separate coils of insulated wire wrapped around an iron core.
transformador Aparato que aumenta o disminuye el voltaje, que consiste de dos bobinas de alambre aislado y devanado sobre un núcleo de hierro.

transpiration The process by which water is lost through a plant's leaves.
transpiración Proceso por el cual las hojas de una planta pierden agua.

tumor A mass of rapidly dividing cells that can damage surrounding tissue.
tumor Masa de células que se dividen rápidamente y que puede dañar los tejidos que la rodean.

U

unconformity A gap in the geologic record that shows where rock layers have been lost due to erosion.
discordancia Interrupción en el récord geológico que muestra dónde las capas rocosas se han perdido a causa de la erosión.

V

variation Any difference between individuals of the same species.
variación Cualquier diferencia entre individuos de la misma especie.

vent The opening through which molten rock and gas leave a volcano.
ventiladero Abertura a través de la que la roca derretida y los gases salen de un volcán.

vertebrate An animal with a backbone.
vertebrado Animal con columna vertebral.

volcanic neck A deposit of hardened magma in a volcano's pipe.
cuello volcánico Depósito de magma solidificada en la chimenea de un volcán.

volcano A weak spot in the crust where magma has come to the surface.
volcán Punto débil en la corteza por donde el magma escapa hacia la superficie.

voltage The difference in electrical potential energy per charge between two places in a circuit.
voltaje Diferencia en el potencial eléctrico que hay entre dos áreas de un circuito.

volume The amount of space that matter occupies.
volumen Cantidad de espacio que ocupa la materia.

W

weight A measure of the force of gravity acting on an object.
peso Medida de la fuerza de gravedad que actúa sobre un cuerpo.

Z

zygote A fertilized egg, produced by the joining of a sperm cell and an egg cell.
cigoto Óvulo fertilizado, producido por la unión de un espermatozoide y un óvulo.

Index

Page numbers for key terms are printed in **boldface** type.

Index

Page numbers for key terms are printed in **boldface** type.

Index

Page numbers for key terms are printed in **boldface** type.

Index

Page numbers for key terms are printed in **boldface** type.

Index

Page numbers for key terms are printed in **boldface** type.

Index

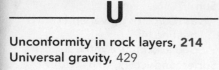

Page numbers for key terms are printed in **boldface** type.

ACKNOWLEDGMENTS

Staff Credits

The people who made up the *Interactive Science* team—representing composition services, core design digital and multimedia production services, digital product development, editorial, editorial services, manufacturing, and production—are listed below:

Jan Van Aarsen, Samah Abadir, Ernie Albanese, Chris Anton, Zareh Artinian, Bridget Binstock, Suzanne Biron, Niki Birbilis, MJ Black, Nancy Bolsover, Stacy Boyd, Jim Brady, Katherine Bryant, Michael Burstein, Pradeep Byram, Jessica Chase, Jonathan Cheney, Arthur Ciccone, Allison Cook-Bellistri, Rebecca Cottingham, AnnMarie Coyne, Bob Craton, Chris Deliee, Paul Delsignore, Michael Di Maria, Diane Dougherty, Kristen Ellis, Kelly Engel, Theresa Eugenio, Amanda Ferguson, Jorgensen Fernandez, Kathryn Fobert, Alicia Franke, Louise Gachet, Julia Gecha, Mark Geyer, Steve Gobbell, Paula Gogan-Porter, Jeffrey Gong, Sandra Graff, Robert M. Graham, Adam Groffman, Lynette Haggard, Christian Henry, Karen Holtzman, Susan Hutchinson, Sharon Inglis, Marian Jones, Sumy Joy, Sheila Kanitsch, Courtenay Kelley, Chris Kennedy, Toby Klang, Greg Lam, Russ Lappa, Margaret LaRaia, Ben Leveillee, Thea Limpus, Charles Luey, Dotti Marshall, Kathy Martin, Robyn Matzke, John McClure, Mary Beth McDaniel, Krista McDonald, Tim McDonald, Rich McMahon, Cara McNally, Bernadette McQuilkin, Melinda Medina, Angelina Mendez, Maria Milczarek, Claudi Mimo, Mike Napieralski, Deborah Nicholls, Dave Nichols, William Oppenheimer, Jodi O'Rourke, Ameer Padshah, Lorie Park, Celio Pedrosa, Jonathan Penyack, Linda Zust Reddy, Jennifer Reichlin, Stephen Rider, Charlene Rimsa, Walter Rodriguez, Stephanie Rogers, Marcy Rose, Rashid Ross, Anne Rowsey, Logan Schmidt, Amanda Seldera, Laurel Smith, Nancy Smith, Ted Smykal, Emily Soltanoff, Cindy Strowman, Dee Sunday, Barry Tomack, Elizabeth Tustian, Patricia Valencia, Ana Sofia Villaveces, Stephanie Wallace, Amanda Watters, Christine Whitney, Brad Wiatr, Heidi Wilson, Heather Wright, Rachel Youdelman.

Photography

All otherwise unacknowledged photos are copyright © 2011 Pearson Education.

Cover

Boy with horn, David Deas/DK Stock/Getty Images; **reflection,** Flirt/SuperStock.

Front Matter

vi, Chris Sattlberger/Digital Vision/Getty Images; **vii,** Stephen Dalton/Minden Pictures; **viii,** Whit Richardson/Getty Images; **ix,** Peter Rowlands/PR Productions; **x,** Pata Roque/AP Images; **xi,** Digital Vision/Photolibrary; **xii,** James L. Amos/Photo Researchers, Inc.; **xiii,** Mark Kostich; **xiv,** Blickwinkel/Alamy; **xv,** HALEY/SIPA/Newscom; **xvi,** Chris Newbert/Minden Pictures; **xvii,** Brian Snyder/Reuters; **xviii,** Construction Photography/Corbis; **xxi laptop,** iStockphoto.com; **xxiii, girl,** JupiterImages/Getty Images; **xxviii l,** Comstock/JupiterUnlimited; **xxviii r,** Kevin Fleming/Corbis; **xxix l,** Flip Nicklin/Minden Pictures; **xxix r,** Reuters/Matangi Tonga Online/Landov; **xxxi l,** ISSD/SuperStock; **xxxi r,** ZSSD/SuperStock; **xxxii, soccer players,** Randy Siner/APImages **xxxiii,** Darryl Leniuk/Getty Images.

Chapter 1

xxxiv–001 spread, Robert Postma/AGE Fotostock; **3 t,** Mark Humphrey/AP Images; **3 tm,** Edgewater Media/Shutterstock; **3 b,** Daniel Templeton/Alamy; **3 bm,** Richard Haynes; **4 m,** Copyright 2006 by The National Academy of Sciences of the USA; **4 tr,** Science Source/Photo Researchers, Inc.; **5 inset,** Inga Spence/Getty Images; **5 bkgrnd,** Tom & Pat Leeson/Photo Researchers, Inc.; **6 tl,** W.D. Brush/USDA-NRCS PLANTS Database; **7 bl,** Thomas Mangelsen/Minden Pictures; **8–9 spread,** Mark Humphrey/AP Images; **10 m,** Indianapolis Recorder Collection, Indiana Historical Society; **14 b,** Edgewater Media/Shutterstock; **15 bkgrnd,** Babak Tafreshi/Photo Researchers, Inc.; **16 tr,** *Untitled* (1920), George Grosz. Oil on canvas. Collection Kunstsammlung Nordrhein-Westfalen, Duesseldorf, Germany/Photo by Erich Lessing/Art Resource, New York/Artwork copyright Estate of George Grosz/Licensed by VAGA, New York, NY; **17 m,** Walter C. Jaap/Sustainable Seas/R. Halley/Courtesy of USGS; **19 b,** Navnit/Shutterstock; **20 m,** Radius Images/Photolibrary New York; **21 br,** Sam Yu/The Frederick News-Post/AP Images; **24 bkgrnd,** Patrick LaRoque/First Light Associated Photographers/Photolibrary New York; **26 bl,** Tim Fitzharris/Minden Pictures; **27 spread,** John Dominis/Index Stock Imagery/Photolibrary New York; **29 r,** Daniel Templeton/Alamy; **29 l,** John Short/Jupiter Images; **31 m,** Inspirestock/Jupiter Images; **32–33 spread,** imagebroker/Alamy; **34 b,** John Short/Jupiter Images; **34 m,** Navnit/Shutterstock; **34 t,** Science Source/Photo Researchers, Inc.; **36,** Barrie Rokeach/Alamy; **38,** Explorer/Photo Researchers, Inc.

Chapter 2

Pages 40–41 spread, NASA Langley Research Center (NASA-LaRC); **43 t,** Paul Burns/Getty Images; **43 tm,** Stem Jems/Photo Researchers, Inc.; **43 bm,** J. I. Alvarez-Hamelin, M. Beiró, L. Dall'Asta, A. Barrat, A. Vespignani; http://xavier.informatics.indiana.edu/lanet-vi/ http://sourceforge.net/projects/lanet-vi/; **45 br,** Zhao Jianwei/Imaginechina/AP Images; **46 t,** Image Source/Getty Images; **47 tr,** Stephen Dalton/Minden Pictures; **47 bkgrnd,** Barry Mansell/Nature Picture Library; **48 bl,** Paul Burns/Getty Images; **49 m,** Image100/SuperStock; **51 spread,** Kenneth Morris/ASP-Covered Images/Zuma Press; **52 b,** Tue Nam Ton/Contra Costa Newspapers/Zuma Press; **52 tl,** Olga Lipatova/Shutterstock; **54 inset,** NOAA; **54 bkgrnd,** Erik Zobrist/NOAA Restoration Center; **55 tr,** Amazon Images/Alamy; **55 br,** Stem Jems/Photo Researchers, Inc.; **56 b,** Richard Haynes; **57 r,** Lukasz Kwapien/iStockphoto.com; **58 t,** Andy Levin/Alamy; **58–59 bkgrnd,** imagebroker/Alamy; **58–59 bkgrnd,** imagebroker/Alamy; **59 r,** Melvyn Longhurst/Alamy; **60 m,** Science & Society Picture Library/Getty Images; **62 b,** Bernd Vogel/Corbis; **63 b,** Chris Parypa/Alamy; **64–65 spread,** Bill Curtsinger/National Geographic Stock; **65 tr,** Valery Rizzo/Alamy; **66 b,** Oliver Burston/Photolibrary New York; **66 tr,** Vladislav Ociacia/Alamy; **67 r,** J. I. Alvarez-Hamelin, M. Beiró, L. Dall'Asta, A. Barrat, A. Vespignani; http://xavier.informatics.indiana.edu/lanet-vi/http://sourceforge.net/projects/lanet-vi/; **68–69 spread,** Agence Zoom/Getty Images; **70 b,** Brian E. Small/VIREO; **72 inset,** Tony Heald/Minden Pictures;

ACKNOWLEDGMENTS

72–73 spread, Suzi Eszterhas/Minden Pictures; **74 tr,** Martin Shields/Alamy; **74 b,** Originalpunkt/Shutterstock; **79 b,** Corbis Super RF/Alamy; **79 bl,** Dave White/iStockphoto.com; **79 ml,** Martin Darley/iStockphoto.com; **79 m,** Vincent P. Walter/Prentice Hall, Inc.; **79 mr,** Chas/Shutterstock.com.

Chapter 2 Feature
Page 84 bkgrnd, AP Images; **84 tl,** Greg Huey/AP Images; **85,** Brian J. Skerry/National Geographic Stock.

Chapter 3
Pages 86–87, Whit Richardson/Getty Images; **89 t,** ©2006 John Eastcott and Yva Momatiuk/Getty Images; **89 m,** Design Pics Inc./Alamy; **89 b,** Rick Price/Nature Picture Library; **90 bkgrnd,** Michael Busselle/Getty Images; **91,** ©2006 John Eastcott and Yva Momatiuk/Getty Images; **92 t,** All Canada Photos/Alamy; **92 m,** Roger Werth/Woodfin Camp/Getty Images; **92 b,** Design Pics Inc./Alamy; **93 inset,** Anna Yu/iStockphoto.com; **92–93,** Marvin Dembinsky Photo Associates/Alamy; **94 l,** Dietrich Rose/zefa/Corbis; **94 r,** Philip Dowell/Dorling Kindersley; **95,** David Jordan/AP Images; **96,** Samuel B. Mukasa; **98,** Tracy Frankel/Getty Images; **99 t,** NASA; **99 tm,** Rick Price/Nature Picture Library; **99 bm,** Harry Taylor/Royal Museum of Scotland, Edinburgh/Dorling Kindersley; **99 b,** Harry Taylor/Dorling Kindersley; **100,** NASA; **101,** NASA; **102–103 earth,** NASA; **102–103 stars,** Markus Gann/Shutterstock; **103,** Copyright © 1990 Richard Megna/Fundamental Photographs **104,** Jupiterimages/Brand X/Alamy; **105 l,** Pancaketom/Dreamstime.com; **105 m,** Bloomimage/Corbis; **105 r,** INSADCO Photography/Alamy; **106 t,** Hall/photocuisine/Corbis; **106 b,** tbkmedia.de/Alamy; **107,** NASA; **108 t,** Design Pics Inc./Alamy; **108 m,** NASA; **108 b,** Hall/Photocuisine/Corbis.

Interchapter Feature
Page 112 bkgrnd, Daniel Sambraus/Photo Researchers, Inc.; **112 b,** Courtesy of Michael Wysession; **113 t,** John McConnico/AP Images; **113 b,** Bryan & Cherry Alexander Photography/Alamy.

Chapter 4
Pages 114–115, Peter Rowlands/PR Productions; **118,** Peter Dennis/Dorling Kindersley; **121,** Francois Gohier/Photo Researchers, Inc.; **122,** The Granger Collection, New York; **123,** moodboard/Corbis; **124 t,** OAR/National Undersea Research Program/Photo Researchers, Inc.; **124 m,** Courtesy of USGS; **124 b,** Paul Zoeller/AP Images; **125,** Sandy Felsenthal/Corbis; **128,** Image Source/Getty Images; **130,** Kristy-Anne Glubish/Design Pics/Corbis; **131,** Daniel Sambraus/Science Photo Library; **132,** Blaine Harrington III/Corbis; **133,** James Balog/Getty Images; **134,** Daniel Sambraus/Science Photo Library.

Interchapter Feature
Page 138, Emory Kristof/National Geographic Stock; **139 t,** Radius Images/Alamy; **139 bkgrnd,** Carsten Peter/National Geographic Stock.

Chapter 5
Pages 140–141, Pata Roque/AP Images; **143 t,** Michael Nichols/Getty Images; **143 b,** D. Parker/Photo Researchers Inc.; **144,** Alan Kearney/Getty Images; **146 l,** Breck P. Kent/Animals Animals/Earth Scenes; **146 r,** Marli Miller/University of Oregon; **147,** D. Parker/Photo Researchers Inc.; **148–149,** Martin Bond/Photo Researchers, Inc.; **150,** Bob Krist/Corbis; **151,** Michael Nichols/Getty Images; **152–153,** AFP/Getty Images/Newscom; **156 l,** Photo Japan/Alamy; **156 r,** Koji Sasahara/AP Images; **157,** Ho New/Reuters; **166 t,** D. Parker/Photo Researchers, Inc.; **166 b,** Koji Sasahara/AP Images; **168,** Jewel Samad/AFP/Getty Images.

Interchapter Feature
Page 170, Gibson Stock Photography; **171 tl,** WENN/Newscom; **171 tr,** Geoff Brightling/Dorling Kindersley; **171 br,** Ajit Kumar/AP Images.

Chapter 6
Pages 172–173, Digital Vision/Photolibrary New York; **175 t,** Danny Lehman/Corbis; **175 b,** Allan Seiden/Pacific Stock; **176,** George Steinmetz/Corbis; **180 inset,** Colin Keates/Natural History Museum, London/Dorling Kindersley; **180 bkgrnd,** Karl Weatherly/Getty Images; **182 tl,** Rainer Albiez/iStockphoto.com; **182–183,** G. Brad Lewis/Omjalla Images; **183 t,** Tui De Roy/Minden Pictures; **183 b,** Dave B. Fleetham/Tom Stack & Associates, Inc.; **184 t,** Pat and Tom Leeson/Photo Researchers, Inc.; **184 b,** U.S. Geological Survey/Geologic Inquiries Group; **184 bkgrnd,** Paul Thompson/Photolibrary New York; **185,** Alberto Garcia/Corbis; **187 l,** Courtesy of USGS; **187 r,** G. Brad Lewis/Omjalla Images; **188 b,** Karen Kasmauski/Corbis; **189,** Allan Seiden/Pacific Stock; **190 t,** Jeffzenner/Shutterstock, Inc.; **190 b,** Rob Reichenfeld/Dorling Kindersley; **192 inset,** Eric & David Hosking/Photo Researchers, Inc.; **192 bkgrnd,** Danny Lehman/Corbis; **193,** David J. Boyle/Animals Animals/Earth Scenes; **194 t,** Dave B. Fleetham/Tom Stack & Associates, Inc.; **194 b,** David J. Boyle/Animals Animals/Earth Scenes.

Interchapter Feature
Page 198 t, Arctic Images/Alamy; **198 bkgrnd,** Bettmann/Corbis; **199 t,** Krafft/Explorer/Photo Researchers, Inc.; **199 b,** Tom Van Sant/Corbis.

Chapter 7
Pages 200–201 spread, Tam C. Nguyen/Phototake; **203 t,** James L. Amos/Photo Researchers, Inc.; **203 m1,** Michael Szoenyi/Photo Researchers, Inc.; **203 m2,** Dr. Marli Miller/Getty Images; **203 m2,** Bedrock Studios/Dorling Kindersley; **204,** Phil Martin/PhotoEdit Inc.; **204 boy,** Diane Diederich/iStockphoto.com; **205,** Stock Connection/Newscom; **206 fern fossils,** Charles R. Belinky/Photo Researchers, Inc.; **206 insect fossil,** Breck P. Kent; **206 dinosaur footprint,** Travel Ink/Getty Images, Inc.; **207 b,** Yva Momatiuk & John Eastcott/Minden Pictures; **207 t,** James L. Amos/Photo Researchers, Inc.; **207 m,** Dave King/Courtesy of the National Museum of Wales/Dorling Kindersley; **208 l,** Courtesy of the Peabody Museum of Natural History, Yale University; **208 r,** Newscom; **208 m,** John Cancalosi/age Fotostock/Photolibrary New York; **209,** Phil Schermeister/Corbis; **211,** Jeff Foott/Discovery Channel Images/Getty Images; **212 t,** Michael Szoenyi/Photo Researchers, Inc.; **212 b,** G. R. Roberts/Photo Researchers, Inc.; **215,** Dr. Marli Miller/Getty Images; **216,** The Granger Collection, New York; **219,** Archaeological Society

SAP/AP Images; **220 r bkgrnd,** Jeremy Walker/Science Photo Library/Photo Researchers; **220 l bkgrnd,** Gianni Tortoli/Photo Researchers, Inc.; **220 br,** Dave King/Dorling Kindersley; **220 t,** Gary Ombler/Robert L. Braun, modelmaker/Dorling Kindersley; **221,** James L. Amos/Corbis; **222 smilodon,** Colin Keates/Courtesy of the Natural History Museum, London/Dorling Kindersley; **222 velociraptor,** Gary Ombler/Luis Rey, Modelmaker/Dorling Kindersley; **222 wiwaxia,** Chase Studio/Photo Researchers, Inc.; **222 chart t,** Peter Johnson/Corbis; **222 chart m2,** Fred Bavendam/Visuals Unlimited; **222 chart m1,** Jeremy Walker/Science Photo Library/Photo Researchers; **222 chart b,** Gianni Tortoli/Photo Researchers, Inc.; **223,** R. Dolton/Alamy; **224 bkgrnd,** National Oceanic and Atmospheric Administration (NOAA); **224 bl inset,** National Oceanic and Atmospheric Administration (NOAA); **224 br inset,** National Oceanic and Atmospheric Administration (NOAA); **227,** Fred Bavendam/Visuals Unlimited; **228 inset,** Francois Gohier/Photo Researchers, Inc.; **228 bkgrnd,** Mark Garlick/Photo Researchers, Inc.; **229 l,** Alan Sirulnikoff/Photo Researchers, Inc.; **229 r,** The Natural History Museum, London; **230,** David Fleetham/Alamy; **232,** Sinclair Stammers/Photo Researchers, Inc.; **233 t,** Gary Ombler/Robert L. Braun, modelmaker/Dorling Kindersley; **233 b,** John Downs/Dorling Kindersley; **233 bkgrnd,** Jeremy Walker/Science Photo Library/Photo Researchers; **233 bkgrnd,** Jeremy Walker/Science Photo Library/Photo Researchers; **235 l,** Harry Taylor/Courtesy of the Natural History Museum, London/Dorling Kindersley; **235 r,** Jerry Young/Dorling Kindersley; **236 sea pen,** Chase Studio/Photo Researchers, Inc.; **236 trilobite,** Chase Studio/Photo Researchers, Inc.; **236 jawless fish,** Zig Leszczynski/Animals Animals/Earth Scenes; **236 ammonite,** Colin Keates/Courtesy of the Natural History Museum, London/Dorling Kindersley; **236 early plant,** Patrice Rossi Calkin; **236 sea scorpion,** Publiphoto/Photo Researchers, Inc.; **236 lava,** Gianni Tortoli/Photo Researchers, Inc.; **237 bkgrnd,** Greg Vaughn/Alamy; **237 bony fish,** Harry Taylor/Courtesy of the Royal Museum of Scotland, Edinburgh/Dorling Kindersley; **237 early amphibian,** Harry Taylor/Courtesy of the Royal Museum of Scotland, Edinburgh/Dorling Kindersley; **237 giant dragonfly,** Steve Gorton/Courtesy of Oxford University Museum of Natural History/Dorling Kindersley; **237 club moss,** Sheila Terry/Photo Researchers, Inc.; **237 dimetrodon,** Bedrock Studios/Dorling Kindersley; **238 coelophysis,** Gary Ombler/Gary Staab, modelmaker/Dorling Kindersley; **238 plateosaurus,** Bedrock Studios/Dorling Kindersley; **238 barosaurus,** Dave King/Jeremy Hunt at Centaur Studios, modelmaker/Dorling Kindersley; **238 early mammal,** Malcolm McGregor/Dorling Kindersley; **238 gigantosaurus,** Jon Hughes/Bedrock Studios/Dorling Kindersley; **238–239 bison bkgrnd,** Peter Johnson/Corbis; **238–239 forest bkgrnd,** Jeremy Walker/Science Photo Library/Photo Researchers; **239 hyracotherium,** Harry Taylor/Courtesy of the Natural History Museum, London/Dorling Kindersley; **239 bat,** Bedrock Studios/Dorling Kindersley; **239 titanis,** Jon Hughes/Bedrock Studios/Dorling Kindersley; **239 early hominid,** Javier Trueba/Madrid Scientific Films/Photo Researchers, Inc.; **239 woolly mammoth,** Dave King/Courtesy of the National Museum of Wales/Dorling Kindersley; **241,** Colin Keates/Dorling Kindersley; **242,** John Cancalosi/Photo Researchers, Inc.; **240 b,** Fred Bavendam/Visuals Unlimited; **240 t,** Dave King/Dorling Kindersley.

Interchapter Feature
Page 244 t, Steppenwolf/Alamy, **244 b,** Louie Psihoyos/Science Faction/Corbis; **245 b,** Morton Beebe/Corbis; **245 tr,** Colin Keates/Courtesy of the Natural History Museum, London/Dorling Kindersley; **245 t bkgrnd,** Russell Sadur/Dorling Kindersley; **245 b inset,** Nick Cobbing/Alamy; **245 tl,** Dorling Kindersley/Getty Images.

Chapter 8
Pages 246–247 spread, Mark Kostich; **249 m2,** O.S.F./Animals Animals/Earth Scenes; **249 b,** Juniors Bildarchiv/Photolibrary New York; **249 m1,** Nigel Bean/Nature Picture Library; **250,** Fletcher & Baylis/Photo Researchers, Inc.; **251 r,** Derek Croucher/Alamy; **251 l,** Lynwood M. Chace/Photo Researchers, Inc.; **252 l,** Peter Hestbaek/Shutterstock; **252–253,** Manfred Kage/Peter Arnold, Inc.; **254–255,** Pakhnyushcha/Shutterstock; **258 tr,** Barry Mansell/Nature Picture Library; **258 tm,** Tom Vezo/Minden Pictures, Inc.; **258 br,** Simon Williams/Nature Picture Library; **258 bl,** Barry Mansell/Nature Picture Library; **258 bm,** Niall Benvie/Nature Picture Library; **258 tl,** Kim Taylor/Nature Picture Library; **260,** Tom Bean/Corbis; **262,** Ed Reschke/Peter Arnold, Inc.; **263 b,** Christine M. Douglas/Dorling Kindersley; **263 t,** Tristan Lafranchis/Bios/Peter Arnold, Inc.; **264–265,** Andrew Browne/Ecoscene/Corbis; **265 t,** Breck P. Kent/Animals Animals/Earth Scenes; **265 m,** Breck P. Kent; **265 b,** Patti Murray/Animals Animals/Earth Scenes; **266 tree,** Medio Images/Photodisc/Photolibrary New York; **266 seedling,** Dwight Kuhn; **267 blackberry bush,** Nigel Bean/Nature Picture Library; **267 ripe blackberry,** Peter Chadwick/Dorling Kindersley; **267 green blackberry,** Peter Chapwick/Dorling Kindersley; **267 developing berry,** Peter Chapwick/Dorling Kindersley; **267 berry blossom,** Peter Chapwick/Dorling Kindersley; **268 b,** Kathy Keatley Garvey/University of California at Davis Department of Entomology; **268 t,** Kathy Keatley Garvey/University of California at Davis Department of Entomology; **269,** Colin Milkins/Photolibrary New York; **270 b,** Paul Bricknell/Dorling Kindersley; **270 t,** Konrad Wothe/Minden Pictures; **271 t,** K.L. Kohn/Shutterstock; **271 b,** Stephen Dalton/Minden Pictures; **274–275,** O.S.F./Animals Animals/Earth Scenes; **276,** David G. Knowles; **277,** Juniors Bildarchiv/Photolibrary New York; **279 r inset,** Alistair Dove/Alamy; **279 bkgrnd,** Andrew J. Martinez/Photo Researchers, Inc.; **279 l inset,** George D. Lepp/Corbis; **280 r,** Ingo Arndt/Minden Pictures; **280 l,** Gladden Williams Willis/Animals Animals/Earth Scenes; **280 m,** SF Photo/Shutterstock; **281 r,** Ingo Arndt/Minden Pictures; **281 l,** Michael Durham/Minden Pictures; **283,** Zigmund Leszczynski/Animals Animals/Earth Scenes; **284–285 t,** WizData, Inc./Shutterstock; **284–285 b,** Robert Sabin/Animals Animals/Earth Scenes; Earth Scenes; **288 t,** Paul Bricknell/Dorling Kindersley; **288 b,** Juniors Bildarchiv/Photolibrary New York;

InterChapter Feature
Page 292, Susumu Nishinaga/Photo Researchers, Inc.; **293,** Ames/NASA.

Chapter 9
Pages 294–295 spread, ZSSD/SuperStock; **297 m1,** Timothy Large/iStockphoto; **297 red & white snapdragons,** Burke/Triolo/JupiterUnlimited; **297 pink snapdragons,** Frank Krahmer/Getty Images; **298 t,** Bettmann/Corbis; **298 b,**

ACKNOWLEDGMENTS

Wally Eberhart/Getty Images; **300 inset,** Andrea Jones/Alamy; **303 l,** Herman Eisenbeiss/Photo Researchers, Inc.; **303 r,** WildPictures/Alamy; **303 bkgrnd,** Monika Gniot/Shutterstock; **304 inset,** J. Pat Carter/AP Images; **304 bkgrnd,** National Oceanic and Atmospheric Administration (NOAA); **305,** Brand X/JupiterImages; **306–307 spread,** Monika Gniot/Shutterstock; **308,** Alexandra Grablewski/JupiterImages; **309 l inset,** Timothy Large/iStockphoto; **309 r inset,** Jomann/Dreamstime; **309 bkgrnd,** Agg/**Dreamstime; 310 inset,** Joel Sartore/Getty Images; **310 bkgrnd,** Erik Rumbaugh/iStockphoto; **311 white chicken,** CreativeAct–Animals series/Alamy**; 311 black & white chicken,** Dorling Kindersley; **311 black chicken,** Mike Dunning/Dorling Kindersley; **311 red & white snapdragons,** Burke/Triolo/JupiterUnlimited; **311 pink snapdragons,** Frank Krahmer/Getty Images; **312 r,** Jay Brousseau/Getty Images; **312 m,** John Daniels/Ardea; **312 l,** Geoff Dann/Dorling Kindersley; **313 tl,** Radius Images/Photolibrary New York; **313 bkgrnd,** Randy Faris/Corbis; **313 tm,** Stuart McClymont/Getty Images; **313 tr,** Blickwinkel/Alamy; **313 bl,** Michael Melford/Getty Images; **313 br,** Naile Goelbasi/Getty Images; **313 pushpins,** Luis Carlos Torres/iStockphoto; **314 white chicken,** Creative Act–Animals Series/Alamy; **314 black & white chicken,** Dorling Kindersley; **314 black chicken,** Mike Dunning/Dorling Kindersley; **314 red & white snapdragons,** Burke/Triolo/JupiterUnlimted; **314 pink snapdragons,** Frank Krahmer/Getty Images; **314 two men,** Radius Images/Photolibrary; **314–315 flowers bkgrnd,** Tomas Bercic/iStockphoto; **314–315 sky bkgrnd,** Serg64/Shutterstock; **315 b,** Joel Sartore/Getty Images; **315 t,** Stuart McClymont/Getty Images; **316 both,** Phototake; **317 r,** Proxyminder/iStockphoto; **317 l,** Eric Isselée/iStockphoto; **317 mr,** Jane Burton/Dorling Kindersley; **317 ml,** Frank Greenaway/Dorling Kindersley; **317 m,** Cathleen Clapper/iStockphoto; **322 l,** Paul Bricknell/Dorling Kindersley; **322 r,** Konrad Wothe/Minden Pictures; **323,** Colin Milkins/Photolibrary New York; **324 bkgrnd,** Miguel Salmeron/Getty Images; **324 inset,** Biophoto Associates/Photo Researchers, Inc.; **325,** Isifa Image Service S.R.O./Alamy; **326 b,** Peter Cade/Getty Images; **326 t,** Russell Glenister/Image100/Corbis; **328 r,** Christian Charisius/Reuters; **328 t,** Jim Stamates/Stone/Getty Images; **329,** Dorling Kindersley; **332 b,** Blickwinkel/Alamy.

InterChapter Feature
Page 336, We Shoot/Alamy; **337,** Dorling Kindersley.

Chapter 10
Pages 338–339 spread, HALEY/SIPA/Newscom; **341 m1,** Oliver Meckes & Nicole Ottawa/Photo Researchers, Inc.; **341 t both,** Addenbrookes Hospital/Photo Researchers, Inc.; **341 m2,** www.splashnews.com/Newscom; **341 b,** Choi Byung-kil/Yonhap/AP Images; **343,** Timothey Kosachev/iStockphoto.com; **344,** China Daily Information Corp-CDIC/Reuters; **345 x chromosomes,** Addenbrookes Hospital/Photo Researchers, Inc.; **345 x and y chromosomes,** Addenbrookes Hospital/SPL/Photo Researchers, Inc.; **346 r,** JupiterImages/Brand X/Alamy; **346 l,** Michael Newman/PhotoEdit, Inc.; **348 l,** Paul Cotney/iStockphoto.com; **348 r,** Lisa Svara/iStockphoto.com; **348 m,** John Long/iStockphoto.com; **349,** Oliver Meckes & Nicole Ottawa/Photo Researchers, Inc.; **341,** Nancy Hamilton/Photo Researchers, Inc.; **352 r,** Dennis Kunkel/Phototake;

352 l, Dennis Kunkel/Phototake; **353 t,** iStockphoto.com; **353 b,** Tomas Ovalle/The Fresno Bee/AP Images; **354 inset,** Udo Richter/AFP/Getty Images; **354–355 bkgrnd,** Anke van Wyk/Shutterstock; **357,** www.splashnews.com/Newscom; **359,** Choi Byung-kil/Yonhap/AP Images; **360,** PeJo/Shu/Shutterstock; **361,** Laura Doss/Photolibrary New York; **361 double helix,** Andrey Prokhorov/iStockphoto.com; **362,** Kenneth C. Zirkel/iStockphoto.com; **362 bkgrnd,** David Fairfield/Getty Images; **364 b,** Tomas Ovalle/The Fresno Bee/AP Images; **364 t,** JupiterImages/Brand X/Alamy; **366,** Dennis Kunkel/Phototake.

Interchapter Feature
Page 368 bkgrnd, Sam Ogden/Photo Researchers, Inc.; **369 bkgrnd,** Phototake Inc./Alamy; **369 inset,** Stocksearch/Alamy.

Chapter 11
Pages 370–371 spread, Chris Newbert/Minden Pictures; **374 bl inset,** Dorling Kindersley; **374 bkgrnd,** Andreas Gross/Westend 61/Alamy; **374 t,** The Gallery Collection/Corbis; **375 bl inset,** Nigel Reed/QED Images/Alamy; **375 br,** Wardene Weisser/Bruce Coleman Inc./Alamy; **375 t,** Ingo Arndt/Minden Pictures; **375 m,** Enzo & Paolo Ragazzini/Corbis; **376 t,** Tui De Roy/Minden Pictures; **376 br,** Joe McDonald/Corbis; **376 bl,** Stuart Westmorland/Visions of Tomorrow, Inc./Science Faction; **378 bkgrnd,** Magdalena Duczkowska/iStockphoto.com; **378 m inset,** Steve Shott/Dorling Kindersley; **378 l inset,** GK Hart/Vikki Hart/Getty Images; **378 r inset,** Dorling Kindersley; **379 m,** PetStock Boys/Alamy; **379 r,** Derrell Fowler Photography; **379 l,** Georgette Douwma/Nature Picture Library; **382,** Mitsuaki Iwago/Minden Pictures; **383 bkgrnd,** Copyright © 2007 Maury Hatfield. All rights reserved; **384 r,** Model by Tyler Keillor/Courtesy of University of Chicago; **384 l,** Gordon Wiltsie/National Geographic Stock; **386 m,** Pacific Stock/SuperStock; **386 l,** Winfried Wisniewski/Zefa/Corbis; **386 r,** SuperStock; **388 tr,** Copyright © 2007 Gerald McCormack/Cook Islands Biodiversity Database, Version 2007.2. Cook Islands Natural Heritage Trust, Rarotonga. Online at http://cookislands.bishopmuseum.org; **388 maggots,** John T. Rotenberry/University of California at Riverside; **389 l inset,** Thomas & Pat Leeson/Photo Researchers, Inc.; **389 r inset,** Thomas & Pat Leeson/Photo Researchers, Inc.; **389 bkgrnd,** Momatiuk-Eastcott/Corbis; **373 t,** Mark Bolton/Photolibrary New York; **373 m,** C Squared Studios/Photodisc/Getty Images; **373 m inset,** C Squared Studios/Photodisc/Getty Images; **373 b,** Digital Vision/Photolibrary New York; **392 r,** Jerome Whittingham/iStockphoto.com; **393 l,** PhotographerOlympus/iStockphoto.com; **393 c,** Burke/Triolo Productions/Brand X/Corbis; **393 tr,** iStockphoto.com; **393 r,** iStockphoto.com; **393 b,** Pete Oxford/Minden Pictures; **392,** kiamsoon/iStockphoto.com; **396,** StockFood America/Buntrock; **397 tr,** ©2007 James D. Watt/Image Quest Marine; **397 br,** Hawaii Dept. of Land and Natural Resources, Betsy Gange/AP Images; **399 tl,** Markus Botzek/zefa/Corbis; **399 tr,** Konrad Wothe/Minden Pictures; **399 tm,** Tom Lazar/Animals Animals/Earth Scenes; **399 bl,** Thomas Wiewandt; **399 bm,** www.operationmigration.org; **399 br,** ©2005 Jason Hahn; **400,** Nevio Doz/Marka/age Fotostock; **401,** Shin Yoshino/Minden Pictures. **402,** Caro/Alamy; **404,** Ethan Miller/Getty Images;

CREDITS

Chapters 1 and 2 taken from Chapters 1 and 2, *Indiana Interactive Science, Grade 8* by Don Buckley, M.Sc., Zipporah Miller, M.A.Ed., Michael J. Padilla, Ph.D., Kathryn Thornton, Ph.D., and Michael E. Wysession, Ph.D.

Chapter 3 taken from Chapter 1, *Interactive Science: Earth's Structure* by Don Buckley, M.Sc., Zipporah Miller, M.A.Ed., Michael J. Padilla, Ph.D., Kathryn Thornton, Ph.D., and Michael E. Wysession, Ph.D.

Chapter 4, taken from Chapter 3, *Interactive Science: Earth's Structure* by Don Buckley, M.Sc., Zipporah Miller, M.A.Ed., Michael J. Padilla, Ph.D., Kathryn Thornton, Ph.D., and Michael E. Wysession, Ph.D.

Chapter 5 taken from Chapter 4, *Interactive Science: Earth's Structure* by Don Buckley, M.Sc., Zipporah Miller, M.A.Ed., Michael J. Padilla, Ph.D., Kathryn Thornton, Ph.D., and Michael E. Wysession, Ph.D.

Chapter 6 taken from Chapter 5, *Interactive Science: Earth's Structure* by Don Buckley, M.Sc., Zipporah Miller, M.A.Ed., Michael J. Padilla, Ph.D., Kathryn Thornton, Ph.D., and Michael E. Wysession, Ph.D.

Chapter 7 taken from Chapter 4, *Interactive Science: Earth's Surface* by Don Buckley, M.Sc., Zipporah Miller, M.A.Ed., Michael J. Padilla, Ph.D., Kathryn Thornton, Ph.D., and Michael E. Wysession, Ph.D.

Chapter 8 taken from Chapter 6, *Louisiana Interactive Science, Grade 8* by Don Buckley, M.Sc., Zipporah Miller, M.A.Ed., Michael J. Padilla, Ph.D., Kathryn Thornton, Ph.D., and Michael E. Wysession, Ph.D.

Chapter 9 taken from Chapter 10, *Louisiana Interactive Science, Grade 7* by Don Buckley, M.Sc., Zipporah Miller, M.A.Ed., Michael J. Padilla, Ph.D., Kathryn Thornton, Ph.D., and Michael E. Wysession, Ph.D.

Chapter 10 taken from Chapter 5, *Interactive Science: Cells and Heredity* by Don Buckley, M.Sc., Zipporah Miller, M.A.Ed., Michael J. Padilla, Ph.D., Kathryn Thornton, Ph.D., and Michael E. Wysession, Ph.D.

Chapter 11 Lessons 1–3 taken from Chapter 6, Lessons 1–3, *Interactive Science: Cells and Heredity* by Don Buckley, M.Sc., Zipporah Miller, M.A.Ed., Michael J. Padilla, Ph.D., Kathryn Thornton, Ph.D., and Michael E. Wysession, Ph.D.

Chapter 11 Lesson 4 taken from Chapter 3, Lesson 5, *Interactive Science: Ecology and the Environment* by Don Buckley, M.Sc., Zipporah Miller, M.A.Ed., Michael J. Padilla, Ph.D., Kathryn Thornton, Ph.D., and Michael E. Wysession, Ph.D.

Chapter 12 Lesson 1 taken from Chapter 1, Lesson 3, and Lessons 2–6 taken from Chapter 2, *Interactive Science: Forces and Energy* by Don Buckley, M.Sc., Zipporah Miller, M.A.Ed., Michael J. Padilla, Ph.D., Kathryn Thornton, Ph.D., and Michael E. Wysession, Ph.D.

Chapter 13 Lessons 1–2 and 5–7 taken from Chapter 7, and Lessons 3–4 taken from Chapter 6 *Interactive Science: Forces and Energy* by Don Buckley, M.Sc., Zipporah Miller, M.A.Ed., Michael J. Padilla, Ph.D., Kathryn Thornton, Ph.D., and Michael E. Wysession, Ph.D.